PRENTICE HALL
Chemistry

Core Teaching Resources

PEARSON

Prentice Hall

Boston, Massachusetts
Upper Saddle River, New Jersey

To the Teacher

Core Teaching Resources contains Section Reviews, Practice Problems, Interpreting Graphics, Vocabulary Reviews, Quizzes and Tests, Laboratory Record Sheets, solutions for chapter assessment questions in *Prentice Hall Chemistry*, and an Answer Key for the worksheets in the Core Teaching Resources.

- The Section Reviews offer students the opportunity to review the content and concepts in each numbered section of the Student Edition.

- Practice Problems extend the multitude of problem-solving opportunities that exist in the Student Edition and on the Interactive Text with Chem ASAP. These extra practice problems are correlated to sections in the student text and include a variety of problems to challenge students.

- The Interpreting Graphics exercises challenge students to analyze processes, data, or information presented graphically.

- The Vocabulary Reviews give students the opportunity to review key vocabulary terms while completing a variety of different exercises.

- A quiz is included for each chapter in the student text. The questions are organized and labeled according to the sections in the text that they correspond to. They can be used as tools for quick assessment as students complete sections.

- There are two tests for each chapter. Both Test A and Test B consist of a variety of testing formats, including multiple-choice and essay questions, matching, completion, problem solving, and true/false. Test questions of greater difficulty are included at the ends of some tests in sections labeled *Additional Problems*, *Matching*, and *True-False*.

- The Laboratory Recordsheets help students organize their laboratory work for the Quick Labs and Small-Scale Labs in the student text. The organization and format of the Laboratory Recordsheets allows teachers to quickly assess students' understanding of the content, application of science processes, and proficiency in using lab skills.

- The Solutions Manual contains complete solutions to all the problems in the student textbook Chapter Assessments.

Cover photograph: Image from Getty Images, Inc.

PEARSON
Prentice
Hall

ISBN 0-13-166233-3

2 3 4 5 6 7 8 9 10   09 08 07 06 05

CONTENTS

CONTENTS

Name _____ Date _____ Class _____

Section Review

Objectives

- Identify five traditional areas of study in chemistry
- Relate pure chemistry to applied chemistry
- Identify reasons to study chemistry

Vocabulary

- matter
- chemistry
- organic chemistry
- inorganic chemistry
- biochemistry
- analytical chemistry
- physical chemistry
- pure chemistry
- applied chemistry
- technology

Part A Completion

Use this completion exercise to check your understanding of the concepts and terms that are introduced in this section. Each blank can be completed with a term, short phrase, or number.

Matter is anything that has ___1___ and occupies ___2___.

    Chemistry is the study of the ___3___ of matter and the

___4___ that matter undergoes. Chemistry has traditionally been

divided into ___5___ areas of study. Organic chemistry is the study

of chemicals that contain ___6___, while inorganic chemistry is

primarily the study of chemicals that do not contain ___7___.

Biochemistry is the study of the processes that take place

in ___8___. ___9___ is focused on the composition of matter,

while ___10___ deals with the mechanism, the rate, and the

___11___ that occurs when matter undergoes a change. A

chemist is likely to be working in ___12___ area of chemistry at

the same time.

1. _____
2. _____
3. _____
4. _____
5. _____
6. _____
7. _____
8. _____
9. _____
10. _____
11. _____
12. _____

Part B True-False

Classify each of these statements as always true, AT; sometimes true, ST; or never true, NT.

_____ **13.** Organic chemistry is the study of chemicals that do not contain carbon.

_____ **14.** The goal of chemistry is to accumulate knowledge.

_____ **15.** Biochemistry involves the study of living organisms.

_____ **16.** An organic chemist uses analytical chemistry.

_____ **17.** Applied chemistry is used to attain specific goals.

Part C Matching

Match each description in Column B to the correct term in Column A.

Column A	Column B
_____ **18.** chemistry	**a.** anything that has mass and occupies space
_____ **19.** pure chemistry	**b.** study of essentially all chemicals that contain carbon
_____ **20.** organic chemistry	**c.** study of the composition of substances
_____ **21.** inorganic chemistry	**d.** study of essentially all chemicals that do not contain carbon
_____ **22.** technology	**e.** study of the chemistry of living organisms
_____ **23.** physical chemistry	**f.** study of the composition of matter and the changes it undergoes
_____ **24.** analytical chemistry	**g.** study of the mechanism, the rate, and the energy transfer that occurs when matter undergoes a change
_____ **25.** matter	**h.** the means by which a society provides its members with those things needed and desired
_____ **26.** biochemistry	**i.** the pursuit of chemistry knowledge for its own sake
_____ **27.** applied chemistry	**j.** research that is directed toward a practical goal or application

Part D Questions and Problems

Answer the following questions in the space provided.

28. Match each activity below to one of the five branches of chemistry.

    a. determining the energy transfer when water boils   _____

    b. finding out how much nitrogen is in a sample of air   _____

    c. studying the process of photosynthesis in plants   _____

    d. manufacturing nylon, which contains carbon   _____

1.2 CHEMISTRY FAR AND WIDE

Section Review

Objectives

- Identify some areas of research affected by chemistry and describe examples of research in chemistry
- Distinguish between macroscopic and microscopic views

Vocabulary

- macroscopic
- microscopic
- biotechnology
- pollutant

Part A Completion

Use this completion exercise to check your understanding of the concepts and terms that are introduced in this section. Each blank can be completed with a term, short phrase, or number.

Chemists design materials to fit __1__ needs. Objects that can be seen only under magnification are part of the __2__ world.

Chemistry is important in the production and conservation of __3__. One of the easiest ways to __4__ energy is through the use of insulation. New kinds of __5__ for the storage of energy are also being developed.

Chemistry plays a role in efforts to increase the __6__ of farmland and to protect __7__ from insect pests. The trend is toward chemicals that treat __8__ problems.

Astronomy and __9__ exploration also benefit from chemistry. For example, a robotic vehicle delivered to the surface of Mars can determine the __10__ of Mars rocks.

1. _____
2. _____
3. _____
4. _____
5. _____
6. _____
7. _____
8. _____
9. _____
10. _____

Part B True-False

Classify each of these statements as always true, AT; sometimes true, ST; or never true, NT.

_____ **9.** Insulin can be produced when genes from bacteria are inserted into humans.

_____ **10.** World energy demand is decreasing.

_____ **11.** Some human genes have been inserted into bacteria.

_____ **12.** Low levels of lead in the blood can permanently damage the nervous system of a growing child.

Part C Matching

Match each description in Column B to the correct term in Column A.

Column A	Column B

_____ **13.** macroscopic

a. material found in air, water, or soil that is harmful to humans or other organisms

_____ **14.** pollutant

b. describes objects that can be seen only under magnification

_____ **15.** biotechnology

c. applies science to the production of biological products or processes

_____ **16.** microscopic

d. describes objects that are large enough to see with the unaided eye

_____ **17.** fossil fuels

e. determined the sequence of genes in human DNA

_____ **18.** Human Genome Project

f. materials formed from the remains of ancient plants and animals

Part D Questions and Problems

Answer the following questions in the space provided.

19. Describe two ways biotechnology can help treat diseases.

_____

_____

_____

20. Name three factors that decrease crop productivity.

_____

_____

_____

21. Explain how scientists know that water once existed on the surface on Mars.

_____

_____

_____

1.3 THINKING LIKE A SCIENTIST

Section Review

Objectives

- Explain how alchemy laid the groundwork for chemistry
- Describe how Lavoisier transformed chemistry
- Identify three steps in the scientific method
- Explain why collaboration and communication are important in science

Vocabulary

- scientific method
- observation
- hypothesis
- experiment
- manipulated variable
- responding variable
- theory
- scientific law

Part A Completion

Use this completion exercise to check your understanding of the concepts and terms that are introduced in this section. Each blank can be completed with a term, short phrase, or number.

Before there were chemists, ____1____ were studying matter.

They developed ____2____ and ____3____ for working with chemicals.

Lavoisier helped make chemistry a science of ____4____.

A logical, ____5____ approach is the best way to solve a difficult

problem. One logical approach to solving scientific problems is the

____6____. This method may begin with an observation, followed

by ____7____, or a proposed explanation for what is observed. You can

conduct an ____8____ to test a hypothesis. If a hypothesis meets

the test of repeated experimentation, it may become a ____9____,

which is a well-tested explanation for a broad set of observations.

A ____10____ is a concise statement that summarizes the results

of many observations and experiments.

1. _____
2. _____
3. _____
4. _____
5. _____
6. _____
7. _____
8. _____
9. _____
10. _____

Part B True-False

Classify each of these statements as always true, AT; sometimes true, ST; or never true, NT.

_____ **11.** A theory can be easily proved.

_____ **12.** Scientific laws explain observations.

_____ **13.** A well-planned experiment will disprove a hypothesis.

Part C Matching

Match each description in Column B to the correct term in Column A.

Column A

_____ **14.** scientific method

_____ **15.** observation

_____ **16.** manipulated variable

_____ **17.** hypothesis

_____ **18.** experiment

_____ **19.** responding variable

Column B

a. variable that one changes during an experiment

b. information obtained through one's senses

c. a logical approach to the solution of scientific problems

d. a means to test a hypothesis

e. a proposed explanation for an observation

f. variable that is observed during an experiment

Part D Questions and Problems

Answer the following questions in the space provided.

20. Classify each step in the following application of the scientific method as an observation, a hypothesis, an experiment, or a scientific law.

a. An iron ball falls to the ground when you drop it.

_____

b. Earth is a giant magnet, which attracts iron objects.

_____

c. An iron ball and a piece of wood are dropped from the same height.

_____

d. The iron ball and wood fall at the same rate.

_____

e. Gravity attracts every object in the universe to every other object.

_____

21. What two processes practiced by scientists increase the likelihood of a successful outcome in science?

_____

1.4 PROBLEM SOLVING IN CHEMISTRY

Section Review

Objectives

- Identify a general approach to solving a problem
- Describe three steps for solving numeric problems
- Describe two steps for solving conceptual problems

Part A Completion

Use this completion exercise to check your understanding of the concepts and terms that are introduced in this section. Each blank can be completed with a term, short phrase, or number.

Effective problem solving involves developing a ___1___ and

___2___ the plan.

    Your textbook teaches a ___3___-step approach to numeric

problem solving. Step 1 is to ___4___ the problem. Identify what is

known and what is ___5___. Then make a ___6___ for getting

from the known to the unknown. Step 2 is to ___7___. If you have

done a good job of planning, this should be straightforward.

Step 3 is to ___8___ your answer. Does the answer make ___9___?

An answer should be expressed in the correct ___10___ and with

the correct number of ___11___.

1. _____
2. _____
3. _____
4. _____
5. _____
6. _____
7. _____
8. _____
9. _____
10. _____
11. _____

Part B True-False

Classify each of these statements as always true, AT; sometimes true, ST; or never true, NT.

_____ **12.** All of the information needed to solve a numeric problem will be given in the problem.

_____ **13.** Problem solving involves developing a plan.

_____ **14.** The first step in solving a numeric problem is to calculate the answer.

_____ **15.** If you have a good problem-solving plan, it is not necessary to check your work.

_____ **16.** Identifying knowns and unknowns is part of the first problem-solving step.

_____ **17.** Analyze and solve are the two steps for solving conceptual problems.

Part C Matching

Match each description in Column B to the correct term in Column A.

Column A		**Column B**

_____ **18.** analyze

a. the starting point for solving a problem

_____ **19.** calculate

b. Step 1 in the three-step problem-solving approach

_____ **20.** evaluate

c. what a problem-solving plan is designed to identify

_____ **21.** known

d. Step 3 in the three-step problem-solving approach

_____ **22.** unknown

e. Step 2 in the three-step problem-solving approach

Part D Questions and Problems

Apply the three-step problem-solving approach to the problems below.

23. What is the length, in centimeters, of a 10.0-inch ruler, given that there are 2.54 centimeters per inch?

24. How many miles are there in 5.0 kilometers, given that there are 0.62 miles per kilometer?

1 INTRODUCTION TO CHEMISTRY

Practice Problems

In your notebook, solve the following problems.

SECTION 1.1 CHEMISTRY

1. Match the project to the appropriate field of chemistry (inorganic chemistry, organic chemistry, biochemistry, analytical chemistry, or physical chemistry).

   a. Determine the composition of a moon rock sample.

   b. Do research on making a new medicine to treat high blood pressure.

   c. Investigate ways to regulate the rate of gasoline burning in an automobile engine.

   d. Develop a plastic that can be decomposed by bacteria.

   e. Improve the method for extracting iron from iron ore.

2. Classify the following examples as examples of pure chemistry or applied chemistry.

   a. developing a shampoo to be used with dry or damaged hair

   b. determining the conditions required for materials to burn

   c. figuring out the general structure of materials such as cotton and silk

   d. designing a large-scale method for producing nylon

   e. explaining why water expands when it freezes

SECTION 1.2 CHEMISTRY FAR AND WIDE

1. Identify three areas of energy research that scientists are working on today.

2. The following statements are all concerned with the work chemists do. Write T for each *true* statement and F for each *false* statement.

   a. Chemists design materials to meet specific needs.

   b. Oil from the soybean plant is used to make biodiesel.

   c. As the world's population increases, the amount of land available to grow food increases.

   d. Many drugs are effective because they interact in a specific way with chemicals in cells.

   e. The trend in crop protection is toward chemicals that are less specific.

   f. The use of lead paint in houses was banned in 1978.

   g. Chemists are doing research to improve batteries.

   h. To study the universe, chemists gather data from afar and analyze matter that is brought back to Earth.

   i. Chemists have developed a plastic "skin" that can heal itself when it cracks to help patients with burns.

SECTION 1.3 THINKING LIKE A SCIENTIST

1. One cold morning your car does not start. Make two hypotheses about why the car will not start.

2. Suppose you try several experiments with your car. You try a battery jump, which does not work. There seems to be enough gas in the car. You wiggle a wire in the engine, and the car starts on the next try. Explain how these tests help you decide what was wrong with the car.

3. The following is a list of observations from everyday experiences:

   Hummingbirds have long beaks.
   Moisture forms on the outside of a cold glass.
   Ice cubes float.
   Oil and water don't mix.
   There are fewer fish in a particular creek this year.

   a. Propose one hypothesis for each observation.

   b. Select one of the hypotheses and describe an experiment that you could do to test it.

4. Discuss the statement "No theory is written in stone."

SECTION 1.4 PROBLEM SOLVING IN CHEMISTRY

1. Apples are selling for $1.50 a pound. Each apple weighs, on average, 0.50 pounds. You have $6.00. How many apples can you purchase?

   a. ANALYZE (List the knowns and unknown.)
   Knowns: Unknown:

   cost of apples =   number of apples purchased = ?

   weight of an apple =

   dollars available =

   b. CALCULATE (Solve for the unknown.)
   Use an expression that converts cost per pound to cost per apple.

   $$\text{cost per apple} = 0.50 \; \cancel{\text{pound}} \times \frac{\$1.50}{1 \; \cancel{\text{pound}}}$$

   cost per apple =

   Use an expression that relates cost per apple to dollars available.

   $$\text{number of apples purchased} = \frac{\$6.00}{\$0.75}$$

   number of apples purchased =

2. Describe an alternate way to solve Problem 1.

INTERPRETING GRAPHICS

1

Use with Section 1.1

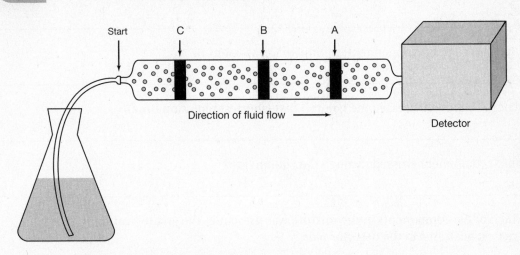

Figure 1 *Separation of a mixture of chemicals. Component A is moving along the column faster than Component B, which is moving faster than Component C.*

Liquid chromatography (LC) is a technique often used by analytical chemists to separate the components of a mixture. In liquid chromatography, a mixture is placed at one end of a long tube, or column, which is packed with microscopic beads. The components in the mixture move from one end of the column to the other by means of a liquid that is flowing through the column. Different components move along the column at different rates. Each component of a mixture has a characteristic *retention time*, or time it takes the component to cross the column.

When a component reaches the end of the column, it passes through a detector, which plots the amount of material exiting the column against time.

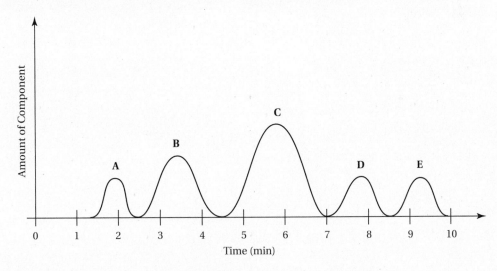

Figure 2 *A typical LC detector plot of a mixture of components.*

1. How many components were present in the original mixture?

   _____

2. Which component has a retention time of approximately 8 minutes?

   _____

3. What is the approximate retention time of Component B?

   _____

4. Which component crossed the column first (shortest retention time)?

   _____

5. Which component crossed through the column last?

   _____

6. Which of the components in the mixture was present in the greatest amount (greatest peak area in the detector plot)?

   _____

1 INTRODUCTION TO CHEMISTRY

Vocabulary Review

Match the correct vocabulary term to each numbered statement. Write the letter of the correct term on the line.

Column A

_____ 1. the pursuit of chemical knowledge for its own sake

_____ 2. the means by which a society provides its members with those things needed and desired

_____ 3. the science concerned with the composition of matter and the changes that matter undergoes

_____ 4. field of chemistry that is concerned with the composition of matter

_____ 5. describe an object that can be seen only under magnification

_____ 6. the study of essentially all chemicals containing carbon

_____ 7. field of study that is concerned with the chemistry of living organisms

_____ 8. a logical approach to the solution of scientific problems

_____ 9. applies science to the production of biological products or processes

_____ 10. information obtained directly by using your senses

_____ 11. a method of testing a hypothesis

_____ 12. variable that one changes during an experiment

_____ 13. a proposed explanation for what is observed

_____ 14. a well-tested explanation for a broad set of observations

_____ 15. describes many observations but does not explain them

Column B

a. chemistry

b. organic chemistry

c. pure chemistry

d. analytical chemistry

e. theory

f. biochemistry

g. observation

h. hypothesis

i. scientific method

j. experiment

k. scientific law

l. technology

m. microscopic

n. biotechnology

o. manipulated variable

1 INTRODUCTION TO CHEMISTRY

Chapter Quiz

Classify each of these statements as true (T) or false (F). Write the letter on the line.

_____ 1. Chemistry is the study of matter and the changes that matter undergoes.

1.1

_____ 2. Pure chemistry is the use of scientific knowledge to attain a specific goal.

1.1

_____ 3. Inorganic chemistry is the study of substances that contain oxygen.

1.1

_____ 4. Agriculture is one area where chemistry has played an important role.

1.2

_____ 5. In chemistry, as in all sciences, patterns can be discovered by making observations and doing experiments.

1.3

Fill in the word(s) that will make each statement true.

6. The _____ _____ is a logical approach to the solution of scientific problems.

1.3

7. An experiment is a means for testing of a(n) _____.

1.3

8. A candle gives off light and heat. These are examples of _____.

1.3

9. A proposed explanation for observations is a(n) _____.

1.3

10. Successful scientific outcomes are more likely when scientists collaborate and _____.

1.3

Write your answer in the space provided.

11. For the following word problems, state whether there is enough information to solve the problem. If not, tell what is needed.

 a. A chemist must fill 10 test tubes with sulfuric acid. What volume of sulfuric acid does she need?

1.4

 b. Earth is 9.3×10^7 miles from the sun. If light travels at 1.86×10^5 miles per second, how many minutes does it take light to reach Earth from the sun?

1.4

1 INTRODUCTION TO CHEMISTRY

Chapter Test A

A. Multiple Choice

Choose the best answer and write its letter on the line.

_____ 1. Identify the activity that belongs in the field of chemistry.
  a. developing medicines
  b. analysis of a compound
  c. production of a new plastic
  d. all of the above

_____ 2. Which of these chemicals is definitely inorganic?
  a. one that is made of carbon and hydrogen
  b. one that is made of nitrogen and carbon
  c. one that is made of nitrogen and hydrogen
  d. one that is made of carbon and oxygen

_____ 3. Which of the following is *not* a step for solving a numeric word problem?
  a. calculate
  b. conclude
  c. analyze
  d. evaluate

_____ 4. Identify the *false* statement.
  a. Chemistry plays an important role in efforts to increase the world's food supply and to protect crops.
  b. Biodiesel is a fossil fuel.
  c. Potato plants with a jellyfish gene will glow when they need to be watered.
  d. Chemists are working to develop more pest-resistant and disease-resistant plants.

_____ 5. A hypothesis is
  a. an observation recorded from an experiment.
  b. a proposed explanation for what is observed.
  c. a summary of the results of many experiments.
  d. a well-tested explanation for many observations.

_____ 6. Which of the following is *not* a part of the scientific method?
  a. experimenting
  b. observing
  c. proving
  d. hypothesizing

_____ 7. Identify the *false* statement.
  a. A scientific law fully explains a set of observations.
  b. The scientific method is a logical, systematic approach to the solution of a problem.
  c. For the results of an experiment to be accepted, the experiment must produce the same results no matter how many times it is repeated.
  d. The scientific method is repeated until a hypothesis either fits all the observed experimental results or the hypothesis is discarded.

_____ **8.** Which of these steps of the scientific method involves stating a
relationship but not proposing an explanation for the relationship?
   a. observation   **c.** theory
   b. scientific law   **d.** hypothesis

B. Questions

Write your answer in the space provided.

  9. Define *chemistry.*

_____

_____

_____

 10. List the major steps in the scientific method and describe each briefly.

_____

_____

_____

_____

_____

_____

Name ______________________ Date ________________ Class ________________

C. Essay

Write a short essay for the following.

11. What are the three steps that you can use to help solve numeric word problems? Describe what you would do in each step.

1 INTRODUCTION TO CHEMISTRY

Chapter Test B

A. Multiple Choice

Choose the best answer and write its letter on the line.

_____ 1. Which of the following tasks would probably not be be assigned to an analytical chemist?
  a. Determine the amount of copper in a sample.
  b. Determine the amount of lead in a blood sample.
  c. Determine the least expensive method to produce nylon.
  d. Determine the amount of pollutants in a local lake.

_____ 2. Which of the following would most likely be an organic substance?
  a. a chemical containing oxygen   c. a chemical containing carbon
  b. a chemical containing hydrogen   d. a chemical containing nitrogen

_____ 3. A biochemist might:
  a. determine the amount of energy released when a fossil fuel burns.
  b. design a method to speed up the production of a metal from its ore.
  c. identify the genes that control the production of insulin.
  d. determine how much table salt will dissolve in a liter of water.

_____ 4. Select the group of materials that were not developed by chemists.
  a. nylon, silk, cotton
  b. cotton, silk, wool
  c. wool, silk, nylon
  d. cotton, nylon, wool

_____ 5. Because the worldwide demand for energy is growing, chemists are working to
  a. find new sources of energy.
  b. develop new ways of conserving energy.
  c. develop new batteries for electric cars.
  d. all of the above

_____ 6. Which of the following is *not* a step for solving numeric word problems?
  a. evaluate   c. calculate
  b. observe   d. analyze

_____ 7. Identify the *false* statement.
   a. Some moon rocks formed from volcanic material.
   b. Analysis of sunlight indicates the presence of oxygen on the sun's surface.
   c. A robotic vehicle delivered to the surface of Mars analyzed and determined the chemical composition of Mars rocks.
   d. The composition of rocks and soil indicates that a large amount of water once existed on the surface of Mars.

_____ 8. A well-tested explanation for a broad set of observations is
   a. a hypothesis.   c. a theory.
   b. an experiment.   d. a scientific law.

_____ 9. To which of the following might a hypothesis be elevated after repeated experimentation?
   a. observation   c. theory
   b. scientific law   d. experiment

_____ 10. Your friend makes the statement that "Water boils at a higher temperature than ethanol." How would you classify this statement?
   a. observation   c. theory
   b. scientific law   d. experiment

B. Problems

Write your answer in the space provided.

11. List the five traditional branches of chemistry and explain what each involves.

_____

_____

_____

_____

_____

_____

_____

12. Discuss the role of chemistry in one of these areas: Materials, Energy, Medicine and Biotechnology, Agriculture, the Environment, or the Universe.

_____

_____

_____

_____

_____

_____

_____

13. You notice that a lawn looks unhealthy and that, perhaps, the grass is dying. Undertake a scientific project to save the lawn.

    a. What is your initial hypothesis, and what experiments can you design to test it?

_____

_____

_____

_____

    b. Often in science you must try several ideas before you find a solution to a problem. Suppose your hypothesis in part **a** is incorrect. Propose an alternative hypothesis. Design a new experiment to test this hypothesis.

_____

_____

_____

Name _____ Date _____ Class _____

QUICK LAB: Bubbles!

Laboratory Recordsheet   Use with Section 1.3

PURPOSE

To test the hypothesis that bubble making can be affected by adding sugar or salt to a bubble-blowing mixture.

MATERIALS

- 3 plastic drinking cups
- measuring cup and spoons
- table sugar
- drinking straw
- liquid dish detergent
- water
- table salt

PROCEDURE

1. Label three drinking cups 1, 2, and 3. Measure and add one teaspoon of liquid dish detergent to each cup. Use the measuring cup to add two thirds of a cup of water to each drinking cup. Then swirl the cups to form a clear mixture. **CAUTION:** *Wipe up any spills immediately so that no one will slip and fall.*

2. Add a half teaspoon of table sugar to cup 2 and add a half teaspoon of table salt to cup 3. Swirl each cup for one minute.

3. Dip the drinking straw into cup 1, remove it, and blow gently into the straw to make the largest bubble you can. Practice making bubbles until you feel you have reasonable control over your bubble production.

4. Repeat Step 3 with the mixtures in cups 2 and 3.

ANALYZE AND CONCLUDE

1. Did you observe any differences in your ability to produce bubbles using the mixtures in cup 1 and cup 2?

   _____

   _____

2. Did you observe any differences in your ability to produce bubbles using the mixtures in cup 1 and cup 3?

   _____

Name ______________________ Date ________________ Class ________________

3. What can you conclude about the effects of table sugar and table salt on your ability to produce bubbles?

____

____

____

4. Propose another hypothesis related to bubble making, and design an experiment to test your hypothesis.

____

____

____

Name _____ Date _____ Class _____

SMALL-SCALE LAB: Laboratory Safety

Laboratory Recordsheet   Use with Section 1.3

PURPOSE

To demonstrate your knowledge of safe laboratory practices.

PROCEDURE

While doing the chemistry experiments in this textbook, you will work with equipment similar to the equipment shown in the photographs. Your success, and your safety, will depend on following instructions and using safe laboratory practices. To test your knowledge of these practices, answer the question after each safety symbol. Refer to the safety rules in Appendix D and any instructions provided by your teacher.

 When should safety goggles be worn?

What should you do if glassware breaks?

If you accidentally spill water near electrical equipment, what should you do?

What precautions should you take when working near an open flame?

After you clean up your work area, what should you do before leaving the laboratory?

Is it always appropriate to dispose of chemicals by flushing them down the sink? Explain.

SMALL SCALE LAB: Laboratory Safety

Laboratory Recordkeeper   Use with Section 1.1

PURPOSE

PROCEDURE

2.1 PROPERTIES OF MATTER

Section Review

Objectives

- Identify physical properties and physical changes
- Distinguish intensive properties from extensive properties
- Differentiate among three states of matter

Vocabulary

- mass
- volume
- extensive property
- intensive property

- substance
- physical property
- solid
- liquid

- gas
- vapor
- physical change

Part A Completion

Use this completion exercise to check your understanding of the concepts and terms that are introduced in this section. Each blank can be completed with a term, short phrase, or number.

Properties used to describe matter can be classified as __1__ or __2__. The __3__ of an object is a measure of the amount of matter the object contains. The __4__ of an object is a measure of the space occupied by the object. An extensive property is one that depends on the __5__ of matter. An intensive property is one that depends on the __6__ of matter.

A __7__ is matter that has uniform and definite composition. A solid has a definite __8__ and __9__. A liquid has a definite volume, but takes the __10__ of its container. A __11__ takes both the shape and volume of its container.

1. _____
2. _____
3. _____
4. _____
5. _____
6. _____
7. _____
8. _____
9. _____
10. _____
11. _____

Part B True-False

Classify each of these statements as always true, AT; sometimes true, ST; or never true, NT.

_____ **11.** Matter has mass and occupies space.

_____ **12.** A liquid has a definite shape.

_____ **13.** Heating a solid to 200°C will cause it to change to a liquid.

_____ **14.** Gases are easier to compress than liquids.

Part C Matching

Match each description in Column B to the correct term in Column A.

Column A   **Column B**

_____ 15. volume   **a.** a quality or condition of a substance that can be observed or
                               measured without changing the substance's composition

_____ 16. mass   **b.** matter that takes both the shape and volume of its container

_____ 17. substance   **c.** matter that has a uniform and definite composition

_____ 18. physical property **d.** measure of the space occupied by an object

_____ 19. solid   **e.** matter that has a definite volume and takes the shape of its
                               container

_____ 20. liquid   **f.** a change to a material that does not change its composition

_____ 21. gas   **g.** gaseous state of a substance that generally exists as a liquid
                               or solid at room temperature

_____ 22. vapor   **h.** matter that has a definite shape and volume

_____ 23. physical change   **i.** the amount of matter that an object contains

_____ 24. extensive property **j.** depends on the type of matter in a sample

_____ 25. intensive property **k.** depends on the amount of matter in a sample

Part D Questions and Problems

Answer the following questions in the space provided.

26. Classify each of the following as a solid, liquid, gas, or vapor.

   a. steam   **a.** _____

   b. apple juice   **b.** _____

   c. gasoline   **c.** _____

   d. hockey puck   **d.** _____

   e. air   **e.** _____

27. State whether the following changes are physical changes.

   a. melting butter   **a.** _____

   b. breaking a window   **b.** _____

   c. burning gasoline   **c.** _____

   d. boiling water   **d.** _____

2.2 MIXTURES

Section Review

Objectives

- Classify a sample of matter as a substance or a mixture
- Distinguish between homogeneous and heterogeneous samples of matter
- Describe two ways that components of mixtures can be separated

Vocabulary

- mixture
- heterogeneous mixture
- homogeneous mixture
- solution
- phase
- filtration
- distillation

Part A Completion

Use this completion exercise to check your understanding of the concepts and terms that are introduced in this section. Each blank can be completed with a term, short phrase, or number.

A physical blend of two or more substances is a ___1___ .

A mixture has a composition that varies. Mixtures may be identified

as ___2___ or ___3___ . Homogeneous mixtures are also known

as ___4___ and have uniform properties. Any part of a sample

with uniform composition and properties is called a ___5___ .

Many mixtures can be separated into their components by

___6___ methods. ___7___ is a method of separation that involves

boiling a liquid, which is then condensed.

1. _____
2. _____
3. _____
4. _____
5. _____
6. _____
7. _____

Part B True-False

Classify each of these statements as always true, AT; sometimes true, ST; or never true, NT.

_____ 8. Homogeneous mixtures can be separated by distillation.

_____ 9. A solution has a uniform composition.

_____ 10. A heterogeneous mixture contains two or more phases.

_____ 11. Solutions are liquids.

Name _____ Date _____ Class _____

Part C Matching

Match each description in Column B to the correct term in Column A.

	Column A		Column B

_____ 12. mixture

   a. a mixture that has a uniform composition throughout

_____ 13. heterogeneous mixture

   b. any part of a sample that has uniform composition and properties

_____ 14. homogeneous mixture

   c. a mixture that is not uniform in composition

_____ 15. solution

   d. separation of a liquid by boiling followed by condensation

_____ 16. phase

   e. another name for a homogeneous mixture

_____ 17. distillation

   f. a physical blend of two or more components

_____ 18. filtration

   g. a method for separating a solid from a liquid in a heterogeneous mixture

Part D Questions and Problems

Answer each of the following questions in the space provided.

19. State whether each of the following is a homogeneous or heterogeneous mixture.

  a. table salt dissolved in water   **a.** _____

  b. carbon mixed with sand   **b.** _____

  c. filtered apple juice   **c.** _____

  d. vegetable soup   **d.** _____

  e. fresh squeezed lemonade   **e.** _____

20. Classify each of the following as a substance or a mixture.

  a. table sugar (sucrose)   **a.** _____

  b. hot tea   **b.** _____

  c. table salt (sodium chloride)   **c.** _____

  d. vinegar   **d.** _____

Name _____ Date _____ Class _____

 2.3 # ELEMENTS AND COMPOUNDS

Section Review

Objectives
- Explain the difference between an element and a compound
- Distinguish between a substance and a mixture
- Identify the chemical symbols of elements, and name elements, given their symbols

Vocabulary
- element
- compound
- chemical change
- chemical symbol

Part A Completion

Use this completion exercise to check your understanding of the concepts and terms that are introduced in this section. Each blank can be completed with a term, short phrase, or number.

A substance is either a(n) ___1___ or a(n) ___2___.

Compounds are made up of ___3___, which are always present in

the same ___4___ in a given compound. Compounds can be

broken down into simpler substances by ___5___ means.

If the composition of a material is fixed, it is a ___6___.

If the composition of a material may vary, it is a ___7___.

Each element is represented by a one- or two-letter ___8___.

For example, carbon is represented by the symbol ___9___, while

potassium is represented by the symbol ___10___.

1. _____

2. _____

3. _____

4. _____

5. _____

6. _____

7. _____

8. _____

9. _____

10. _____

Part B True-False

Classify each of these statements as always true, AT; sometimes true, ST; or never true, NT.

_____ 9. Heating a chemical compound produces elements.

_____ 10. Compounds can be broken down into elements by physical means.

_____ 11. An element is the simplest form of matter that has a unique set of properties.

_____ 12. Compounds are represented by chemical formulas.

Part C Matching

Match each description in Column B to the correct term in Column A.

	Column A		Column B
_____	**13.** element	**a.**	substance that can be separated into simpler substances only by chemical means
_____	**14.** compound	**b.**	a physical blend of two or more components
_____	**15.** mixture	**c.**	one or two letters that represent an element
_____	**16.** chemical symbol	**d.**	simplest form of matter that has a unique set of properties
_____	**17.** chemical change	**e.**	a change that produces matter with a different composition than the original matter

Part D Questions and Problems

Answer the following questions in the space provided.

18. Classify each substance as an element or a compound.

   a. water   **a.** _____

   b. oxygen   **b.** _____

   c. table salt   **c.** _____

   d. sucrose   **d.** _____

   e. gold   **e.** _____

19. Write the chemical symbols for each of the following elements.

   a. potassium   **a.** _____

   b. lead   **b.** _____

   c. sodium   **c.** _____

   d. chlorine   **d.** _____

   e. sulfur   **e.** _____

20. Name the chemical elements represented by the following symbols.

   a. Cu   **a.** _____

   b. H   **b.** _____

   c. Ag   **c.** _____

   d. Fe   **d.** _____

   e. N   **e.** _____

2.4 CHEMICAL REACTIONS

Section Review

Objectives

- Describe what happens during a chemical change
- Identify four possible clues that a chemical change has taken place
- Apply the law of conservation of mass to chemical reactions

Vocabulary

- chemical property
- chemical reaction
- reactant
- product
- precipitate
- law of conservation of mass

Part A Completion

Use this completion exercise to check your understanding of the concepts and terms that are introduced in this section. Each blank can be completed with a term, short phrase, or number.

Substances change into new substances during a(n) ___1___ reaction. A change in which the properties of a substance change, but not its composition, is a ___2___ change. If the composition changes, then a ___3___ change has occurred. In a chemical reaction, ___4___ are converted to products. The only way to be sure a ___5___ change has occurred is to test the ___6___ composition of a sample before and after a change. The law of ___7___ states that mass is conserved in any physical change or chemical reaction. In other words, ___8___ is neither created nor destroyed.

1. _____
2. _____
3. _____
4. _____
5. _____
6. _____
7. _____
8. _____

Part B True-False

Classify each of these statements as always true, AT; sometimes true, ST; or never true, NT.

_____ 9. A physical change is reversible.

_____ 10. In a chemical reaction, reactants are changed into products.

_____ 11. The amount of matter present appears to change during a chemical reaction.

_____ **12.** Matter can be created during a chemical reaction.

_____ **13.** The substances formed in a chemical reaction are called reactants.

Part C Matching

Match each description in Column B to the correct term in Column A.

Column A	**Column B**

_____ **14.** chemical reaction

a. solid that forms and settles out of a liquid mixture

_____ **15.** reactants

b. starting substances in a chemical reaction

_____ **16.** product

c. ability of a substance to undergo a specific chemical change

_____ **17.** chemical property

d. substance formed in a chemical reaction

_____ **18.** precipitate

e. process in which one or more substances change into one or more new substances

Part D Questions and Problems

Answer the following questions in the space provided.

19. When 400 grams of wood are burned, 30 grams of ash remain. What happened to the missing 370 grams of matter?

_____

_____

20. Some car batteries give off a potentially explosive mixture of gases. What kind of change is taking place in the battery?

_____

_____

21. When 16 grams of methane gas combine with 64 grams of oxygen, 44 grams of carbon dioxide form, plus water. What mass of water is produced?

_____

_____

2 MATTER AND CHANGE

Practice Problems

In your notebook, solve the following problems.

SECTION 2.1 PROPERTIES OF MATTER

1. Which of the following is *not* a physical change?

   a. dissolving sugar in water

   b. burning gasoline in an engine

   c. evaporating sea water to obtain salt

   d. slicing a piece of bread

2. Which of the following is *not* a property of a gas?

   a. has a definite shape

   b. has an indefinite volume

   c. assumes the shape of its container

   d. is easily compressed

3. Which of the following is *not* a physical property of sucrose?

   a. solid at room temperature

   b. decomposes when heated

   c. dissolves in water

   d. tastes sweet

4. Which of the following is in a different physical state at room temperature than the other three?

   a. salt   b. sugar   c. flour   d. water

5. Complete the following table.

Physical state	Definite Shape?	Definite Volume?	Easily Compressed?
gas			
	no		no
	yes		

Use the Table 2.1 to answer the following questions.

6. Which substance is a colored gas?

7. Which liquids boil at a lower temperature than water?

8. Classify the following properties as extensive or intensive.

   a. color   b. volume   c. mass   d. boiling point

SECTION 2.2 MIXTURES

1. How might you separate a mixture of water and salt?

2. What is a homogeneous mixture?

3. Which of the following mixtures are homogeneous? Which are heterogeneous?

   a. gasoline   **b.** chunky peanut butter   **c.** oil and vinegar salad dressing

4. Which of the following are substances? Which are mixtures?

   a. ethanol   **b.** motor oil   **c.** vinegar   **d.** neon

SECTION 2.3 ELEMENTS AND COMPOUNDS

1. What elements make up ammonia, chemical formula NH_3?

2. Name the elements represented by the following chemical symbols.

   a. Pb   **b.** K   **c.** Au   **d.** Fe

3. Classify the following as elements, compounds, or mixtures.

   a. table salt   **b.** water   **c.** iron   **d.** stainless steel

4. Write the chemical symbol for each of the following elements.

   a. tin   **b.** sodium   **c.** silver   **d.** carbon

5. A liquid is allowed to evaporate and leaves no residue. Can you determine whether it was an element, a compound, or a mixture?

6. Which of the following is not an element?

   a. copper   **b.** sulfur   **c.** sucrose   **d.** helium

SECTION 2.4 CHEMICAL REACTIONS

1. Which one of the following is a chemical change?

   a. Gasoline boils.   **c.** Gasoline burns.

   b. Oxygen is added to gasoline.   **d.** Gasoline is poured into a tank.

2. Classify each of the following changes as physical or chemical.

   a. A puddle is dried by the sun.   **c.** Bread is toasted.

   b. A dark cloth is faded by sunlight.   **d.** Soap is mixed with water.

3. Carbon dioxide plus water yields carbonic acid.

   a. Name the product(s) of this reaction.

   b. Name the reactant(s) of this reaction.

4. If 44 grams of carbon dioxide react completely with 18 grams of water, what is the mass of carbonic acid formed?

5. In an engine, octane combines with oxygen to form carbon dioxide and water. If 22.8 grams of octane combine completely with 80 grams of oxygen to form 70.4 grams of carbon dioxide, what mass of water is formed?

6. What is the name of the chemical law on which problems 4 and 5 are based?

Name _____ Date _____ Class _____

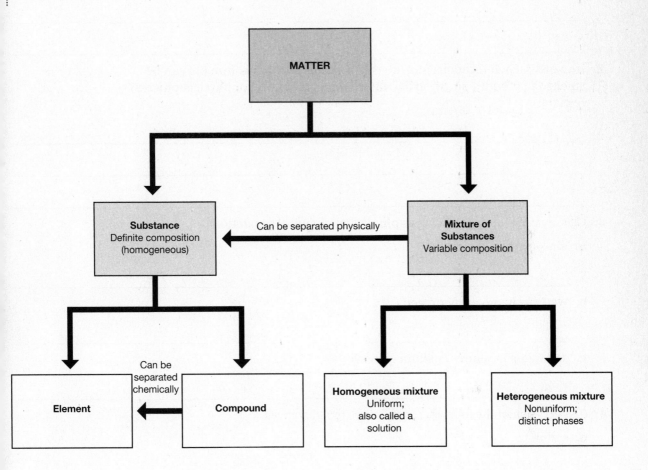

Use the flowchart on the previous page, redrawn from Figure 2.8 in your textbook, to answer the following questions.

   1. Motor oil is available in various grades (10W30, 10W40, and so on). Is motor oil a homogenous mixture or a compound? Explain.

   _____

   _____

   _____

   2. Iron ore is a heterogenous mixture that contains iron oxide. Iron ore can be smelted to produce pure iron. Is iron smelting a chemical or physical process? Explain.

   _____

   _____

   _____

   3. Classify each of the following as physical or chemical separations.

   a. air → oxygen + nitrogen

   _____

   b. water → hydrogen + oxygen

   _____

   c. salt water → water + sodium chloride

   _____

   4. Classify each of the following as mixtures or substances.

   a. sulfur

   _____

   b. air

   _____

   c. concrete

   _____

   d. water

   _____

Name _____ Date _____ Class _____

MATTER AND CHANGE

2

Vocabulary Review

Each clue describes a vocabulary term. Read the clues and write the letters of each term on the lines provided.

1. Clue: part of a system having uniform composition and properties.

    ___ ___ ___ ___ ◯

2. Clue: one- or two-letter designation for an element. (2 words)

    ◯ ___ ___ ___ ___ ___ ___ ___   ___ ___ ___ ◯ ___ ___

3. Clue: another name for a homogeneous mixture.

    ___ ___ ___ ___ ◯ ___ ___ ___

4. Clue: simplest form of matter that has a unique set of properties.

    ___ ___ ___ ___ ___ ◯ ___

5. Clue: the amount of matter an object contains.

    ___ ___ ___ ◯

6. Clue: matter that has a definite shape and volume.

    ◯ ___ ___ ___ ___

7. Clue: a physical blend of two or more components.

    ___ ___ ___ ___ ◯ ___ ___

8. Clue: matter that takes both the shape and volume of its container.

    ___ ◯ ___

Write the letters found inside the circles on the lines below. Then unscramble them to find the term that describes matter that has a uniform and definite composition.

Scrambled letters:

___ ___ ___ ___ ___ ___ ___ ___ ___

Solution:

___ ___ ___ ___ ___ ___ ___ ___ ___

2 MATTER AND CHANGE

Chapter Quiz

Choose the best answer and write its letter on the line.

_____ **1.** A liquid is a form of matter that   2.1
    a. flows.   **c.** has no definite volume.
    b. is easily compressed.   **d.** has a definite shape.

_____ **2.** Examples of physical changes include   2.1
    a. freezing and melting.   **c.** boiling and condensing.
    b. cutting and grinding.   **d.** all of the above

_____ **3.** Which of the following is *not* a physical property of water?   2.1
    a. boiling point of 100°C   **c.** able to dissolve table salt
    b. colorless liquid   **d.** separates into hydrogen and oxygen

_____ **4.** Which of the following cannot be classified as a substance?   2.2
    a. table salt   **c.** iron
    b. air   **d.** sulfur

_____ **5.** An example of a change of state is   2.1
    a. boiling water to form a vapor. **c.** spraying water on plants.
    b. pouring water through a filter. **d.** all of the above

_____ **6.** Which statement is true of any chemical reaction?   2.4
    a. The mass of the reactants is always greater than the mass of the products.
    b. The mass of the products is always greater than the mass of the reactants.
    c. There is no relationship between the mass of the reactants and products.
    d. The mass of the reactants equals the mass of the products.

_____ **7.** In the chemical reaction sodium plus chlorine → sodium chloride,   2.4
    a. sodium chloride is a reactant.
    b. sodium and chlorine are products.
    c. sodium is a product.
    d. sodium is a reactant.

Fill in the word(s) that will make each statement true.

8. Mixtures are a ___**8**___ of two or more components.   **8.** _____   2.2

9. The simplest form of matter with a unique set of   **9.** _____   2.3

    properties is a(n) ___**9**___ .   **10.** _____   2.3

10. The composition of heterogeneous and homogeneous   **11a.** _____   2.2

    mixtures may ___**10**___ .   **11b.** _____   2.3

11. The formula for potassium hydroxide is KOH. It contains   **11c.** _____

    the elements ___**11a**___ , ___**11b**___ , and ___**11c**___ .

2 MATTER AND CHANGE

Chapter Test A

A. Matching

Match each description in Column B to the correct term in Column A. Write the letter of the correct description on the line.

Column A	Column B
_____ 1. product	**a.** matter that flows but has a definite volume
_____ 2. phase	**b.** amount of matter that an object contains
_____ 3. physical change	**c.** starting substance in a chemical reaction
_____ 4. liquid	**d.** homogeneous mixture
_____ 5. mass	**e.** the simplest form of matter with a unique set of properties
_____ 6. element	**f.** a part of a sample with uniform composition and properties
_____ 7. solid	**g.** alters a substance without changing its composition
_____ 8. solution	**h.** matter with a definite shape and volume
_____ 9. compound	**i.** substance formed in a chemical reaction
_____ 10. reactant	**j.** contains two or more elements chemically combined in a fixed proportion

B. Multiple Choice

Choose the best answer and write its letter on the line provided.

_____ 11. All of the following are general characteristics of a substance in the liquid state *except*
    a. definite volume.   **c.** not easily compressed.
    b. able to flow.   **d.** definite shape.

_____ 12. In the chemical reaction iron plus oxygen → iron oxide,
    a. iron oxide is a reactant.   **c.** oxygen is a product.
    b. iron is a reactant.   **d.** iron is a product.

_____ 13. Which term does not fit with the others listed?
    a. solid   **c.** gas
    b. reactant   **d.** liquid

_____ **14.** The chemical symbol for sodium is
    a. NA.
    b. Na.
    c. SO.
    d. So.

_____ **15.** A basketball has more mass than a golf ball because:
    a. the basketball takes up more space.
    b. the basketball contains more matter.
    c. the golf ball contains a different kind of matter.
    d. the golf ball has an indefinite composition.

_____ **16.** A gas is a form of matter that
    a. has a definite volume.
    b. is generally a liquid or solid at room temperature.
    c. takes the shape and volume of its container.
    d. is difficult to compress.

_____ **17.** Homogeneous mixtures
    a. are always liquids.
    b. consist of two or more phases.
    c. have a composition that is fixed.
    d. are known as solutions.

_____ **18.** A compound
    a. is a substance.
    b. has a composition that varies.
    c. can be physically separated into its elements.
    d. has properties similar to those of its elements.

_____ **19.** Physical properties of a substance include
    a. color and odor.
    b. melting and boiling points.
    c. malleability.
    d. all of the above.

_____ **20.** When iron and oxygen combine to form iron oxide,
    a. a physical change occurs.
    b. a change of state occurs.
    c. a change in mass occurs.
    d. a chemical change occurs.

C. True-False

Classify each of these statements as always true, AT; sometimes true, ST; or never true NT.

_____ **21.** Any part of a sample with uniform composition and properties is
called a phase.

_____ **22.** A substance does not have a fixed composition.

_____ **23.** A heterogeneous mixture consists of two or more phases.

_____ **24.** A vapor is a gaseous substance that is generally a liquid at room
temperature.

_____ **25.** A compound can be physically separated into its elements.

Name _____ Date _____ Class _____

D. Completion

Fill in the word(s) that will make each statement true.

26. During chemical and physical changes, substances can absorb or give off __26__ .

26. _____

27. During __27__ , a liquid is boiled to produce a vapor that is then condensed again to a liquid.

27. _____

28. Mixtures differ from substances because the composition of a mixture can __28__ .

28. _____

29. When iron and sulfur combine to form iron sulfide, a __29__ change takes place.

29. _____

30. A __30__ property is a quality of a substance that can be observed or measured without changing the composition of the substance.

30. _____

31. Elements combine chemically to form __31__ .

31. _____

32. Fe is the chemical symbol for the element __32__ .

32. _____

33. A __33__ mixture has a uniform composition throughout.

33. _____

34. In any physical or chemical change, mass is __34__ .

34. _____

35. In a chemical reaction, the new substances formed are called __35__ .

35. _____

E. Essay

Write a short essay for the following.

36. Distinguish between physical changes and chemical changes and give two examples of each. Then, list three clues that are often indications of chemical changes.

_____

_____

_____

_____

_____

_____

_____

_____

Name _____ Date _____ Class _____

Chapter Test B

A. Matching

Match each description in Column B with the correct term in Column A. Write the letter of the correct description on the line.

Column A	Column B
_____ 1. a physical blend of two or more components	**a.** solution
_____ 2. the change of one or more substances into new substances	**b.** element
_____ 3. amount of matter that an object contains	**c.** substance
_____ 4. a homogeneous mixture	**d.** chemical reaction
_____ 5. a substance that can be separated into simpler substances only by chemical means	**e.** gas
_____ 6. the simplest form of matter that has a unique set of properties	**f.** intensive property
_____ 7. depends on the type of matter in a sample	**g.** physical property
_____ 8. matter that takes both the shape and the volume of its container	**h.** mass
_____ 9. matter that has a uniform and definite composition	**i.** mixture
_____ 10. a quality or condition of a substance that can be observed or measured without changing the substance's composition	**j.** compound

B. Multiple Choice

Choose the best answer for each question and write its letter on the line.

_____ 11. Another name for homogenous mixture is
    a. solution.   **c.** element.
    b. matter.   **d.** mass.

_____ 12. The chemical symbol for iron is:
    a. Ir.   **c.** Fe.
    b. FE.   **d.** I.

_____ 13. Which of the following is a physical property?
    a. color   **c.** freezing point
    b. hardness   **d.** all of the above

_____ **14.** Which of the following statements describes a solid?
      a. It takes the shape of its container.
      b. It takes the volume of its container.
      c. Its particles are packed together tightly.
      d. It is easily compressed.

_____ **15.** At room temperature, which of the following is typically in a physical state different from that of the other three?
      a. water   **c.** grape juice
      b. milk   **d.** oxygen

_____ **16.** Which term does not fit with the others listed?
      a. ice   **c.** salt
      b. steam   **d.** water

_____ **17.** Which of the following is an example of a physical change?
      a. toasting bread   **c.** digesting a banana
      b. cooking a hamburger   **d.** melting butter

_____ **18.** An example of a heterogeneous mixture would be
      a. sugar.   **c.** tap water.
      b. salt water.   **d.** vegetable soup.

_____ **19.** Which of the following is a compound?
      a. carbon   **c.** oxygen
      b. hydrogen   **d.** water

_____ **20.** Iron is an example of a(n)
      a. element.   **c.** heterogeneous mixture.
      b. compound.   **d.** homogeneous mixture.

_____ **21.** The element whose chemical symbol is C is
      a. calcium.   **c.** copper.
      b. carbon.   **d.** chlorine.

_____ **22.** Which of the following events can best distinguish a physical change from a chemical change?
      a. Energy is absorbed or released.   **c.** A gas is produced.
      b. a different chemical composition   **d.** Mass is conserved.

_____ **23.** Which of the following is an example of a chemical change?
      a. cooking meat   **c.** dissolving sugar in iced tea
      b. slicing cheese   **d.** freezing water

C. True-False

Classify each of these statements as always true (AT), sometimes true (ST), or never true (NT).

_____ **24.** In a chemical reaction, mass is neither created nor destroyed; it is conserved.

_____ **25.** Dissolving salt in water is a chemical change.

_____ **26.** Physical changes are not easily reversed.

_____ **27.** Elements can be separated into simpler substances by chemical reactions.

_____ **28.** Energy is transferred during chemical reactions.

D. Completion

Fill in the word(s) that will make each statement true.

29. A _____ is a form of matter that flows, has a fixed volume, and takes the shape of its container.

30. A _____ is a gaseous substance that is generally a liquid or solid at room temperature.

31. A tossed green salad is an example of a _____ mixture.

32. The chemical symbol for the element nitrogen is _____.

33. In a chemical reaction, the starting substances are called _____.

34. The burning of wood is an example of a _____ change.

35. The evaporation of water is an example of a _____ change.

36. Any matter that has a uniform and definite composition is a(n)

_____.

E. Essay

Write a short essay for the following.

37. Name at least one physical property of each of the following four materials that could be used to separate it from a mixture of all four. Describe how you would separate a mixture of salt, water, iron filings, and sawdust.

_____

_____

_____

_____

_____

_____

_____

_____

QUICK LAB: Mixtures

Laboratory Recordsheet   Use with Section 2.2

PURPOSE

To separate a mixture using paper chromatography.

MATERIALS

- green marking pen
- metric ruler
- pencil
- clear plastic drinking cup
- filter paper strip
- clear plastic tape
- rubbing alcohol
- clear plastic wrap

PROCEDURE

1. Use the marking pen to draw a line across a strip of filter paper as shown in the drawing. The line should be 2 cm from one end of the strip.

2. Tape the unmarked end of the filter paper to the center of a pencil so that the strip hangs down when the pencil is held horizontally.

3. Working in a well-ventilated room, pour rubbing alcohol into a plastic cup to a depth of 1 cm.

4. Rest the pencil on the rim of the cup so that the ink end of the strip touches the alcohol, but does not extend below its surface. Use plastic wrap to cover the top of the cup.

5. Observe the setup for 15 minutes.

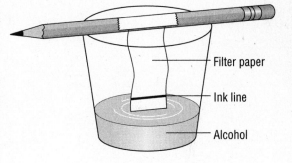

Filter paper

Ink line

Alcohol

ANALYSES AND CONCLUSIONS

1. How did the appearance of the filter paper change during the procedure?

_____

_____

_____

2. What evidence is there that green ink is a mixture?

_____

_____

3. How could you use this procedure to identify an unknown type of green ink?

_____

_____

SMALL-SCALE LAB: 1 + 2 + 3 = BLACK!

Laboratory Recordsheet   Use with Section 2.4

SAFETY

Wear your safety glasses and follow standard safety procedures.

PURPOSE

To make macroscopic observations of chemical reactions and use them to solve problems.

MATERIALS

- paper
- materials shown in grid
- metric ruler

- reaction surface
- pipet, medicine droppers, and spatulas

PROCEDURE

1. Draw two copies of the grid on separate sheets of paper. Make each square in the grid 2 cm on each side.

2. Place a reaction surface over one of the grids. Use the second grid as a data table to record your observations.

3. Use the column and row labels to determine which materials belong in each square. Depending on the material, add one drop, one piece, or a few grains.

4. Stir each mixture by forcing air from an empty pipet as directed by your teacher.

	NaClO	H_2O_2	$CuSO_4$
KI			
KI + Starch			
KI + Paper			
KI + Cereal			

ANALYSES AND CONCLUSIONS

Using your experimental data, record the answers to the following questions.

1. What color is a mixture of sodium hypochlorite (NaClO) and potassium iodide (KI)?

   _____

2. What happens when you mix NaClO, KI, and starch?

   _____

   _____

3. What do NaClO, H_2O_2, and $CuSO_4$ have in common?

   _____

   _____

   _____

4. What substance is found in both paper and cereal? How do you know?

   _____

   _____

5. If you used NaClO instead of $CuSO_4$ in reactions other than the reaction with KI and starch, would you expect the results to always be identical? Explain your answer.

   _____

   _____

YOU'RE THE CHEMIST

Use the space below to write your observations to the small-scale activities in the *You're the Chemist* section.

3.1 MEASUREMENTS AND THEIR UNCERTAINTY

Section Review

Objectives

- Convert measurements to scientific notation
- Distinguish among the accuracy, precision, and error of a measurement
- Identify the number of significant figures in a measurement and in the result of a calculation

Vocabulary

- measurement
- scientific notation
- accuracy
- precision
- accepted value
- experimental value
- error
- percent error
- significant figures

Key Equations

- Error = experimental value − accepted value

- Percent error = $\dfrac{|\text{error}|}{\text{accepted value}} \times 100\%$

Part A Completion

Use this completion exercise to check your understanding of the concepts and terms that are introduced in this section. Each blank can be completed with a term, short phrase, or number.

The __1__ of a measurement describes how close the

measurement comes to the true value. The __2__ of a measure-

ment depends on its reproducibility. An __3__ is a value

measured in the lab. __4__ is calculated by subtracting the

__5__ from an experimental value. Percent error is calculated

by dividing the __6__ of the error by the accepted value and

then multiplying by __7__.

Large and small numbers are more easily handled when

expressed in __8__. Significant figures in a measurement include

all of the digits that are __9__ plus a last digit that is __10__.

1. _____

2. _____

3. _____

4. _____

5. _____

6. _____

7. _____

8. _____

9. _____

10. _____

Part B True-False

Classify each of these statements as always true, AT; sometimes true, ST; or never true, NT.

_____ **11.** Scientific notation is used to express large numbers in convenient form.

_____ **12.** Significant figures include all the digits that can be known accurately plus a last digit that must be estimated.

_____ **13.** An answer to calculations done with scientific measurements cannot be more precise than the least precise measurement.

Part C Matching

Match each description in Column B to the correct term in Column A.

Column A	**Column B**
_____ **14.** accuracy	**a.** measure of how close a series of measurements are to one another
_____ **15.** measurement	**b.** measure of how close a measurement comes to the actual value
_____ **16.** precision	**c.** digits in a measurement that are known plus one that is estimated
_____ **17.** scientific notation	**d.** a value determined in the laboratory
_____ **18.** experimental value	**e.** a quantity that has both a number and a unit
_____ **19.** significant figures	**f.** a method of expressing numbers as a product of a coefficient and a power of 10.

Part D Questions and Problems

Answer the following questions or solve the following problems in the space provided. Show your work.

20. Give the number of significant figures in the following measurements.

    a. 3.85×10^{-3} dm   **a.** _____

    b. 17.30 cm^3 **b.** _____

    c. 0.0037 mm   **c.** _____

21. Perform the following operations and give the answers in standard exponential form with the correct number of significant figures.

    a. 37.2 mL + 18.0 mL + 380 mL =

    b. 0.57 cm $\times$ 0.86 cm $\times$ 17.1 cm =

    c. $(8.13 \times 10^4) \div (3.8 \times 10^2) =$

3.2 THE INTERNATIONAL SYSTEM OF UNITS

Section Review

Objectives

- List SI units of measurement and common SI prefixes
- Distinguish between the mass and weight of an object
- Convert between Celsius and Kelvin temperature scales

Vocabulary

- International System of Units (SI)
- meter (m)
- liter (L)
- weight

- kilogram (kg)
- gram (g)
- temperature
- Celsius scale
- Kelvin scale

- absolute zero
- energy
- joule (J)
- calorie (cal)

Part A Completion

Use this completion exercise to check your understanding of the concepts and terms that are introduced in this section. Each blank can be completed with a term, short phrase, or number.

The International System of Units (SI) is a revision of the __1__ system. There are __2__ SI base units. In SI, the base unit of length is the __3__.

The space taken up by a cube that is 10 cm on each edge is one __4__. A measure of the pull of gravity on an object of given mass is its __5__. The mass of one cubic centimeter of water at 4°C is one __6__. Scientists commonly use two equivalent units of temperature, the degree __7__ and the __8__. The __9__ and the __10__ are common units of energy.

1. _____
2. _____
3. _____
4. _____
5. _____
6. _____
7. _____
8. _____
9. _____
10. _____

Part B True-False

Classify each of these statements as always true, AT; sometimes true, ST; or never true, NT.

_____ **11.** The SI base unit of mass is the milliliter.

_____ **12.** A decigram is 100 times smaller than a gram.

_____ **13.** The SI unit of volume is derived from the unit of length.

_____ **14.** There are six basic SI units of measurement.

Part C Matching

Match each description in Column B to the correct term in Column A.

Column A

_____ **15.** Kelvin scale

_____ **16.** International System of Units (SI)

_____ **17.** temperature

_____ **18.** meter

_____ **19.** calorie

_____ **20.** Celsius scale

_____ **21.** liter

_____ **22.** joule

_____ **23.** weight

_____ **24.** absolute zero

_____ **25.** kilogram

_____ **26.** gram

_____ **27.** energy

Column B

a. quantity of heat that raises the temperature of 1 g of pure water by 1°C.

b. the capacity to do work or to produce heat

c. the SI unit of energy

d. non-SI unit of volume

e. standardized system of measurement based on the metric system

f. mass unit commonly used in chemistry

g. the SI unit of length

h. force that measures the pull of gravity on a given mass

i. zero point on the Kelvin scale equal to $-273.15°C$

j. SI base unit of mass

k. temperature scale on which the freezing point of water is 273.15° and its boiling point is 373.15°

l. temperature scale that sets the freezing point of water at 0° and its boiling point at 100°

m. measure of how hot or cold an object is

Name _____ Date _____ Class _____

Part D Questions and Problems

Answer the following in the space provided.

28. What is the volume of a board that measures 1.8 cm by 8.8 cm by 30.5 cm?

_____

_____

29. Hydrogen boils at 20K. What is the boiling point of hydrogen on the Celsius scale?

_____

_____

30. What is the symbol and meaning of each prefix?

    a. *pico-*   **a.** _____

    b. *kilo-*   **b.** _____

    c. *micro-*   **c.** _____

    d. *centi-*   **d.** _____

Name _____ Date _____ Class _____

3.3 CONVERSION PROBLEMS

Section Review

Objectives

- Construct conversion factors from equivalent measurements
- Apply the techniques of dimensional analysis to a variety of conversion problems
- Solve problems by breaking the solution into steps
- Convert complex units, using dimensional analysis

Vocabulary

- conversion factor
- dimensional analysis

Part A Completion

Use this completion exercise to check your understanding of the concepts and terms that are introduced in this section. Each blank can be completed with a term, short phrase, or number.

Whenever two measurements are equal, or equivalent, a ratio of these two measurements will equal __1__.

A ratio of equivalent measurements is called a __2__. When a measurement is multiplied by a conversion factor, the value of the measurement __3__.

In __4__, the units that are a part of the measurements are used to help solve the problem. The form of the conversion factor that is used is the one in which the unit of the __5__ is in the denominator.

Many complex word problems can be solved by breaking the solution into __6__. When converting between units, it is often necessary to use more than one __7__.

In doing multistep problems, it is important to check that the numerator and __8__ of each conversion factor are equivalent. When the __9__ cancel, you should be left with the unit of the __10__.

1. _____

2. _____

3. _____

4. _____

5. _____

6. _____

7. _____

8. _____

9. _____

10. _____

60   *Core Teaching Resources*

Part B True-False

Classify each of these statements as always true, AT; sometimes true, ST; or never true, NT.

_____ **11.** The units of a conversion factor must cancel.

_____ **12.** The conversion factor for changing between grams and milligrams is
$\dfrac{1\text{ g}}{1000\text{ mg}}$.

_____ **13.** Multiple conversion factors can be used to solve complex conversion problems.

_____ **14.** If density = mass/volume, then mass = density/volume.

_____ **15.** When two measurements are equal, a ratio of these two measurements will equal unity.

Part C Questions and Problems

Answer the following in the space provided.

16. Make the following conversions using Tables 3.1 and 3.2. Write your answers in scientific notation.

   a. 125 g to kilograms

   b. 0.12 L to mL

17. If 1500 white blood cells are lined up side by side, they would form a row 1.0 inch long. What is the average diameter in micrometers of a single white blood cell? (1 inch = 2.54 cm)

18. A radio wave travels 186,000 miles per second. How many kilometers will the wave travel in one microsecond? (1 mile = 1.61 km)

3.4 DENSITY

Section Review

Objectives

- Calculate the density of a material from experimental data
- Describe how density varies with temperature

Key Term

- density

Key Equation

- $\text{Density} = \dfrac{\text{mass}}{\text{volume}}$

Part A Completion

Use this completion exercise to check your understanding of the concepts and terms that are introduced in this section. Each blank can be completed with a term, short phrase, or number.

The ratio of the mass of an object to its volume is its ___1___. 1. _____

Density is an ___2___ property that depends only on the ___3___ 2. _____

of a substance, not on the size of the sample. 3. _____

Part B True-False

Classify each of these statements as always true, AT; sometimes true, ST; or never true, NT.

_____   4. The density of a substance decreases as its temperature is increased.

_____   5. Density has units of grams per cubic centimeter.

Name _____ Date _____ Class _____

Part D Questions and Problems

Solve the following problems in the space provided. Show your work.

6. A rock has a mass of 127 g and displaces 32.1 mL of water. What is the density of the rock?

_____

_____

7. A 1.00-L sample of carbon tetrachloride has a mass of 1.58 kg. What is the density of this substance in g/cm^3?

_____

_____

3 SCIENTIFIC MEASUREMENT

Practice Problems

In your notebook, solve the following problems.

SECTION 3.1 MEASUREMENTS AND THEIR UNCERTAINTY

Using different rulers, Bruce and Pete each measure the length of the same object three times.

1. Bruce's three measurements are 19 cm, 20 cm, and 22 cm. Calculate the average value of his measurements and express the answer with the correct number of significant figures.

2. Pete's three measurements are 20.9 cm, 21.0 cm, and 21.0 cm. Calculate the average value of his measurements and express the answer with the correct number of significant figures.

3. Multiply the answer to problem 1 by the answer to problem 2. Express the answer in scientific notation with the correct number of significant figures.

4. Whose measurements are more precise?

5. The actual length of the object is 20 cm. Whose measurements are more accurate?

6. What is the error of Pete's average measurement?

7. What is the percent error of Pete's average measurement?

8. Four boards each measuring 1.5 m are laid end to end. Multiply to determine the combined length of the boards, expressed with the correct number of significant figures.

SECTION 3.2 THE INTERNATIONAL SYSTEM OF UNITS (SI)

A fish tank measures 0.40 meter long by 0.20 meter wide by 0.30 meter high.

1. What is the width of the tank in centimeters?

2. What is the length of the tank in millimeters?

3. What is the volume of the tank in liters?

4. What is the mass of water, in grams, that would fill the tank halfway?

5. An astronaut in her spacesuit weighs 300 lb on Earth. What would her weight be on the moon?

6. How many nanoseconds are there in one minute?

7. A chemical reaction takes place at 20°C. What is this temperature in kelvins?

8. A typical refrigerator keeps food at 277 K. What is this temperature in degrees Celsius?

Name _____ Date _____ Class _____

SECTION 3.3 CONVERSION PROBLEMS

1. The population of San Francisco is 750,000 in an area of 49 square miles. What is the population density in San Francisco? Express your answer in people per acre. (1 mi^2 = 640 acres)

2. A sugar-free powdered drink mix sells for $2.99 per can. Each can of the mix contains 50.2 g of powder, which, when added to water, will make 8 quarts of drink. What is the cost of the powdered drink mix in dollars/lb? (454 g = 1 lb)

3. A car is travelling at 60 miles per hour. Express this speed in kilometers per hour (km/h). (1 mi = 1.609 km)

4. A whole chicken sells for $7.06 and has a mass of 1.5 kg. A beef shank sells for $10.00 with a mass of 2.5 kg. Compare the per pound cost for each item. (1 kg = 2.2 lb)

5. How many seconds are there in a day? (1 day = 24 h)

6. The speed limit on a certain highway is 72 km/h. What is this speed in cm/s?

7. Gold has a density of 19.3 g/cm^3. What is the mass, in kilograms, of one cubic meter of gold?

8. An automobile can travel 40.0 miles on one gallon of gasoline. How many kilometers per liter is this? (1.61 km = 1 mi; 1 L = 0.264 gal)

9. Suppose that gold is selling at $375/ounce. How many milligrams of gold could you buy for one cent? (16 oz = 1 lb; 1 lb = 454 g)

SECTION 3.4 DENSITY

Use the data in Table 3.7 to solve problems 1–4.

1. What is the mass at 20°C of 5 liters of air?

2. A balloon filled with air is released in a room filled with carbon dioxide. Will the balloon float to the ceiling or sink to the floor?

3. What is the volume in liters of a kilogram of ice at 0°C?

4. What is the mass of a bar of aluminum measuring 1.0 cm by 1.0 cm by 10.0 cm?

Name _____ Date _____ Class _____

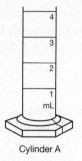

Cylinder A

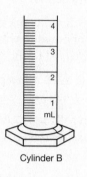

Cylinder B

Figure 1

Use Figure 1 to answer the following questions.

1. Cylinder A is used to measure liquids up to 4 mL. To what number of significant figures could liquids be measured using cylinder A?

   _____

   _____

2. Cylinder B is also used to measure liquids up to 4 mL. To what number of significant figures could liquids be measured using cylinder B?

   _____

   _____

3. A student is asked to measure out 2.55 mL of water. Which cylinder(s) would be suitable for this measurement?

   _____

   _____

4. A student is asked to measure out 3 mL of methanol. Which cylinder(s) would be suitable for this measurement?

   _____

   _____

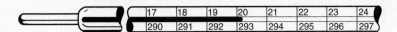

Figure 2

Figure 2 shows a thermometer that is calibrated in both Celsius and Kelvin scales. Use Figure 2 to answer the following questions.

5. Which temperature scale is shown at the top of the drawing?

_____

_____

6. Which temperature scale is shown at the bottom of the drawing?

_____

_____

7. A student reported the temperature shown to be 20°C. Is this the correct number of significant figures? Why?

_____

_____

8. In what physical state does water exist at the temperature shown?

_____

_____

SCIENTIFIC MEASUREMENT

3

Vocabulary Review

Match the correct vocabulary term to each numbered statement. Write the letter of the correct term on the line.

Column A

_____ 1. the ratio of the mass of an object to its volume

_____ 2. closeness of a measurement to the true value

_____ 3. the mass of 1 L of water at 4°C

_____ 4. difference between the experimental value and the accepted value

_____ 5. the degree of hotness or coldness of an object

_____ 6. the SI base unit of length

_____ 7. a ratio of equivalent measurements

_____ 8. a quantity that has both a number and a unit

_____ 9. temperature scale on which water freezes at 0° and boils at 100°

_____ 10. a way to analyze and solve problems, using the units of the measurements

_____ 11. a method of expressing numbers as a product of a coefficient and a power of 10

_____ 12. the SI unit of energy

_____ 13. the capacity to do work or to produce heat

Column B

a. Celsius scale

b. measurement

c. scientific notation

d. joule

e. energy

f. error

g. density

h. kilogram

i. accuracy

j. meter

k. temperature

l. conversion factor

m. dimensional analysis

SCIENTIFIC MEASUREMENT

3

Chapter Quiz

Answer the following questions and write the answers on the line.

1. If you measure a line three times with the same ruler, do your measurements become more accurate?

   1. _____ *3.1*

2. Which form of the conversion factor would you use to convert 75 g to kg?

   2. _____ *3.3*

3. How many significant figures does the measurement 0.4006 m have?

   3. _____ *3.1*

4. Round off the following measurements to two significant figures.

   a. 0.0828 m

   4a. _____ *3.1*

   b. 19.75°C

   4b. _____

   c. 6906 km

   4c. _____

5. Write the answers to question 4 in scientific notation.

   5a. _____ *3.1*

   5b. _____

   5c. _____

Choose the best answer and write its letter on the line.

_____ 6. Which of these is the smallest? *3.2*
   a. one liter
   b. one microliter
   c. one milliliter

_____ 7. The metric prefix *kilo-* means: *3.2*
   a. one thousand times smaller.
   b. ten times smaller.
   c. one thousand times larger.

Solve the following problems in the space provided.

8. Convert −55°C to K. (Recall that °C = K − 273.) *3.2*

9. The density of a substance, as measured by a student, is 4.80 g/cm^3. The accepted value, as printed in a reliable handbook, is 5.10 g/cm^3. Calculate the percent error. *3.1*

SCIENTIFIC MEASUREMENT

3

Chapter Test A

A. Matching

Match each description in Column B with the correct term in Column A. Write the letter of the correct description on the line.

Column A		**Column B**
_____ **1.** error	**a.**	a measure of the pull of gravity on a given mass
_____ **2.** precision	**b.**	concerned with the reproducibility of measurements
_____ **3.** 1 liter	**c.**	a ratio of equivalent measurements
_____ **4.** temperature	**d.**	originally defined as the mass of 1 L of water at 4°C
_____ **5.** density	**e.**	a way to analyze and solve problems, using the units of a measurement
_____ **6.** conversion factor	**f.**	the ratio of the mass of an object to its volume
_____ **7.** dimensional analysis	**g.**	the degree of hotness or coldness of an object
_____ **8.** weight	**h.**	closeness of a measurement to the true value
_____ **9.** 1 kilogram	**i.**	difference between the experimental value and the accepted value
_____ **10.** accuracy	**j.**	the volume of a cube 10 cm on each edge

B. Multiple Choice

Choose the best answer and write its letter on the line.

_____ **11.** How many significant figures are in the measurement 2103.2 g?
  a. 2   **c.** 4
  b. 3   **d.** 5

_____ **12.** Which of these equalities is *not* correct?
  a. 100 cg = 1 g   **c.** $1 cm^3$ = 1 mL
  b. 1000 mm = 1 m   **d.** 10 kg = 1 g

_____ **13.** How many of the zeros in the measurement 0.000 040 200 m are significant?
  a. 2   **c.** 7
  b. 3   **d.** 8

_____ **14.** How many milligrams are in 2.5 kg?
    a. 2.5×10^6 mg   **c.** 2.5×10^{-4} mg
    b. 25 mg   **d.** 2.5×10^2 mg

_____ **15.** The closeness of a measurement to its true value is a measure of its:
    a. usefulness.   **c.** accuracy.
    b. precision.   **d.** reproducibility.

_____ **16.** Which of these measurements is expressed to three significant figures?
    a. 0.070 mm   **c.** 7007 mg
    b. 7.30×10^{-7} km   **d.** 0.007 m

_____ **17.** A metric unit of volume is the:
    a. L.   **c.** km.
    b. mg.   **d.** K.

_____ **18.** The number of seconds in a 40-hour work week can be calculated as follows:

    a. $60 \text{ s} \times \dfrac{1 \text{ min}}{60 \text{ s}} \times \dfrac{1 \text{ h}}{60 \text{ min}} =$ **c.** $40 \text{ h} \times \dfrac{60 \text{ min}}{1 \text{ h}} \times \dfrac{60 \text{ s}}{1 \text{ min}} =$

    b. $1 \text{ s} \times \dfrac{1 \text{ min}}{60 \text{ s}} \times \dfrac{40 \text{ h}}{60 \text{ min}} =$ **d.** $40 \text{ h} \times \dfrac{60 \text{ min}}{40 \text{ h}} \times \dfrac{60 \text{ s}}{60 \text{ min}} =$

_____ **19.** The metric prefix *kilo-* means:
    a. 100 times smaller.   **c.** 1000 times smaller.
    b. 1000 times larger.   **d.** 100 times larger.

_____ **20.** What is the volume of 60.0 g of ether if the density of ether is 0.70 g/mL?
    a. 86 mL   **c.** 2.4×10^{-2} mL
    b. 1.2×10^{-2} mL   **d.** 42 mL

_____ **21.** The temperature reading of $-14°C$ corresponds to a Kelvin reading of:
    a. 297.6 K.   **c.** 287 K.
    b. -287 K.   **d.** 259 K.

_____ **22.** Concentrated hydrochloric acid has a density of 1.19 g/mL. What is the mass, in grams, of 2.00 liters of this acid?
    a. 2.38×10^3 g   **c.** 4.20×10^{-4} g
    b. 2.38 g   **d.** 4.20×10^{-4} g

_____ **23.** A conversion factor:
    a. is equal to 1.
    b. is a ratio of equivalent measurements.
    c. does not change the value of a measurement.
    d. all of the above

_____ **24.** Chlorine boils at 239 K. What is the boiling point of chlorine expressed in degrees Celsius?
    a. 93°C   **c.** $-61°C$
    b. 34°C   **d.** $-34°C$

_____ **25.** A student measures a volume as 25 mL, whereas the correct volume is 23 mL. What is the percent error?
    a. 0.087%   **c.** 0.92%
    b. 8.7%   **d.** 8.0%

C. True-False

Classify each of these statements as always true, AT; sometimes true, ST; or never true, NT.

_____ **26.** Precise measurements are also accurate measurements.

_____ **27.** Zeros in a measurement are significant.

_____ **28.** In converting between units, it is necessary to use more than one conversion factor.

_____ **29.** When converting complex units, you should check that the units cancel, the conversion factors are correct, and the answer has the correct units.

_____ **30.** The weight of an object changes with its location.

_____ **31.** A kilogram is the mass of 1 mL of water at 4°C.

_____ **32.** The density of a substance decreases at its temperature increases.

_____ **33.** Heat transfers from objects at high temperatures to objects at low temperatures.

_____ **34.** To convert density from g/cm^3 to kg/m^3, one of the conversion factors you could use is mg^3/kg.

D. Problems

Solve the problems in the space provided. Show your work.

35. A cube of gold-colored metal with a volume of 64 cm^3 has a mass of 980 g. The density of pure gold is 19.3 g/cm^3. Is the metal pure gold?

36. Perform the following operations. Make sure that your answers have the correct number of significant digits.

  a. 4.15 cm $\times$ 1.8 cm

  b. 13.00 m $-$ 0.54 m

  c. $(1.7 \times 10^{-5}\ m) \times (3.72 \times 10^{-4}\ m)$

Name ______________________ Date ________________ Class ________________

37. Calculate the density of a liquid that has a mass of 14.0 g and a volume of 18.0 cm^3.

E. Essay

Write a short essay for the following.

38. Explain how density differs from volume.

3 SCIENTIFIC MEASUREMENT

Chapter Test B

A. Matching

Match each term in Column B with the correct description in Column A. Write the letter of the correct term on the line.

Column A   **Column B**

_____ 1. how close a single measurement comes to the actual value of whatever is being measured

a. density

_____ 2. a way to analyze and solve problems, using the units of a measurement

b. precision

_____ 3. the SI base unit of length

c. conversion factor

_____ 4. the mass of 1 L of water at 4°C.

d. temperature

_____ 5. a ratio of equivalent measures

e. accuracy

_____ 6. how close several measurements are to each other

f. 1 kilogram

_____ 7. a measure of the pull on a given mass by Earth's gravity

g. meter

_____ 8. the ratio of the mass of an object to its volume

h. 1 liter

_____ 9. the volume of a cube 10 cm on each edge

i. dimensional analysis

_____ 10. the degree of hotness or coldness of an object

j. weight

B. Multiple Choice

Choose the best answer and write its letter on the line.

_____ 11. The number of seconds in a 40-hour work week can be calculated as follows:

a. $60 \text{ s} \times \dfrac{1 \text{ min}}{60 \text{ s}} \times \dfrac{1 \text{ h}}{60 \text{ min}} =$ **c.** $40 \text{ h} \times \dfrac{60 \text{ min}}{1 \text{ h}} \times \dfrac{60 \text{ s}}{1 \text{ min}} =$

b. $1 \text{ s} \times \dfrac{1 \text{ min}}{60 \text{ s}} \times \dfrac{40 \text{ h}}{60 \text{ min}} =$ **d.** $40 \text{ h} \times \dfrac{60 \text{ min}}{40 \text{ h}} \times \dfrac{60 \text{ s}}{60 \text{ min}} =$

_____ 12. Which of the following is the correct scientific notation for 0.000 008 62?
    a. 86.2×10^{7} **c.** 86.2×10^{-7}
    b. 8.62×10^{6} **d.** 8.62×10^{-6}

_____ **13.** The measurement 4.06×10^{-5} g represents:
    a. 0.000 040 6 g.   **c.** 406 000 g.
    b. 0.000 004 06 g.   **d.** 40 600 000 g.

_____ **14.** The largest number from among the following is:
    a. 1.80×10^{-4}.   **c.** 1.80×10^{-2}.
    b. 1.80×10^{-6}.   **d.** 1.80×10^{-8}.

_____ **15.** According to the rules of significant figures, the number of digits that are estimated in a measurement is:
    a. one.   **c.** three.
    b. two.   **d.** none.

_____ **16.** How many significant figures are in the measurement 603.040 g?
    a. 3   **c.** 5
    b. 4   **d.** 6

_____ **17.** How many of the zeros in the measurement 0.050 060 m are significant?
    a. 1   **c.** 3
    b. 2   **d.** 4

_____ **18.** Which of these measurements is expressed to four significant figures?
    a. 0.108 m   **c.** 2.6×10^4 m
    b. 16.530 m   **d.** 5.300×10^{-7} m

_____ **19.** The thickness of a dime is approximately:
    a. 1 m.   **c.** 1 cm.
    b. 1 dm.   **d.** 1 mm.

_____ **20.** Which of these equalities is correct?
    a. 1 g = 1000 kg   **c.** 1 L = 1000 mL
    b. 1 cm = 100 m   **d.** 1 mm = 10 cm

_____ **21.** How many centimeters are in 25 kilometers?
    a. 2.5×10^3 cm   **c.** 2.5×10^5 cm
    b. 2.5×10^4 cm   **d.** 2.5×10^6 cm

_____ **22.** The metric prefix *milli-* means:
    a. 100 times smaller.   **c.** 1000 times larger.
    b. 1000 times smaller.   **d.** 100 times larger.

_____ **23.** The smallest volume from among the following is:
    a. 0.012 L.   **c.** 18 cm^3.
    b. 25 mL.   **d.** 1.6×10^{-2} L.

_____ **24.** What volume of water at 4°C can be held in a cube whose edge is 3.0 cm long?
    a. 3.0 mL   **c.** 27 mL
    b. 9.0 cm^2 **d.** 12 cm^3

_____ **25.** What is the density of an object with a mass of 40.0 g and a volume of 80.0 cm^3?
    a. 0.500 g/cm^3 **c.** 3.20×10^3 g/cm^3
    b. 2.00 cm^3/g   **d.** 1.20×10^2 g/cm^3

_____ **26.** What is the volume of 25.0 g of copper if the density of copper is
8.9 g/cm^3?
    a. 2.8 cm^3 **c.** 220 cm^3
    b. 0.36 cm^3 **d.** 34 cm^3

_____ **27.** What is the mass of 72 cm^3 of silver if the density of silver is 10.5 g/cm^3?
    a. 6.8 g   **c.** 0.15 g
    b. 760 g   **d.** 83 g

_____ **28.** A conversion factor:
    a. is equal to 1.
    b. is a ratio of equivalent measurements.
    c. does not change the value of a measurement.
    d. all of the above

_____ **29.** If water boils at 100°C, this is a Kelvin reading of:
    a. 100 K.   **c.** 373 K.
    b. 273 K.   **d.** 173 K.

_____ **30.** A Kelvin reading of 50 K is the same as a Celsius reading of:
    a. −223°C.   **c.** 223°C.
    b. 323°C.   **d.** 50°C.

_____ **31.** A student estimated a mass to be 250 g but, upon carefully measuring
it, found the value to be 240 g. What is the percent error of the
estimated mass if the measured value is the accepted one?
    a. 4.0%   **c.** −4.0%
    b. −4.2%   **d.** 4.2%

C. True-False

Classify each of these statements as always true, AT; sometimes true, ST; or never true, NT.

_____ **32.** When converting complex units, you should check that the units cancel,
the conversion factors are correct, and the answer has the correct units.

_____ **33.** A reproducible measurement is an accurate one.

_____ **34.** Zero digits in a measurement are significant.

_____ **35.** One mL of water has a mass of 1 g at 4°C.

_____ **36.** One milliliter occupies the same volume as one cubic centimeter.

_____ **37.** The mass of an object changes with its location.

_____ **38.** In converting between units, it is never necessary to use more than
one conversion factor.

_____ **39.** The density of a substance decreases as its volume decreases.

D. Problems

Solve the following problems in the space provided. Show your work.

40. Perform the following operations. Express your answers in the correct number of significant figures.

    a. 36.47 + 2.721 cm + 15.1 cm

    c. $(5.6 \times 10^7 \text{ m}) \times (3.60 \times 10^{-2} \text{ m})$

    b. 148.576 g − 35.41 g

    d. $(8.74 \times 10^9 \text{ m}) / (4.2 \times 10^{-6})$

41. a. Find the volume, in both cm^3 and L, of a metal box 0.60 m long, 10.0 cm wide, and 50.0 mm deep.

    b. If the box is filled with water, what would be the mass of the water inside?

42. A block of silver-colored metal with a volume of 65.0 cm^3 has a mass of 750.0 g. The density of pure silver is 10.5 g/cm^3. Is the metal pure silver?

E. Essay

Write a short essay for the following.

43. Using the following problem as an example, explain and illustrate, step by step, how the use of units can help you solve problems correctly. Example: Find the volume, in liters, of a rectangular box 25 cm long, 10 cm wide, and 8 cm deep.

_____

_____

_____

_____

_____

QUICK LAB: Accuracy and Precision

Laboratory Recordsheet   Use with Section 3.1

PURPOSE

To measure the dimensions of an object as accurately and precisely as possible and to apply rules for rounding answers calculated from the measurements.

MATERIALS

- 3 inch × 5 inch index card
- metric ruler

PROCEDURE

1. Use a metric ruler to measure in centimeters the length and width of an index card as accurately and precisely as you can. The hundredths place in your measurement should be estimated.

2. Calculate the perimeter [2 × (length + width)] and the area (length × width) of the index card. Write both your unrounded answers and your correctly rounded answers on the chalkboard.

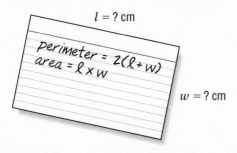

$l = ?$ cm

perimeter = $2(l + w)$
area = $l \times w$

$w = ?$ cm

ANALYSES AND CONCLUSIONS

1. How many significant figures are in your measurements of length and of width?

   _____

2. How do your measurements compare with those of your classmates?

   _____

   _____

3. How many significant figures are in your calculated value for the area? In your calculated value for the perimeter? Do your rounded answers have as many significant figures as your classmates' measurements?

_____

_____

_____

4. Assume that the correct (accurate) length and width of the card are 12.70 cm and 7.62 cm, respectively. Calculate the percent error for each of your two measurements.

_____

_____

QUICK LAB: Dimensional Analysis

Laboratory Recordsheet   Use with Section 3.3

PURPOSE

To apply the problem-solving technique of dimensional analysis to conversion problems.

MATERIALS

- 3 inch × 5 inch index cards or paper cut to approximately the same size
- pen

PROCEDURE

A conversion factor is a ratio of equivalent measurements. For any relationship, you can write two ratios. On a conversion factor card, you can write one ratio on each side of the card.

1. Make a conversion factor card for each metric relationship shown in Tables 3.3, 3.4, and 3.5. Show the inverse of the conversion factor on the back of each card.

2. Use the appropriate conversion factor cards to set up solutions to Sample Problems 3.7 and 3.8. Notice that in each solution, the unit in the denominator of the conversion factor cancels the unit in the numerator of the previous conversion factor.

ANALYSES AND CONCLUSIONS

1. What is the effect of multiplying a given measurement by one or more conversion factors?

   _____

   _____

2. Use your conversion factor cards to set up solutions to these problems.

   a. 78.5 cm = _____ m   **d.** 0.098 nm = _____ dm

   b. 0.056 L = _____ cm^3 **e.** 0.96 cm = _____ μm

   c. 77 kg = _____ mg   **f.** 0.0067 mm = _____ nm

SMALL-SCALE LAB: Now What Do I Do?

Laboratory Recordsheet   Use with Section 3.4

PURPOSE

To solve problems by making accurate measurements and applying mathematics.

MATERIALS

- pencil
- paper
- meter stick
- balance
- pair of dice
- aluminum can

- calculator
- small-scale pipet
- water
- a pre- and a post-1982 penny
- 8-well strip
- plastic cup

PROCEDURE

1. Determine the mass, in grams, of one drop of water. To do this, measure the mass of an empty cup. Add 50 drops of water from a small-scale pipet to the cup and measure its mass again. Subtract the mass of the empty cup from the mass of the cup with water in it. To determine the average mass in grams of a single drop, divide the mass of the water by the number of drops (50). Repeat this experiment until your results are consistent.

2. Determine the mass of a pre-1982 penny and a post-1982 penny.

ANALYSIS

Using your experimental data, record the answers to the following questions.

1. What is the average mass of a single drop of water in milligrams? (1 g = 1000 mg)

2. The density of water is 1.00 g/cm³. Calculate the volume of a single drop in cm^3 and mL. (1 mL = 1 cm³) What is the volume of a drop in microliters (μL)? (1000 μL = 1 mL)

3. What is the density of water in units of mg/cm³ and mg/mL? (1 g = 1000 mg)

4. Pennies made before 1982 consist of 95.0% copper and 5.0% zinc. Calculate the mass of copper and the mass of zinc in the pre-1982 penny.

5. Pennies made after 1982 are made of zinc with a thin copper coating. They are 97.6% zinc and 2.4% copper. Calculate the mass of copper and the mass of zinc in the newer penny.

6. Why does one penny have less mass than the other?

_____

_____

_____

YOU'RE THE CHEMIST

Use the space below to write your observations to the small-scale activities in the *You're the Chemist* section.

Name _____ Date _____ Class _____

4.1 DEFINING THE ATOM

Section Review

Objectives

- Describe Democritus's ideas about atoms
- Explain Dalton's atomic theory
- Describe the size of an atom

Vocabulary

- atom
- Dalton's atomic theory

Part A Completion

Use this completion exercise to check your understanding of the concepts and terms that are introduced in this section. Each blank can be completed with a term, short phrase, or number.

Elements are composed of tiny particles called ___1___.

Atoms of any one element are ___2___ from those of any

other element. Atoms of different elements can form ___3___

by combining in whole-number ratios. Chemical reactions

 occur when atoms are ___4___ .

1. _____

2. _____

3. _____

4. _____

Part B True-False

Classify each of these statements as always true, AT; sometimes true, ST; or never true, NT.

_____ 5. Atoms of one element change into atoms of another element during chemical reactions.

_____ 6. Atoms combine in one-to-one ratios to form compounds.

_____ 7. Atoms of one element are different from atoms of other elements.

Part C Matching

Match each description in Column B to the correct term in Column A.

Column A	**Column B**
_____ **8.** atom	**a.** an instrument used to generate images of individual atoms
_____ **9.** scanning tunneling microscope	**b.** Greek philosopher who was among the first to suggest the existence of atoms
_____ **10.** John Dalton	**c.** the smallest particle of an element that retains its identity in a chemical reaction
_____ **11.** Democritus	**d.** English chemist and schoolteacher who formulated a theory to describe the structure and chemical reactivity of matter in terms of atoms

Part D Questions and Problems

Answer the following questions in the space provided.

12. In what type of ratios do atoms combine to form compounds?

_____

_____

_____

13. How many copper atoms would you have to line up side by side to form a line 1 m long?

_____

_____

_____

4.2 STRUCTURE OF THE NUCLEAR ATOM

Section Review

Objectives

- Identify three types of subatomic particles
- Describe the structure of atoms according to the Rutherford model

Vocabulary

- electrons
- cathode ray
- protons
- neutrons
- nucleus

Part A Completion

Use this completion exercise to check your understanding of the concepts and terms that are introduced in this section. Each blank can be completed with a term, short phrase, or number.

Dalton theorized that atoms are indivisible, but the discovery of __1__ particles changed this theory. Scientists now know that atoms are made up of electrons, which have a __2__ charge; __3__, which have a positive charge; and __4__, which are neutral. The latter two particles are found in the __5__ of the atom. It was __6__ who discovered the nucleus of the atom. The nucleus, which has a __7__ charge, occupies a very small volume of the atom. In contrast, the negatively charged __8__ occupy most of the volume of the atom.

1. _____
2. _____
3. _____
4. _____
5. _____
6. _____
7. _____
8. _____

Part B True-False

Classify each of these statements as always true, AT; sometimes true, ST; or never true, NT.

_____ 9. According to Dalton's atomic theory, atoms are composed of protons, electrons, and neutrons.

_____ 10. Atoms of elements are electrically neutral.

_____ 11. The mass of an electron is equal to the mass of a neutron.

_____ 12. The charge on all protons is the same.

Part C Matching

Match each description in Column B to the correct term in Column A

Column A

_____ **13.** electrons

_____ **14.** cathode ray

_____ **15.** protons

_____ **16.** neutrons

_____ **17.** nucleus

Column B

a. stream of electrons produced at the negative electrode of a tube containing a gas at low pressure

b. the central core of an atom, which is composed of protons and neutrons

c. negatively charged subatomic particles

d. subatomic particles with no charge

e. positively charged subatomic particles

Part D Questions and Problems

Answer the following questions in the space provided.

18. Which subatomic particles are found in the nucleus of an atom?

_____

_____

19. Which subatomic particles are charged?

_____

_____

20. Describe Rutherford's model of the atom, including the location of protons, neutrons, and electrons with respect to the nucleus. How does this model explain the deflections of a beam of alpha particles aimed at a sheet of gold foil?

_____

_____

_____

_____

_____

Name _____ Date _____ Class _____

4.3 DISTINGUISHING BETWEEN ATOMS

Section Review

Objectives

- Explain how isotopes differ from one another
- Use the atomic number and mass number of an element to find the numbers of protons, electrons, and neutrons
- Calculate the atomic mass of an element from isotope data

Vocabulary

- atomic number
- mass number
- isotopes
- atomic mass unit (amu)
- atomic mass
- periodic table
- period
- group

Key Equations

- atomic number = number of protons = number of electrons
- number of neutrons = mass number − atomic number

Part A Completion

Use this completion exercise to check your understanding of the concepts and terms that are introduced in this section. Each blank can be completed with a term, short phrase, or number.

The number of __1__ in the nucleus of an atom is the atomic __2__ of that element. Because atoms are electrically neutral, the number of protons and __3__ in an atom are equal. The total number of __4__ and neutrons in an atom is the mass number. Atoms of the same element are identical in most respects, but they can differ in the number of __5__ in the nucleus. Atoms that have the same number of protons but different mass numbers are called __6__ .

The __7__ of an element is the weighted average of the masses of the isotopes of that element. Each of the three known isotopes of hydrogen has __8__ proton(s) in the nucleus. The most common hydrogen isotope has __9__ neutrons. It has a mass number of __10__ and is called hydrogen-1.

1. _____
2. _____
3. _____
4. _____
5. _____
6. _____
7. _____
8. _____
9. _____
10. _____

Name _____ Date _____ Class _____

Part B True-False

Classify each of these statements as always true, AT; sometimes true, ST; or never true, NT.

_____ **11.** The atomic number of an element is the sum of the protons and electrons in an atom of that element.

_____ **12.** The atomic number of an atom is the total number of protons in an atom of that element.

_____ **13.** An atom of nitrogen has 7 protons and 7 neutrons.

_____ **14.** Relative atomic masses are expressed in amus.

_____ **15.** The number of neutrons in the nucleus can be calculated by subtracting the atomic number from the mass number.

Part C Matching

Match each description in Column B to the correct term in Column A

Column A	**Column B**
_____ **16.** atomic number	**a.** atoms that have the same number of protons but different numbers of neutrons
_____ **17.** periodic table	**b.** weighted average mass of the atoms in a naturally occurring sample of an element
_____ **18.** mass number	**c.** equals the number of neutrons plus the number of protons in an atom
_____ **19.** group	**d.** $\frac{1}{12}$ the mass of a carbon-12 atom
_____ **20.** isotopes	**e.** the number of protons in the nucleus of an atom of an element
_____ **21.** atomic mass unit (amu)	**f.** an arrangement of elements according to similarities in their properties
_____ **22.** atomic mass	**g.** a vertical column of elements in the periodic table
_____ **23.** period	**h.** a horizontal row of the periodic table

Part D Questions and Problems

Solve the following problem in the space provided.

24. Given the relative abundance of the following naturally occurring isotopes of oxygen, calculate the average atomic mass of oxygen.

oxygen-16:   99.76%
oxygen-17:   0.037%
oxygen-18:   0.204%

ATOMIC STRUCTURE

4

Practice Problems

In your notebook, solve the following problems.

SECTION 4.1 DEFINING THE ATOM

1. According to Figure 5.2, 100,000,000 copper atoms would form a line 1 cm long. How long would a line formed by 1×10^7 copper atoms be? Express your answer in millimeters.

SECTION 4.2 STRUCTURE OF THE NUCLEAR ATOM

1. A sulfur-32 atom contains 16 protons, 16 neutrons, and 16 electrons. What is the mass (in grams) of a sulfur-32 atom?

2. The mass of a neutron is 1.67×10^{-24} g. Approximately what number of neutrons would equal a mass of one gram?

3. Which statement is consistent with the results of Rutherford's gold foil experiment?

   a. All atoms have a positive charge.

   b. Atoms are mostly empty space.

   c. The nucleus of an atom contains protons and electrons.

   d. Mass is spread uniformly throughout an atom.

SECTION 4.3 DISTINGUISHING BETWEEN ATOMS

1. How many protons are found in an atom of each of the following?
   a. boron   c. neon
   b. sulfur   d. lithium

2. Complete the table for the following elements.

Element	Number of Protons	Number of Electrons	Number of Neutrons	Atomic Number	Mass Number
Manganese	25		30		
Sodium		11	12		
Bromine	35		45		
Yttrium				39	89
Arsenic		33			75
Actinium					227

3. How many neutrons are in each atom?
   a. $^{23}_{11}$Na
   c. $^{81}_{35}$Br
   b. $^{238}_{92}$U
   d. $^{19}_{9}$F

4. The two most abundant isotopes of carbon are carbon-12 (mass = 12.00 amu) and carbon-13 (mass = 13.00 amu). Their relative abundances are 98.9% and 1.10%, respectively. Calculate the atomic mass of carbon.

5. Element X has two isotopes: X-100 and X-104. If the atomic mass of X is 101 amu, what is the relative abundance of each isotope in nature?

4 | ATOMIC STRUCTURE

Vocabulary Review

Match the correct vocabulary term to each numbered statement. Write the letter of the correct term on the line.

Column A	Column B

Column A

_____ 1. defined as $\frac{1}{12}$ the mass of a carbon-12 atom

_____ 2. central core of an atom, which contains most of the atom's mass

_____ 3. a vertical column of elements in the periodic table

_____ 4. subatomic particles with no charge

_____ 5. positively charged subatomic particles

_____ 6. the smallest particle of an element that retains its identity in a chemical reaction

_____ 7. the number of protons in the nucleus of an element

_____ 8. negatively charged subatomic particles

_____ 9. atoms with the same number of protons but different numbers of neutrons

_____ 10. an arrangement of elements according to similarities in their properties

Column B

a. isotopes

b. neutrons

c. atom

d. electrons

e. atomic number

f. atomic mass unit

g. group

h. nucleus

i. periodic table

j. protons

4 ATOMIC STRUCTURE

Chapter Quiz

Fill in the word(s) that will make each statement true.

1. Dalton's atomic theory included the idea that the atoms of different elements can chemically combine in __1__ ratios.

1. _____

2. An atom is the smallest particle of an element that retains its identity in a __2__ .

2. _____

3. __3__ are subatomic particles with a negative charge.

3. _____

4. The nucleus of an atom is composed of __4__ and protons.

4. _____

5. A neutron has no charge, but its mass is almost the same as that of a __5__ .

5. _____

6. The number of protons in an atom is called its __6__ number.

6. _____

7. There are 10 neutrons and __7__ electrons in an atom of oxygen-18.

7. _____

8. Isotopes of an element have different numbers of neutrons. They also have different __8__ numbers.

8. _____

9. The total number of protons, neutrons, and electrons in an atom of silver-109 (atomic number 47) is __9__ .

9. _____

10. The mass number of an element with 14 electrons and 16 neutrons is __10__ .

10. _____

11. The horizontal rows of the periodic table are called __11__ .

11. _____

12. The elements in the periodic table are listed in order of increasing __12__ .

12. _____

Name _____ Date _____ Class _____

4 ATOMIC STRUCTURE

Chapter Test A

A. Matching

Match each description in Column B with the correct term in Column A. Write the letter of the correct description on the line.

Column A	Column B

_____ **1.** proton

a. the total number of protons and neutrons in the nucleus of an atom

_____ **2.** atom

b. the weighted average mass of the atoms in a naturally occurring sample of an element

_____ **3.** mass number

c. $\frac{1}{12}$ the mass of a carbon-12 atom

_____ **4.** atomic mass unit

d. the number of protons in the nucleus of an element

_____ **5.** electron

e. atoms with the same number of protons but different numbers of neutrons

_____ **6.** isotopes

f. negatively charged subatomic particle

_____ **7.** atomic number

g. the smallest particle of an element that retains its identity in a chemical reaction

_____ **8.** atomic mass

h. a horizontal row of the periodic table

_____ **9.** period

i. subatomic particle with no charge

_____ **10.** neutron

j. positively charged subatomic particle

B. Multiple Choice

Choose the best answer and write its letter on the line.

_____ **11.** Which of the following is *not* a part of Dalton's atomic theory?
 a. All elements are composed of atoms.
 b. Atoms of the same element are alike.
 c. Atoms are always in motion.
 d. Atoms that combine do so in simple whole-number ratios.

_____ **12.** The nucleus of an atom is
 a. negatively charged and has a low density.
 b. negatively charged and has a high density.
 c. positively charged and has a low density.
 d. positively charged and has a high density.

_____ **13.** Dalton theorized that atoms are indivisible and that all atoms of an element are identical. Scientists now know that
  a. Dalton's theories are completely correct.
  b. atoms of an element can have different numbers of protons.
  c. atoms are all divisible.
  d. all atoms of an element are not identical but they all have the same mass.

_____ **14.** The number of neutrons in the nucleus of an atom can be calculated by
  a. adding together the numbers of electrons and protons.
  b. subtracting the number of protons from the number of electrons.
  c. subtracting the number of protons from the mass number.
  d. adding the mass number to the number of protons.

_____ **15.** The sum of the protons and neutrons in an atom equals the
  a. atomic number.   **c.** atomic mass.
  b. number of electrons.   **d.** mass number.

_____ **16.** All atoms of the same element have the same:
  a. number of protons.   **c.** mass number.
  b. number of neutrons.   **d.** mass.

_____ **17.** Which of these statements is false?
  a. Electrons have a negative charge.
  b. Electrons have a mass of 1 amu.
  c. The nucleus of an atom is positively charged.
  d. The neutron is found in the nucleus of an atom.

_____ **18.** An atom of an element with atomic number 48 and mass number 120 contains
  a. 48 protons, 48 electrons, and 72 neutrons.
  b. 72 protons, 48 electrons, and 48 neutrons.
  c. 120 protons, 48 electrons, and 72 neutrons.
  d. 72 protons, 72 electrons, and 48 neutrons.

_____ **19.** How do the isotopes hydrogen-2 and hydrogen-3 differ?
  a. Hydrogen-3 has one more electron than hydrogen-2.
  b. Hydrogen-3 has two neutrons.
  c. Hydrogen-2 has three protons.
  d. Hydrogen-2 has no protons.

_____ **20.** The number 80 in the name bromine-80 represents
  a. the atomic number.
  b. the mass number.
  c. the sum of protons and electrons.
  d. none of the above

_____ **21.** Which of these statements is *not* true?
  a. Atoms of the same elements can have different masses.
  b. The nucleus of an atom has a positive charge.
  c. Atoms of isotopes of an element have different numbers of protons.
  d. Atoms are mostly empty space.

_____ **22.** Relative atomic masses are measured in

    a. nanograms.   **c.** angstroms.

    b. grams.   **d.** amus.

_____ **23.** If E is the symbol for an element, which two of the following symbols represent isotopes of the same element?

    1. $^{24}_{12}E$ **2.** $^{24}_{13}E$ **3.** $^{25}_{11}E$ **4.** $^{25}_{12}E$

    a. 1 and 2   **c.** 1 and 4

    b. 3 and 4   **d.** 2 and 3

C. Problems

Solve the following problem in the space provided. Show your work.

24. There are five naturally occurring isotopes of the element zinc. The relative abundance and mass of each are as follows.

$^{64}_{30}Zn$ = 48.89%, 63.929 amu

$^{66}_{30}Zn$ = 27.81%, 65.926 amu

$^{67}_{30}Zn$ = 4.11%, 66.927 amu

$^{68}_{30}Zn$ = 18.57%, 67.925 amu

$^{70}_{30}Zn$ = 0.62%, 69.925 amu

Calculate the average atomic mass of zinc.

25. Complete this table.

Atomic Number	Mass Number	Number of Protons	Number of Neutrons	Number of Electrons
9			10	
	14		7	
			21	20
13	27			
	56	26		

26. List the number of protons, neutrons, and electrons in each of the following atoms.

	Protons	Neutrons	Electrons
$^{13}_{6}C$			
$^{10}_{4}Be$			
$^{20}_{10}Ne$			
$^{11}_{5}B$			
$^{33}_{16}S$			

D. Essay

Write a short essay to answer the following.

27. Explain how the atoms of one element differ from those of another element. Then explain how the atoms of one isotope differ from those of other isotopes of the same element.

_____

_____

_____

_____

_____

_____

ATOMIC STRUCTURE

4

Chapter Test B

A. Matching

Match each term in Column B with the correct description in Column A. Write the letter of the correct term on the line.

Column A	Column B

_____ 1. the number of protons in the nucleus of an element

_____ 2. the smallest particle of an element that retains its identity in a chemical reaction

_____ 3. the total number of protons and neutrons in the nucleus of an atom

_____ 4. a positively charged subatomic particle

_____ 5. atoms with the same number of protons but different numbers of neutrons

_____ 6. a negatively charged subatomic particle

_____ 7. $\frac{1}{12}$ the mass of a carbon-12 atom

_____ 8. an arrangement of elements in which the elements are separated into groups based on a set of repeating properties

_____ 9. a subatomic particle with no charge

_____ 10. the weighted average of the mass of the atoms in a naturally occurring sample of an element

a. electron

b. mass number

c. atomic number

d. atomic mass

e. neutron

f. atomic mass unit

g. proton

h. isotopes

i. atom

j. periodic table

B. Multiple Choice

Choose the best answer and write its letter on the line.

_____ 11. Which of these statements is included in Dalton's atomic theory?
    a. Chemical reactions occur when atoms are separated, joined, or rearranged.
    b. Some but not all elements are composed of atoms.
    c. Atoms of the same element can have different numbers of protons.
    d. Atoms are divisible.

_____ 12. Which of the following statements is correct?
    a. Electrons are positively charged.
    b. Protons are negatively charged.
    c. Neutrons have no charge.
    d. Atoms are positively charged.

_____ **13.** Which of the following correctly lists the particles in order from least massive to most massive?

    a. proton, electron, hydrogen atom, helium atom

    b. proton, helium atom, hydrogen atom, electron

    c. hydrogen atom, electron, helium atom, proton

    d. electron, proton, hydrogen atom, helium atom

_____ **14.** Which of the following statements is *not* consistent with the results obtained in Rutherford's gold foil experiment?

    a. The nucleus of an atom is positively charged.

    b. The nucleus of an atom contains almost all the mass of the atom.

    c. Atoms are composed mainly of empty space.

    d. Electrons are contained in the nucleus of an atom.

_____ **15.** The identity of an element can be determined on the basis of which of the following?

    a. the number of protons in an atom of the element

    b. the number of neutrons in an atom of the element

    c. the mass number of the element

    d. the atomic mass of the element

_____ **16.** What is the atomic number and the mass number of an atom with 11 protons and 12 neutrons?

    a. atomic number = 11 and mass number = 12

    b. atomic number = 12 and mass number = 11

    c. atomic number = 11 and mass number = 23

    d. atomic number = 23 and mass number = 12

_____ **17.** An atom of hydrogen-2 contains

    a. 2 protons, 2 electrons, and 2 neutrons.

    b. 2 protons, 2 electrons, and 4 neutrons.

    c. 1 proton, 1 electron, and 1 neutron.

    d. 1 proton, 1 electron, and 2 neutrons.

_____ **18.** Which of the following statements is correct?

    a. Each vertical column of elements in the periodic table is called a period.

    b. The elements in any group of the periodic table have similar physical and chemical properties.

    c. Group 1A contains the elements hydrogen and helium.

    d. In the modern periodic table, elements are listed in order of increasing atomic mass.

_____ **19.** Isotopes of the same element have

    a. the same number of protons but different numbers of neutrons.

    b. the same number of protons but different numbers of electrons.

    c. the same number of neutrons but different numbers of protons.

    d. the same number of neutrons but different numbers of electrons.

_____ **20.** Which symbol correctly represents an element (D) whose atoms contain 15 protons and 20 neutrons?

    a. $^{20}_{15}D$ **c.** $^{35}_{15}D$

    b. $^{15}_{20}D$ **d.** $^{15}_{35}D$

_____ **21.** If Z is the symbol for an element, which pair among the following represents isotopes of the same element?

    a. $^{51}_{25}Z$ and $^{51}_{26}Z$ **c.** $^{50}_{25}Z$ and $^{50}_{27}Z$

    b. $^{51}_{25}Z$ and $^{50}_{25}Z$ **d.** $^{51}_{26}Z$ and $^{50}_{25}Z$

_____ **22.** The relative abundance of each isotope of an element determines its

    a. atomic number.   **c.** number of electrons.

    b. atomic mass.   **d.** number of protons.

_____ **23.** Three isotopes of oxygen occur in nature: oxygen-16, oxygen-17, and oxygen-18. If the atomic mass of oxygen is 15.9994, which of the three isotopes, if any, is the most abundant?

    a. oxygen-16   **c.** oxygen-18

    b. oxygen-17   **d.** All are equally abundant.

_____ **24.** Element Z has two naturally occurring isotopes: Z-20 and Z-22. If the atomic mass of Z is 21.5 amu, what is the relative abundance of each isotope in nature?

    a. one Z-20 to one Z-22   **c.** two Z-20s to one Z-22

    b. one Z-20 to two Z-22s   **d.** one Z-20 to three Z-22s

C. Problems

Solve the following problems in the space provided. Show your work.

25. The element argon contains three naturally occurring isotopes:

$$^{36}_{18}Ar \qquad ^{38}_{18}Ar \qquad ^{40}_{18}Ar$$

The relative abundances and atomic masses are 0.337% (mass = 35.978 amu), 0.063% (mass = 37.963 amu), and 99.600% (mass = 39.962 amu), respectively. Calculate the average atomic mass of argon.

26. List the numbers of protons, neutrons, and electrons in each of the following atoms.

	Protons	Neutrons	Electrons
$^{19}_{9}F$			
$^{27}_{13}Al$			
$^{40}_{18}Ar$			
$^{65}_{30}Zn$			
$^{108}_{47}Ag$			

27. Complete the following table.

Atomic Number	Mass Number	Number of Protons	Number of Neutrons	Number of Electrons	Symbol
12					$^{24}_{12}\text{Mg}$
	39		20		
			30	26	
					$^{80}_{35}\text{Br}$
	79	118			

D. Essay

Write a short essay for the following.

28. Explain how the isotopes of one element are alike and how they are different. Give at least two examples of each.

_____

_____

_____

_____

_____

_____

Name _____ Date _____ Class _____

QUICK LAB: Using Inference: The Black Box

Laboratory Recordsheet   Use with Section 4.2

PURPOSE

To determine the shape of a fixed object inside a sealed box without opening the box.

MATERIALS

- box containing a regularly shaped object fixed in place and a loose marble

PROCEDURE

1. Do not open the box.

2. Carefully manipulate the box so that the marble moves around the fixed object.

3. Gather data (clues) that describe the movement of the marble.

4. Sketch a picture of the object in the box, showing its shape, size, and location within the box.

5. Repeat this activity with a different box containing a different object.

ANALYSES AND CONCLUSIONS

1. Find a classmate who had the same lettered box that you had. Compare your findings and try to come to agreement about the shape and location of the fixed object.

   _____

   _____

   _____

2. What experiment that contributed to a better understanding of the atom does this activity remind you of?

   _____

   _____

   _____

SMALL-SCALE LAB: The Atomic Mass of Candium

Laboratory Recordsheet   Use with Section 4.3

PURPOSE

To analyze the isotopes of candium and to calculate its atomic mass.

MATERIALS

- sample of "candium"
- balance
- pencil
- paper

PROCEDURE

Obtain a sample of "candium" that contains three different brands of round, coated candy. Treat each brand of candy as an isotope of candium. Separate the three isotopes into groups labeled A, B, and C, and measure the mass of each isotope. Count the number of atoms in each sample. Make a table similar to the one below to record your measured and calculated data.

	A	B	C	Totals
Total mass (grams)				
Number				
Average mass (grams)				
Relative abundance				
Percent abundance				
Relative mass				

Figure A

ANALYSIS

Using the experimental data, record the answers to the following questions.

1. Calculate the average mass of each isotope by dividing its total mass by the number of particles of that isotope. Record your data in Figure A.

2. Calculate the relative abundance of each isotope by dividing its number of particles by the total number of particles.

3. Calculate the percent abundance of each isotope by multiplying the relative abundance from Step 2 by 100.

4. Calculate the relative mass of each isotope by multiplying its relative abundance from Step 2 by its average mass.

5. Calculate the weighted average mass of all candium particles by adding the relative masses. This weighted average mass is the atomic mass of candium.

6. Explain the difference between percent abundance and relative abundance. What is the result when you total the individual percent abundances? The individual relative abundances?

_____

_____

7. The percent abundance of each kind of candy tells you how many of each kind of candy there are in every 100 particles. What does relative abundance tell you?

_____

_____

8. Compare the total values for rows 3 and 6 in the table. Explain why the totals differ and why the value in row 6 best represents atomic mass.

_____

_____

9. Explain any differences between the atomic mass of your candium sample and that of your neighbor. Explain why the difference would be smaller if larger samples were used.

_____

_____

YOU'RE THE CHEMIST

Use the space below to write about the small-scale activities in the *You're the Chemist* section.

_____

_____

_____

_____

_____

_____

_____

_____

_____

_____

_____

_____

_____

_____

_____

_____

Name _____ Date _____ Class _____

5.1 MODELS OF THE ATOM

Section Review

Objectives

- Identify inadequacies in the Rutherford atomic model
- Identify the new assumption in the Bohr model of the atom
- Describe the energies and positions of electrons according to the quantum mechanical model
- Describe how the shapes of orbitals at different sublevels vary

Vocabulary

- energy levels
- quantum
- quantum mechanical model
- atomic orbital

Part A Completion

Use this completion exercise to check your understanding of the concepts and terms that are introduced in this section. Each blank can be completed with a term, short phrase, or number.

The chemical properties of atoms, ions, and molecules are related to the arrangement of the __1__ within them.

The first modern atomic theory, proposed by __2__, portrayed the atom as a solid, indivisible mass. After the discovery of the electron by __3__, the atomic model was revised to include them. J.J. Thomson's model is referred to as the __4__ model. Rutherford pictured the atom as a dense __5__ surrounded by electrons. In the Bohr model, the electrons move in __6__ paths. The __7__ model is the modern description of the electrons in atoms. This model estimates the __8__ of finding an electron within a certain volume of space surrounding the nucleus.

1. _____
2. _____
3. _____
4. _____
5. _____
6. _____
7. _____
8. _____

Part B True-False

Classify each of these statements as always true, AT; sometimes true, ST; or never true, NT.

_____ 9. Electrons must have a certain minimum amount of energy called a quantum in order to move from one energy level to the next higher energy level.

_____ 10. The electron probability clouds for atomic orbitals are spherical in shape.

_____ 11. The number of sublevels in an energy level is equal to the square of the principal quantum number of that energy level.

_____ 12. The maximum number of electrons that can occupy the fourth principal energy level of an atom is 32.

_____ 13. The higher the energy level occupied by an electron the more energetic it is.

_____ 14. The principal quantum number equals the number of sublevels within that principal energy level.

Part C Matching

Match each description in Column B to the correct term in Column A.

Column A	**Column B**
_____ 15. quantum	**a.** a region in space around the nucleus of an atom where an electron is likely to be moving
_____ 16. atomic orbitals	**b.** the regions around the nucleus within which the electrons have the highest probability of being found
_____ 17. energy level	**c.** the amount of energy required to move an electron from its present energy level to the next higher one
_____ 18. quantum mechanical model	**d.** the modern description of the behavior of electrons in atoms

Part D Questions and Problems

Answer the following in the space provided.

19. Summarize the development of atomic theory.

_____

_____

_____

_____

_____

20. How many orbitals are in each of the following sublevels?

a. $4p$ sublevel _____

b. $3d$ sublevel _____

c. $4f$ sublevel _____

d. $2s$ sublevel _____

Name _____ Date _____ Class _____

Section Review

Objectives
- Describe how to write the electron configuration for an atom
- Explain why the actual electron configurations for some elements differ from those predicted by the Aufbau principle

Vocabulary
- electron configurations
- Aufbau principle
- Pauli exclusion principle
- Hund's rule

Part A Completion

Use this completion exercise to check your understanding of the concepts and terms that are introduced in this section. Each blank can be completed with a term, short phrase, or number.

The ways in which electrons are arranged around the nuclei of atoms are called ___1___. The ___2___ describes the sequence in which orbitals are filled. The various orbitals within a sublevel of a principle energy level are always of ___3___ energy. The ___4___ principle states that a maximum of only ___5___ electrons can occupy each orbital. To occupy the same orbital, two electrons must have ___6___ spins. Hund's rule states that the electrons pair up only after each orbital in a sublevel is occupied by ___7___. When using the shorthand method for showing the electron configuration of an atom, ___8___ are used to indicate the number of ___9___ occupying each sublevel.

Correct electron configurations can be obtained by using the Aufbau diagram for the elements up to and including vanadium. ___10___ and copper are exceptions to the Aufbau principle.

1. _____
2. _____
3. _____
4. _____
5. _____
6. _____
7. _____
8. _____
9. _____
10. _____

Part B True-False

Classify each of these statements as always true, AT; sometimes true, ST; or never true, NT.

_____ **11.** The orbitals of a principal energy level are lower in energy than the orbitals in the next higher principal energy level.

_____ **12.** The configuration $3d^4 4s^2$ is more stable than the configuration $3d^5 4s^1$.

_____ **13.** As many as four electrons can occupy the same orbital.

_____ **14.** The Pauli exclusion principle states that an atomic orbital may describe at most two electrons.

_____ **15.** The electron configuration for potassium is $1s^2 2s^2 2p^6 3s^2 3p^6 4s^1$.

_____ **16.** The electron configuration for copper is $1s^2 2s^2 2p^6 3s^2 3p^6 4s^2 3d^9$.

Part C Matching

Match each description in Column B to the correct term in Column A.

Column A	Column B
_____ **17.** electron configuration	**a.** When electrons occupy orbitals of equal energy, one electron enters each orbital until all the orbitals contain one electron with parallel spins.
_____ **18.** Aufbau principle	**b.** An atomic orbital may describe at most two electrons.
_____ **19.** Pauli exclusion principle	**c.** $1s^2 2s^2 2p^6$
_____ **20.** Hund's rule	**d.** Electrons enter orbitals of lowest energy first.
_____ **21.** neon	**e.** the most stable arrangement of electrons around the nucleus of an atom

Part D Questions and Problems

Answer the following in the space provided.

22. Write the electron configurations for the following atoms.

a. C _____

c. K _____

b. S _____

d. Ar _____

23. Identify the elements described below:

a. Contains a full third energy level.

_____

b. Contains the first *p* electron.

_____

5.3 PHYSICS AND THE QUANTUM MECHANICAL MODEL

Section Review

Objectives

- Describe the relationship between the wavelength and frequency of light
- Explain how the frequencies of light are related to changes in electron energies
- Distinguish between quantum mechanics and classical mechanics
- Identify the cause of the atomic emission spectrum

Vocabulary

- amplitude
- wavelength (λ)
- frequency (ν)
- hertz (Hz)

- electromagnetic radiation
- spectrum
- atomic emission spectrum
- ground state

- photons
- Heisenberg uncertainty principle

Key Equations

- $c = \lambda \nu$
- $E = h \times \nu$
- $\lambda = \dfrac{h}{m\nu}$

Part A Completion

Use this completion exercise to check your understanding of the concepts and terms that are introduced in this section. Each blank can be completed with a term, short phrase, or number.

According to quantum mechanics, the motions of subatomic

particles may be described as ___1___ . The frequency and

wavelength of all waves are ___2___ related.

Every element emits ___3___ if it is heated by passing an

electric discharge through its gas or vapor. Passing this emission

through a prism gives the ___4___ of the element.

The quantum concept developed from Planck's studies of

___5___ and Einstein's explanation of the ___6___ effect. Planck

showed that the amount of radiant energy absorbed or emitted by

a body is proportional to the ___7___ of the radiation.

1. _____

2. _____

3. _____

4. _____

5. _____

6. _____

7. _____

Part B True-False

Classify each of these statements as always true, AT; sometimes true, ST; or never true, NT.

_____ **8.** The speed of light is a constant that can be obtained by dividing the frequency of light by its wavelength.

_____ **9.** The amplitude of a wave is the distance between the crests.

_____ **10.** The energy of a body can change only in small discrete units.

_____ **11.** The position and velocity of an electron in an atom can be determined with great certainty.

_____ **12.** The photoelectric effect will occur no matter what frequency of light strikes a metal.

Part C Matching

Match each description in Column B to the correct term in Column A.

Column A	Column B
_____ **13.** photons	**a.** predicts that all matter exhibits wavelike motions
_____ **14.** de Broglie's equation	**b.** the distance between two consecutive wave crests
_____ **15.** visible light	**c.** light quanta
_____ **16.** ground state	**d.** the lowest energy level for a given electron
_____ **17.** wavelength	**e.** example of electromagnetic radiation

Part D Questions and Problems

Answer the following in the space provided.

18. What is the frequency of radiation whose wavelength is 2.40×10^{-5} cm?

19. Apply quantum theory to explain the photoelectric effect.

_____

_____

_____

5 | ELECTRONS IN ATOMS

Practice Problems

In your notebook, solve the following problems.

SECTION 5.1 MODELS OF THE ATOM

1. How many sublevels are in the following principal energy levels?

   a. $n = 1$ c. $n = 3$ e. $n = 5$

   b. $n = 2$ d. $n = 4$ f. $n = 6$

2. How many orbitals are in the following sublevels?

   a. $1s$ sublevel   d. $4f$ sublevel   g. fifth principal energy level

   b. $5s$ sublevel   e. $7s$ sublevel   h. $6d$ sublevel

   c. $4d$ sublevel   f. $3p$ sublevel

3. What are the types of sublevels and number of orbitals in the following energy levels?

   a. $n = 1$ c. $n = 3$ e. $n = 5$

   b. $n = 2$ d. $n = 4$

SECTION 5.2 ELECTRON ARRANGEMENT IN ATOMS

1. Write a complete electron configuration of each atom.

   a. hydrogen   d. barium   g. krypton

   b. vanadium   e. bromine   h. arsenic

   c. magnesium   f. sulfur   i. radon

SECTION 5.3 PHYSICS AND THE QUANTUM MECHANICAL MODEL

1. What is the wavelength of the radiation whose frequency is 5.00×10^{15} s^{-1}? In what region of the electromagnetic spectrum is this radiation?

2. An inexpensive laser that is available to the public emits light that has a wavelength of 670 nm. What are the color and frequency of the radiation?

3. What is the energy of a photon whose frequency is 2.22×10^{14} s^{-1}?

4. What is the frequency of a photon whose energy is 6.00×10^{-15} J?

5. Arrange the following types of electromagnetic radiation in order of increasing frequency.

   a. infrared   c. visible light   e. microwaves

   b. gamma rays   d. radio waves   f. ultraviolet

6. Suppose that your favorite AM radio station broadcasts at a frequency of 1600 kHz. What is the wavelength in meters of the radiation from the station?

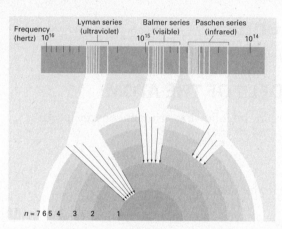

5 INTERPRETING GRAPHICS

Use with Section 5.3

Figure 1 The emission spectrum and orbit-transition diagram for hydrogen.

Table 1

Transition	E (J)	ν (s^{-1})	λ(m)	Type of Radiation
$n = 6 \rightarrow n = 5$	2.66×10^{-20}			
$n = 6 \rightarrow n = 4$	7.57×10^{-20}			
$n = 6 \rightarrow n = 3$	1.82×10^{-19}			
$n = 6 \rightarrow n = 2$	4.84×10^{-19}			
$n = 6 \rightarrow n = 1$	2.12×10^{-18}			
$n = 5 \rightarrow n = 4$	4.91×10^{-20}			
$n = 5 \rightarrow n = 3$	1.55×10^{-19}			
$n = 5 \rightarrow n = 2$	4.56×10^{-19}			
$n = 5 \rightarrow n = 1$	2.09×10^{-18}			
$n = 4 \rightarrow n = 3$	1.06×10^{-19}			
$n = 4 \rightarrow n = 2$	4.09×10^{-19}			
$n = 4 \rightarrow n = 1$	2.04×10^{-18}			
$n = 3 \rightarrow n = 2$	3.03×10^{-19}			
$n = 3 \rightarrow n = 1$	1.94×10^{-18}			
$n = 2 \rightarrow n = 1$	1.64×10^{-18}			

Name _____ Date _____ Class _____

1. Figure 1 summarizes the quantum model of the hydrogen atom originally proposed by Neils Bohr to account for the interaction of hydrogen with electromagnetic radiation. The energy changes associated with each electron transition for the lowest six energy levels of hydrogen are listed in Table 1. Calculate the frequency of the emitted radiation for each transition.

2. Calculate the wavelength in meters for each energy level transition and fill in the column for wavelength.

3. Determine the type of radiation (ultraviolet, visible, or infrared) that corresponds to each wavelength.

4. Which transitions result in the emission of visible light?

_____

_____

_____

_____

5. If the wavelengths of blue, green, and red light are approximately 400 nm, 500 nm, and 650 nm, respectively, what colors in the visible spectrum correspond to the transitions stated in your answer to question 4?

_____

_____

_____

_____

6. What is the common feature among transitions where the resulting radiation lies within the visible light range of the electromagnetic spectrum?

_____

_____

_____

_____

7. The Bohr model, although historically important, was limited in its ability to explain the behavior of more complex elements and ions. To which of the following atoms or ions would you expect the Bohr model to apply?

   Be, He^+, K, Li^{2+}

_____

5 ELECTRONS IN ATOMS

Vocabulary Review

Choose the term from the following list that best matches each description.

quantum
photons
hertz
Pauli exclusion principle
wavelength

Hund's rule
atomic emission spectrum
photoelectrons
Aufbau principle
quantum mechanical model

1. The lowest-energy arrangement of electrons in a subshell is obtained by putting electrons into separate orbitals of the subshell before pairing electrons.

   _____

2. packets/quanta of electromagnetic energy

   _____

3. the SI unit of frequency

   _____

4. An atomic orbital can hold no more than two electrons.

   _____

5. the amount of energy required to move an electron from its present energy level to the next higher one

   _____

6. the modern description of the location and energy of electrons in an atom

   _____

7. This principle states that electrons enter orbitals of lowest energy first.

   _____

8. the distance between two adjacent crests of an electromagnetic wave

   _____

9. This is produced by passing the light emitted by an element through a prism.

   _____

10. These are sometimes produced when light shines on metals.

   _____

5 ELECTRONS IN ATOMS

Chapter Quiz

Classify each of these statements as always true, AT; sometimes true, ST; or never true, NT.

_____ 1. The orbitals of a principal energy level are lower in energy than the orbitals in the next higher principal energy level. 5.1

_____ 2. The configuration $3d^4 4s^2$ is more stable than the configuration $3d^5 4s^1$. 5.2

_____ 3. In the quantum mechanical model of the atom, the probability of finding an electron within a certain volume of space surrounding the nucleus can be portrayed as a fuzzy cloud. 5.3

_____ 4. The fourth principal energy level of an atom contains 32 electrons. 5.1

_____ 5. There are five orbitals in the $4d$ energy level. 5.1

_____ 6. The amplitude of a wave is the distance between the crests. 5.3

Fill in the word(s) that will make each statement true.

7. In the equation $E = h \times v$, h is called ___7___. 7. _____ 5.3

8. The electron in a hydrogen atom has the least energy in the ___8___. 8. _____ 5.3

9. Einstein proposed that light is composed of particle-like quanta of energy; light quanta are known as ___9___. 9. _____ 5.3

10. The ___10___ effect occurs when light above the threshold frequency strikes a metal. 10. _____ 5.3

11. De Broglie developed the idea that matter in motion exhibits ___11___ properties. 11. _____ 5.3

5 ELECTRONS IN ATOMS

Chapter Test A

A. Matching

Match each description in Column B with the correct term in Column A. Write the letter of the correct description on the line.

Column A	Column B
_____ 1. hertz	**a.** the number of wave cycles that pass a given point per unit of time
_____ 2. atomic orbital	**b.** the SI unit of frequency
_____ 3. spectrum	**c.** lines of colored light obtained by passing the light emitted by an element through a prism
_____ 4. atomic emission spectrum	**d.** the region around an atomic nucleus where an electron is likely to be moving
_____ 5. quantum of energy	**e.** a range of colors seen when light passes through a prism
_____ 6. amplitude	**f.** Electrons enter orbitals of lowest energy first.
_____ 7. wavelength	**g.** a region outside the nucleus where there is high probability of finding an electron
_____ 8. energy level	**h.** the amount of energy required to move an electron from one energy level to the next higher one
_____ 9. Aufbau principle	**i.** the distance between crests of waves
_____ 10. frequency	**j.** the height of a wave from the origin to the crest

B. Multiple Choice

Choose the best answer and write its letter on the line.

_____ 11. The fourth principal energy level has
    a. 4 orbitals.   **c.** 32 orbitals.
    b. 16 orbitals.   **d.** 9 orbitals.

_____ 12. If the electron configuration of an element is $1s^2 2s^2 2p^6 3s^2 3p^5$, the element is
    a. iron.   **c.** chlorine.
    b. bromine.   **d.** phosphorus.

_____ **13.** The quantum mechanical model of the atom
   a. is concerned with the probability of finding an electron in a certain position.
   b. was proposed by Neils Bohr.
   c. defines the exact path of an electron around the nucleus.
   d. has many analogies in the visible world.

_____ **14.** The electron configuration of calcium is
   a. $1s^2 2s^2 2p^2 3s^2 3p^3 4s^2$.
   c. $1s^2 2s^2 3s^2 3p^6\ 3d^8$.
   b. $1s^2 2s^2 2p^{10} 3s^2 3p^4$.
   d. $1s^2 2s^2 2p^6 3s^2 3p^6 4s^2$.

_____ **15.** The maximum number of electrons that can occupy the third principal energy level is
   a. 18.
   c. 2.
   b. 32.
   d. 8.

_____ **16.** As the frequency of light increases, the wavelength
   a. increases.
   c. decreases.
   b. remains the same.
   d. approaches the speed of light.

_____ **17.** The formula $2n^2$ represents
   a. the number of sublevels in any energy level.
   b. the maximum number of electrons that can occupy an energy level.
   c. the number of orbitals in a sublevel.
   d. none of the above

_____ **18.** In order to occupy the same orbital, two electrons must have
   a. the same direction of spin.
   c. opposite charge.
   b. low energy.
   d. opposite spin.

_____ **19.** Stable electron configurations are likely to contain
   a. high-energy electrons.
   b. unfilled s orbitals.
   c. fewer electrons than unstable configurations.
   d. filled energy sublevels.

_____ **20.** According to Hund's rule, when electrons occupy orbitals of equal energy, one electron enters each orbit until
   a. all the orbitals contain one electron, with spins parallel.
   b. all the orbitals contain one electron, with opposite spins.
   c. there are two electrons in each orbital.
   d. electron velocities become constant.

C. Problems

Solve the following problems in the space provided. Show your work.

21. Write electron configurations for these atoms, using arrows to represent electrons. Then, use the shorthand method to write the configurations.

   a. S
   b. Na

22. What is the frequency of radiation whose wavelength is 2.40×10^{-5} cm?

23. Identify the elements that have the following electron configurations.

    a. $1s^2 2s^2 2p^6 3s^2 3p^1$

    a. _____

    b. $1s^2 2s^2 2p^6 3s^2 3p^6 3d^{10} 4s^2 4p^6$

    b. _____

    c. $1s^2 2s^2 2p^6 3s^2 3p^6 3d^7 4s^2$

    c. _____

24. Consider the elements neon, bromine, and phosphorus. Which has

    a. three electrons in its $3p$ sublevel?

    a. _____

    b. its highest energy level completely filled?

    b. _____

    c. the highest occupied energy level?

    c. _____

25. What is the maximum number of electrons that can occupy each of the first five principal energy levels?

D. Essay

Write a short essay for the following.

26. Explain why the $5s$ sublevel fills before any electrons are added to the $4d$ sublevel.

_____

_____

_____

_____

_____

_____

Name _____ Date _____ Class _____

E. Additional Matching

Match each description in Column B with the correct term in Column A. Write the letter of the correct description on the line.

Column A

_____ 27. ground state

_____ 28. photoelectric effect

_____ 29. photons

_____ 30. Heisenberg uncertainty principle

_____ 31. de Broglie's equation

_____ 32. Planck's constant

Column B

a. a process in which electrons are ejected by metals when certain wavelengths of light shine on them

b. the lowest energy level for a given electron

c. predicts that all matter exhibits wavelike motions

d. 6.6262×10^{-34} Js

e. It is impossible to know both the velocity and the position of a particle at the same time.

f. quanta of light

F. True-False

Classify each of these statements as always true, AT; sometimes true, ST; or never true, NT.

_____ 33. The energy of a body can change only in small discrete units.

_____ 34. The position and velocity of an electron in an atom can be determined with great certainty.

_____ 35. Above the threshold frequency, increasing the intensity of the light striking a metal increases the number of electrons ejected.

_____ 36. Electrons moving from one energy level to another emit photons.

_____ 37. The photoelectric effect will occur no matter what frequency of light strikes a metal.

_____ 38. In the Bohr model of the hydrogen atom, when the electron is in the ground state, $n = 1$.

_____ 39. The lines in the emission spectrum of hydrogen can be correlated to transitions of electrons from higher energy levels to lower energy levels.

_____ 40. The outermost *s* orbital of an atom contains two electrons.

_____ 41. According to quantum mechanics, the motions of subatomic particles may be described as wavelike.

5 ELECTRONS IN ATOMS

Chapter Test B

A. Matching

Match each term in Column B with the correct description in Column A. Write the letter of the correct term on the line.

Column A   **Column B**

_____ 1. the ways in which electrons are arranged around the nuclei of atoms

a. Aufbau principle

_____ 2. the ejection of electrons by metals when light shines on them

b. quantum

_____ 3. the region around the nucleus of an atom where an electron is likely to be moving

c. photoelectric effect

_____ 4. An atomic orbital may describe at most two electrons.

d. atomic orbitals

_____ 5. the regions within which electrons have the highest probability of being found

e. Pauli exclusion principle

_____ 6. When electrons occupy orbitals of equal energy, one electron enters each orbital until all the orbitals contain one electron.

f. energy level

_____ 7. the amount of energy required to move an electron from its present energy level to the next higher one

g. Hund's rule

_____ 8. light quanta

h. electron configurations

_____ 9. Electrons enter orbitals of lowest energy first.

i. quantum mechanical model

_____ 10. the modern description of the electrons in atoms

j. photons

B. Multiple Choice

Choose the best answer and write its letter on the line.

_____ 11. Bohr's contribution to the development of atomic structure
   a. was referred to as the "plum pudding model."
   b. was the discovery that electrons surround a dense nucleus.
   c. was proposed that electrons travel in circular orbits around the nucleus.
   d. is the quantum mechanical model.

_____ 12. What is the total number of orbitals in the third principal energy level?
   a. 1   **c.** 9
   b. 4   **d.** 16

_____ 13. What is the maximum number of electrons allowed in the third energy
level?
a. 2
b. 8
c. 18
d. 32

_____ 14. What is the maximum number of electrons that can occupy one orbital?
a. 1
b. 2
c. 8
d. 18

_____ 15. The electron configuration for fluorine is
a. $1s^2 2s^2 2p^3$.
b. $1s^2 2s^2 2p^5$.
c. $1s^2 2s^2 2p^6$.
d. $1s^2 2s^2 2p^6 3s^2$.

_____ 16. The first three electrons that enter into p orbitals must have
a. parallel spins.
b. opposite spins.
c. low energy levels.
d. opposite charges.

_____ 17. The atom whose electron configuration is $1s^2 2s^2 2p^6 3s^2 3p^1$ is
a. B.
b. Na.
c. Al.
d. Ga.

_____ 18. The configuration for the outermost energy level in Ca is
a. $3s^2$.
b. $4s^2$.
c. $2s^1$.
d. $4s^1$.

_____ 19. The element having the same s and p configurations for principal
energy level 3 as the element F has for its principal energy level 2 is
a. Na.
b. Al.
c. P.
d. Cl.

_____ 20. The frequency and wavelength of all waves are
a. directly related.
b. inversely related.
c. unrelated.
d. equal.

_____ 21. The SI unit of cycles per second is called a
a. photon.
b. quantum.
c. hertz.
d. hund.

_____ 22. Among the following groups of atoms, which have the same outer
energy level configurations?
a. H, He
b. Li, Be, N, Ne
c. Mg, Al, Ca, Ga
d. N, P, As, Bi

_____ 23. The wavelength of light with a frequency of 2.50×10^{13} s^{-1} is
a. 1.20×10^5 m.
b. 8.33×10^5 m.
c. 1.20×10^{-5} m.
d. 8.33×10^{-5} m.

_____ 24. Once the electron in a hydrogen atom absorbs a quantum of energy, it
a. is now in its ground state.
b. is now in its excited state.
c. has released a photon.
d. none of the above

C. Problems

Solve the following problems in the space provided. Show your work.

25. Write the electron configurations for the following atoms.

   a. Mg

   b. P

   c. Br

   d. Xe

26. Identify the elements described below.

   a. Configuration = $1s^2 2s^2 2p^6 3s^2 3p^4$

   b. Contains a full second energy level

   c. Contains the first d electron

   d. Contains seven electrons in its fourth energy level

   e. Contains only two electrons in its fifth energy level

   f. Contains three unpaired electrons in its third energy level

   g. Contains five electrons in its $3d$ orbitals

   h. Has its outermost electron in $7s^1$

27. What is the frequency of radiation whose wavelength is 6.25×10^{-5} cm?

28. What is the energy of a photon whose frequency is $5.2 \times 10^{15}\ s^{-1}$?
$h = 6.6262 \times 10^{-34}\ Js$

D. Essay

Write a short essay for the following.

29. Distinguish between the Bohr model and the quantum mechanical model of an atom in terms of the positions of the electrons in an atom.

_____

_____

_____

_____

_____

_____

E. Additional Matching

Match each term in Column B with the correct description in Column A. Write the letter of the correct term on the line.

Column A

_____ **30.** the lowest energy level within which an electron can be found

_____ **31.** the height of an electromagnetic wave from the origin to the crest

_____ **32.** It is impossible to know exactly both the velocity and the position of a particle at the same time.

_____ **33.** the number of electromagnetic wave cycles to pass a given point per unit of time

_____ **34.** All matter exhibits wavelike motion.

_____ **35.** the distance between the crests of an electromagnetic wave

Column B

a. Heisenberg uncertainty principle

b. wavelength

c. ground state

d. amplitude

e. de Broglie's equation

f. frequency

F. True-False

Classify each of these statements as always true, AT; sometimes true, ST; or never true, NT.

_____ **36.** The energy levels in an atom can be viewed like the rungs on a ladder.

_____ **37.** The electrons in an atom are arranged in concentric orbits around the nucleus.

_____ **38.** The principal quantum number equals the number of sublevels within that principal energy level.

_____ **39.** As many as eight electrons may occupy the same orbital.

_____ **40.** In all natural phenomena, change proceeds toward the lowest possible energy state.

_____ **41.** The photoelectric effect will occur only if the frequency of light striking an electron in a metal is above a certain threshold frequency.

_____ **42.** The behavior of light can be explained in terms of waves.

_____ **43.** According to the Heisenberg uncertainty principle, as the velocity of a moving particle is known with increasing accuracy, the position of that particle becomes less accurately known.

_____ **44.** Quantum mechanics describes the motions of subatomic particles and atoms as waves that gain or lose energy in packages called quanta.

SMALL-SCALE LAB: Atomic Emission Spectra

Laboratory Recordsheet   Use with Section 5.2

PURPOSE

To build a spectroscope and use it to measure the wavelengths, frequencies, and energies of atomic emission lines.

MATERIALS

- cereal box
- diffraction grating
- tape
- ruler
- pencil
- scissors
- black construction paper
- white notebook paper

PROCEDURE

Tape together two 2.0 cm × 10 cm strips of black construction paper so that they are parallel and form a narrow slit about 2 mm wide. Remove the top of a cereal box and tape the construction paper slit near one edge of the open end of the box. Cover the remainder of the opening with white notebook paper. On the end of the box opposite the slit, cut a square hole (approximately 2 cm per side) and tape a diffraction grating over the hole. Point the spectroscope toward a fluorescent light and view the spectrum through the diffraction grating. Tape up any light leaks. Your lab partner should mark the exact positions of all the colored emission lines you see on the notebook paper at the end of the box. Measure the distances between the violet line and the other lines you have marked.

ANALYSIS

Using your experimental data, record the answers to the following questions.

1. How many distinct lines do you see and what are their colors?

_____

_____

_____

_____

_____

_____

2. Each line you see has a different value of a property called its wavelength. The prominent violet line has a wavelength of 436 nm and the prominent green line is 546 nm. How many mm apart are the lines on the paper? How many nm do their wavelengths differ? How many nanometers of wavelength are represented by each millimeter you measured?

_____

_____

_____

_____

_____

_____

_____

3. Using the nm/mm value you calculated in Step 2 and the mm distance you measured for each line from the violet reference line, calculate the wavelength of all the other lines you see.

_____

_____

_____

_____

_____

_____

_____

4. Each wavelength corresponds to another property of light called its frequency. Use the wavelength value of each line to calculate its frequency given that $v = c/\lambda$ where $c = 2.998 \times 10^{17}$ nm/s (2.998×10^3 m/s).

_____

_____

_____

_____

_____

_____

_____

_____

5. The energy (E) of a quantum of light an atom emits is related to its frequency (v) by $E = h \times v$. Use the frequency value for each line and $h = 6.63 \times 10^{-34}$ J·s to calculate its corresponding energy.

_____

_____

_____

_____

_____

_____

_____

_____

Name ______________________ Date ________________ Class ________________

YOU'RE THE CHEMIST

Use the space below to write your observations to the small-scale activities in the *You're the Chemist* section.

QUICK LAB: Flame Tests

Laboratory Recordsheet   Use with Section 5.3

PURPOSE

Use the flame test to determine the identity of the cation in an unknown solution based on its characteristic color.

MATERIALS

- Bunsen burner
- small beaker
- 6 small test tubes
- test-tube rack
- tongs
- flame test wire (10-cm length of nichrome wire)
- $6M$ HCl
- $0.1M$ NaCl
- $0.1M$ CaCl$_2$
- $0.1M$ LiCl
- $0.1M$ CuCl$_2$
- $0.1M$ BaCl$_2$
- unknown solution

PROCEDURE

1. Make a two-column data table. Label column one Cation. Label column two Flame Color. Enter the name of the cation of each salt solution in column one.

2. Label each of five test tubes with the name of a salt solution; label the sixth tube Unknown. Add 1 mL of each salt solution to the appropriately labeled test tube. Add 5 mL HCl to the beaker.

3. Grasp one end of the nichrome wire with the tongs. Clean the wire by alternately heating it in the hot burner flame and dipping it into the hydrochloric acid. Repeat several times until the flame remains almost colorless when the wire is heated.

4. Dip the clean wire into the sodium chloride solution and then hold it in the hot burner flame. Record the color of the flame. Repeat Step 3 to clean the wire.

5. Repeat Step 4 for each of the remaining salt solutions.

6. Perform a flame test with the unknown solution. Note the color of the flame.

ANALYSES AND CONCLUSIONS

1. What is the identity of the cation in the unknown?

   _____

   _____

2. Each known salt solution has a unique color. Would you expect this based on the modern view of the atom? Explain.

   _____

   _____

   _____

3. Some commercially available fireplace logs burn with a red and/or green flame. On the basis of your data, what elements could be responsible for these colored flames?

   _____

   _____

4. Aerial fireworks contain gunpowder and chemicals that produce colors. What elements would you include to produce the following colors?

   a. crimson red

   _____

   _____

   b. yellow

   _____

   _____

6.1 ORGANIZING THE ELEMENTS

Section Review

Objectives

- Explain how elements are organized in a periodic table
- Compare early and modern periodic tables
- Identify three broad classes of elements

Vocabulary

- periodic law
- metals
- nonmetals
- metalloids

Part A Completion

Use this completion exercise to check your understanding of the concepts and terms that are introduced in this section. Each blank can be completed with a term, short phrase, or number.

Chemists used the ___1___ of elements to sort them into groups.   1. _____

The periodic table organizes the elements into vertical ___2___   2. _____

and horizontal ___3___ in order of increasing ___4___. The table is   3. _____

constructed so that elements that have similar chemical properties   4. _____

are in the same ___5___. ___6___ have a high luster, or sheen,   5. _____

when cut. Most nonmetals are ___7___ at room temperature.   6. _____

Elements with properties that are similar to those of metals   7. _____

and nonmetals are called ___8___. Across the periodic table,   8. _____

the properties of elements become ___9___ metallic and   9. _____

___10___ nonmetallic.   10. _____

Part B True-False

Classify each of these statements as always true, AT; sometimes true, ST; or never true, NT.

_____ **10.** In his periodic table, Mendeleev arranged the elements in order of atomic number.

_____ **11.** There are six periods in a periodic table.

_____ **12.** Most of the elements in the periodic table are metals.

_____ **13.** The elements within a period have similar properties.

Part C Matching

Match each description in Column B to the correct term in Column A

Column A	**Column B**
_____ **14.** metals	**a.** a vertical column of elements in the periodic table
_____ **15.** periods	**b.** good conductors of heat and electric current
_____ **16.** group	**c.** poor conductors of heat and electric current
_____ **17.** nonmetals	**d.** have properties that are similar to those of metals and nonmetals
_____ **18.** metalloids	**e.** the horizontal rows of the periodic table

Part D Questions and Problems

Answer the following questions in the space provided.

19. List the elements of Group 5A. Tell whether each is a metal, nonmetal, or metalloid.

_____

_____

20. List three properties of metals.

_____

_____

21. Name two elements that have similar properties to those of chlorine.

_____

_____

6.2 CLASSIFYING THE ELEMENTS

Section Review

Objectives

- Describe the information in a periodic table
- Classify elements based on electron configuration
- Distinguish representative elements and transition metals

Vocabulary

- alkali metals
- alkaline earth metals
- halogens
- noble gases
- representative elements
- transition metals
- inner transition metals

Part A Completion

Use this completion exercise to check your understanding of the concepts and terms that are introduced in this section. Each blank can be completed with a term, short phrase, or number.

The periodic table displays the symbols and __1__ of

the elements along with information about the structures of their

__2__. The Group 1A elements are called __3__, and the

Group 2A elements are called __4__. The elements in Groups 1A

through 7A are called the __5__. The nonmetals of Group 7A

are __6__, and the __7__ make up Group 8A. Between Groups

2A and 3A, there are __8__ in periods 4 through 7 and __9__

in periods 6 and 7.

The atoms of the noble gas elements have their highest occupied

s and __10__ sublevels filled. The highest occupied *s* and *p*

sublevels of the representative elements are __11__.

1. _____

2. _____

3. _____

4. _____

5. _____

6. _____

7. _____

8. _____

9. _____

10. _____

11. _____

Part B True-False

Classify each of these statements as always true, AT; sometimes true, ST; or never true, NT.

_____ **12.** Group A elements are representative elements.

_____ **13.** Chlorine has the electron configuration $1s^22s^22p^63s^23p^7$.

_____ **14.** The element in Group 4A, period 3, is gallium.

_____ **15.** There is a relationship between the electron configurations of elements and their chemical and physical properties.

Part C Matching

Match each description in Column B to the correct term in Column A.

Column A	Column B
_____ **16.** alkali metals	**a.** nonmetals of Group 7A
_____ **17.** inner transition metal	**b.** an element in which the highest occupied *s* and *p* sublevels are filled
_____ **18.** representative element	**c.** Group 2A elements
_____ **19.** transition metal	**d.** an element whose highest occupied *s* sublevel and a nearby *d* sublevel contain electrons
_____ **20.** noble gas	**e.** an element whose highest occupied *s* sublevel and a nearby *f* sublevel generally contain electrons
_____ **21.** alkaline earth metals	**f.** Group 1A elements
_____ **22.** halogens	**g.** an element whose highest occupied *s* or *p* sublevels are partially filled

Part D Questions and Problems

Answer the following in the space provided.

23. List the electron configurations for the highest occupied energy level of the elements in period 3 from left to right.

_____

_____

_____

24. List the elements of Group 6A. Tell whether each is a solid, liquid, or gas at room temperature and whether it is a metal, nonmetal, or metalloid.

_____

_____

_____

Name _____ Date _____ Class _____

6.3 PERIODIC TRENDS

Section Review

Objectives

- Describe trends among elements for atomic size
- Explain how ions form
- Describe and explain periodic trends for first ionization energy, ionic size, and electronegativity

Vocabulary

- atomic radius
- ion
- cation
- anion
- ionization energy
- electronegativity

Part A Completion

Use this completion exercise to check your understanding of the concepts and terms that are introduced in this section. Each blank can be completed with a term, short phrase, or number.

Atomic radii generally ___1___ as you move from left to right in a period. Atomic size ___2___ with atomic number within a group because there are more occupied ___3___ and an increased shielding effect, despite an increase in nuclear ___4___.

The energy required to remove an electron from an atom is known as ___5___ energy. This quantity generally ___6___ as you move left to right across a period. Ions form when ___7___ are transferred between atoms. Cations are always ___8___ than the atoms from which they form. The ability of an atom to attract electrons when it is in a compound is called ___9___, and this value ___10___ as you move from left to right across a period.

1. _____
2. _____
3. _____
4. _____
5. _____
6. _____
7. _____
7. _____
8. _____
9. _____
10. _____

Part B True-False

Classify each of these statements as always true, AT; sometimes true, ST; or never true, NT.

_____ 11. Compounds are composed of particles called ions.

_____ **12.** Removing one electron from an atom results in the formation of a positive ion with a 1+ charge.

_____ **13.** An anion has more electrons than protons.

_____ **14.** Elements with a high electronegativity value tend to form positive ions.

Part C Matching

Match each description in Column B to the correct term in Column A.

Column A	Column B
_____ **15.** ion	**a.** half the distance between the nuclei of two atoms of the same element when the atoms are joined
_____ **16.** ionization energy	**b.** a negatively charged ion
_____ **17.** electronegativity	**c.** the energy required to remove an electron from an atom in its gaseous state
_____ **18.** atomic radius	**d.** an atom or group of atoms that has a positive or negative charge
_____ **19.** cation	**e.** a positively charged ion
_____ **20.** anion	**f.** the ability of an atom of an element to attract electrons when the atom is in a compound

Part D Questions and Problems

Answer the following in the space provided.

21. For the following pairs of atoms, tell which one of each pair has the largest ionic radius.

    a. Al, B _____

    b. S, O _____

    c. Br, Cl _____

    d. Na, Al _____

    e. O, F _____

22. Indicate which element of the following pairs is the most electronegative.

    a. calcium, gallium _____

    b. lithium, oxygen _____

    c. chlorine, sulfur _____

    d. bromine, arsenic _____

Name _____ Date _____ Class _____

THE PERIODIC TABLE

Practice Problems

In your notebook, solve the following problems.

SECTION 6.1 ORGANIZING THE ELEMENTS

1. Which element listed below should have chemical properties similar to fluorine (F)?

   a. Li

   b. Si

   c. Br

   d. Ne

2. Identify each element as a metal, metalloid, or nonmetal.

   a. fluorine

   b. germanium

   c. zinc

   d. phosphorus

   e. lithium

3. Which of the following is *not* a transition metal?

   a. magnesium

   b. titanium

   c. chromium

   d. mercury

4. Name two elements that have properties similar to those of the element potassium.

5. Elements in the periodic table can be divided into three broad classes based on their general characteristics. What are these classes and how do they differ?

SECTION 6.2 CLASSIFYING THE ELEMENTS

1. Use the periodic table to write the electron configuration for silicon. Explain your thinking.

2. Use the periodic table to write the electron configuration for iodine. Explain your thinking.

3. Which group of elements is characterized by an s^2p^3 configuration?

4. Name the element that matches the following description.

   a. one that has 5 electrons in the third energy level

   b. one with an electron configuration that ends in $4s^24p^5$

   c. the Group 6A element in period 4

5. Identify the elements that have electron configurations that end as follows.

   a. $2s^22p^4$

   b. $4s^2$

   c. $3d^{10}4s^2$

6. What is the common characteristic of the electron configurations of the elements Ne and Ar? In which group would you find them?

7. Why would you expect lithium (Li) and sulfur (S) to have different chemical and physical properties?

8. What characterizes the electron configurations of transition metals such as silver (Ag) and iron (Fe)?

SECTION 6.3 PERIODIC TRENDS

1. Explain why a magnesium atom is smaller than atoms of both sodium and calcium.

2. Predict the size of the astatine (At) atom compared to that of tellurium (Te). Explain your prediction.

3. Would you expect a Cl^- ion to be larger or smaller than an Mg^{2+} ion? Explain.

4. Which effect on atomic size is more significant, an increase in nuclear charge across a period or an increase in occupied energy levels within a group? Explain.

5. Explain why the sulfide ion (S^{2-}) is larger than the chloride ion (Cl^-).

6. Compare the first ionization energy of sodium to that of potassium.

7. Compare the first ionization energy lithium to that of beryllium.

8. Is the electronegativity of barium larger or smaller than that of strontium? Explain.

9. What is the most likely ion for magnesium to form? Explain.

10. Arrange oxygen, fluorine, and sulfur in order of increasing electronegativity.

INTERPRETING GRAPHICS

6

Use with Section 6.2

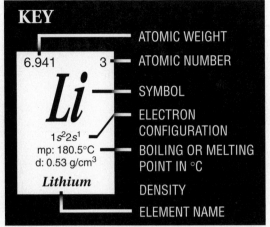

Key to periodic table A

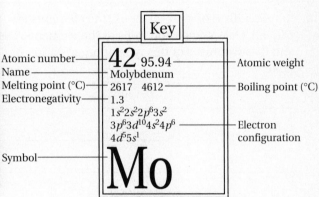

Key to periodic table B

Thousands of periodic tables have been published since Mendeleev published his table. Each one is a little different from the rest. Shown above are keys to two of the hundreds of periodic tables now available. A key is an example or roadmap for using a periodic table. Use the above keys to answer the following questions.

1. What is the atomic number of molybdenum?

_____

2. On which table(s) can the densities of the elements be found?

_____

3. What term is used in both keys as a synonym for average atomic mass?

_____

4. What is the density of lithium?

_____

5. What is the melting point of molybdenum?

_____

6. Which table do you think would be easier to use if you were only interested in finding atomic numbers?

_____

7. To how many significant figures is the atomic mass of lithium given?

_____

8. Compare the keys to periodic tables A and B to the key to the periodic table in your textbook. What other information is provided in your textbook's periodic table that is not provided in the examples shown above?

_____

_____

9. In Appendix B of your textbook, the elements are listed in alphabetical order. Table B.2 lists some properties of the elements. Discuss some of the advantages and disadvantages of this type of organization of data compared to the periodic table.

_____

_____

_____

_____

10. Find Li and Mo on the periodic table in your textbook.

   a. List the group number and period number for each element.

   _____

   b. Would you expect Li and Mo to have similar physical and chemical properties?

   _____

   _____

   c. Classify each element, Li and Mo, as an alkali metal, an alkaline earth metal, a transition metal, a nonmetal, or a metalloid.

   _____

   d. Name one other element in the periodic table whose physical and chemical properties you would expect to be similar to those of lithium.

   _____

11. Create you own key. Using the information given in Table 2.1 and in the periodic table in your textbook, create a key for one of the elements listed in Table 2.1. What information not listed in the periodic table would you have to include in your version of the periodic table?

6 THE PERIODIC TABLE

Vocabulary Review

Match the correct vocabulary term to each numbered statement. Write the letter of the correct term on the line.

Column A

_____ 1. The highest occupied *s* and *p* sublevels are partially filled.

_____ 2. The highest occupied *s* sublevel and a nearby *d* sublevel contain electrons.

_____ 3. metals having only 2 electrons in the highest occupied energy level

_____ 4. one half the distance between the nuclei of two atoms of the same element when the atoms are joined

_____ 5. decreases for cations and anions from left to right across a period

_____ 6. measures the ability of an atom to attract electrons when the atom is in a compound

_____ 7. an atom or group of atoms that has a positive or negative charge

_____ 8. elements in which the highest occupied *s* and *p* sublevels are filled

_____ 9. nonmetals of Group 7A

_____ 10. The highest occupied *s* sublevel and a nearby *f* sublevel contain electrons.

_____ 11. energy required to remove an electron from an atom

_____ 12. positively charged ion

_____ 13. Group 1A elements

_____ 14. good conductors of heat and electric current

_____ 15. negatively charged ion

_____ 16. poor conductors of heat and electric current

Column B

a. representative elements

b. electronegativity

c. atomic radius

d. metals

e. ionization energy

f. cation

g. noble gases

h. alkali metals

i. inner transition metals

j. nonmetals

k. ionic radius

l. ion

m. Group 2A

n. transition metal

o. halogens

p. anion

6 THE PERIODIC TABLE

Chapter Quiz

Fill in the word(s) that will make each statement true.

1. In the modern periodic table, when elements are arranged according to their atomic ___1___, there is a periodic repetition of properties.

1. _____ 6.1

2. There are ___2___ periods in the periodic table.

2. _____ 6.1

3. The elements in any ___3___ in the periodic table have similar physical and chemical properties.

3. _____ 6.1

4. Oxygen and sulfur, Group 6A elements, have ___4___ electrons in their highest occupied energy level.

4. _____ 6.2

5. For the inner transition elements, electrons are added to an *f* sublevel with a principal energy level that is ___5___ than the period number.

5. _____ 6.2

Classify each of these statements as always true, AT; sometimes true, ST; or never true, NT.

_____ 6. The atomic radius of an element in period 3 is larger that the atomic radius of an element in period 2.

6.3

_____ 7. For Group 3A elements, there is a relatively small increase in ionization energy between the second and third ionization energies.

6.3

_____ 8. Anions are smaller than the neutral atoms from which they are formed.

6.3

_____ 9. Atoms with low electronegativity values tend to form positive ions.

6.3

_____ 10. As a group, alkali metals have the highest electronegativities.

6.3

6 THE PERIODIC TABLE

Chapter Test A

A. Matching

Match each description in Column B with the correct term in Column A. Write the letter of the correct description on the line.

Column A	Column B
_____ 1. metal	**a.** positively charged ion
_____ 2. halogen	**b.** an element whose highest occupied *s* or *p* sublevels are partially filled
_____ 3. inner transition metal	**c.** the energy needed to remove an electron from an atom in the gaseous state
_____ 4. representative element	**d.** good conductor of heat and electric current
_____ 5. ionization energy	**e.** an element whose highest occupied *s* sublevel and a nearby *d* sublevel contain electrons
_____ 6. alkaline earth metal	**f.** any nonmetal in Group 7A
_____ 7. cation	**g.** the tendency of an atom to attract electrons when the atom is in a compound
_____ 8. electronegativity	**h.** an element in which the highest occupied *s* and *p* sublevels are filled
_____ 9. transition metal	**i.** an element in Group 2A
_____ 10. noble gas	**j.** an element whose highest occupied *s* sublevel and a nearby *f* sublevel contain electrons

B. Multiple Choice

Choose the best answer and write its letter on the line.

_____ 11. In the periodic table, there is a periodic pattern in the physical and chemical properties of elements when they are arranged in order of
   a. increasing atomic mass.
   b. increasing electronegativity.
   c. increasing atomic radius.
   d. increasing atomic number.

_____ 12. Which sublevel corresponds to the transition metals in the periodic table?
    a. s **c.** d
    b. p **d.** f

_____ 13. The representative elements are
    a. inner transition metals.   **c.** Group B elements.
    b. transition metals.   **d.** Group A elements.

_____ 14. Which of the following elements is a metalloid?
    a. As   **c.** Br
    b. Se   **d.** Kr

_____ 15. When a strontium atom loses two electrons to form an Sr^{2+} ion, the electrons are lost from the
    a. $5s$ orbital.   **c.** $3d$ orbital.
    b. $5p$ orbital.   **d.** $4f$ orbital.

_____ 16. The element iodine, I, is a
    a. period 5 alkali metal.   **c.** period 5 halogen.
    b. period 4 halogen.   **d.** period 5 transition metal.

_____ 17. The subatomic particle that plays the greatest role in determining the physical and chemical properties of an element is the
    a. proton.   **c.** electron.
    b. neutron.   **d.** photon.

_____ 18. Which of the following atoms would you expect to have the largest atomic radius?
    a. I   **c.** Ca
    b. K   **d.** Rb

_____ 19. From left to right across the second period of the periodic table,
    a. first ionization energy increases.   **c.** electronegativity decreases.
    b. atomic radii increase.   **d.** atomic mass decreases.

_____ 20. For which element would you expect a large jump between the first and second ionization energies?
    a. F   **c.** Fe
    b. Ca   **d.** Na

_____ 21. The category of elements that is characterized by the filling of f orbitals is the
    a. inner transition metals.   **c.** alkali earth metals.
    b. alkali metals.   **d.** transition metals.

_____ 22. Electronegativity
    a. generally decreases from left to right across a period.
    b. is the energy change that accompanies the loss of an electron from a gaseous atom.
    c. generally decreases from top to bottom within a group.
    d. is generally higher for metals than for nonmetals.

_____ **23.** Atomic size generally
    a. increases from left to right across a period.
    b. decreases from top to bottom within a group.
    c. remains constant within a period.
    d. decreases from left to right across a period.

_____ **24.** Of the following atoms, which one has the smallest first ionization energy?
    a. boron   **c.** nitrogen
    b. aluminum   **d.** silicon

_____ **25.** The alkali metals do *not* include
    a. Li.   **c.** Na.
    b. Ca.   **d.** Rb.

C. Questions

Answer the following in the space provided.

26. For the elements whose electron configurations end as follows, state the period and the group to which each element belongs.

    a. $5s^2$ _____

    b. $4s^2 4p^4$ _____

    c. $6s^2 6p^2$ _____

27. Write the configurations for the highest occupied energy level for each of the following elements.

    a. He   _____

    b. K   _____

    c. Al   _____

    d. Kr   _____

    e. O   _____

28. Arrange the following elements in order of decreasing ionization energy:

    a. Cs, Li, K   _____

    b. Cl, Si, P, Ar   _____

    c. Ca, Ba, Be, Sr   _____

Name ______________________ Date ______________ Class ______________

29. Tell whether each of the following elements is an inner transition metal, a noble gas, an alkali metal, an alkaline earth metal, or a halogen. Then give its period and group numbers.

a. calcium ____________________

b. cesium ____________________

c. fluorine ____________________

d. chromium ____________________

e. neon ____________________

f. silver ____________________

30. Which element in each pair has the higher electronegativity value?

a. Na, Mg ____________________

b. Rb, I ____________________

c. Cl, Br ____________________

D. Essay

Write a short essay for the following.

31. Why does atomic size generally *increase* as you move down a group of the periodic table and *decrease* as you move from left to right across a period?

____

____

____

____

THE PERIODIC TABLE

6

Chapter Test B

A. Matching

Match each term in Column B with the correct description in Column A. Write the letter of the correct term on the line.

Column A	Column B

_____ 1. half the distance between the nuclei of two atoms of the same element when the atoms are joined

    a. electronegativity

_____ 2. negatively charged ion

    b. groups

_____ 3. the vertical columns of the periodic table

    c. atomic radius

_____ 4. the nonmetallic elements of Group 7A

    d. ionization energy

_____ 5. elements in which the highest occupied *s* and *p* sublevels are filled

    e. periodic law

_____ 6. the tendency for the atoms of an element to attract electrons when the atoms are in a compound

    f. alkali metals

_____ 7. positively charged ion

    g. halogens

_____ 8. the energy required to remove an electron from an atom in the gaseous state

    h. noble gases

_____ 9. the Group 1A elements

    i. anion

_____ 10. When elements are arranged in order of increasing atomic number, there is a periodic repetition of their physical and chemical properties.

    j. cation

B. Multiple Choice

Choose the best answer and write its letter on the line.

_____ 11. The modern periodic table is arranged in order of increasing
    a. atomic mass.
    c. atomic size.
    b. atomic number.
    d. atomic radius.

_____ 12. The elements in Groups 1A through 7A are
    a. alkali metals.
    c. transition metals.
    b. alkaline earth metals.
    d. representative elements.

_____ **13.** Which of the following is true concerning the noble gases?
    a. Their highest occupied s and p sublevels are filled.
    b. They belong to Group 8A.
    c. They are sometimes referred to as the inert gases.
    d. all of the above

_____ **14.** What is the number of electrons in the highest occupied energy level of an element in Group 5A?
    a. 5   **c.** 8
    b. 3   **d.** 18

_____ **15.** Among the groups of elements listed below, which have the same number of electrons in their highest occupied energy levels?
    a. Li, B, C, F   **c.** K, Ca, Rb, Sr
    b. Na, Mg, Al, S   **d.** N, P, As, Sb

_____ **16.** An element that contains an electron in a d sublevel is
    a. Mg.   **c.** Fe.
    b. O.   **d.** Ne.

_____ **17.** The elements that contain electrons in an f sublevel near the highest occupied energy level are referred to as
    a. alkali metals.   **c.** transition metals.
    b. alkaline earth metals.   **d.** inner transition metals.

_____ **18.** The electron configuration of the element chlorine ends in
    a. $3s^2$.   **c.** $3s^23p^5$.
    b. $3p^6$.   **d.** $3s^23p^7$.

_____ **19.** The element with 8 electrons in its $3d$ sublevel is
    a. O.   **c.** Ar.
    b. Ne.   **d.** Ni.

_____ **20.** As you move down a group in the periodic table, atomic size generally
    a. increases.   **c.** remains the same.
    b. decreases.   **d.** varies randomly.

_____ **21.** The largest atom from among the following is
    a. Li.   **c.** Rb.
    b. Na.   **d.** Fr.

_____ **22.** The smallest atom from among the following is
    a. Na.   **c.** Si.
    b. Mg.   **d.** Cl.

_____ **23.** As the number of electrons added to the same principal energy level increases, atomic size generally
    a. increases.   **c.** remains the same.
    b. decreases.   **d.** varies randomly.

_____ **24.** Removing one electron from an atom results in the formation of an
    a. ion with a 1+ charge.   **c.** ion with a 7+ charge.
    b. ion with a 1− charge.   **d.** ion with a 7− charge.

_____ 25. Among the elements listed, which would show the largest increase
between the second and third ionization energies?
a. B   c. Ca
b. P   d. Zn

_____ 26. Among the following, which element has the lowest ionization energy?
a. Na   c. Cs
b. Cl   d. I

_____ 27. Among the following, which element has the highest second
ionization energy?
a. Na   c. Cs
b. Cl   d. I

_____ 28. Which of the following are always larger than the neutral atoms from
which they are formed?
a. positive ions   c. cations
b. negative ions   d. none of the above

_____ 29. The smallest particle from among the following is
a. Li.   c. F.
b. Li^+.   d. F^-.

_____ 30. The least electronegative element from among the following is
a. Na.   c. Cs.
b. Cl.   d. S.

C. Questions

Answer the following in the space provided.

31. Given the outermost energy level configurations below, complete the table by
providing the period number, group number, group name (if appropriate), and
symbol for each element identified.

Element	Period No.	Group No.	Group Name	Symbol
a. $2s^2$				
b. $3s^23p^3$				
c. $3s^23p^6$				
d. $4s^1$				
e. $3d^14s^2$				
f. $4s^24p^5$				

32. Arrange the following elements as described below.
Li, C, K, F, Cs

   a. In order of decreasing atomic size

   _____

   b. In order of increasing ionization energy

   _____

   c. In order of decreasing electronegativity

   _____

33. Among the following pairs of atoms, identify the larger of the two, the one with the greater first ionization energy, and the one with the lower electronegativity.

Atom	Larger	Greater Ionization Energy	Lower Electronegativity
a. Li, K			
b. C, F			
c. Mg, Ca			
d. O, S			

34. The outermost energy level configurations for the theoretical elements A–E are listed below. Use the symbols A through E to answer each of the questions that follow.

$A = 3s^2$ $B = 3s^1$ $C = 2s^2 2p^6$ $D = 2s^2 2p^5$ $E = 2s^2 2p^3$

   a. Which has the lowest first ionization energy?   _____

   b. Which is a noble gas?   _____

   c. Which has the highest electronegativity?   _____

   d. Which has the highest second ionization energy?   _____

   e. Which is the largest atom?   _____

D. Essay

Write a short essay for the following statement.

35. Explain why elements with high first ionization energies typically also have high electronegativity values.

_____

_____

_____

_____

QUICK LAB: Periodic Trends in Ionic Radii

Laboratory Recordsheet   Use with Section 6.3

PURPOSE

Make a graph of ionic radius versus atomic number and use the graph to identify periodic and group trends.

MATERIALS

- graph paper

PROCEDURE

Use the data presented in Figure 6.19 to plot ionic radius versus atomic number.

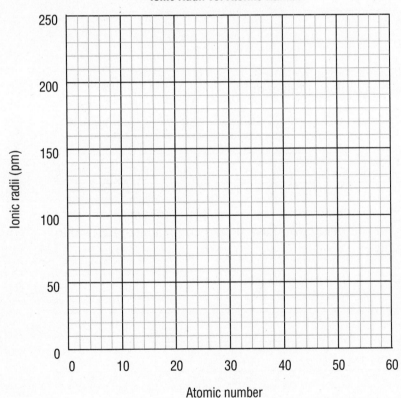

ANALYSES AND CONCLUSIONS

1. Describe how the size changes when an atom forms a cation and when an atom forms an anion.

   _____

   _____

   _____

2. How do the ionic radii vary within a group of metals? How do they vary within a group of nonmetals?

   _____

   _____

   _____

3. Describe the shape of a portion of the graph that corresponds to one period.

   _____

   _____

   _____

   _____

4. Is the trend across a period similar or different for periods 2, 3, 4, and 5?

   _____

   _____

   _____

   _____

5. Propose explanations for the trends you have described for ionic radii within groups and across periods.

   _____

   _____

   _____

   _____

   _____

   _____

SMALL-SCALE LAB: Periodicity in Three Dimensions

Laboratory Recordsheet   Use with Section 6.3

SAFETY

Wear your safety glasses and follow standard safety procedures.

PURPOSE

To build three-dimensional models for periodic trends.

MATERIALS

- 96-well spot plate
- straws
- scissors
- metric ruler
- permanent fine-line marker

PROCEDURE

1. Measure the depth of a well in the spot plate by inserting a straw into a well and holding the straw upright as shown in the photograph. Make a mark on the straw at the point where the straw meets the surface of the plate. Measure the distance from the end of the straw to the mark in centimeters. Record this distance as well depth.

2. Cut the straw to a length that is 4.0 cm plus well depth. The straw will extend exactly 4.0 cm above the surface of the plate.

3. Fluorine has an electronegativity value of 4.0. On a scale of one cm equals one unit of electronegativity, the portion of the straw that extends above the surface of the plate represents the electronegativity value for fluorine. Using the same scale, cut straws to represent the electronegativity values for all the elements listed in Table 6.2. Remember to add the well depth to the electronegativity value before cutting a straw. As you cut the straws, mark each straw with the chemical symbol of the element that the straw represents.

4. Arrange the straws in the spot plate in rows and columns to match the locations of the elements in the periodic table.

5. Make a rough sketch of your completed model.

ANALYSES AND CONCLUSIONS

Observe your model and record the answers to the following questions below your sketch.

1. Which element represented in your model is the most electronegative?

2. Based on your model, what is the general trend in electronegativity from left to right across a period?

3. Relate the trend in electronegativity across a period to the location of metals and nonmetals in the periodic table.

4. What is the general trend in electronegativity within a group? Are there any notable exceptions?

5. Why do you think that the electronegativity value for hydrogen is so high given its location in the table?

YOU'RE THE CHEMIST

Use the space below to write your observations to the small-scale activities in the *You're the Chemist* section.

Name _____ Date _____ Class _____

7.1 IONS

Section Review

Objectives

- Determine the number of valence electrons in an atom of a representative element
- Explain the octet rule
- Describe how cations form
- Explain how anions form

Vocabulary

- valence electrons
- electron dot structures
- octet rule
- halide ions

Part A Completion

Use this completion exercise to check your understanding of the concepts and terms that are introduced in this section. Each blank can be completed with a term, short phrase, or number.

Elements within the same group of the periodic table behave similarly because they have the same number of ___1___. The ___2___ number of a representative element indicates how many valence electrons that element has. Diagrams that show valence electrons as dots are called ___3___. Gilbert Lewis's ___4___ states that in forming compounds, atoms tend to achieve the electron configuration of a noble gas.

The transfer of valence electrons produces positively charged ions, or ___5___, and negatively charged ions called ___6___. The cations of Group 1A elements always have a charge of ___7___.

___8___ are produced when atoms of the elements in Group 7A ___9___ an electron. For transition metals, the ___10___ of cations may vary.

1. _____
2. _____
3. _____
4. _____
5. _____
6. _____
7. _____
8. _____
9. _____
10. _____

Part B True-False

Classify each of these statements as always true, AT; sometimes true, ST; or never true, NT.

_____ **11.** The chlorine atom gains seven electrons when it becomes an ion.

_____ **12.** The chemical properties of an element are largely determined by the number of valence electrons the element has.

_____ **13.** Atoms acquire the stable electron structure of a noble gas by losing electrons.

_____ **14.** An atom of an element in Group 1A has seven valence electrons.

_____ **15.** Among the Group 1A and 2A elements, the group number of each element is equal to the number of valence electrons in an atom of that element.

_____ **16.** Sulfur and magnesium both have two valence electrons.

Part C Matching

Match each description in Column B to the correct term in Column A.

Column A

_____ **17.** electron dot structure

_____ **18.** valence electron

_____ **19.** octet rule

_____ **20.** cations

_____ **21.** anions

_____ **22.** halide ions

_____ **23.** chloride ion

Column B

a. ions that are produced when halogens gain electrons

b. a depiction of valence electrons around the symbol of an element

c. has the electron configuration of argon

d. an electron in the highest occupied energy level of an element's atom

e. Atoms in compounds tend to have the electron configuration of a noble gas.

f. atoms or groups of atoms with a negative charge

g. atoms or groups of atoms with a positive charge

Part D Questions and Problems

Answer the following in the space provided.

24. Write the electron dot structures for the following atoms.

a. silicon   _____

b. rubidium   _____

c. barium   _____

Name ______________________ Date ________________ Class ________________

25. State the number of electrons lost or gained in forming each of these ions. Name the ions and tell whether it is an anion or a cation.

a. Mg^{2+} ______________________ **c.** Br^{-} ______________________

b. Ca^{2+} ______________________ **d.** Ag^{+} ______________________

26. Describe the formation of an ion from a metal and a nonmetal in terms of the octet rule.

____

____

____

7.2 IONIC BONDS AND IONIC COMPOUNDS

Section Review

Objectives

- Explain the electrical charge of an ionic compound
- Describe three properties of ionic compounds

Vocabulary

- ionic compounds
- ionic bonds
- chemical formula
- formula unit
- coordination number

Part A Completion

Use this completion exercise to check your understanding of the concepts and terms that are introduced in this section. Each blank can be completed with a term, short phrase, or number.

Anions and cations attract one another by means of __1__.

1. _____

The forces of attraction that hold __2__ charged ions together in

2. _____

ionic compounds are called __3__. Although they are composed

3. _____

of ions, ionic compounds are electrically __4__. The lowest whole-

4. _____

number ratio of ions in an ionic compound is called a __5__.

5. _____

Nearly all ionic compounds are solid __6__ at room

6. _____

temperature. Ionic compounds in general have very __7__

7. _____

melting temperatures. This is because the __8__ attractive

8. _____

forces between the ions result in a very __9__ structure.

9. _____

Ionic compounds conduct an electric current when in the

10. _____

__10__ state or dissolved in water.

Part B True-False

Classify each of these statements as always true, AT; sometimes true, ST; or never true, NT.

_____ 11. During the formation of the compound NaCl, one electron is transferred from a sodium atom to a chlorine atom.

_____ **12.** The coordination number of an ion is the number of ions of positive charge that surround the ion in a crystal.

_____ **13.** The coordination number of the ion Na^+ in NaCl is 6.

_____ **14.** In forming an ionic compound, an atom of an element gains electrons.

_____ **15.** Ionic compounds cannot conduct electricity if they are dissolved in water.

Part C Matching

Match each description in Column B to the correct term in Column A.

Column A	**Column B**
_____ **16.** ionic compounds	**a.** the number of ions of opposite charge surrounding each ion in a crystal
_____ **17.** ionic bonds	**b.** compounds composed of cations and anions
_____ **18.** chemical formula	**c.** shows the kinds and numbers of atoms in the smallest representative unit of a substance
_____ **19.** formula unit	**d.** lowest whole-number ratio of ions in an ionic compound
_____ **20.** coordination number	**e.** the electrostatic forces of attraction binding oppositely charged ions together

Part D Questions and Problems

Answer the following in the space provided.

21. List the characteristics of an ionic bond.

_____

_____

_____

22. Explain the electrical conductivity of melted and of aqueous solutions of ionic compounds using the characteristics of ionic compounds.

_____

_____

_____

7.3 BONDING IN METALS

Section Review

Objectives

- Model the valence electrons of metal ions
- Describe the arrangement of atoms in a metal
- Explain the importance of alloys

Vocabulary

- metallic bonds
- alloys

Part A Completion

Use this completion exercise to check your understanding of the concepts and terms that are introduced in this section. Each blank can be completed with a term, short phrase, or number.

Metals consist of closely packed ___1___ that are surrounded

by a sea of ___2___. This arrangement constitutes the ___3___

bond. The electron mobility accounts for the excellent

___4___ conductivity of metals and helps explain why

metals are ___5___ and ___6___. Metal atoms are commonly

packed in a ___7___ cubic, a ___8___ cubic, or a ___9___

arrangement. When two or more elements, at least one of which

is a metal, are mixed together, the resulting mixture is called

an ___10___.

1. _____

2. _____

3. _____

4. _____

5. _____

6. _____

7. _____

8. _____

9. _____

10. _____

Part B True-False

Classify each of these statements as always true, AT; sometimes true, ST; or never true, NT.

_____ **11.** In a body-centered cubic structure, each atom has 12 neighbors.

_____ **12.** Metallic objects are formed from pure metals.

_____ 13. Metals that are good conductors of electricity are said to be ductile.

_____ 14. Drifting valence electrons insulate cations from one another and contribute to the malleability of a metal.

_____ 15. Metals are good conductors of electricity because electrons can flow freely in them.

Part C Matching

Match each description in Column B to the correct term in Column A.

Column A	Column B
_____ 16. ductile	a. an alloy whose component atoms are different sizes
_____ 17. metallic bonds	b. a mixture of two or more elements, at least one of which is a metal
_____ 18. alloy	c. can be hammered or forced into shapes
_____ 19. malleable	d. can be drawn into wires
_____ 20. interstitial alloy	e. the attraction of valence electrons for positive metal ions

Part D Questions and Problems

Answer the following in the space provided.

21. Explain the physical properties of metals, using the theory of metallic bonding.

_____

_____

_____

22. Explain why the properties of alloys are generally superior to their constituent components.

_____

_____

_____

IONIC AND METALLIC BONDING

7

Practice Problems

In your notebook, answer the following.

SECTION 7.1 IONS

1. For each element below, state (i) the number of valence electrons in the atom, (ii) the electron dot structure, and (iii) the chemical symbol(s) for the most stable ion.

   a. Ba   **b.** I   **c.** K

2. How many valence electrons does each of the following atoms have?

   a. gallium   **b.** fluorine   **c.** selenium

3. Write the electron configuration for each of the following atoms and ions.

   a. Ca   **c.** Na^+ **e.** O^{2-}

   b. chlorine atom   **d.** phosphide ion

4. What is the relationship between the group number of the representative elements and the number of valence electrons?

5. How many electrons will each element gain or lose in forming an ion? State whether the resulting ion is a cation or an anion.

   a. strontium   **c.** tellurium   **e.** bromine

   b. aluminum   **d.** rubidium   **f.** phosphorus

6. Give the name and symbol of the ion formed when

   a. a chlorine atom gains one electron.

   b. a potassium atom loses one electron.

   c. an oxygen atom gains two electrons.

   d. a barium atom loses two electrons.

7. How many electrons are lost or gained in forming each of the following ions?

   a. Mg^{2+} **b.** Br^- **c.** Ag^+ **d.** Fe^{3+}

8. Classify each of the following as a cation or an anion.

   a. Na^+ **c.** I^- **e.** Ca^{2+}

   b. Cu^{2+} **d.** O^{2-} **f.** Cs^+

SECTION 7.2 IONIC BONDS AND IONIC COMPOUNDS

1. Use electron dot structures to predict the formula of the ionic compounds formed when the following elements combine.

   a. sodium and bromine

   b. sodium and sulfur

   c. calcium and iodine

   d. aluminum and oxygen

   e. barium and chlorine

2. Which of these combinations of elements are most likely to react to form ionic compounds?

   a. sodium and magnesium

   b. barium and sulfur

   c. potassium and iodine

   d. oxygen and argon

3. What is the meaning of coordination number?

4. How is the coordination number determined?

SECTION 7.3 BONDING IN METALS

1. What is a metallic bond?

2. How is the electrical conductivity of a metal explained by metallic bonds?

3. Are metals crystalline? Explain.

4. Give three possible crystalline arrangements of metals. Describe each.

5. What is an alloy?

6. Name the principal elements present in each of the following alloys.

   a. brass

   b. bronze

   c. stainless steel

   d. sterling silver

   e. cast iron

   f. spring steel

7 INTERPRETING GRAPHICS

Use with Section 7.2

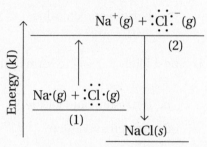

Figure 1 The energetic relationships in the formation
of an ionic solid from its elements.

Sodium metal reacts with chlorine gas to produce a stable ionic compound. The diagram in Figure 1 is a simplified version of a Born-Haber cycle, which shows some of the steps in this chemical process. The Born-Haber cycle was introduced by the German scientists Max Born and Fritz Haber to analyze the factors contributing to the stability of ionic compounds. Note that the Born-Haber method of analysis envisions the reaction as occurring between two gaseous particles. Use the diagram to answer the following questions.

1. Write the electron configurations for sodium and chlorine. How many
   valence electrons does each element have?

   _____

   _____

   _____

   _____

2. Explain the event occurring in Step 1 in Figure 1.

   _____

   _____

   _____

   _____

Name ______________________ Date ________________ Class ______________

3. Describe the event occurring in Step 2 of the Born-Haber cycle.

____

____

____

____

____

4. Explain how the energetic relationships shown in Figure 1 support the observation that ionic compounds are typically hard materials with high melting points.

____

____

____

____

Name _____ Date _____ Class _____

 IONIC AND METALLIC BONDING

Vocabulary Review

Match the correct vocabulary term to each numbered statement. Write the letter of the correct term on the line.

Column A	Column B

Column A

_____ 1. compounds composed of cations and anions

_____ 2. the attraction of free-floating valence electrons for positively charged metal ions

_____ 3. the lowest whole-number ratio of ions in an ionic compound

_____ 4. the electrostatic attraction that binds oppositely charged ions together

_____ 5. the number of ions of opposite charge that surround the ion in a crystal

_____ 6. negatively charged ions

_____ 7. shows the kinds and numbers of atoms in the smallest representative unit of a substance

_____ 8. a diagram that shows valence electrons as dots

_____ 9. a negative ion formed when a halogen atom gains an electron

_____ 10. In forming compounds, atoms tend to react so as to acquire the stable electron configuration of a noble gas.

_____ 11. electrons in the highest occupied energy level of an element's atoms.

_____ 12. a mixture of two or more elements, at least one of which is a metal

_____ 13. positively charged ions

Column B

a. chemical formula

b. valence electrons

c. electron dot structure

d. octet rule

e. halide ion

f. formula unit

g. ionic bonds

h. coordination number

i. metallic bonds

j. ionic compounds

k. alloy

l. anions

m. cations

7 IONIC AND METALLIC BONDING

Chapter Quiz

Classify each of these statements as always true, AT; sometimes true, ST; or never true, NT.

_____ 1. When a metal atom in a metal crystal has 12 neighbors, the
arrangement is a face-centered cube.   7.3

_____ 2. The chlorine atom gains seven electrons when it becomes an ion.   7.1

_____ 3. Ionic compounds conduct electricity better in the molten state than in
the solid state.   7.2

_____ 4. During the formation of the compound NaCl, one electron is
transferred from a sodium atom to a chlorine atom.   7.2

_____ 5. A piece of metal consists of closely packed cations surrounded by
mobile valence electrons.   7.3

Fill in the word(s) that will make each statement true.

6. The electrons in the highest occupied energy level of an   6. _____   7.1
atom are called the ___6___ electrons.

7. The ___7___ rule states that atoms in compounds tend to   7. _____   7.1
have the electron configuration of a noble gas.

8. An oxygen atom attains a stable electron configuration by   8. _____   7.1
___8___ two electrons.

9. Atoms and ions with ___9___ electrons in their highest   9. _____   7.1
energy levels are very stable.

10. Silver forms a cation by attaining a ___10___ electron   10. _____   7.1
configuration with 18 outer electrons including
d electrons.

11. ___11___ tend to lose electrons when they react to form   11. _____   7.1
compounds.

12. An ___12___ is any atom or group of atoms with a   12. _____   7.1
negative charge.

13. The lowest whole-number ratio of ions in an ionic compound   13. _____   7.1
is known as a ___13___ .

IONIC AND METALLIC BONDING

Chapter Test A

A. Matching

Match each description in Column B with the correct term in Column A. Write the letter of the correct description on the line.

Column A		Column B
_____	**1.** electron dot structure	**a.** a mixture of two or more elements, at least one of which is a metal
_____	**2.** ionic compound	**b.** the number of ions of opposite charge surrounding each ion in a crystal
_____	**3.** valence electron	**c.** the force of attraction binding oppositely charged ions together
_____	**4.** ionic bond	**d.** the attraction of valence electrons for positive metal ions
_____	**5.** chemical formula	**e.** a depiction of valence electrons around the symbol of an element
_____	**6.** halide ion	**f.** compound of cations and anions
_____	**7.** alloy	**g.** an anion of a halogen
_____	**8.** octet rule	**h.** an electron in the highest occupied energy level of an atom
_____	**9.** formula unit	**i.** Atoms in most compounds tend to achieve the electron configuration of a noble gas.
_____	**10.** coordination number	**j.** shows the kinds and numbers of atoms in the smallest representative unit of a substance
_____	**11.** metallic bond	**k.** lowest whole-number ratio of ions in an ionic compound

B. Multiple Choice

Choose the best answer and write its letter on the line.

_____ **12.** How many valence electrons does an atom of any element in Group 6A have?

    a. 2   **c.** 6

    b. 4   **d.** 8

_____ 13. The electron dot structure for an atom of phosphorus is

    a. ·Ṗ·

    b. ·P̈·

    c. ·P·

    d. :P̈·

_____ 14. When an aluminum atom loses its valence electrons, what is the charge on the resulting ion?

    a. 2+

    b. 2−

    c. 3+

    d. 1+

_____ 15. The electron configuration of a fluoride ion, F^-, is

    a. $1s^2 2s^2 2p^5$.

    b. the same as that of the neon atom.

    c. $1s^2 2s^2 2p^6 3s^1$.

    d. the same as that of a potassium ion.

_____ 16. Metals are good conductors of electricity because they

    a. form crystal lattices.

    b. contain positive ions.

    c. contain mobile valence electrons.

    d. form ionic bonds.

_____ 17. In forming chemical bonds, atoms tend to attain

    a. a state of higher energy.

    b. the electron configuration of noble gas atoms.

    c. the electron configuration of halogen atoms.

    d. all of the above

_____ 18. An ionic compound is

    a. electrically neutral.

    b. held together by ionic bonds.

    c. composed of anions and cations.

    d. all of the above

_____ 19. Which of these is *not* a characteristic of most ionic compounds?

    a. solid at room temperature

    b. has a low melting point

    c. conducts an electric current when melted

    d. produced by reaction between metallic and nonmetallic elements

_____ 20. A metallic bond is a bond between

    a. valence electrons and positively charged metal ions.

    b. the ions of two different metals.

    c. a metal and nonmetal.

    d. none of the above

_____ 21. Which element when combined with chlorine would most likely form an ionic compound?

    a. lithium

    b. carbon

    c. phosphorus

    d. bromine

_____ 22. A cation is any atom or group of atoms with

    a. a positive charge.

    b. no charge.

    c. a negative charge.

    d. more electrons than the corresponding atoms.

_____ **23.** The cation Fe^{3+} is formed when
   a. an atom of iron loses two electrons.
   b. an atom of zinc loses two electrons.
   c. an atom of iron loses three electrons.
   d. an atom of iron gains three electrons.

C. True-False

Classify each of these statements as always true, AT; sometimes true, ST; or never true, NT.

_____ **24.** The chemical properties of an element are largely determined by the number of valence electrons the element has.

_____ **25.** Fluorine and chlorine each have one valence electron.

_____ **26.** The coordination number gives the total number of ions in a crystal.

_____ **27.** Atoms acquire the stable electron structure of a noble gas by losing electrons.

_____ **28.** An alloy is a mixture of two or more elements, of which at least one is a metal.

_____ **29.** The crystal structure of ionic compounds such as sodium chloride is very unstable.

_____ **30.** When melted, ionic compounds conduct electricity.

_____ **31.** Metals are ductile because the cations in a piece of pure metal are insulated from one another by a sea of electrons.

_____ **32.** Metal atoms are arranged in a face-centered cubic structure.

_____ **33.** During the formation of ionic compounds, electrons are transferred from one atom to another.

D. Questions

Answer the following in the space provided.

34. Write electron dot structures for the atoms and ions of each of the following elements.

   Atoms   Ions

   a. Ca _____

   b. Br _____

   c. Al _____

35. Write the formulas obtained when each of these atoms loses or gains valence electrons and becomes an ion. Tell whether each is a cation or an anion.

   a. Cl _____   **c.** Na _____

   b. Be _____   **d.** O _____

36. Write the complete electron configurations for the ions in problem 35.

a. _____

b. _____

c. _____

d. _____

37. Use electron dot structures to predict the structure of the ionic compound composed of aluminum and chlorine.

38. Write the electron configuration diagram that shows the transfer of electrons that takes place to form the compound sodium fluoride. Include the electron configurations of the ions formed. Which noble gas configuration does each ion have?

E. Essay

Write a short essay for the following.

39. Explain how scientists have used the concept of metallic bonding to account for many of the physical properties of metals, such as electrical conductivity and malleability.

_____

_____

_____

_____

_____

_____

_____

_____

Name _____ Date _____ Class _____

IONIC AND METALLIC BONDING

Chapter Test B

A. Matching

Match each term in Column B with the correct description in Column A. Write the letter of the correct term on the line.

Column A

Column B

_____ 1. compound composed of cations and anions

a. halide ions

_____ 2. the forces of attraction that bind oppositely charged ions together

b. alloy

_____ 3. lowest whole-number ratio of ions in an ionic compound

c. octet rule

_____ 4. a depiction of the valence electrons as dots around the symbol for an element

d. formula unit

_____ 5. a mixture of two or more elements, at least one of which is a metal

e. electron dot structure

_____ 6. the attraction of the free-floating valence electrons for the positively charged metal ions

f. ionic compound

_____ 7. ions of the halogen atoms

g. ionic bonds

_____ 8. the electron(s) in the highest occupied energy level of an atom

h. coordination number

_____ 9. the number of ions of opposite charge that surround each ion in a crystal

i. chemical formula

_____ 10. Atoms in a compound tend to have the electron configuration of a noble gas.

j. valence electrons

_____ 11. Shows the kinds and numbers of atoms in the smallest representative unit of a substance

k. metallic bond

Name _____ Date _____ Class _____

B. Multiple Choice

Choose the best answer and write its letter on the line.

_____ 12. All the elements in a particular group of the periodic table have the same number of
  a. electrons. c. valence electrons.
  b. energy levels. d. protons.

_____ 13. What is the number of valence electrons in an atom of Al?
  a. 13 c. 10
  b. 3 d. 8

_____ 14. Among the following, the element with six valence electrons is
  a. C. c. O.
  b. Cs. d. Ne.

_____ 15. The electron dot structure for Cl is
  a. $:\overset{\cdot}{\underset{\cdot}{Cl}}:$ c. $:\overset{\cdot}{\underset{\cdot}{Cl}}:$
  b. Cl d. $\cdot\overset{}{\underset{\cdot}{Cl}}:$

_____ 16. In general, metals react by:
  a. losing valence electrons.
  b. gaining valence electrons.
  c. sharing valence electrons.
  d. sometimes gaining and sometimes losing valence electrons.

_____ 17. An ion of K has the same electron configuration as
  a. Na^+. c. Ar.
  b. Ca. d. Kr.

_____ 18. The outer energy level configuration for O^{2-} is
  a. $2s^2$. c. $2s^2\,2p^5$.
  b. $2s^2 2p^4$. d. $2s^2\,2p^6$.

_____ 19. The general electron dot structure $\cdot X\colon$ could represent
  a. Li. c. B.
  b. Na. d. N.

_____ 20. The chemical properties of an element are largely determined by its
  a. number of energy levels.
  b. period number.
  c. number of protons.
  d. number of valence electrons.

_____ 21. Which of the following has a noble gas electron configuration?
  a. Na c. Al^{3+}
  b. Mg^+ d. Br

_____ 22. Atoms of Ca and S would be expected to react in a ratio of
  a. 1:1. c. 2:1.
  b. 1:2. d. 3:1.

_____ **23.** The chemical formula for the ionic compound formed when elements
of Ca and N react is

    a. CaN.   **c.** Ca_3N_2.

    b. Ca_2N_3.   **d.** Ca_5N_2.

_____ **24.** In general, ionic compounds

    a. are amorphous solids at room temperature.

    b. conduct electricity when in the solid state.

    c. conduct electricity when they are dissolved in water.

    d. all of the above

_____ **25.** Metals typically are

    a. good conductors of electrical current.

    b. malleable.

    c. ductile.

    d. all of the above

_____ **26.** Which of the following is an anion?

    a. O^{2-} **c.** Al^{3+}

    b. Mg^{2+} **d.** H

_____ **27.** The nonmetals in Groups 5A, 6A, and 7A

    a. lose electrons when they form ions.

    b. form positively charged ions.

    c. form ions with charges of $3-$, $2-$, and $1-$, respectively.

    d. form ions with a numerical charge equal to their group number.

_____ **28.** Among the following, which atom is most likely to form an ion with a
charge of $2+$?

    a. O   **c.** Al

    b. Na   **d.** Ca

C. True-False

Classify each of these statements as always true, AT; sometimes true, ST; or never true, NT.

_____ **29.** Among Groups 1A and 2A, the group number of each element is equal
to the number of valence electrons in an atom of that element.

_____ **30.** Alloys are mixtures with at least one metal.

_____ **31.** In general, atoms react in an attempt to attain the electron
configuration of a noble gas.

_____ **32.** The loss of valence electrons from an atom produces an anion.

_____ **33.** Nonmetals typically react by gaining electrons to attain noble gas
electron configurations.

_____ **34.** Ions have more electrons than the atoms from which they were
formed.

_____ **35.** In the formation of an ionic compound, a single electron is transferred
from one atom to the other.

_____ **36.** Each metal atom in a body-centered cubic structure has eight neighboring atoms.

_____ **37.** The atoms of Group 7A elements gain electrons when they form ions.

_____ **38.** An atom with a positive charge is an anion.

_____ **39.** The ionic charge of an element in Group 6A is 2^-.

D. Questions

Answer the following in the space provided.

40. Complete the following table by providing the electron configurations for the outermost energy level, the number of valence electrons, and the electron dot structure for each of the elements given.

Element	Configuration	No. Valence e^-	Electron Dot
a. Li			
b. N			
c. Si			
d. Br			

41. Write the formula and the complete electron configuration for each of the following.

	Formula	Electron Configuration
a. Na ion		
b. F ion		
c. K ion		
d. Sr ion		

42. Write the electron dot structures for each of the following atom-ion pairs.

	Atom	Ion
a. Na, Na ion		
b. Cl, Cl ion		
c. P, P ion		
d. Ca, Ca ion		

43. Write the chemical formula for the ionic compound formed when the following pairs of elements combine.

	Chemical Formula
a. Na, F	
b. Mg, Cl	
c. Ca, S	
d. Al, O	

E. Essay

Write a short essay for the following.

44. Explain the relationship between the group number, the number of valence electrons lost or gained, and the formula of the compound that results between Ca and F.

_____

_____

_____

_____

_____

_____

_____

_____

_____

QUICK LAB: Solutions Containing Ions

Laboratory Recordsheet   Use with Section 7.2

PURPOSE

To show that ions in solution conduct an electric current.

MATERIALS

- 3 D-cell batteries
- masking tape
- 2 30-cm lengths of bell wire with ends scraped bare
- clear plastic cup
- distilled water
- tap water
- vinegar
- sucrose
- sodium chloride
- baking soda
- conductivity probe (optional)

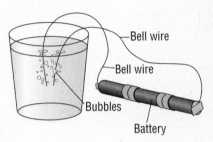

PROCEDURE

1. Tape the batteries together so the positive end of one touches the negative end of another. Tape the bare end of one wire to the positive terminal of the battery assembly and the bare end of the other wire to the negative terminal.

2. Half fill the cup with distilled water. Hold the bare ends of the wires close together in the water. Look for the production of bubbles. They are a sign that the solution conducts electricity.

3. Repeat Step 2 with tap water, vinegar, and concentrated solutions of sucrose, sodium chloride, and baking soda (sodium hydrogen carbonate).

ANALYSES AND CONCLUSIONS

1. Which solutions produced bubbles of gas? Explain.

   _____

   _____

   _____

Name ______________________ Date ________________ Class ________________

2. Which samples did not produce bubbles of gas? Explain.

____

____

____

3. Would you expect the same results if you used only one battery? If you used six batteries? Explain your answer.

____

____

____

____

SMALL-SCALE LAB: Analysis of Anions and Cations

Laboratory Recordsheet   Use with Section 7.2

SAFETY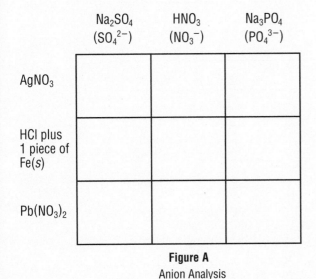

Wear safety glasses and follow the standard safety procedures outlined on page 7 of this manual.

PURPOSE

To develop tests for various ions and use the tests to analyze unknown substances.

MATERIALS

- pencil
- ruler
- cotton swab
- medicine droppers
- chemicals shown in Figures A and B
- paper
- reaction surface
- pipet

PROCEDURE

On a separate sheet of paper, draw grids similar to Figure A and Figure B. Make each square 2 cm on each side. Place a reaction surface over the grids on the sheet of paper and add one drop of each solution or one piece of each solid as shown in Figures A and B. Stir each solution by blowing air through an empty pipet. Use the grids below as data tables to record your observations for each solution. Draw a black X in each square of the grid.

	Na_2SO_4 (SO_4^{2-})	HNO_3 (NO_3^-)	Na_3PO_4 (PO_4^{3-})
$AgNO_3$			
HCl plus 1 piece of Fe(s)			
$Pb(NO_3)_2$			

Figure A
Anion Analysis

	KI (K^+)	$CaCl_2$ (Ca^{2+})	$FeCl_3$ (Fe^{3+})
NaOH			
KSCN			

Figure B
Cation Analysis

Name ______________________ Date ______________ Class ______________

ANALYSIS

Using your experimental data, record the answers to the following questions.

1. Carefully examine the reaction of Fe(*s*) and HCl in the presence of HNO_3. What is unique about this reaction? How can you use it to identify nitrate ion?

2. Which solutions from Figure A are the best for identifying each anion? Which solutions from Figure B are the best for identifying each cation? Explain.

3. Can your experiments conclusively identify K^+ ions? Explain.

YOU'RE THE CHEMIST

Use the space below to write your observations to the small-scale activities in the *You're the Chemist* section.

8.1 MOLECULAR COMPOUNDS

Section Review

Objectives

- Distinguish molecular compounds from ionic compounds
- Identify the information a molecular formula provides

Vocabulary

- covalent bond
- molecule
- diatomic molecule
- molecular compound
- molecular formula

Part A Completion

Use this completion exercise to check your understanding of the concepts and terms that are introduced in this section. Each blank can be completed with a term, short phrase, or number.

Every substance is either an element or a(n) __1__.

A compound is either __2__ or ionic in nature. Most molecular

compounds are composed of two or more __3__. Molecules

consisting of two atoms are __4__ molecules. The chemical

formula of a molecular compound is a __5__. Molecular

compounds tend to have __6__ melting and boiling points, while

ionic compounds tend to have __7__ melting and boiling points.

A molecular formula shows how many __8__ of each

element a molecule contains, but it does not indicate the

__9__ of the molecule.

1. _____

2. _____

3. _____

4. _____

5. _____

6. _____

7. _____

8. _____

9. _____

Part B True-False

Classify each of these statements as always true, AT; sometimes true, ST; or never true, NT.

_____ 10. A diatomic molecule contains two or three atoms.

_____ 11. Molecular compounds have relatively high boiling points.

_____ **12.** The molecular structure of carbon dioxide is one carbon atom with two oxygen atoms on opposite sides of it.

_____ **13.** Covalent bonds exist when combining atoms give up or accept electrons.

_____ **14.** A molecule contains two atoms.

Part C Matching

Match each description in Column B to the correct term in Column A.

Column A	Column B
_____ **15.** molecule	**a.** compound composed of molecules
_____ **16.** molecular compound	**b.** a molecule consisting of two atoms
_____ **17.** covalent bond	**c.** shows the kinds and numbers present in a molecule of a compound
_____ **18.** diatomic molecule	**d.** joins atoms held together by sharing electrons
_____ **19.** molecular formula	**e.** an electrically neutral group of atoms joined together by covalent bonds

Part D Questions and Problems

Answer the following in the space provided.

20. A compound has a boiling point of 40°C. Is this compound most likely an ionic or a molecular compound?

_____

21. Identify the number and kinds of atoms present in a molecule of each compound.

a. butane (C_4H_{10}) _____

b. fluorobenzene (C_6H_5F) _____

22. Classify each particle as an atom or a molecule.

a. CH_4 _____   **d.** He _____

b. Ne _____   **e.** CO_2 _____

c. O_2 _____

8.2 THE NATURE OF COVALENT BONDING

Section Review

Objectives

- State a rule that usually tells how many electrons are shared to form a covalent bond
- Describe how electron dot formulas are used
- Predict when two atoms are likely to be joined by a double or a triple covalent bond
- Distinguish between a single covalent bond and other covalent bonds
- Describe how the strength of a covalent bond is related to its bond dissociation energy
- Describe how resonance structures explain bonding
- Identify some exceptions to the octet rule

Vocabulary

- single covalent bond
- structural formulas
- unshared pairs
- double covalent bonds
- triple covalent bonds
- coordinate covalent bond
- polyatomic ion
- bond dissociation energy
- resonance structures

Part A Completion

Use this completion exercise to check your understanding of the concepts and terms that are introduced in this section. Each blank can be completed with a term, short phrase, or number.

When atoms share electrons to gain the ___1___ configuration of a noble gas, the bonds formed are ___2___. A ___3___ pair of valence electrons constitutes a ___4___ covalent bond. Pairs of valence electrons that are not shared between atoms are called ___5___. Sometimes two or three pairs of electrons may be shared to give ___6___ covalent bonds. In some cases, only one of the atoms in a bond provides the pair of bonding electrons; this is a ___7___. ___8___ is required to break covalent bonds between atoms. The total energy required to break the bond between two covalently bonded atoms is known as the ___9___.

When it is possible to write two or more valid electron dot formulas for a molecule or ion, each formula is referred to as a ___10___.

1. _____

2. _____

3. _____

4. _____

5. _____

6. _____

7. _____

8. _____

9. _____

10. _____

Part B True-False

Classify each of these statements as always true, AT; sometimes true, ST; or never true, NT.

_____ **11.** The modern interpretation of resonance is that electron pairs rapidly flip back and forth between the various electron dot structures.

_____ **12.** The compound NH_3 contains two double covalent bonds.

_____ **13.** The chemical formulas of molecular compounds show the number and type of atoms in each molecule.

_____ **14.** A molecule of bromine has six unshared pairs of electrons.

_____ **15.** Carbon forms four single covalent bonds with other atoms.

_____ **16.** A bond in which one atom contributes both bonding electrons is called a polyatomic covalent bond.

Part C Matching

Match each description in Column B to the correct term in Column A.

Column A

_____ **17.** single covalent bond

_____ **18.** structural formula

_____ **19.** bond dissociation energy

_____ **20.** polyatomic ion

_____ **21.** coordinate covalent bond

Column B

a. a chemical formula that shows the arrangement of atoms in a molecule or a polyatomic ion

b. the amount of energy required to break a covalent bond between atoms

c. a tightly bound group of atoms that has a positive or negative charge and behaves as a unit

d. a covalent bond in which one atom contributes both bonding electrons

e. a chemical bond in which only one pair of electrons is shared by two bonded atoms

Part D Questions and Problems

Answer the following in the space provided.

22. Draw electron dot structures for each of the following compounds

   a. Br_2

   b. HCN

   c. NH_4^+

Name _____ Date _____ Class _____

8.3 BONDING THEORIES

Section Review

Objectives
- Identify the difference between atomic and molecular orbits
- Describe how VSEPR theory helps predict the shapes of molecules
- Identify the ways in which orbital hybridization is useful in describing molecules

Vocabulary
- molecular orbitals
- bonding orbital
- sigma bond
- pi bond
- tetrahedral angle
- VSEPR theory
- hybridization

Part A Completion

Use this completion exercise to check your understanding of the concepts and terms that are introduced in this section. Each blank can be completed with a term, short phrase, or number.

The quantum mechanical model of bonding assumes that atomic orbitals overlap to produce ___1___. A molecular orbit that can be occupied by two electrons of a covalent bond is called a ___2___, whose energy is ___3___ than that of the atomic orbitals from which it formed. When two atomic orbitals combine to form a molecular orbital that is symmetrical around the axis connecting two atomic nuclei, a ___4___ bond is formed. When atomic orbitals overlap side by side, they produce ___5___ bonds.

Electron dot structures fail to reflect the ___6___ shapes of molecules. ___7___ states that because electron pairs repel, molecular shape adjusts so the valence-electron pairs are as far apart as possible. Another way to describe molecules that provides information about both molecular bonding and molecular shape is ___8___.

1. _____
2. _____
3. _____
4. _____
5. _____
6. _____
7. _____
8. _____

Part B True-False

Classify each of these statements as always true, AT; sometimes true, ST; or never true, NT.

_____ **9.** Unshared pairs of electrons affect the shape of molecules.

_____ **10.** Molecular orbitals involve pi bonding.

_____ **11.** A bonding orbital is a molecular orbital whose energy is higher than that of the atomic orbitals from which it is formed.

_____ **12.** With hybridization, several atomic orbitals overlap to form the same total number of equivalent hybrid orbitals.

_____ **13.** Sigma and pi bonds are found in the same molecule.

_____ **14.** The methane molecule has four orbitals with tetrahedral angles of 109.5°.

Part C Matching

Match each description in Column B to the correct term in Column A.

Column A	**Column B**
_____ **15.** sigma bond	**a.** states that because electron pairs repel, molecules adjust their shapes so that valence-electron pairs are as far apart as possible
_____ **16.** pi bond	**b.** a process in which several atomic orbitals overlap to form the same number of equivalent hybrid orbitals
_____ **17.** VSEPR theory	**c.** a term used to describe the shape of certain molecules such as CO_2
_____ **18.** hybridization	**d.** a bond formed when two atomic orbitals combine to form a molecular orbital that is symmetrical along the axis connecting the two atomic nuclei
_____ **19.** linear molecule	**e.** a bond in which the bonding electrons are most likely to be found in the sausage-shaped regions above and below the nuclei of the bonded atoms

Part D Questions and Problems

Answer the following in the space provided.

20. Indicate the hybrid orbitals used by each carbon atom in the following compound.

$$H_3C - C = C - C \equiv C - CH_3$$
$$\qquad\quad | \quad |$$
$$\qquad\quad H \quad H$$

8.4 POLAR BONDS AND MOLECULES

Section Review

Objectives

- Describe how electronegativity values determine the charge distribution in a polar bond
- Describe what happens to polar molecules when placed between oppositely charged metal plates
- Distinguish intermolecular attractions from ionic bonds and from covalent bonds
- Identify the reason network solids have high melting points or decompose without melting

Vocabulary

- nonpolar covalent bond
- polar covalent bond
- polar bond
- polar molecule

- dipole
- van der Waals forces
- dipole interactions

- dispersion forces
- hydrogen bonds
- network solids

Part A Completion

Use this completion exercise to check your understanding of the concepts and terms that are introduced in this section. Each blank can be completed with a term, short phrase, or number.

When like atoms are joined by a covalent bond, the bonding

electrons are shared ___1___, and the bond is ___2___. When the

atoms in a bond are not the same, the bonding electrons are shared

___3___, and the bond is ___4___. The degree of polarity of a bond

between any two atoms is determined by consulting a table of

___5___. The attractions between opposite poles of polar molecules

are called ___6___. Another strong intermolecular attractive force

is the ___7___, in which a hydrogen covalently bonded to a very

___8___ atom, such as ___9___, is also weakly bonded to an

unshared electron pair of another electronegative atom.

1. _____

2. _____

3. _____

4. _____

5. _____

6. _____

7. _____

8. _____

9. _____

Part B True-False

Classify each of these statements as always true, AT; sometimes true, ST; or never true, NT.

_____ **10.** In a polar covalent bond, the more electronegative atom has a slight positive charge.

_____ **11.** In general, the electronegativity values of nonmetallic elements are greater than the electronegativity values of metallic elements.

_____ **12.** A molecule with polar bonds is dipolar.

_____ **13.** Covalent compounds are network solids.

_____ **14.** If the electronegativity difference between two atoms is greater than 2.0, they will form an ionic bond.

_____ **15.** Dispersion forces are weaker than hydrogen bonds.

Part C Matching

Match each description in Column B to the correct term in Column A.

Column A

_____ **16.** nonpolar covalent bond

_____ **17.** polar covalent bond

_____ **18.** polar molecule

_____ **19.** van der Waals forces

_____ **20.** network solid

Column B

a. a substance in which all of the atoms are covalently bonded to each other

b. a bond formed when the atoms in a molecule are alike and the bonding electrons are shared equally

c. a term used to describe the weakest intermolecular attractions; these include dispersion forces and dipole interactions

d. a bond formed when two different atoms are joined by a covalent bond and the bonding electrons are shared unequally

e. a molecule in which one end is slightly positive and the other end is slightly negative

Name ______________________ Date ________________ Class ________________

Part D Questions and Problems

Answer the following in the space provided.

21. Arrange the following intermolecular attractions in order of increasing strength: dipole interactions, dispersion forces, and hydrogen bonds.

____

22. State whether the following compounds contain polar covalent bonds, nonpolar covalent bonds, or ionic bonds, based on their electronegativities.

a. KF **a.** ____________________

b. SO_2 **b.** ____________________

c. NO_2 **c.** ____________________

d. Cl_2 **d.** ____________________

8 COVALENT BONDING

Practice Problems

In your notebook, solve the following problems.

SECTION 8.1 MOLECULAR COMPOUNDS

1. Classify each of the following as an atom or a molecule.

   a. Be   **c.** N_2 **e.** Ne

   b. CO_2 **d.** H_2O

2. Which of the following are diatomic molecules?

   a. CO_2 **c.** O_2 **e.** CO

   b. N_2 **d.** H_2O

3. What types of elements tend to combine to form molecular compounds?

4. What information does a molecule's molecular structure give?

5. How do ionic compounds and molecular compounds differ in their relative melting and boiling points?

SECTION 8.2 THE NATURE OF COVALENT BONDING

1. Draw the electron dot structure for hydrogen fluoride, HF.

2. Draw the electron dot structure for phosphorus trifluoride, PF_3.

3. Draw the electron dot structure for nitrogen trichloride, NCl_3.

4. Draw the electron dot configuration for acetylene, C_2H_2.

5. How many resonance structures can be drawn for CO_3^{2-}? Show the electron dot structures for each.

SECTION 8.3 BONDING THEORIES

1. Predict the shape and bond angle for the compound carbon tetrafluoride, CF_4.

2. Predict the shape and bond angle for phosphorus trifluoride, PF_3.

3. Predict the type of hybridized orbitals involved in the compound boron trichloride, BCl_3.

4. What types of hybrid orbitals are involved in the bonding of the silicon atoms in silicon tetrafluoride, SiF_4?

5. Predict the shape and bond angle of fluorine monoxide, F_2O.

6. Predict the shape of the CH_2CF_2 molecule. What hybridization is involved in the carbon-carbon bonds?

7. How many sigma and pi bonds are used by each of the carbon atoms in the following compound?

$$
\begin{array}{c}
\quad\quad H\ \ddot{\ddot{O}}\ \\
H:\!\overset{\displaystyle H}{\underset{\displaystyle H}{C_1}}\!:\!C_2\!:\!\ddot{O}\!:H
\end{array}
$$

SECTION 8.4 POLAR BONDS AND MOLECULES

1. What type of bond—nonpolar covalent, polar covalent, or ionic—will form between each pair of atoms?

    a. Na and O   **b.** O and O   **c.** P and O

2. Explain why most chemical bonds would be classified as either polar covalent or ionic.

3. Would you expect carbon monoxide and carbon dioxide to be polar or nonpolar molecules?

4. Draw the structural formulas for each molecule and identify polar covalent bonds by assigning the slightly positive ($\delta+$) and slightly negative ($\delta-$) symbols to the appropriate atoms.

    a. NH_3 **b.** CF_3

5. Which would you expect to have the higher melting point, CaO or CS_2?

INTERPRETING GRAPHICS

8

Use with Section 8.3

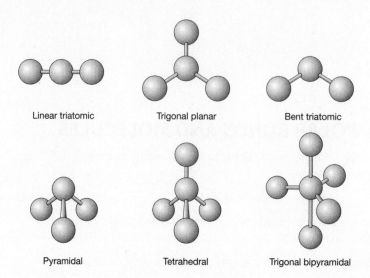

Figure 1 Common Molecular Shapes

Use what you have learned in Chapter 8 to complete the table on the following page.

Table 1 Arrangement of electron pairs about an atom

Number of valence electron pairs about the central atom	Arrangement of valence-electron pairs
2	linear
3	trigonal planar
4	tetrahedral
5	trigonal bipyramidal

Table 2 Molecular Geometries

Molecule	Electron Dot Structure	Shape	Bond Angle	Resonance Structures
1. CO_2				
2. CH_4				
3. SO_3				
4. BeF_2				
5. PF_3				
6. PCl_5				
7. H_2O				

8. If you have access to a molecular model set, construct three-dimensional models of each of the molecules in the table. Compare your models to the shapes shown in Figure 1. With a protractor, measure all the bond angles in your models. Compare these angles to those predicted by VSEPR theory and label each of the illustrations in Figure 1 with the correct bond angles.

COVALENT BONDING

°8

Vocabulary Review

Select the term from the following list that best matches each description.

polyatomic ion   VSEPR theory   bonding molecular orbital
coordinate covalent bond   sigma bond   van der Waals forces
hybridization   molecule   bond dissociation energy
hydrogen bond

1. a bond in which one atom contributes both bonding electrons to a covalent bond

_____

2. the total energy required to break the bond between two covalently bonded atoms

_____

3. a molecular orbital whose energy is lower than that of the atomic orbitals from
    which it is formed

_____

4. molecular orbital that lies along the axis connecting two atomic nuclei

_____

5. states that because electron pairs repel, molecules adjust their shapes so that
    valence-electron pairs are as far apart as possible

_____

6. a process in which several atomic orbitals mix to form the same number of
    equivalent hybrid orbitals

_____

7. a tightly bound group of atoms that behaves as a unit and carries a charge

_____

8. a term that collectively refers to dispersion forces and dipole interactions

_____

9. a relatively strong intermolecular attraction in which a hydrogen that is
    covalently bonded to a very electronegative atom is also weakly bonded to an
    unshared pair of electrons of another electronegative atom

_____

10. a tightly connected group of two or more atoms of nonmetallic elements that
    behave as an electrically neutral unit

_____

Name _____ Date _____ Class _____

<table>
<tr><td>**8**</td><td># COVALENT BONDING</td></tr>
</table>

Chapter Quiz

Choose the best answer and write its letter on the line.

_____ 1. A bond in which each atom contributes two electrons is   8.2
  a. a double covalent bond. **c.** a polar covalent bond.
  b. an ionic bond. **d.** a coordinate covalent bond.

_____ 2. The electron dot structure for hydrogen sulfide, H_2S, is   8.2

     a. H:̈S̈:   **c.** H:S̈:
         H   H

     b. H::S::H   **d.** H:H:S̈:

_____ 3. Which electron dot structure represents a nonpolar molecule?   8.2

     a. H:Ö:H   **c.** H:C̈l:

     b. :C̈l:C̈l: **d.** H:C:C:F

_____ 4. Bond dissociation energy   8.2
  a. is the energy required to break a single bond.
  b. of a C — H bond is high.
  c. of a C — C bond is high.
  d. all of the above

_____ 5. A covalent bond formed between two elements that have an   8.4
  electronegativity difference of 1.6 would be
  a. a nonpolar bond. **c.** a moderately polar bond.
  b. a very polar bond. **d.** an ionic bond.

_____ 6. You would expect a bond formed between a silicon atom and an   8.4
  oxygen atom to be
  a. an ionic bond. **c.** a polar covalent bond.
  b. a coordinate covalent bond. **d.** a nonpolar covalent bond.

Classify each of these statements as always true, AT; sometimes true, ST; or never true, NT.

_____ 7. Molecular orbitals involve pi bonding.   8.3

_____ 8. An antibonding orbital is a molecular orbital whose energy is lower   8.3
  than that of the atomic orbitals from which it is formed.

_____ 9. A three-atom molecule is bent.   8.3

_____ 10. Sigma and pi bonds are found in the same molecule.   8.3

_____ 11. A molecule contains two atoms.   8.1

COVALENT BONDING

8

Chapter Test A

A. Matching

Match each description in Column B with the correct term in Column A. Write the letter of the correct description on the line.

Column A	Column B
_____ 1. coordinate covalent bond	**a.** shows the kinds and numbers present in a molecule of a compound
_____ 2. nonpolar covalent bond	**b.** chemical formula that shows the arrangement of atoms in molecules and polyatomic ions
_____ 3. hydrogen bond	**c.** a covalent bond between two atoms of different electronegativities in which the bonding electrons are not shared equally
_____ 4. double covalent bond	**d.** interaction caused by the motion of electrons
_____ 5. dispersion force	**e.** a covalent bond formed by the equal sharing of bonding electrons by two atoms
_____ 6. molecular formula	**f.** a covalent bond involving two pairs of electrons; each atom donates one pair of electrons to the bond
_____ 7. structural formula	**g.** a covalent bond in which three pairs of electrons are shared by two bonded atoms
_____ 8. polar bond	**h.** substance in which all of the atoms are covalently bonded to each other
_____ 9. triple covalent bond	**i.** a covalent bond between two atoms in which the shared electron pair comes from only one of the atoms
_____ 10. network solid	**j.** force that occurs when a hydrogen atom that is covalently bonded to a very electronegative atom is also weakly bonded to an unshared pair of electrons in the same or a nearby molecule

Name _____ Date _____ Class _____

B. Multiple Choice

Choose the best answer and write its letter on the line.

_____ 11. Which of these elements does *not* exist as a diatomic molecule?
  a. I
  b. F
  c. H
  d. He

_____ 12. Which one of the following compounds is *not* covalent?
  a. SCl_2
  b. KCl
  c. HCl
  d. S_2Cl_2

_____ 13. How many valence electrons does an atom of any halogen have?
  a. 1
  b. 2
  c. 4
  d. 7

_____ 14. A diatomic molecule with a triple covalent bond is
  a. N_2.
  b. Br_2.
  c. H_2.
  d. O_2.

_____ 15. A molecule of nitrous oxide, N_2O, $:N \equiv N \rightarrow \overset{\cdot\cdot}{\underset{\cdot\cdot}{O}}$ contains all of the following *except*
  a. a coordinate covalent bond.
  b. a triple bond.
  c. a double bond.
  d. nonbonding pairs of electrons.

_____ 16. If a bonding pair of electrons is unequally shared between two atoms, the bond is
  a. ionic.
  b. nonpolar covalent.
  c. coordinate covalent.
  d. polar covalent.

_____ 17. What is the electron dot structure for water?
  a. $H :: O :: H$

  b. $H : H \overset{\cdot\cdot}{\underset{\cdot\cdot}{O}} :$

  c. $H \overset{\cdot\cdot}{:O:} \\ \quad H$

  d. $H \overset{\cdot\cdot}{:O:} \\ \quad \overset{\cdot\cdot}{H}$

_____ 18. Which of the following compounds is *not* ionic?
  a. NaI
  b. $CaCl_2$
  c. CO_2
  d. Na_2O

_____ 19. A covalent bond forms
  a. when an element becomes a noble gas.
  b. when atoms share electrons.
  c. between metals and nonmetals.
  d. when electrons are transferred from one atom to another.

_____ 20. What is the electron dot structure for the polyatomic ion OH^-?
  a. $[:\overset{\cdot\cdot}{O}: H]^-$
  b. $[H:\overset{\cdot\cdot}{\underset{\cdot\cdot}{O}}\cdot]^-$
  c. $[H :: \overset{\cdot\cdot}{O}]^-$
  d. $[\cdot\overset{\cdot\cdot}{O}:H]^-$

_____ 21. Which of these compounds would *not* have covalent bonds?
  a. NO_2
  b. K_2O
  c. N_2O_4
  d. H_2O_2

_____ **22.** A molecule with a single covalent bond is

    a. CO_2.
    b. F_2.
        c. NO.
        d. N_2.

_____ **23.** Chlorine is a gas, bromine is a liquid, and iodine is a solid because of differences in the strength of their

    a. hydrogen bonds.
    b. dispersion forces.
        c. dipole interactions.
        d. polar bonds.

_____ **24.** When H^+ forms a bond with H_2O to form hydronium ion, H_3O^+, this bond is called a coordinate covalent bond because

    a. both bonding electrons come from the oxygen atom.
    b. it is an especially strong bond.
    c. the electrons are equally shared.
    d. the oxygen no longer has eight electrons surrounding it.

_____ **25.** Which of the following molecules has one lone pair of electrons?

    a. CH_4
    b. HCl
        c. H_2O
        d. NH_3

_____ **26.** Which of the following is the weakest?

    a. hydrogen bond
    b. polar covalent bond
        c. dipole interaction
        d. ionic bond

_____ **27.** The carbon tetrachloride molecule is

    a. four-cornered.
    b. square.
        c. tetrahedral.
        d. pyramidal.

C. Questions

Answer the following questions in the space provided.

28. Draw structural formulas for the following substances.

    a. Br_2

    b. N_2

    c. CO

29. State whether the following compounds contain polar covalent bonds, nonpolar covalent bonds, or ionic bonds. (You may refer to the table of electronegativities on the top of the next page.)

    a. KF _____

    b. SO_2 _____

    c. NO_2 _____

    d. HBr _____

Reference Section

Electronegativities								
1A								0
H 2.1	2A	3A	4A	5A	6A	7A		He —
Li 1.0	Be 1.5	B 2.0	C 2.5	N 3.0	O 3.5	F 4.0		Ne —
Na 0.9	Mg 1.2	Al 1.5	Si 1.8	P 2.1	S 2.5	Cl 3.0		Ar —
K 0.8	Ca 1.0	Ga 1.6	Ge 1.8	As 2.0	Se 2.4	Br 2.8		Kr —

30. The following covalent molecules have only single covalent bonds. Draw an electron dot structure for each one.

   a. HBr

                                                        c. PCl_3

   b. H_2O_2

D. Essay

31. Describe a network solid and give two examples.

_____

_____

_____

_____

E. Additional Questions and Problems

Answer the following in the space provided. Show your work.

32. Calculate the total energy needed to dissociate all the bonds in one mole of ethyl alcohol, C_2H_5OH. (Assume that the total energy is the sum of the individual bond dissociation energies.) The structural formula of ethyl alcohol is

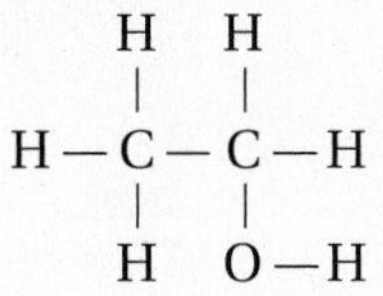

$$
\begin{array}{ccc}
 & H & H \\
 & | & | \\
H- & C- & C-H \\
 & | & | \\
 & H & O-H
\end{array}
$$

Bond	Energy (kJ/mol)
H — H	435
C — H	393
C — O	356
O — H	464
C — C	347

33. With the aid of a diagram, describe how the overlap of one $2p$ orbital from each of two atoms forms a sigma bond, but the overlap of the remaining two $2p$ orbitals from each atom forms pi bonds.

_____

_____

_____

_____

_____

_____

34. Indicate the hybrid orbitals used by each carbon atom in the following compound. The carbons are numbered for easy reference.

_____

_____

35. Draw electron dot structures for PCl_5 and SF_6. (*Hint:* These compounds are exceptions to the octet rule.)

8 COVALENT BONDING

Chapter Test B

A. Matching

Match each term in Column B with the correct description in Column A. Write the letter of the correct term on the line.

Column A	Column B
_____ 1. the mixing of several atomic orbitals to form the same number of equivalent hybrid orbitals	**a.** molecular compound
_____ 2. two or more valid electron dot formulas that can be written for the same molecule	**b.** VSEPR theory
_____ 3. a chemical formula that shows the arrangement of atoms in molecules and polyatomic ions	**c.** van der Waals forces
_____ 4. the weakest attractions that exist between molecules	**d.** single covalent bond
_____ 5. Because electron pairs repel, molecules adjust their shapes so that the valence-electron pairs are as far apart as possible.	**e.** resonance structures
_____ 6. a covalent bond in which one pair of electrons is shared between two atoms	**f.** polar molecule
_____ 7. a molecule in which one end is slightly negative and the other end is slightly positive	**g.** hybridization
_____ 8. a covalent bond formed between two different atoms in which the bonding electrons are shared unequally	**h.** structural formula
_____ 9. an electrically neutral group of atoms joined together by covalent bonds	**i.** polar covalent bond
_____ 10. a covalent bond in which one atom contributes both bonding electrons	**j.** coordinate covalent bond

B. Multiple Choice

Choose the best answer and write its letter on the line.

_____ 11. Which of the following exists as a diatomic molecule?
a. He   c. Cl
b. Ar   d. Na

_____ 12. The diatomic molecule among the following that contains a single covalent bond is
a. F_2.   c. N_2.
b. O_2.   d. O^{2-}.

_____ 13. Atoms share electrons in order to acquire the electron configurations of
a. alkali metals.   c. halogens.
b. alkaline earth metals.   d. noble gases.

_____ 14. In Cl_2, what is the total number of unshared pairs of electrons?
a. 1   c. 4
b. 2   d. 6

_____ 15. The diatomic molecule among the following that contains a triple covalent bond is
a. O_2.   c. H_2.
b. Cl_2.   d. N_2.

_____ 16. In the N_2 molecule, what is the number of unshared pairs of electrons in each nitrogen atom?
a. 1   c. 3
b. 2   d. 4

_____ 17. The covalent molecule among the following is
a. NaCl.   c. CaO.
b. NH_3.   d. KF.

_____ 18. How many single covalent bonds are there in a molecule of CH_4?
a. 1   c. 3
b. 2   d. 4

_____ 19. How many double covalent bonds are there in a molecule of CO_2?
a. 1   c. 3
b. 2   d. 4

_____ 20. The molecule among the following that contains only one single covalent bond is
a. NH_3.   c. HI.
b. N_2.   d. H_2O.

_____ 21. In forming the molecule HF, the F atom attains the electron configuration of
a. He.   c. Ar.
b. Ne.   d.. Cl.

_____ 22. Which molecule among the following contains a coordinate covalent bond?
  a. CO
  b. NH_3
  c. H_2O
  d. CCl_4

_____ 23. The molecule among the following that exhibits resonance structures is
  a. CO_2.
  b. CH_4.
  c. O_3 (ozone).
  d. NH_3.

_____ 24. Resonance structures can be considered
  a. polar molecules.
  b. hybrids.
  c. coordinate covalent molecules.
  d. none of the above

_____ 25. Substances that show relatively strong attractions to an external magnetic field are said to be
  a. diamagnetic.
  b. paramagnetic.
  c. nonmagnetic.
  d. none of the above

_____ 26. Oxygen is an example of a substance that is
  a. diamagnetic.
  b. paramagnetic.
  c. nonmagnetic.
  d. none of the above

_____ 27. When two atomic orbitals combine to form a molecular orbital that is symmetrical along the axis connecting the two atomic nuclei, the bond that is produced is referred to as a(n)
  a. ionic bond.
  b. pi bond.
  c. sigma bond.
  d. none of the above

_____ 28. The shape of a molecule of NH_3 is said to be
  a. tetrahedral.
  b. pyramidal.
  c. bent.
  d. linear.

_____ 29. In a methane (CH_4) molecule, the mixing of one $2s$ orbital with three $2p$ orbitals forms
  a. one sp^4 hybrid orbital.
  b. four sp hybrid orbitals.
  c. one sp^3 hybrid orbital.
  d. four sp^3 hybrid orbitals.

_____ 30. The overlap of atomic s orbitals produces a(n)
  a. ionic bond.
  b. pi bond.
  c. sigma bond.
  d. none of the above

_____ 31. Which of the following contains a polar covalent bond?
  a. O_2
  b. $MgCl_2$
  c. CaO
  d. HF

_____ 32. What type of bond would be expected in a molecule of LiF?
  a. ionic bond
  b. polar covalent bond
  c. nonpolar covalent bond
  d. none of the above

_____ **33.** Among the following molecules, the one containing the most polar
bond is

    a. HF.   **c.** HBr.
    b. HCl.   **d.** H_2O.

_____ **34.** The polar molecule among the following is

    a. CCl_4.   **c.** H_2O.
    b. CO_2.   **d.** N_2.

_____ **35.** The strongest intermolecular attractive forces from among those listed are

    a. dispersion forces.   **c.** hydrogen bonds.
    b. dipole interactions.   **d.** cannot be determined

_____ **36.** The melting and boiling points of most molecular compounds are

    a. lower than those of most ionic compounds.
    b. about the same as those of most ionic compounds.
    c. higher than those of most ionic compounds.
    d. sometimes higher and sometimes lower than those of most ionic
compounds.

_____ **37.** Network solids

    a. have low melting points.   **c.** are extremely hard.
    b. have low boiling points.   **d.** are generally ductile.

C. Questions

Answer the following in the space provided.

38. Write both the electron dot structure and the structural formula for each of the
following covalent molecules:

	Electron Dot Structure	**Structural Formula**
a. H_2		
b. N_2		
c. H_2O		
d. NH_3		
e. CO		

Name ______________________ Date __________________ Class ________________

39. Write the electron dot formula for each of the following polyatomic ions.

a. NH_4^+

b. PO_4^{3-}

D. Essay

40. Distinguish between ionic and covalent bonds in terms of how each is formed and how to predict which will be formed when various elements combine.

E. Additional Questions and Problems

Answer the following in the space provided. Show your work.

41. Use the electronegativity table below to determine the type of bond (polar covalent, nonpolar covalent, or ionic) that would be formed between each of the following elements. Give the electronegativity difference in each case.

Reference Section

Electronegativities								
1A								0
H 2.1	2A	3A	4A	5A	6A	7A		He —
Li 1.0	Be 1.5	B 2.0	C 2.5	N 3.0	O 3.5	F 4.0		Ne —
Na 0.9	Mg 1.2	Al 1.5	Si 1.8	P 2.1	S 2.5	Cl 3.0		Ar —
K 0.8	Ca 1.0	Ga 1.6	Ge 1.8	As 2.0	Se 2.4	Br 2.8		Kr —

	Bond Type	Electronegativity Difference
a. H, Cl		
b. H, S		
c. S, Cl		
d. Na, F		
e. Cl, Br		
f. Al, Br		

42. Given the following bond dissociation energy values, calculate the total energy that would be required to break all of the covalent bonds in 0.25 mol of ethane (C_2H_6). C—C = 347 kJ/mol and C—H = 393 kJ/mol

Name _____ Date _____ Class _____

QUICK LAB: Strengths of Covalent bonds

Laboratory Recordsheet   Use with Section 8.2

PURPOSE

To compare and contrast the stretching of rubber bands and the dissociation energy of covalent bonds.

MATERIALS

- 170-g (6-oz) can of food
- 2 454-g (16-oz) cans of food
- 3 No. 25 rubber bands
- metric ruler
- coat hanger
- plastic grocery bag
- paper clip
- graph paper
- pencil
- motion detector (optional)

PROCEDURE

1. Bend the coat hanger to fit over the top of a door. The hook should hang down on one side of the door. Measure the length of the rubber bands (in cm). Hang a rubber band on the hook created by the coat hanger.

2. Place the 170-g can in the plastic grocery bag. Use a paper clip to fasten the bag to the end of the rubber band. Lower the bag gently until it is suspended from the end of the rubber band. Measure and record the length of the stretched rubber band. Using different food cans, repeat this process three times with the following masses: 454 g, 624 g, and 908 g.

3. Repeat Step 2, first using two rubber bands to connect the hanger and the paper clip, and then using three.

4. Graph the length difference: (stretched rubber band) − (unstretched rubber band) on the *y*-axis versus mass (kg) on the *x*-axis for one, two, and three rubber bands. Draw the straight line that you estimate best fits the points for each set of data. (Your graph should have three separate lines.) The *x*-axis and *y*-axis intercepts of the lines should pass through zero, and the lines should extend past 1 kg on the *x*-axis. Determine the slope of each line in cm / kg.

Name ______________________ Date ________________ Class ________________

ANALYSES AND CONCLUSIONS

1. Assuming the rubber bands are models for covalent bonds, what can you conclude about the relative strengths of single, double, and triple bonds?

____

____

____

2. How does the behavior of the rubber bands differ from that of covalent bonds?

____

____

____

SMALL-SCALE LAB: Paper Chromatography
of Food Dyes

Laboratory Recordsheet   Use with Section 8.4

SAFETY

Use safe and proper laboratory procedures.

PURPOSE

To use paper chromatography to separate and identify food dyes in various samples.

MATERIALS

- pencil
- paper
- ruler
- scissors
- toothpicks

- 4 different colors of food coloring
- plastic cup
- 0.1% NaCl solution
- chromatography paper

PROCEDURE

Cut a 5 cm × 10 cm strip of chromatography paper and label it with a pencil as shown in Figure A. Use a different toothpick to place a spot of each of the four food colors on the X's on your chromatography paper. Allow the spots to dry for a few minutes. Fill the plastic cup so its bottom is just covered with the solvent (0.1% NaCl solution). Wrap the chromatography paper around a pencil. Remove the pencil and place the chromatography paper, color-spot side down, in the solvent. When the solvent reaches the top of the chromatography paper, remove the paper and allow it to dry.

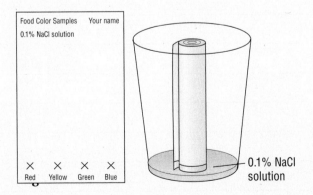

ANALYSIS

Using your experimental data, record the answers to the following questions.

  1. If a food color sample yields a single streak or spot, it is usually a pure compound. Which food colors consist of pure compounds?

_____

_____

  2. Which food colors are mixtures of compounds?

_____

_____

  3. Food colors often consist of a mixture of three colored dyes: Red No. 40, Yellow No. 5, and Blue No. 1. Read the label on the food color package. Which dyes do your food color samples contain?

_____

_____

_____

  4. Identify each spot or streak on your chromatogram as Red No. 40, Yellow No. 5, or Blue No. 1.

  5. Paper chromatography separates polar covalent compounds on the basis of their relative polarities. The most polar dyes migrate the fastest and appear at the top of the paper. Which dye is the most polar? The least polar?

_____

_____

_____

YOU'RE THE CHEMIST

Use the space below to write your observations to the small-scale activities in the *You're the Chemist* section.

_____

_____

_____

_____

_____

_____

_____

9.1 NAMING IONS

Section Review

Objectives

- Determine the charges of monatomic ions by using the periodic table and write the names of the ions
- Define a polyatomic ion and write the names and formulas of the most common polyatomic ions
- Identify the two common endings for the names of most polyatomic ions.

Vocabulary

- monatomic ions
- polyatomic ions

Part A Completion

Use this completion exercise to check your understanding of the concepts and terms that are introduced in this section. Each blank can be completed with a term, short phrase, or number.

Ions that consist of a single atom are called __1__ ions.

Metallic elements tend to __2__ electrons. Group 1A ions have a

__3__ charge, whereas Group 2A metals form ions with a __4__

charge, and Group 3A metals form ions with a __5__ charge.

The charge of a Group A nonmetal ion is determined by

subtracting __6__ from the group number. For example, the

Group 7A elements form ions with a charge of __7__.

Many of the __8__ have more than one common ionic

charge. These ions are named using either the __9__ system

or the __10__ naming system.

Ions containing more than one atom are called __11__ ions.

The names of most common polyatomic ions end in either

__12__ or __13__.

1. _____

2. _____

3. _____

4. _____

5. _____

6. _____

7. _____

8. _____

9. _____

10. _____

11. _____

12. _____

13. _____

Part B True-False

Classify each of these statements as always true, AT; sometimes true, ST; or never true, NT.

_____ **14.** The names of polyatomic ions end in *-ite* or *-ate*.

_____ **15.** In polyatomic ions for which there is an *-ite/-ate* pair, the *-ite* ending will always indicate one less oxygen atom than the *-ate* ending.

_____ **16.** Polyatomic ions are anions.

_____ **17.** The charge on Group A metal ions is determined by subtracting the group number from 8.

_____ **18.** The Group 6A ions have a charge of $2-$.

Part C Matching

Match each description in Column B to the correct term in Column A.

Column A	Column B
_____ **19.** monatomic ions	**a.** negatively charged ions
_____ **20.** polyatomic ions	**b.** ions formed from single atoms
_____ **21.** cations	**c.** a traditional way of naming transition metal cations
_____ **22.** anions	**d.** positively charged ions
_____ **23.** classical naming system	**e.** ions formed from groups of atoms

Part D Questions and Problems

Answer the following in the space provided.

24. What is the charge on a typical ion for each of the following groups?

    a. 1A _____

    c. 7A _____

    b. 6A _____

    d. 2A _____

25. Write the name of each of the following polyatomic ions.

    a. HCO_3^- _____

    c. MnO_4^- _____

    b. NH_4^+ _____

    d. OH^- _____

26. How many electrons does the neutral atom gain or lose to form each of the following ions?

    a. Ca^{2+} _____

    c. I^- _____

    b. S^{2-} _____

    d. Mn^{3+} _____

9.2 NAMING AND WRITING FORMULAS FOR IONIC COMPOUNDS

Section Review

Objectives

- Apply the rules for naming and writing formulas for binary ionic compounds
- Apply the rules for naming and writing formulas for compounds with polyatomic ions

Vocabulary

- binary compound

Part A Completion

Use this completion exercise to check your understanding of the concepts and terms that are introduced in this section. Each blank can be completed with a term, short phrase, or number.

Binary ionic compounds are named by writing the name of

the ___1___ followed by the name of the ___2___. Names of

binary compounds end in ___3___. For example, NaI is ___4___.

When a cation has more than one ionic charge, a ___5___

is used in the name.

Compounds with polyatomic ions whose names end in *-ite*

or *-ate* contain a polyatomic ___6___ that includes ___7___.

In writing the formula of an ionic compound, the net ionic charge

must be ___8___.

1. _____

2. _____

3. _____

4. _____

5. _____

6. _____

7. _____

8. _____

Part B True-False

Classify each of these statements as always true, AT; sometimes true, ST; or never true, NT.

_____ 9. The systematic name for baking soda ($NaHCO_3$) is sodium bicarbonate.

_____ 10. In writing a formula for an ionic compound, the net ionic charge of the formula must be zero.

_____ **11.** Anions that contain oxygen end in *-ite* or *-ate*.

_____ **12.** The cation name is placed first when naming ionic compounds.

Part C Matching

Match each description in Column B to the correct term in Column A.

Column A	Column B
_____ **13.** binary compounds	**a.** ions that consist of a single atom
_____ **14.** monatomic ions	**b.** ionic compounds composed of two elements
_____ **15.** polyatomic ions	**c.** Group B metals, many of which have more than one common ionic charge
_____ **16.** transition metals	**d.** ions that consist of more than one atom

Part D Questions and Problems

Answer the following in the space provided.

17. Name the following compounds and tell what type of compound they are (binary ionic or ionic with a polyatomic ion).

a. $FeBr_3$ _____

b. KOH _____

c. $Na_2Cr_2O_7$ _____

18. Write the formulas for the following compounds.

a. sodium chlorate _____

b. lead(II) phosphate _____

c. magnesium hydrogen carbonate _____

9.3 NAMING AND WRITING FORMULAS FOR MOLECULAR COMPOUNDS

Section Review

Objectives

- Interpret the prefixes in the names of molecular compounds in terms of their chemical formulas
- Apply the rules for naming and writing formulas for binary molecular compounds

Part A Completion

Use this completion exercise to check your understanding of the concepts and terms that are introduced in this section. Each blank can be completed with a term, short phrase, or number.

Binary molecular compounds are composed of two ___1___

elements. The name of this type of compound ends in ___2___.

Prefixes are used to show how many ___3___ of each element

are present in a molecule of the compound. For example,

the name of As_2S_5 is ___4___.

1. _____

2. _____

3. _____

4. _____

Part B True-False

Classify each of these statements as always true, AT; sometimes true, ST; or never true, NT.

_____ 5. Binary molecular compounds contain carbon.

_____ 6. Charges must be balanced when writing formulas for molecular compounds.

_____ 7. CO_2 is named monocarbon dioxide.

Part C Matching

Match each description in Column B to the correct term in Column A.

Column A   **Column B**

_____ **8.** binary molecular   **a.** used to indicate the relative number of atoms of an
             compound   element in a molecular compound

_____ **9.** prefix   **b.** prefix indicating one atom of an element in a molecule

_____ **10.** *mono-*   **c.** prefix indicating four atoms of an element in a molecule

_____ **11.** *tetra-*   **d.** nonionic compound containing atoms of two elements

Part D Questions and Problems

Answer the following in the space provided.

12. Name each of the following compounds.

   a. PCl_5 _____

   b. SO_2 _____

   c. P_4S_{10} _____

13. Write formulas for the following compounds.

   a. carbon tetrabromide _____

   b. dinitrogen tetroxide _____

9.4 NAMING AND WRITING FORMULAS FOR ACIDS AND BASES

Section Review

Objectives

- Apply three rules for naming acids
- Apply the rules in reverse to write formulas of acids
- Apply the rules for naming bases

Vocabulary

- acid
- base

Part A Completion

Use this completion exercise to check your understanding of the concepts and terms that are introduced in this section. Each blank can be completed with a term, short phrase, or number.

An acid is a compound that contains one or more ___1___

atoms and produces ___2___ when dissolved in water. There

are rules for naming acids. For example, HBr is called

___3___ acid, whereas HNO_3 is called ___4___ acid.

A base is a(n) ___5___ compound that produces ___6___ when

dissolved in water. Ionic compounds that are bases are named

in the same way as other ___7___ compounds, that is, the name

of the ___8___ is followed by the name of the ___9___.

1. _____

2. _____

3. _____

4. _____

5. _____

6. _____

7. _____

8. _____

9. _____

Part B True-False

Classify each of these statements as always true, AT; sometimes true, ST; or never true, NT.

_____ **10.** A compound that contains hydrogen atoms will be an acid when dissolved in water.

_____ **11.** An acid contains one or more hydroxide ions.

_____ **12.** Chemists have a special system for naming bases.

Part C Matching

Match each description in Column B to the correct term in Column A.

Column A		**Column B**
_____ **13.** acid		**a.** a compound containing hydrogen that ionizes to yield hydrogen ions in solution
_____ **14.** base		**b.** a solution in which the solvent is water
_____ **15.** aqueous solution		**c.** a compound that produces hydroxide ions in water

Part D Questions and Problems

Answer the following in the space provided.

16. Write the formula for each acid or base.

    a. magnesium hydroxide

    b. hydrofluoric acid

    c. phosphoric acid

    d. lithium hydroxide

17. Name each acid or base.

    a. KOH

    b. HI

    c. H_2SO_4

9.5 THE LAWS GOVERNING FORMULAS AND NAMES

Section Review

Objectives

- Define the laws of definite proportions and multiple proportions
- Apply the rules for writing chemical formulas by using a flowchart
- Apply the rules for naming chemical compounds by using a flowchart

Vocabulary

- law of definite proportions
- law of multiple proportions

Part A Completion

Use this completion exercise to check your understanding of the concepts and terms that are introduced in this section. Each blank can be completed with a term, short phrase, or number. [Use Figure 9.20 to complete this exercise.]

The law of ___1___ states that in samples of any chemical

compound, the masses of the elements are always in the same

___2___. The law of ___3___ states that whenever the same two

elements form more than one compound, the different masses

of one element that combine with the same mass of the other

element are in the ratio of ___4___ numbers.

    H_3PO_4 is a(n) ___5___. It is called ___6___.

    CCl_4 is not a(n) ___7___. It contains two elements, so it is a

___8___ compound. It does not contain a metal, so it is a binary

___9___ compound. The compound is called ___10___.

    $Pb(C_2H_3O_2)_2$ is not a(n) ___11___. It contains more than two

___12___. $C_2H_3O_2^-$ is a polyatomic ___13___. Pb is a Group ___14___

metal. The compound is called ___15___.

1. _____

2. _____

3. _____

4. _____

5. _____

6. _____

7. _____

8. _____

9. _____

10. _____

11. _____

12. _____

13. _____

14. _____

15. _____

Part B True-False

Classify each of these statements as always true, AT; sometimes true, ST; or never true, NT.

_____ **16.** Roman numerals are used when naming Group B metal cations.

_____ **17.** Names of compounds containing polyatomic anions end in *-ide*.

_____ **18.** Prefixes are used when naming binary ionic compounds.

_____ **19.** Compounds containing two elements are called binary compounds.

Part C Questions and Problems

Answer the following in the space provided.

20. Name the following compounds.

  a. $Pb(C_2H_3O_2)_4$ _____

  b. HF _____

  c. P_2O_5 _____

  d. LiBr _____

21. Write formulas for the following compounds.

  a. phosphorus pentachloride _____

  b. iron(II) oxide _____

  c. nitric acid _____

  d. potassium chloride _____

  e. calcium nitrate _____

9 CHEMICAL NAMES AND FORMULAS

Practice Problems

In your notebook, solve the following problems.

SECTION 9.1 NAMING IONS

1. What is the charge on the ion typically formed by each element?

   a. oxygen

   b. iodine

   c. sodium

   d. aluminum

   e. nickel, 2 electrons lost

   f. magnesium

2. How many electrons does the neutral atom gain or lose when each ion forms?

   a. Cr^{3+}

   b. P^{3-}

   c. Li^+

   d. Ca^{2+}

   e. Cl^-

   f. O^{2-}

3. Name each ion. Identify each as a cation or an anion.

   a. Sn^{2+}

   b. Co^{3+}

   c. Br^-

   d. K^+

   e. H^-

   f. Mn^{2+}

4. Write the formula (including charge) for each ion. Use Table 9.3 if necessary.

   a. carbonate ion

   b. nitrite ion

   c. sulfate ion

   d. hydroxide ion

   e. chromate ion

   f. ammonium ion

5. Name the following ions. Identify each as a cation or an anion.

   a. CN^-

   b. HCO_3^-

   c. PO_4^{3-}

   d. Cl^-

   e. Ca^{2+}

   f. SO_3^{2-}

SECTION 9.2 NAMING AND WRITING FORMULAS FOR IONIC COMPOUNDS

1. Write the formulas for these binary ionic compounds.

   a. magnesium oxide

   b. tin(II) fluoride

   c. potassium iodide

   d. aluminum chloride

   e. sodium sulfide

   f. ferric bromide

2. Write the formulas for the compounds formed from these pairs of ions.

   a. Ba^{2+}, Cl^-

   b. Ag^+, I^-

   c. Ca^{2+}, S^{2-}

   d. K^+, Br^-

   e. Al^{3+}, O^{2-}

   f. Fe^{2+}, O^{2-}

3. Name the following binary ionic compounds.

   a. MnO_2

   b. Li_3N

   c. $CaCl_2$

   d. $SrBr_2$

   e. $NiCl_2$

   f. K_2S

   g. $CuCl_2$

   h. $SnCl_4$

4. Write formulas for the following ionic compounds.

    a. sodium phosphate   **c.** sodium hydroxide   **e.** ammonium chloride

    b. magnesium sulfate   **d.** potassium cyanide   **f.** potassium dichromate

5. Write formulas for compounds formed from these pairs of ions.

    a. NH_4^+, SO_4^{2-} **c.** barium ion and hydroxide ion

    b. K^+, NO_3^- **d.** lithium ion and carbonate ion

6. Name the following compounds.

    a. NaCN   **c.** Na_2SO_4 **e.** $Cu(OH)_2$

    b. $FeCl_3$ **d.** K_2CO_3 **f.** $LiNO_3$

7. Name and give the charge of the metal cation in each of the following ionic compounds.

    a. Na_3PO_4 **c.** CaS   **e.** $FeCl_3$

    b. $NiCl_2$ **d.** K_2S **f.** CuI

SECTION 9.3 NAMING AND WRITING FORMULAS FOR MOLECULAR COMPOUNDS

1. Name the following molecular compounds.

    a. PCl_5 **c.** NO_2 **e.** P_4O_6 **g.** SiO_2

    b. CCl_4 **d.** N_2F_2 **f.** XeF_2 **h.** Cl_2O_7

2. Write the formulas for the following binary molecular compounds.

    a. nitrogen tribromide   **c.** sulfur dioxide

    b. dichlorine monoxide   **d.** dinitrogen tetrafluoride

SECTION 9.4 NAMING AND WRITING FORMULAS FOR ACIDS AND BASES

1. Name the following compounds as acids.

    a. HNO_2 **b.** H_2SO_4 **c.** HF   **d.** H_2CO_3

2. Write the formulas for the following bases.

    a. calcium hydroxide   **c.** aluminum hydroxide

    b. ammonium hydroxide   **d.** lithium hydroxide

SECTION 9.5 THE LAWS GOVERNING FORMULAS AND NAMES

1. Write the formulas for these compounds.

    a. potassium sulfide   **e.** hydrobromic acid   **i.** sulfur hexafluoride

    b. tin(IV) chloride   **f.** aluminum fluoride   **j.** magnesium chloride

    c. hydrosulfuric acid   **g.** dinitrogen pentoxide   **k.** phosphoric acid

    d. calcium oxide   **h.** iron(III) carbonate   **l.** nitric acid

Name _____ Date _____ Class _____

2. Complete this table by writing correct formulas for the compounds formed by combining positive and negative ions.

	SO_4^{2-}	NO_3^-	OH^-	PO_4^{3-}
Ca^{2+}				
Al^{3+}				
Na^+				
Pb^{4+}				

3. Name the following compounds.

a. K_3PO_4

b. $Al(OH)_3$

c. $NaHSO_4$

d. HgO

e. N_2O_5

f. NBr_3

g. PI_3

h. $(NH_4)_2SO_4$

4. Explain the difference between the law of definite proportions and the law of multiple proportions.

_____

_____

_____

9 INTERPRETING GRAPHICS

Use with Section 9.1

Group 1A							8A
1 **H** Hydrogen	2A	3A	4A	5A	6A	7A	2 **He** Helium
3 **Li** Lithium	4 **Be** Beryllium	5 **B** Boron	6 **C** Carbon	7 **N** Nitrogen	8 **O** Oxygen	9 **F** Fluorine	10 **Ne** Neon
11 **Na** Sodium	12 **Mg** Magnesium	13 **Al** Aluminum	14 **Si** Silicon	15 **P** Phosphorus	16 **S** Sulfur	17 **Cl** Chlorine	18 **Ar** Argon
19 **K** Potassium	20 **Ca** Calcium						

Use the abbreviated periodic table above to answer the following questions.

1. Which group on the periodic table contains magnesium (Mg)?

   _____

2. How many electrons does a magnesium atom lose to form a magnesium cation?

   _____

3. How many electrons does a neutral magnesium atom contain?

   _____

4. How many electrons does a magnesium cation contain?

   _____

5. Which group on the periodic table contains fluorine (F)?

   _____

6. How many electrons does a fluorine atom gain to form a fluoride anion?

   _____

7. How many electrons does a neutral fluorine atom contain?

   _____

Name ______________________ Date ______________ Class ______________

8. How many electrons does a fluoride anion contain?

____

9. How many electrons does a sodium cation contain?

____

10. How many electrons does an oxide anion contain?

____

11. How many electrons does each of the following ions contain?

a. S^{2-} ______________________________

b. Ca^{2+} ______________________________

c. K^{+} ______________________________

d. Cl^{-} ______________________________

CHEMICAL NAMES AND FORMULAS

9

Vocabulary Review

Match the correct vocabulary term to each numbered statement. Write the letter of the correct term on the line.

Column A

_____ 1. compounds that contain one or more hydrogen atoms and produce hydrogen ions in solution

_____ 2. an ionic compound that produces hydroxide ions when dissolved in water

_____ 3. any atom or group of atoms that has a positive charge

_____ 4. compounds composed of metal cations and nonmetal anions

_____ 5. composed of two elements and can be either ionic or molecular

_____ 6. an ion consisting of a single atom with a positive or negative charge

_____ 7. Whenever two elements form more than one compound, the different masses of one element that combine with the same mass of the other element are in the ratio of small whole numbers.

_____ 8. a tightly bound group of atoms that behaves as a unit and carries a charge

_____ 9. In samples of any chemical compound, the masses of the elements are always in the same proportions.

_____ 10. any atom or group of atoms that has a negative charge

Column B

a. anion

b. law of multiple proportions

c. base

d. ionic compounds

e. binary compound

f. monatomic ion

g. cation

h. polyatomic ion

i. acids

j. law of definite proportions

9 | CHEMICAL NAMES AND FORMULAS

Chapter Quiz

Fill in the word(s) that will make each statement true.

1. __1__ tend to lose electrons when they react to form compounds.

2. The formula for phosphorus pentachloride is __2__.

3. A(n) __3__ is any atom or group of atoms with a negative charge.

4. The law of __4__ states that in any chemical compound, the elements are always combined in the same proportion by mass.

5. The charge on an ion of a Group A nonmetal is determined by subtracting 8 from __5__.

6. The metals in Groups 1A, 2A, and 3A __6__ electrons when they form ions.

7. The two common polyatomic ions whose names end in *-ide* are the cyanide ion and the __7__ ion.

8. The formula for the dihydrogen phosphate ion is __8__.

9. The systematic name for laughing gas (N_2O) is __9__.

Write your answer in the space provided.

10. What is the formula for iron(II) chloride?

11. Name the compound whose formula is SnS_2.

12. Name the compound N_2O_5.

13. Name the compound $NaHCO_3$.

14. Write the formula for copper(II) hydroxide.

15. Name the compound HNO_3 as an acid.

1. _____ 9.1

2. _____ 9.3

3. _____ 9.1

4. _____ 9.5

5. _____ 9.1

6. _____ 9.1

7. _____ 9.1

8. _____ 9.1

9. _____ 9.3

10. _____ 9.2

11. _____ 9.2

12. _____ 9.3

13. _____ 9.2

14. _____ 9.2

15. _____ 9.4

CHEMICAL NAMES AND FORMULAS

Chapter Test A

A. Matching

*Match each description in Column B to the correct term in Column A. Write the
letter of the correct description in the blank.*

Column A	Column B
_____ 1. cation	**a.** any atom or group of atoms with a negative charge
_____ 2. anion	**b.** When two elements combine to form more than one compound, the different masses of one element that combine with the same mass of the other element are in the ratio of small whole numbers.
_____ 3. law of definite proportions	**c.** tightly bound group of atoms that behaves as a unit and carries a charge
_____ 4. acid	**d.** a compound that produces hydroxide ions when dissolved in water
_____ 5. base	**e.** a compound composed of two different elements
_____ 6. law of multiple proportions	**f.** any atom or group of atoms with a positive charge
_____ 7. polyatomic ion	**g.** In all samples of the same chemical compound, the elements are always combined in the same proportion by mass.
_____ 8. monatomic ion	**h.** a compound that produces hydrogen ions when dissolved in water
_____ 9. binary compound	**i.** consists of a single atom with a positive or negative charge

B. Multiple Choice

Choose the best answer and write its letter on the line.

_____ 10. The correct name for the N^{3-} ion is the:
    a. nitrate ion.   **c.** nitride ion.
    b. nitric ion.   **d.** nitrite ion.

_____ **11.** Elements of Group 4A:
  a. generally form positive ions.
  b. generally form negative ions.
  c. do not commonly form ions.
  d. do not combine with other elements.

_____ **12.** What is the ionic charge on the chromium ion in the ionic compound that has the formula Cr_2O_3?
  a. 3+   **c.** 5−
  b. 2−   **d.** 5+

_____ **13.** Which element when combined with chlorine would most likely form an ionic compound?
  a. lithium   **c.** phosphorus
  b. carbon   **d.** bromine

_____ **14.** What is the formula for calcium hydrogen phosphate?
  a. $CaHPO_4$ **c.** $Ca(H_2PO_4)_2$
  b. Ca_2HPO_4 **d.** $Ca(HPO_4)_2$

_____ **15.** A cation is any atom or group of atoms with:
  a. a positive charge.
  b. no charge.
  c. a negative charge.
  d. more electrons than the corresponding atoms.

_____ **16.** The cation Fe^{3+} is formed when:
  a. an atom of iron loses two electrons.
  b. an atom of zinc loses two electrons.
  c. an atom of iron loses three electrons.
  d. an atom of iron gains three electrons.

_____ **17.** A molecular formula:
  a. gives information about molecular geometry.
  b. can be written for ionic compounds.
  c. shows the number and kinds of atoms in a molecule of a compound.
  d. uses superscripts to show the number of atoms of each kind.

_____ **18.** The metals in Groups 1A, 2A, and 3A:
  a. gain electrons when they form ions.
  b. form ions with a charge found by subtracting 8 from the group number.
  c. all form ions with a 1+ charge.
  d. lose electrons when they form ions.

_____ **19.** When naming an ion of a transition metal that has more than one common ionic charge, the numerical value of the charge is indicated by a:
  a. prefix.
  b. suffix.
  c. Roman numeral following the name.
  d. superscript after the name.

_____ **20.** In naming a binary molecular compound, the number of atoms of each element present in the molecule is indicated by:
    a. Roman numerals.   **c.** prefixes.
    b. superscripts.   **d.** suffixes.

_____ **21.** An -*ite* or -*ate* ending on the name of a compound indicates that the compound:
    a. is a binary ionic compound.
    b. is a binary molecular compound.
    c. contains a polyatomic anion.
    d. contains a polyatomic cation.

_____ **22.** What is the formula for sulfuric acid?
    a. H_2S_2 **c.** H_2SO_3
    b. H_2SO_4 **d.** H_2S

C. Completion

Fill in the word(s) that will make each statement true.

23. The ionic charge of lead, Pb, in the compound PbS_2 is ___23___ .   **23.** _____

24. The typical ionic charge of an ion formed by an element in Group 7A is ___24___ .   **24.** _____

25. Atoms that have a positive or negative charge are called ___25___ .   **25.** _____

26. The name of a monatomic anion ends in ___26___ .   **26.** _____

27. The ionic charge of chlorine, Cl, in the compound $MgCl_2$ is ___27___ .   **27.** _____

28. In a polyatomic ion, the -*ite* ending indicates one fewer ___28___ atom than the -*ate* ending.   **28.** _____

29. Binary molecular compounds are composed of two ___29___ elements.   **29.** _____

30. Acids are compounds that produce ___30___ ions when dissolved in water.   **30.** _____

D. Problems

Write the answers in the space provided.

31. Write the formulas for these compounds.

    a. magnesium cyanide   **a.** _____

    b. mercury(II) bromide   **b.** _____

    c. sulfur hexafluoride   **c.** _____

Name ______________________ Date ________________ Class ________________

32. Name these compounds.

a. CuCl **a.** ______________________

b. N_2O_3 **b.** ______________________

c. $KC_2H_3O_2$ **c.** ______________________

E. Essay

Write a short essay for the following.

33. Why was it necessary for chemists to develop a system for naming chemical compounds?

CHEMICAL NAMES AND FORMULAS

9

Chapter Test B

A. Matching

Match each term in Column B to the correct description in Column A. Write the letter of the correct description on the line.

Column A	Column B
_____ 1. a compound composed of two elements	**a.** law of definite proportions
_____ 2. a compound that produces hydrogen ions when dissolved in water	**b.** acid
_____ 3. When two elements combine to form more than one compound, the different masses of one element that combine with the same mass of the other element are in the ratio of small whole numbers.	**c.** law of multiple proportions
_____ 4. an atom or group of atoms with a negative charge	**d.** base
_____ 5. consists of a single atom with a positive or negative charge	**e.** polyatomic ion
_____ 6. In any sample of a chemical compound, the elements are always combined in the same proportions by mass.	**f.** cation
_____ 7. any atom or group of atoms with a positive charge	**g.** monatomic ion
_____ 8. tightly bound group of atoms that behaves as a unit and carries a charge	**h.** anion
_____ 9. compound that produces hydroxide ions when dissolved in water	**i.** binary compound

B. Multiple Choice

Choose the best answer and write its letter on the line.

_____ 10. Which of the following is a nonmetal?
    a. iron   **c.** oxygen
    b. silver   **d.** copper

_____ 11. Which of the following is an anion?
    a. O^{2-} **c.** Al^{3+}
    b. Mg^{2+} **d.** H

_____ **12.** Nitrogen reacts with oxygen to form two compounds. Compound A contains 2.8 g of nitrogen for each 1.6 g of oxygen. Compound B contains 5.6 g of nitrogen for each 9.6 g of oxygen. What is the lowest whole-number mass ratio of nitrogen that combines with a given mass of oxygen?

    a. 3:1   **c.** 4:7

    b. 2:1   **d.** 1:6

_____ **13.** The nonmetals in Groups 5A, 6A, and 7A:

    a. lose electrons when they form ions.

    b. form positively charged ions.

    c. form ions with charges of 3−, 2−, and 1−, respectively.

    d. form ions with a numerical charge equal to their group number.

_____ **14.** Among the following, which atom is most likely to form an ion with a charge of 2+?

    a. O   **c.** Al

    b. Na   **d.** Ca

_____ **15.** The correct name for the ion Fe^{2+} is:

    a. ferric.   **c.** ferrous.

    b. iron(II).   **d.** both b and c.

_____ **16.** Among these element groups, which is least likely to form ions?

    a. 1A   **c.** 4A

    b. 3A   **d.** 7A

_____ **17.** The sulfate ion is written in which of the following ways?

    a. S^{2-} **c.** $SO_4{}^{2-}$

    b. $SO_3{}^{2-}$ **d.** none of the above

_____ **18.** What is the formula for aluminum oxide?

    a. AlO_3 **c.** Al_3O_2

    b. Al_2O_3 **d.** Al_2O

_____ **19.** Among the following, which is a binary molecular compound?

    a. CO_2 **c.** FeO

    b. NaCl   **d.** MgS

_____ **20.** What is the formula for carbon tetrachloride?

    a. CCl   **c.** CCl_3

    b. CCl_2 **d.** CCl_4

_____ **21.** The compound H_3PO_4 is named:

    a. nitric acid.   **c.** phosphoric acid.

    b. sulfuric acid.   **d.** ethanoic acid.

C. Completion

Fill in the word(s) that will make each statement true.

22. The atoms of Group 7A elements _____ electrons when they form ions.

23. The atoms of Group B elements _____ electrons when they form ions.

24. An atom or group of atoms with a positive charge is a(n) _____.

25. The law of _____ states that in all samples of the same chemical compound, the masses of the elements are always in the same proportions.

26. The ionic charge of an element in Group 6A is _____.

27. The symbol for the ammonium ion is _____.

28. The name of the compound $Mg(NO_3)_2$ is _____.

29. The names of all binary compounds, both ionic and molecular, end in the

letters _____.

30. The formula for calcium phosphate is _____.

31. In a polyatomic ion, the *-ate* ending indicates one _____ oxygen than the *-ite* ending.

D. Questions

Answer the following questions in the space provided.

32. For each pair of ions listed, write the correct formula and then name the compound formed by combining the two ions.

	Formula	Name
a. Ca^{2+} and NO_3^-		
b. Na^+ and SO_4^{2-}		
c. Fe^{3+} and O^{2-}		
d. Al^{3+} and CO_3^{2-}		

Name ______________________ Date ________________ Class ______________

33. Write the formulas for the following compounds.

a. silicon dioxide ______________________

b. carbon tetrafluoride ______________________

c. zinc hydroxide ______________________

d. phosphorus tribromide ______________________

e. nitric acid ______________________

f. silver nitrate ______________________

g. ferric sulfate ______________________

h. mercury(II) chloride ______________________

34. Name the following compounds:

a. CS_2 ______________________

b. $(NH_4)_2CO_3$ ______________________

c. As_2O_5 ______________________

d. CO ______________________

e. $Sn(OH)_4$ ______________________

f. H_2SO_4 ______________________

g. PI_5 ______________________

h. $KMnO_4$ ______________________

E. Essay

Write a short essay for the following.

35. Distinguish between ionic and molecular compounds, both in terms of composition and method of naming.

SMALL-SCALE LAB: Names and Formulas for Ionic Compounds

Laboratory Recordsheet   Use with Section 9.2

SAFETY 🔬🥼☠️🧪🔥

Wear safety glasses and follow the standard safety procedures, as outlined in the Small-Scale Lab Manual.

PURPOSE

To observe the formation of compounds, and to write their names and formulas.

MATERIALS

- pencil
- paper
- ruler
- small-scale reaction surface
- spatula
- chemicals shown in Figure A

PROCEDURE

On a separate sheet of paper, draw a grid similar to Figure A. Make each square 2 cm on each side. Draw a black X in each square of the grid. Place a reaction surface over the grid and add the chemicals as shown in Figure A. Use the grid in Figure A as a data table to record your observations of each solution. Draw a black X in each square of the grid.

	$AgNO_3$ (Ag^+)	$Pb(NO_3)_2$ (Pb^{2+})	$CaCl_2$ (Ca^{2+})
Na_2CO_3 (CO_3^{2-})	a	e	i
Na_3PO_4 (PO_4^{3-})	b	f	j
$NaOH$ (OH^-)	c	g	k
Na_2SO_4 (SO_4^{2-})	d	h	l

Figure A

ANALYSES AND CONCLUSIONS

Using the experimental data, record the answers to the following questions.

1. Describe each precipitate that forms as milky, grainy, cloudy, or gelatinous. Which mixture(s) did not form a precipitate?

_____

2. Write the formulas and names of the chemical compounds produced in the mixings.

_____

_____

_____

_____

_____

_____

YOU'RE THE CHEMIST ☠ ☣ ☢

Use the space below to write what you observed in the small-scale activities in the *You're the Chemist* section.

_____

_____

_____

_____

_____

_____

_____

_____

_____

_____

_____

_____

_____

_____

_____

_____

QUICK LAB: Making Ionic Compounds

Laboratory Recordsheet   Use with Section 9.5

PURPOSE

To mix solutions containing cations and anions to make ionic compounds.

MATERIALS

- 9 small test tubes
- test-tube rack
- paper
- pencil
- ruler
- 6 solutions in plastic dropper bottles containing the following ions:
- Solution A
  (Fe^{3+} ion)
- Solution B
  (Ag^+ ion)
- Solution C
  (Pb^{2+} ion)
- Solution X
  (CO_3^{2-} ion)
- Solution Y
  (OH^- ion)
- Solution Z
  (PO_4^{3-} ion)

PROCEDURE

1. Label three test tubes A, three test tubes B, and three test tubes C.

2. Add 10 drops (approximately 0.5 mL) of solutions A, B, and C to appropriately labeled test tubes.

3. Add 10 drops of solution X to one test tube of A, 10 drops to one test tube of B, and 10 drops to one test tube of C. Observe each for the formation of a solid.

4. Make a 3-inch by 3-inch grid in which to record your observations. Label the rows A, B, and C. Label the columns X, Y, and Z. Describe any solid material you observe.

5. Repeat Step 3, adding 10 drops of solution Y to test tubes A, B, and C. Record your observations.

6. Repeat Step 3, adding 10 drops of solution Z to test tubes A, B, and C. Record your observations.

ANALYSES AND CONCLUSIONS

1. Some ionic compounds are insoluble (do not dissolve in water). Explain what you observed.

_____

_____

2. Write the formula for each ionic compound formed.

_____

_____

_____

_____

3. Name each ionic compound formed.

_____

_____

_____

_____

4. Will mixing any cation with any anion always lead to the formation of an insoluble ionic compound? Explain.

_____

_____

_____

THE MOLE: A MEASUREMENT OF MATTER

10.1

Section Review

Objectives

- Relate Avogadro's number to a mole of a substance
- Calculate the mass of a mole of any substance
- Describe methods of measuring the amount of something
- Compare and contrast the atomic mass of an element and its molar mass

Vocabulary

- mole (mol)
- Avogadro's number
- representative particle
- molar mass

Key Equations

- $\text{moles} = \text{representative particles} \times \dfrac{1 \text{ mole}}{6.02 \times 10^{23} \text{ representative particles}}$

- $\text{representative particles} = \text{moles} \times \dfrac{6.02 \times 10^{23} \text{ representative particles}}{1 \text{ mole}}$

Part A Completion

Use this completion exercise to check your knowledge of the terms and your understanding of the concepts introduced in this section. Each blank can be completed with a term, short phrase, or number.

Chemists relate units of counting, of mass, and of volume to a single quantity called the ___1___. The number of representative particles in a mole of a substance is ___2___.

To find the mass of a mole of a compound, scientists add together the ___3___ of the atoms making up the compound. When you substitute the unit *grams* for amu, you obtain the ___4___ of the compound. There are ___5___ representative particles in a mole of any substance.

1. _____
2. _____
3. _____
4. _____
5. _____

Name _____ Date _____ Class _____

Part B True-False

Classify each of these statements as always true, AT; sometimes true, ST; or never true, NT.

_____ **6.** A mole of a pure substance contains 6.02×10^{23} atoms.

_____ **7.** The representative particle of a compound is the molecule.

_____ **8.** A mole of CCl_4 is composed of one atom of carbon and four atoms of chlorine.

_____ **9.** A mole of carbon atoms has a mass approximately three times as great as the mass of a mole of helium atoms.

_____ **10.** The molar mass of nitrogen gas is 14.0 g.

Part C Matching

Match each description in Column B to the correct term in Column A.

Column A	Column B
_____ **11.** Avogadro's number	**a.** the atoms, molecules, or ions present in a substance
_____ **12.** molar mass	**b.** 6.02×10^{23}
_____ **13.** mole	**c.** the mass of one mole of a substance
_____ **14.** representative particles	**d.** SI unit that measures the amount of a substance

Part D Problems

Solve the following problems in the space provided. Show your work.

15. How many moles of Pb is 9.3×10^{15} atoms of Pb?

16. What is the molar mass of ethane, C_2H_6?

17. Find the mass of 3.65×10^{-2} mol K_2SO_4.

18. How many representative particles are in 2.5 mol H_2O_2?

Name _____ Date _____ Class _____

MOLE-MASS AND MOLE-VOLUME RELATIONSHIPS

Section Review

Objectives

- Convert the mass of a substance to the number of moles of a substance, and the number of moles of a substance to mass
- Calculate the volume of a quantity of gas at STP

Vocabulary

- Avogadro's hypothesis
- standard temperature and pressure (STP)
- molar volume

Key Equations

- $$\text{mass (grams)} = \text{number of moles} \times \frac{\text{mass (grams)}}{1 \text{ mole}}$$

- $$\text{moles} = \text{mass (grams)} \times \frac{1 \text{ mole}}{\text{mass (grams)}}$$

- $$\frac{\text{grams}}{\text{mole}} = \frac{\text{grams}}{\text{L}} \times \frac{22.4 \text{ L}}{1 \text{ mole}}$$

- $$\text{volume of gas} = \text{moles of gas} \times \frac{22.4 \text{ L}}{1 \text{ mole}}$$

Part A Completion

Use this completion exercise to check your knowledge of the terms and your understanding of the concepts introduced in this section. Each blank can be completed with a term, short phrase, or number.

At STP (0°C and 1 atmosphere pressure), one mole of any gas

occupies a volume of ___1___ L. This quantity is known as the

___2___ of the gas. To determine the volume in liters of 2.00 mol

of SO_2 gas at STP, you would use ___3___ as a conversion factor.

___4___, expressed in the units g/L, is used as a conversion factor

when converting from volume to molar mass. When converting

between numbers of representative particles, masses, and volumes,

you must always convert to ___5___ as an intermediate step.

1. _____

2. _____

3. _____

4. _____

5. _____

Part B True-False

Classify each of these statements as always true, AT; sometimes true, ST; or never true, NT.

_____ **6.** One mole of any gas occupies a volume of 22.4 L.

_____ **7.** For a substance of known molar mass, the number of moles of a sample can be calculated from the mass of the sample.

_____ **8.** The volume occupied by one mole of a gas is dependent on the molar mass of the gas.

_____ **9.** The volume of a gas at STP can be calculated from the number of molecules of the gas.

Part C Matching

Match each description in Column B to the correct term in Column A.

Column A	Column B
_____ **10.** molar mass	**a.** 22.4 L of a gas at STP
_____ **11.** standard temperature	**b.** 101.3 kPa or 1 atm
_____ **12.** molar volume	**c.** 0°C
_____ **13.** standard pressure	**d.** mass (in grams) of one mole of a substance
_____ **14.** molar road map	**e.** a means of relating mass, number of representative particles, and gaseous volume of a substance

Part D Problems

Solve the following problems in the space provided. Show your work.

15. What is the density of N_2O, a gas, at STP?

16. What is the mass of two moles of NaCl?

17. How many moles are in 16 grams of O_2?

18. What is the volume of 16 grams of O_2 at STP?

10.3 PERCENT COMPOSITION AND CHEMICAL FORMULAS

Section Review

Objectives

- Calculate the percent by mass of an element in a compound
- Interpret an empirical formula
- Compare and contrast empirical and molecular formulas

Vocabulary

- percent composition
- empirical formula

Key Equation

- $\% \text{ mass of element} = \dfrac{\text{mass of element}}{\text{mass of compound}} \times 100\%$

Part A Completion

Use this completion exercise to check your knowledge of the terms and your understanding of the concepts introduced in this section. Each blank can be completed with a term, short phrase, or number.

The __1__ of a compound is the percent by mass of each element in a compound. The percent by mass of an element in a compound is the number of grams of the element per __2__ g of the compound, multiplied by 100%. To calculate the percent by mass of an element in a known compound, divide the mass of the element in one mole by the __3__ and multiply by 100%.

A(n) __4__ formula represents the lowest __5__ ratio of the elements in a compound. It can be calculated from a compound's percent composition. The __6__ formula of a compound is either the same as its empirical formula, or it is some whole-number multiple of it.

1. _____

2. _____

3. _____

4. _____

5. _____

6. _____

Part B True-False

Classify each of these statements as always true, AT; sometimes true, ST; or never true, NT.

_____ **7.** It is necessary to know the formula of a compound in order to calculate its percent composition.

_____ **8.** If the percent by mass of carbon in methane, CH_4, is 75%, then 100 grams of methane contain 25.0 grams of hydrogen.

_____ **9.** The formula for methane, CH_4, is both a molecular and an empirical formula.

_____ **10.** The empirical formula for glucose, $C_6H_{12}O_6$, is $C_2H_4O_2$.

Part C Matching

Match each description in Column B to the correct term in Column A.

Column A	**Column B**
_____ **11.** percent composition	**a.** describes the actual number of atoms of each element in a molecule of a compound
_____ **12.** empirical formula	**b.** the lowest whole-number ratio of atoms of the elements in a compound
_____ **13.** molecular formula	**c.** the percent by mass of each element in a compound

Part D Problems

Solve the following problems in the space provided. Show your work.

14. What is the percent composition of each of the following?

    a. Cr_2O_3 **c.** HgS

    b. $Mn_2P_2O_7$ **d.** $Ca(NO_3)_2$

15. Determine the empirical formula of the compound with the percent composition of 29.1% Na, 40.5% S, and 30.4% O.

16. How many kilograms of iron can be recovered from 639 kilograms of the ore Fe_2O_3?

10 CHEMICAL QUANTITIES

Practice Problems

In your notebook, solve the following problems.

SECTION 10.1 THE MOLE: A MEASUREMENT OF MATTER

1. What is the molar mass of sucrose ($C_{12}H_{22}O_{11}$)?

2. What is the molar mass of each of the following compounds?

    a. phosphorus pentachloride (PCl_5)

    b. uranium hexafluoride (UF_6)

3. Calculate the molar mass of each of the following ionic compounds:

    a. $KMnO_4$

    b. $Ca_3(PO_4)_2$

4. How many moles is 3.52×10^{24} molecules of water?

5. How many atoms of zinc are in 0.60 mol of zinc?

6. What is the mass of 1.00 mol of oxygen (O_2)?

SECTION 10.2 MOLE–MASS AND MOLE–VOLUME RELATIONSHIPS

1. What is the molar mass of each of the following compounds?

    a. $C_6H_{12}O_6$ b. $NaHCO_3$ c. C_7H_{12} d. KNH_4SO_4

2. Calculate the mass in grams of each of the following:

    a. 8.0 mol lead oxide (PbO)

    b. 0.75 mol hydrogen sulfide (H_2S)

    c. 0.00100 mol silicon tetrahydride (SiH_4)

    d. 1.50×10^{-2} mol molecular oxygen (O_2)

    e. 2.30 mol ethylene glycol ($C_2H_6O_2$)

3. How many grams are in 1.73 mol of dinitrogen pentoxide (N_2O_5)?

4. How many grams are in 0.658 mol of calcium phosphate [$Ca_3(PO_4)_2$]?

5. Calculate the number of moles in each of the following:

    a. 0.50 g sodium bromide (NaBr)

    b. 13.5 g magnesium nitrate [$Mg(NO_3)_2$]

    c. 1.02 g magnesium chloride ($MgCl_2$)

    d. 0.00100 g monochloromethane (CH_3Cl)

    e. 1.50×10^{-3} g propylene glycol [$C_3H_6(OH)_2$]

6. A chemist plans to use 435.0 grams of ammonium nitrate (NH_4NO_3) in a reaction. How many moles of the compound is this?

7. A solution is to be prepared in a laboratory. The solution requires 0.0465 mol of quinine ($C_{20}H_{24}N_2O_2$). What mass, in grams, should the laboratory technician obtain in order to make the solution?

8. What is the volume at STP of 2.66 mol of methane (CH_4) gas?

9. How many moles is 135 L of ammonia (NH_3) gas at STP?

10.3 PERCENT COMPOSITION AND CHEMICAL FORMULAS

1. A sample of a compound analyzed in a chemistry laboratory consists of 5.34 g of carbon, 0.42 g of hydrogen, and 47.08 g of chlorine. What is the percent composition of this compound?

2. Find the percent composition of a compound containing tin and chlorine if 18.35 g of the compound contains 5.74 g of tin.

3. If 3.907 g of carbon combines completely with 0.874 g of hydrogen to form a compound, what is the percent composition of this compound?

4. From the formula for calcium acetate, $Ca(C_2H_3O_2)_2$, calculate the mass of carbon that can be obtained from 65.3 g of the compound.

5. How many grams of aluminum are in 25.0 g of aluminum oxide (Al_2O_3)?

6. How many grams of iron are in 21.6 g of iron(III) oxide (Fe_2O_3)?

7. Determine the empirical formula of each of the following compounds from the percent composition:

   a. 7.8% carbon and 92.2% chlorine

   b. 10.0% C, 0.80% H, 89.1% Cl

INTERPRETING GRAPHICS

10

Use with Section 10.3

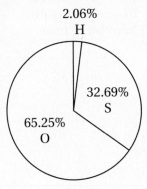

Acid X

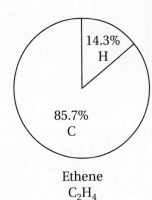

Cyclohexane
C_6H_{12}

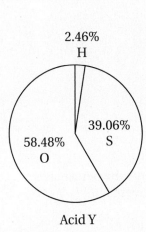

Acid Y

Ethene
C_2H_4

Use the circle graphs above to answer the following questions.

1. What is the percent of carbon in 50.0 g of cyclohexane?

2. Calculate the mass of hydrogen in 150.0 g of ethene.

3. Using the circle graphs, explain why percent composition alone is not sufficient to distinguish one compound from another.

_____

_____

4. What information, in addition to percent composition, is needed to distinguish ethene from cyclohexane?

_____

5. Scientists can use reactivity as a means of distinguishing between compounds with the same empirical formula. Ethene reacts with bromine to form dibromoethane, $C_2H_4Br_2$. Cyclohexane does not react with bromine. Create a circle graph to show the percent composition of dibromoethane.

6. Which of the circle graphs, labeled Acid X and Acid Y, represents the percentage composition of sulfuric acid, H_2SO_4? Which represents the percentage composition of sulfurous acid, H_2SO_3?

Name _____ Date _____ Class _____

 CHEMICAL QUANTITIES

10

Vocabulary Review

Select the term from the following list that best matches each description.

mole   percent composition
Avogadro's number   empirical formula
molar mass   standard temperature and pressure (0° C, 1 atm)
22.4 L

1. a description of the relative amounts of each element in a compound

_____

2. the lowest whole-number ratio of the atoms of the elements in a compound

_____

3. the volume occupied by one mole of any gas at STP

_____

4. the mass (in grams) of one mole of a compound

_____

5. the SI unit representing 6.02×10^{23} representative particles of a substance

_____

6. 6.02×10^{23} particles

_____

7. the temperature and pressure at which one mole of gas occupies a volume
of 22.4 L

_____

10 CHEMICAL QUANTITIES

Chapter Quiz

Fill in the word(s) that will make each statement true.

1. Counting, finding mass, and finding volume are all ways of measuring the amount of ___1___.

   1. _____   *10.1*

2. The ___2___ is the mass, in amus, of one atom of a monatomic element.

   2. _____   *10.1*

3. The ___3___ is the mass in grams of one mole of a substance.

   3. _____   *10.2*

4. The representative particle of most elements is the ___4___.

   4. _____   *10.2*

5. To convert moles of oxygen gas (O_2) to mass in grams, you can use the conversion factor ___5___.

   5. _____   *10.2*

Classify each of these statements as always true, AT; sometimes true, ST; or never true, NT.

_____ 6. The density of ethane gas, C_2H_6, at STP is 1.34 g/L.   *10.2*

_____ 7. The volume of 3 moles of oxygen at STP is 67.2 L.   *10.2*

_____ 8. One mole of a gas occupies 22.4 L.   *10.2*

_____ 9. To convert a volume of 3.20 L of hydrogen gas to the number of moles, you would use the conversion factor $\dfrac{22.4 \text{ L}}{1.00 \text{ mol } H_2}$.   *10.2*

_____ 10. The density of a gas at STP can be used to calculate the molar mass of that gas.   *10.2*

Solve the following problems. Show your work in the space provided.

11. What mass of gold contains as many atoms as 3.05 g of silver?   *10.2*

12. What is the empirical formula of a compound that is 40.7% carbon, 54.2% oxygen, and 5.1% hydrogen?   *10.3*

CHEMICAL QUANTITIES

10

Chapter Test A

A. Matching

Match each description in Column B to the correct term in Column A. Write the letter of the correct description on the line.

Column A	Column B

_____ 1. standard temperature and pressure

_____ 2. molar volume

_____ 3. representative particle

_____ 4. molar mass

_____ 5. atomic mass

_____ 6. Avogadro's number

_____ 7. mole (mol)

_____ 8. empirical formula

_____ 9. percent composition

_____ 10. molar mass

a. the volume occupied by a mole of any gas at STP (22.4 L)

b. the mass in amus of an atom of an element

c. the number of representative particles in a mole of a substance

d. the percent by mass of each element in a compound

e. the mass of a mole of a substance

f. the formula that gives the lowest whole-number ratio of the elements in a compound

g. an atom, a formula unit, or a molecule

h. the mass in grams of a mole of any pure substance

i. 6.02×10^{23} representative particles of a substance

j. 0°C and 101.3 kPa

B. Multiple Choice

Choose the best answer and write its letter on the line.

_____ 11. How many hydrogen atoms are in 4 molecules of isopropyl alcohol, C_3H_8O?
  a. $4 \times (6.02 \times 10^{23})$ c. 32
  b. 4   d. $32 \times (6.02 \times 10^{23})$

_____ 12. The mass of a mole of NaCl is its:
  a. molar mass.   c. gram atomic mass.
  b. empirical formula.   d. atomic mass.

_____ 13. The chemical formula of aspirin is $C_9H_8O_4$. What is the mass of 0.200 mol of aspirin?

a. 22.5 g

b. 5.4 g

c. 80 g

d. 36.0 g

_____ 14. How many moles of SO_3 are in 2.4×10^{24} molecules of SO_3?

a. 0.25

b. 3.4×10^{22}

c. 4.0

d. 2.9×10^{-23}

_____ 15. What is the volume (in liters at STP) of 2.50 mol of carbon monoxide?

a. 0.112 L

b. 3.10 L

c. 56.0 L

d. 8.96 L

_____ 16. The molar mass of molecular oxygen is:

a. equal to the mass of one mole of oxygen atoms.

b. 16.0 g.

c. 32.0 g.

d. none of the above

_____ 17. At STP, 1 mol each of hydrogen, oxygen, nitrogen, and fluorine:

a. have different densities.

b. occupy different volumes.

c. are monatomic elements.

d. contain twice Avogadro's number of representative particles.

_____ 18. A large weather balloon filled with helium has a volume of 7.00×10^2 L at STP. Which expression should be used to find the mass of helium in the balloon?

a. $\dfrac{22.4 \text{ L}}{\text{mol}} \times \dfrac{4 \text{ g He}}{\text{mol}}$

c. $\dfrac{22.4 \text{ L/mol}}{7.00 \times 10^2 \text{ L}} \times \dfrac{4 \text{ g He}}{\text{mol}}$

b. $\dfrac{7.00 \times 10^2}{\text{L}} \times \dfrac{4 \text{ g He}}{\text{mol}}$

d. $\dfrac{7.00 \times 10^2 \text{ L}}{22.4 \text{ L/mol}} \times \dfrac{4 \text{ g He}}{\text{mol}}$

_____ 19. The molar mass of a gas can be determined from:

a. the density of the gas at STP.

b. the volume of a mole of the gas.

c. Avogadro's number.

d. none of the above

_____ 20. What is the percent by mass of carbon in acetone, C_3H_6O?

a. 1.60%

b. 30.0%

c. 62%

d. 20.7%

_____ 21. Which of the following is *not* an empirical formula?

a. Na_2SO_4

b. C_6H_5Cl

c. N_2H_4

d. $Sn_3(PO_4)_4$

_____ 22. Which expression represents the percent by mass of nitrogen in NH_4NO_3?

a. $\dfrac{14.0 \text{ g}}{80.0 \text{ g}} \times 100$

c. $\dfrac{80.0 \text{ g}}{14.0 \text{ g}} \times 100$

b. $\dfrac{28.0 \text{ g}}{80.0 \text{ g}} \times 100$

d. $\dfrac{80.0 \text{ g}}{28.0 \text{ g}} \times 100$

_____ **23.** A compound has the empirical formula C_2H_3O and a molar mass of
172 g. What is its molecular formula?

    a. $C_6H_9O_3$ **c.** $C_9H_{16}O_3$

    b. $C_8H_{12}O_4$ **d.** $C_7H_8O_5$

_____ **24.** The empirical formula of a compound is CH_2F. The molar mass of this
compound is 66.0 g. The molecular formula of the compound is:

    a. $C_4H_8F_4$.   **c.** $C_2H_4F_2$.

    b. $C_4H_4F_4$.   **d.** CH_2F.

C. Problems

Solve the following problems in the space provided. Show your work.

25. Find the mass, in grams, of 5.00×10^{23} molecules of F_2.

26. The polymer used for the nonstick surface of cooking utensils is 24.0% C and
76.0% F by mass. What is the empirical formula of this polymer?

27. Find the number of moles of argon in 364 g of argon.

D. Essay

Write a short essay for the following.

28. The adjective *molar* in the phrase *molar mass* means "of or pertaining to a
mole." How does this definition support your understanding of molar mass as it
is applied to atoms, molecules, ions, formula units, and other particles?

_____

_____

_____

_____

_____

_____

10 **CHEMICAL QUANTITIES**

Chapter Test B

A. Matching

Match each term in Column B with the correct description in Column A. Write the letter of the correct term on the line.

Column A

_____ **1.** the percent by mass of each element in a compound

_____ **2.** 0°C and 101.3 kPa or 1 atmosphere

_____ **3.** the lowest whole-number ratio of the atoms of elements in a compound

_____ **4.** the species present in a substance—usually atoms, molecules, or formula units

_____ **5.** 6.02×10^{23} representative particles of a substance

_____ **6.** the mass of an atom of an element

_____ **7.** the mass of one mole of any element or compound

_____ **8.** 22.4 L of any gas measured at STP

Column B

a. molar mass

b. empirical formula

c. atomic mass

d. molar volume

e. representative particle

f. percent composition

g. one mole

h. standard temperature and pressure

B. Multiple Choice

Choose the best answer and write its letter on the line.

_____ **9.** How many oxygen atoms are in 10 formula units of $Al_2(SO_4)_3$?
  a. 10 atoms O
  b. 7 atoms O
  c. 70 atoms O
  d. 120 atoms O

_____ **10.** How many molecules are in 4.50 moles of H_2O?
  a. 450 molecules
  b. 2.71×10^{24} molecules
  c. 6.02×10^{23} molecules
  d. 3.00 molecules

_____ **11.** How many moles are in 8.5×10^{25} molecules of CO_2?
  a. 1.4×10^2 mol
  b. 7.1×10^{-3} mol
  c. 5.1×10^{49} mol
  d. 8.5×10^{25} mol

_____ 12. What is the molar mass of C_3H_8?
    a. 36.0 g   **c.** 44.0 g
    b. 11.0 g   **d.** 6.02×10^{23} g

_____ 13. The representative particle for nitrogen is:
    a. an atom.   **c.** a formula unit.
    b. a molecule.   **d.** none of the above

_____ 14. What is the molar mass of $MgCl_2$?
    a. 59.8 g   **c.** 125.8 g
    b. 95.3 g   **d.** 76.4 g

_____ 15. How many grams are in 6.50 moles of H_2SO_4?
    a. 638 g   **c.** 15.1 g
    b. 98.1 g   **d.** 0.0663 g

_____ 16. Find the number of moles in 3.30 g of $(NH_4)_2SO_4$?
    a. 132.1 mol   **c.** 0.0279 mol
    b. 40.0 mol   **d.** 0.0250 mol

_____ 17. What is the mass of 2.56×10^{-4} moles of Fe_2O_3?
    a. 4.09×10^{-2} g   **c.** 6.23×10^5
    b. 159.6 g   **d.** 1.60×10^{-6} g

_____ 18. At STP, one mole of any gas occupies a volume of:
    a. 1 L.   **c.** 22.4 L.
    b. 6.02×10^{23} L.   **d.** none of the above

_____ 19. What is the volume, in liters, of 3.75 moles of O_2 gas at STP?
    a. 3.75 L   **c.** 84.0 L
    b. 32.0 L   **d.** 1.20×10^2 L

_____ 20. Determine the number of moles in 625 L of H_2 gas at STP.
    a. 3.58×10^{-2} mol   **c.** 1.40×10^4 mol
    b. 27.9 mol   **d.** 1250 mol

_____ 21. The density of a gaseous compound is 1.623 g/L at STP. Determine the molar mass of the compound.
    a. 13.80 g   **c.** 1.623 g
    b. 7.246×10^{-2} g   **d.** 36.36 g

_____ 22. How many atoms are contained in 12.5 grams of silver?
    a. 6.97×10^{22} atoms   **c.** 0.116 atoms
    b. 7.52×10^{24} atoms   **d.** 1.92×10^{-25} atoms

_____ 23. What is the percent of aluminum in $Al_2(SO_4)_3$?
    a. 28.1%   **c.** 15.8%
    b. 54.0%   **d.** 56.7%

_____ 24. What is the mass of hydrogen in 50.0 g of propane, C_3H_8?
    a. 18.2 g   **c.** 44.0 g
    b. 9.1 g   **d.** 81.8 g

_____ **25.** What is the empirical formula of a compound that is 3.05% carbon, 0.26% hydrogen, and 96.69% iodine?

    a. C_2HI_7 **c.** $C_3H_2I_{11}$

    b. CH_2I_5 **d.** CHI_3

_____ **26.** A compound has an empirical formula of $C_3H_5O_2$ and a molar mass of 146.14 g. What is the molecular formula of this compound?

    a. $C_6H_5O_4$ **c.** $C_6H_{10}O_4$

    b. $C_9H_{15}O_6$ **d.** $C_{12}H_{20}O_8$

C. Problems

Solve the following problems in the space provided. Show your work.

27. How many atoms are contained in 0.25 moles of Fe?

28. Find the mass, in grams, of 6.25 mol H_2SO_4.

29. What is the volume, in liters, of 15.0 kg of CO_2 at STP?

30. Determine the molar mass of a compound that has a density of 0.650 g/L at STP.

31. What is the mass, in grams, of 3.75×10^{15} atoms of gold?

32. Calculate the percent composition of $Mg(NO_3)_2$.

33. What is the empirical formula of a compound that is 27.3% C and 72.7% O?

34. A compound consisting of 56.38% phosphorus and 43.62% oxygen has a molar mass of 219.9 g/mol. Determine its molecular formula.

D. Essay

Write a short essay for the following.

35. Explain how the mass of a single atom in an element (in amu), the mass of one mole of atoms of that element, and Avogadro's number are related.

_____

_____

_____

_____

_____

_____

_____

_____

SMALL-SCALE LAB: Counting by Measuring Mass

Laboratory Recordsheet   Use with Section 10.2

SAFETY

Wear your safety glasses and follow standard safety procedures as outlined in the Small-Scale Lab Manual.

PURPOSE

To determine the mass of several samples of chemical compounds and use the data to count atoms.

MATERIALS

- chemicals shown in the table
- plastic spoon
- weighing paper
- watchglass or small beaker
- balance
- paper
- pencil
- ruler

PROCEDURE

Measure the mass of one level teaspoon of sodium chloride (NaCl), water (H_2O), and calcium carbonate ($CaCO_3$). Record your measured and calculated data in Figure A.

	$H_2O(l)$	$NaCl(s)$	$CaCO_3(s)$
Mass (grams)			
Molar Mass (g/mol)			
Moles of each compound			
Moles of each element			
Atoms of each element			

Figure A

ANALYSES AND CONCLUSIONS

Using your experimental data, record the answers to the following questions.

1. Calculate the moles of NaCl contained in one level teaspoon and record the result in your table.

$$\text{moles of NaCl} = ? \text{ g NaCl} \times \frac{1 \text{ mol NaCl}}{58.5 \text{ g}}$$

2. Repeat Step 1 for the other compounds in Figure A. Use the periodic table to calculate the molar mass of water and calcium carbonate.

3. Calculate the number of moles of each element present in the teaspoon-sized sample of H_2O.

$$\text{moles of H} = \text{? mol } H_2O \times \frac{2 \text{ mol H}}{1 \text{ mol } H_2O}$$

Repeat for all the other compounds in your table.

4. Calculate the number of atoms of each element present in the teaspoon-sized sample of H_2O.

$$\text{atoms of H} = \text{? mol H} \times \frac{6.02 \times 10^{23} \text{ atoms H}}{1 \text{ mol } H_2O}$$

Repeat for all the other compounds in your table.

5. Which of the three teaspoon-sized samples contains the greatest number of moles?

_____

6. Which of the three compounds contains the most atoms?

_____

YOU'RE THE CHEMIST

Use the space below to write your observations of the small-scale activities in the *You're the Chemist* section.

_____

_____

_____

_____

_____

Name _____ Date _____ Class _____

QUICK LAB: Percent Composition

Laboratory Recordsheet   Use with Section 10.3

PURPOSE

To measure the percent of water in a series of crystalline compounds called hydrates.

MATERIALS

- centigram balance
- 3 medium-sized test tubes
- test-tube rack
- hydrated salts of copper(II) sulfate, calcium chloride, and sodium sulfate
- burner
- test-tube holder
- spatula

PROCEDURE

1. Label each test tube with the name of a salt. Weigh and record its mass.

2. Add 2–3 g of salt (a good-sized spatula full) to the appropriately labeled test tube. Measure and record the mass of each test tube and salt.

3. Hold one of the tubes at a 45° angle and gently heat its contents over the burner, slowly passing it in and out of the flame. Note any change in the appearance of the solid salt.

4. As moisture begins to condense in the upper part of the test tube, gently heat the entire length of the tube. Continue heating until all of the moisture is driven from the tube. This may take 2–3 minutes. Repeat Steps 3 and 4 for the other two tubes.

5. Allow each tube to cool. Then measure and record the mass of each test tube and the heated salt.

THINK ABOUT IT!

1. Set up a data table so you can subtract the mass of the empty tube from the mass of the salt and the test tube, both before and after heating.

2. Calculate the difference between the mass of each salt before and after heating. This difference represents the amount of water lost by the hydrate on heating.

3. Calculate the percent by mass of water lost by each compound.

4. Which compound lost the greatest percent by mass of water? The smallest?

_____

_____

Name _____ Date _____ Class _____

Section Review

Objectives

- Explain how to write a word equation
- Describe how to write a skeleton equation
- List the steps for writing a complete chemical equation

Vocabulary

- chemical equation
- skeleton equation
- catalyst
- coefficients
- balanced equation

Part A Completion

Use this completion exercise to check your understanding of the concepts and terms that are introduced in this section. Each blank can be completed with a term, short phrase, or number.

A chemical reaction can be concisely represented by a chemical __1__. The substances that undergo a chemical change are the __2__. The new substances formed in a chemical reaction are the __3__. In accordance with the law of conservation of __4__, a chemical equation must be balanced. When balancing an equation, you place __5__ in front of reactants and products so that the same number of atoms of each __6__ are on each side of the equation. An equation must never be balanced by changing the __7__ in the chemical formula of a substance.

Special symbols are used to show the physical state of a substance in a reaction. The symbol for a liquid is __8__; for a solid, __9__; and for a gas, __10__. A substance dissolved in water is designated __11__. If a __12__ is used to increase the rate of a chemical reaction, its formula is written above the arrow.

1. _____
2. _____
3. _____
4. _____
5. _____
6. _____
7. _____
8. _____
9. _____
10. _____
11. _____
12. _____

Part B True-False

Classify each of these statements as always true, AT; sometimes true, ST; or never true, NT.

_____ **13.** In an equation, a substance is shown to be in the gaseous state by placing an upward-pointing arrow after its formula.

_____ **14.** The symbol Δ placed over the arrow in an equation means that heat is supplied to the reaction.

_____ **15.** Atoms are destroyed in a chemical reaction.

_____ **16.** A skeleton equation is not a balanced equation.

Part C Matching

Match each description in Column B to the correct term in Column A.

Column A	Column B
_____ **17.** chemical equation	**a.** an equation in which each side has the same number of atoms of each element
_____ **18.** skeleton equation	**b.** a substance that speeds up the rate of a reaction
_____ **19.** catalyst	**c.** a symbolic way of describing a chemical reaction
_____ **20.** coefficients	**d.** substances that undergo chemical change
_____ **21.** balanced equation	**e.** a chemical equation that does not indicate the amounts of substances involved
_____ **22.** reactants	**f.** new substances formed in a chemical reaction
_____ **23.** products	**g.** numbers used to balance a chemical equation

Part D Questions and Problems

Answer the following in the space provided.

24. Write a balanced equation for each of these chemical reactions. Include appropriate symbols from Table 11.1.

a. Aluminum reacts with aqueous hydrochloric acid to form hydrogen gas and aqueous aluminum chloride.

_____

b. Acetylene gas (C_2H_2) burns in a welding torch with oxygen to form carbon dioxide gas and water vapor.

_____

TYPES OF CHEMICAL REACTIONS

11.2

Section Review

Objectives

- Describe the five general types of reactions
- Predict the products of the five general types of reactions

Vocabulary

- combination reaction
- decomposition reaction
- single-replacement reaction
- activity series
- double-replacement reaction
- combustion reaction

Part A Completion

Use this completion exercise to check your understanding of the concepts and terms that are introduced in this section. Each blank can be completed with a term, short phrase, or number.

It is possible to ___1___ the products of some chemical

reactions. In order to do this, you must be able to recognize at least

five general types of reactions. For example, in a ___2___ reaction,

the reactants are two or more ___3___ and/or compounds and

there is always a ___4___ product. In a ___5___ reaction, a single

compound is broken down into two or more simpler substances.

In a ___6___ reaction, the reactants and products are an

element and a compound. The ___7___ can be used to predict

whether most single-replacement reactions will take place.

A ___8___ reaction involves the exchange of ions between two

compounds. This reaction generally takes place between two ionic

compounds in ___9___ solution. One of the reactants in a

combustion reaction is ___10___. The products of the complete

combustion of a hydrocarbon are ___11___ and ___12___.

1. _____

2. _____

3. _____

4. _____

5. _____

6. _____

7. _____

8. _____

9. _____

10. _____

11. _____

12. _____

Part B True-False

Classify each of these statements as always true, AT; sometimes true, ST; or never true, NT.

_____ **13.** In a decomposition reaction, there is a single reactant.

_____ **14.** The activity series of metals can be used to predict products in double-replacement reactions.

_____ **15.** Carbon dioxide and water are the products of the combustion of hexane (C_6H_{14}).

_____ **16.** A nonmetal can replace another nonmetal from a compound in a single-replacement reaction.

_____ **17.** One of the products of a double-replacement reaction is a gas that bubbles out of the mixture.

Part C Matching

Match each description in Column B to the correct term in Column A.

Column A

_____ **18.** combination reaction

_____ **19.** decomposition reaction

_____ **20.** single-replacement reaction

_____ **21.** combustion reaction

Column B

a. reaction in which atoms of one element replace atoms of a second element in a compound

b. a reaction in which two or more substances combine to form a single substance

c. reaction of a compound with oxygen to produce energy

d. reaction in which a single compound is broken down into two or more products

Part D Questions and Problems

Answer the following in the space provided.

22. Identify the type of each of the following reactions.

   a. $2C_6H_{14}(l) + 19O_2(g) \rightarrow 12CO_2(g) + 14H_2O(g)$ **b.** $2Fe(s) + 3Br_2(l) \rightarrow 2FeBr_3(s)$

   _____   _____

23. Complete and balance the following equation. What must be true of one of the products?

   $Li_3PO_4 + Zn(NO_3)_2 \rightarrow$

_____

_____

Name _____ Date _____ Class _____

Section Review

Objectives

- Describe the information found in a net ionic equation
- Predict the formation of a precipitate in a double-replacement reaction

Vocabulary

- complete ionic equation
- spectator ion
- net ionic equation

Part A Completion

Use this completion exercise to check your understanding of the concepts and terms that are introduced in this section. Each blank can be completed with a term, short phrase, or number.

Many important chemical reactions take place in __1__, which makes up 66 percent of the human body. Reactions in water are said to take place in __2__ solution.

A double-replacement reaction can be written as a __3__, which shows dissolved ionic compounds as their free ions. Ions that appear on both sides of the equation and are not directly involved in the reaction are called __4__. Canceling these ions from the equation leaves the __5__, which indicates only those particles that take part in the reaction.

When balancing a net ionic equation, it is necessary to balance the electric __6__ as well as the number of __7__.

When mixing solutions of ions, it is possible to predict the formation of a __8__. This prediction can be made using the general rules for __9__ of ionic compounds.

1. _____

2. _____

3. _____

4. _____

5. _____

6. _____

7. _____

8. _____

9. _____

Part B True-False

Classify each of these statements as always true, AT; sometimes true, ST; or never true, NT.

_____ **10.** A precipitate is formed when two ionic solutions are mixed.

_____ **11.** Spectator ions are not part of a net ionic equation.

_____ **12.** Balancing the atoms in a net ionic equation will cause the charges to balance.

_____ **13.** A net ionic equation shows all ions present.

Part C Matching

Match each description in Column B to the correct term in Column A.

Column A

_____ **14.** complete ionic equation

_____ **15.** spectator ions

_____ **16.** net ionic equation

_____ **17.** precipitate

_____ **18.** aqueous reaction

_____ **19.** ionic solubility rules

Column B

a. equation that indicates only the particles that take part in a reaction

b. solid product of reaction in solution

c. reaction that occurs in water

d. equation that shows dissolved ionic compounds as free ions

e. used to predict whether a precipitate will form in an aqueous reaction

f. ions that do not participate in a reaction

Part D Questions and Problems

Answer the following in the space provided.

20. Identify the spectator ion(s) and write a balanced net ionic equation for this reaction.

$Cl_2(g) + NaBr(aq) \rightarrow Br_2(l) + NaCl(aq)$

_____

_____

21. Predict which precipitate, if any, will form in the following reactions:

  a. $AgNO_3(aq) + NaCl(aq) \rightarrow$

  b. $CaCl_2(aq) + Na_2CO_3(aq) \rightarrow$

  c. $Fe(NO_3)_3(aq) + KCl(aq) \rightarrow$

  d. $Pb(NO_3)_2(aq) + HCl(aq) \rightarrow$

CHEMICAL REACTIONS

11

Practice Problems

In your notebook, solve the following problems. Use the 3-step problem-solving approach you learned in Chapter 1.

SECTION 11.1 DESCRIBING CHEMICAL REACTIONS

1. Write the skeleton equation for the reaction between hydrogen and oxygen that produces water.

2. Write the skeleton equation for the reaction that produces iron(II) sulfide from iron and sulfur.

3. Write the skeleton equation representing the heating of magnesium carbonate to produce solid magnesium oxide and carbon dioxide gas.

4. Write a balanced equation for the production of HCl gas from its elements.

5. Write a sentence that completely describes the chemical reaction represented by this balanced equation.

$$2HCl(aq) + CaCO_3(s) \rightarrow CO_2(g) + CaCl_2(aq) + H_2O(l)$$

6. Write the word equation for the following equation. Write a sentence fully describing the reaction. Is the equation correctly balanced? Explain.

$$2Ag(s) + S(s) \rightarrow Ag_2S(s)$$

7. Write a balanced equation representing the formation of aqueous sulfuric acid from water and sulfur trioxide gas.

8. Write a balanced equation from this word equation.

   aqueous silver nitrate + copper metal → silver metal + aqueous copper nitrate

9. Write a balanced equation for the following word equation.

   phosphorus + oxygen → tetraphosphorous decoxide

SECTION 11.2 TYPES OF CHEMICAL REACTIONS

1. Write a balanced equation representing the reaction of magnesium with oxygen gas to produce magnesium oxide.

2. Write the balanced equation for the reaction that occurs between aluminum and fluorine.

3. Write the balanced equation for the production of oxygen gas and potassium chloride from the decomposition of potassium chlorate.

4. Write the balanced equation for the reaction between hydrochloric acid and calcium metal. The products are hydrogen gas and calcium chloride.

5. Write the balanced equation for the combustion of propane (C_3H_8) to produce carbon dioxide and water vapor.

6. Write the balanced equation for the reaction between iron(III) chloride and sodium hydroxide. The products are iron(III) hydroxide and sodium chloride.

7. Classify each of the reactions in problems 1–6 as to type.

8. Use the activity series of metals (Table 11.2) and your knowledge of the relative reactivity of the halogens to predict whether the following reactions will occur. Write balanced equations for those reactions that do occur.

   a. $Br_2(l) + NaCl(aq) \rightarrow$

   b. $Ca(s) + Mg(NO_3)_2(aq) \rightarrow$

   c. $K(s) + H_2SO_4(aq) \rightarrow$

   d. $Zn(s) + NaOH(aq) \rightarrow$

SECTION 11.3 REACTIONS IN AQUEOUS SOLUTION

1. Write the net ionic equation for the reaction between aqueous barium nitrate, $Ba(NO_3)_2$, and sodium sulfate, Na_2SO_4.

2. Magnesium reacts with HCl to form hydrogen and magnesium chloride. Write the balanced net ionic equation for this reaction.

3. The double-replacement reaction below results in the formation of the precipitate lead chloride. Balance the equation and write the net ionic equation.

$$Pb(NO_3)_2(aq) + NH_4Cl(aq) \rightarrow PbCl_2(s) + NH_4NO_3(aq)$$

4. Identify the precipitate formed when solutions of the following ionic compounds are mixed. If no precipitate is formed, write *no precipitate*.

   a. $Zn(NO_3)_2 + SnCl_2 \rightarrow$

   b. $KCl + AgNO_3 \rightarrow$

   c. $Cu(NO_3)_2 + Na_2S \rightarrow$

   d. $Al_2(SO_4)_3 + 3Mg(OH)_2 \rightarrow$

Name _____ Date _____ Class _____

INTERPRETING GRAPHICS
Use with Section 11.3

Chemists often use molecular structures rather than chemical formulas to represent compounds. Below are ball-and-stick structures of several simple molecules. Using the key below, write the chemical formula of each compound in the space provided.

Key: ● ○ ◍ ⊜

carbon   hydrogen   oxygen   nitrogen

nitrous oxide

_____

nitric oxide

_____

oxygen

_____

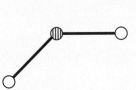

carbon dioxide

_____

water

_____

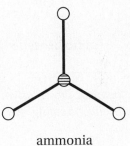

ammonia

_____

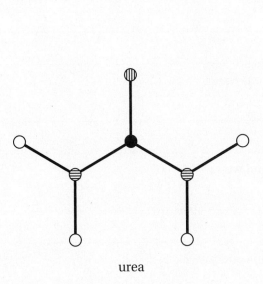

urea

_____

benzene

_____

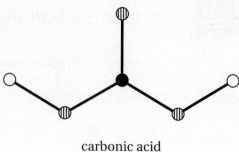

carbonic acid

_____

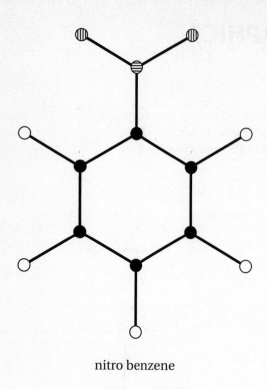

nitro benzene

_____

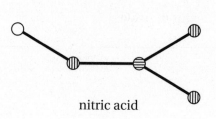

nitric acid

_____

Using the chemical formulas you wrote, write skeleton equations and balanced equations for the following reactions.

Example:

Water and carbon dioxide combine to form carbonic acid.

Skeleton equation: $H_2O + CO_2 \rightarrow H_2CO_3$
Balanced equation: balanced as written

1. Nitrous oxide and oxygen combine to form nitric oxide.

Skeleton equation   _____

Balanced equation   _____

2. Benzene burns in oxygen to form carbon dioxide and water.

Skeleton equation   _____

Balanced equation   _____

3. Ammonia and carbon dioxide react to form urea and water.

Skeleton equation   _____

Balanced equation   _____

4. Benzene reacts with nitric acid to form nitrobenzene and water.

Skeleton equation   _____

Balanced equation   _____

11 CHEMICAL REACTIONS

Vocabulary Review

Each clue describes a vocabulary term. Read the clues and write the letters of each term on the lines provided.

1. Clue: the complete reaction of a hydrocarbon with oxygen to produce carbon dioxide and water.

   __ __ __ __ __ __ Ⓞ __ __ __

2. Clue: a single compound is broken down into two or more products.

   __ Ⓞ __ __ __ Ⓞ __ __ __ __ __ __ __

3. Clue: the equation indicating only those particles that actually take part in a chemical reaction in an aqueous solution.

   __ __ __ Ⓞ __ __ Ⓞ __   __ __ __ __ __ __ __ __

4. Clue: a substance that speeds up the rate of a chemical reaction.

   __ Ⓞ __ __ __ __ __ __

5. Clue: the elements or compounds on the left side of a chemical equation.

   Ⓞ __ __ __ __ __ __ __ __

6. Clue: ions that do not participate in an aqueous chemical reaction.

   __ Ⓞ __ __ __ __ __ __ __

7. Clue: reaction in which atoms of one element replace the atoms of a second, less reactive, element in a compound.

   __ __ __ __ __ __   __ __ __ __ __ __ __ __ __ __ Ⓞ

8. Clue: a chemical equation that is consistent with the law of conservation of mass.

   __ __ __ __ __ __ Ⓞ __ __   __ __ __ __ __ __ __ __ __

9. Clue: numbers placed in front of chemical symbols or formulas in a chemical reaction.

   Ⓞ __ __ __ __ __ __ __ __ __ __ __ __

Write the letters found inside the circles on the lines below. Then unscramble them to find the term used to describe an insoluble salt.

Scrambled letters:

__ __ __ __ __ __ __ __ __ __ __ __

Solution:

a __ __ __ __ __ __ __ __ __ __ __ __

11 CHEMICAL REACTIONS

Chapter Quiz

Fill in the word(s) that will make each statement true.

1. A(n) __1__ equation is one in which the relative amounts of the reactants and products are not indicated.

2. A chemical reaction can be represented by a chemical __2__.

3. The first step in balancing an equation is to write the correct __3__ for all the reactants and products.

4. An equation obeys the laws of conservation of mass if it has been properly __4__.

5. In an equation, the formulas for the products appear on the __5a__ and the formulas for the reactants appear on the __5b__.

6. The symbol for "yields" or "reacts to produce" is a(n) __6__.

1. _____ *11.1*

2. _____ *11.1*

3. _____ *11.1*

4. _____ *11.1*

5a. _____ *11.1*

5b. _____ *11.1*

6. _____ *11.1*

Balance the following equations and identify any precipitate formed. Complete the equation first if necessary. Write your answer in the space provided.

7. $HgO(s) \rightarrow Hg(l) + O_2(g)$

_____ *11.2*

8. $Ag^+(aq) + Na^+(aq) + NO_3^-(aq) + CO_3^{2-}(aq) \rightarrow$
   (*Hint:* Write two equations—a complete ionic equation and a net ionic equation.)

_____ *11.3*

9. $C_4H_8(g) + O_2(g) \rightarrow CO_2(g) + H_2O(g)$

_____ *11.2*

10. $Na(s) + Br_2(l) \rightarrow$

_____ *11.2*

CHEMICAL REACTIONS

Chapter Test A

A. Matching

Match each description in Column B with the correct term in Column A. Write the letter of the correct description on the line.

Column A	Column B
_____ 1. coefficient	**a.** a chemical equation that does not indicate relative amounts of reactants and products
_____ 2. spectator ion	**b.** a starting substance in a chemical reaction
_____ 3. combustion reaction	**c.** a list of metals in order of decreasing reactivity
_____ 4. reactant	**d.** a reaction in which a single compound is broken down into simpler substances
_____ 5. skeleton equation	**e.** a whole number that appears before a formula in an equation
_____ 6. balanced equation	**f.** a new substance formed in a chemical reaction
_____ 7. activity series	**g.** a particle not directly involved in a chemical reaction
_____ 8. product	**h.** an equation in which each side has the same number of atoms of each element
_____ 9. decomposition reaction	**i.** a reaction in which the atoms of one element replace the atoms of a second element
_____ 10. single-replacement reaction	**j.** a reaction in which oxygen reacts with another substance, often producing heat or light

B. Multiple Choice

Choose the best answer and write its letter on the line.

_____ **11.** The symbol Δ in a chemical equation means:
  a. heat is supplied to the reaction.
  b. a catalyst is needed.
  c. yields.
  d. precipitate.

_____ **12.** A catalyst is:
  a. a solid product of a reaction.
  b. one of the reactants in a single-replacement reaction.
  c. not used up in a reaction.
  d. the product of a combustion reaction.

_____ 13. When the equation $Fe + O_2 \rightarrow Fe_2O_3$ is balanced, the coefficient for O_2 is:

a. 4   c. 2
b. 3   d. 1

_____ 14. The reaction in question 13 is an example of a(n):
a. aqueous reaction.   c. combination reaction.
b. single-replacement reaction.   d. decomposition reaction.

_____ 15. The equation $H_3PO_4 + 3KOH \rightarrow K_3PO_4 + 3H_2O$ is an example of which type of reaction?
a. double-replacement   c. decomposition
b. combination   d. single-replacement

_____ 16. In a double-replacement reaction:
a. the reactants are usually a metal and a nonmetal.
b. the reactants are generally two ionic compounds in aqueous solution.
c. one of the reactants is often water.
d. energy in the form of heat or light is always produced.

_____ 17. In order for the reaction $2Al(s) + 6HCl(aq) \rightarrow 2AlCl_3(aq) + 3H_2(g)$ to occur, which of the following must be true?
a. Al must be above Cl on the activity series.
b. Al must be above H on the activity series.
c. Heat must be supplied for the reaction.
d. $AlCl_3$ must be a precipitate.

_____ 18. In a double-replacement reaction:
a. one of the products is always a gas.
b. one of the products must be an element.
c. positive ions are exchanged between two compounds.
d. all of the above

_____ 19. When the following equation is balanced, the coefficient in front of HCl is:

$$Ba(s) + HCl(aq) \rightarrow BaCl_2(aq) + H_2(g)$$

a. 6   c. 1
b. 3   d. 2

_____ 20. The equation in question 19 is an example of which type of reaction?
a. combustion   c. decomposition
b. single-replacement   d. double-replacement

_____ 21. This symbol $\rightleftharpoons$ indicates:
a. that heat must be applied.
b. an incomplete combustion reaction.
c. that a gas is formed by the reaction.
d. that the reaction is reversible.

_____ **22.** Which of the following statements is *incorrect*?
  a. Complete combustion has occurred when all the carbon in the product is in the form of carbon dioxide.
  b. A single reactant is the identifying characteristic of a decomposition reaction.
  c. The only way to determine the products of a reaction is to perform the reaction.
  d. All chemical reactions can be classified as one of four general types.

_____ **23.** A chemical formula written above or below the yield sign indicates:
  a. that a gas is formed.
  b. that the substance is used as a catalyst.
  c. that heat must be supplied.
  d. a reversible reaction.

_____ **24.** The equation $2C_3H_7OH(g) + 9O_2(g) \rightarrow 6CO_2(g) + 8H_2O(g)$ is an example of which type of reaction?
  a. combustion
  b. combination
  c. double-replacement
  d. decomposition

_____ **25.** A double-replacement reaction takes place when aqueous K_2SO_4 reacts with aqueous $Pb(NO_3)_2$. You would expect one of the products of this reaction to be:
  a. K_2S.
  b. NaPb.
  c. $PbSO_4$.
  d. CNO_3.

C. Problems

Solve the following problems in the space provided. Show your work.

26. Balance the following equations:

  a. $Ca(s) + H_3PO_4(aq) \rightarrow Ca_3(PO_4)_2(s) + H_2(g)$

  b. $KBrO_3(s) \rightarrow KBr(s) + O_2(g)$

  c. $(NH_4)_2CO_3(aq) + NaOH(aq) \rightarrow Na_2CO_3(aq) + NH_3(g) + H_2O(l)$

27. For each equation in question 26, identify the type of reaction.

  a. _____

  b. _____

  c. _____

Name ______________________ Date ______________ Class ______________

28. Balance the following equations. Indicate whether combustion is complete or incomplete.

a. $C_5H_{10}(g) + O_2(g) \rightarrow CO(g) + H_2O(g)$

b. $C_3H_7OH(l) + O_2(g) \rightarrow CO_2(g) + H_2O(g)$

29. Complete and balance the following equations. Then write each as a net ionic equation.

a. $K_3PO_4(aq) + MgCl_2(aq) \rightarrow$

b. $Fe(NO_3)_3(aq) + Na_2CO_3(aq) \rightarrow$

D. Essay

Write a short essay for the following.

30. What determines whether one metal will replace another metal from a compound in a single-replacement reaction?

___

___

___

___

___

CHEMICAL REACTIONS

11

Chapter Test B

A. Matching

Match each term in Column B with the correct description in Column A. Write the letter of the correct term on the line.

Column A

_____ **1.** a reaction in which an element or compound reacts with oxygen, often producing energy in the form of heat or light

_____ **2.** a reaction in which two or more substances react to form a single substance

_____ **3.** an equation that indicates only those particles that actually take part in the reaction

_____ **4.** a substance that speeds up a reaction without being used up

_____ **5.** ions that are not directly involved in a reaction

_____ **6.** a reaction in which a single compound is broken down into two or more products

_____ **7.** an equation in which each side has the same number of atoms of each element

_____ **8.** a reaction in which atoms of an element replace the atoms of a second element in a compound

_____ **9.** a list of metals in order of decreasing reactivity

_____ **10.** a reaction that involves an exchange of positive ions between two compounds

Column B

a. decomposition reaction

b. activity series

c. spectator ions

d. balanced equation

e. double-replacement reaction

f. catalyst

g. combustion reaction

h. combination reaction

i. net ionic equation

j. single-replacement reaction

B. Multiple Choice

Choose the best answer and write its letter on the line.

_____ **11.** In the chemical equation $2H_2O_2(aq) \xrightarrow{MnO_2} 2H_2O(l) + O_2(g)$, the MnO_2 is a:
   a. reactant.   **c.** spectator ion.
   b. product.   **d.** catalyst.

_____ **12.** When the equation $Mg(s) + HCl(aq) \rightarrow MgCl_2(aq) + H_2(g)$ is balanced, what is the coefficient for HCl?
   a. 1   **c.** 3
   b. 2   **d.** 4

_____ **13.** The reaction in question 12 is an example of a:
    a. combination reaction.   **c.** single-replacement reaction.
    b. decomposition reaction.   **d.** double-replacement reaction.

_____ **14.** When the equation $Fe(s) + O_2(g) \rightarrow Fe_2O_3(s)$ is balanced, what is the coefficient for Fe_2O_3?
    a. 1   **c.** 3
    b. 2   **d.** 4

_____ **15.** The reaction in question 14 is an example of a:
    a. combination reaction.   **c.** single-replacement reaction.
    b. decomposition reaction.   **d.** double-replacement reaction.

_____ **16.** Which binary compound decomposes to form $K + I_2$?
    a. KI_2 **c.** K_2I
    b. KI **d.** none of the above

_____ **17.** In order for the reaction $Cu(s) + 2AgNO_3(aq) \rightarrow Cu(NO_3)_2(aq) + 2Ag(s)$ to occur, which of the following must be true?
    a. Cu must be above Ag in the activity series.
    b. Ag must be above Cu in the activity series.
    c. Cu must be above H in the activity series.
    d. Ag must be above H in the activity series.

_____ **18.** Water is often a product in:
    a. combination reactions.   **c.** single-replacement reactions.
    b. decomposition reactions.   **d.** combustion reactions.

_____ **19.** Among the elements listed, which one could replace all of the rest as an ion from a compound in aqueous solution?
    a. Cu   **c.** Fe
    b. Ca   **d.** Ag

_____ **20.** The complete combustion of octane (C_8H_{18}) would:
    a. require $25\ O_2(g)$.   **c.** produce $18\ H_2O(g)$.
    b. produce $16\ CO_2(g)$.   **d.** all of the above

_____ **21.** Double-replacement reactions are generally driven by the formation of:
    a. a precipitate.   **c.** water.
    b. a gaseous product.   **d.** all of the above

_____ **22.** If butane (C_4H_{10}) undergoes complete combustion:
    a. $8\ CO_2$ is one product.   **c.** $9\ O_2$ is one reactant.
    b. $8\ CO$ is one product.   **d.** $10\ O_2$ is one reactant.

_____ **23.** When $H_2SO_4(aq)$ and $NaOH(aq)$ react by double-replacement:
    a. $2\ H_2SO_4(aq)$ are required.   **c.** $2\ H_2O(l)$ are produced.
    b. $1\ NaOH(aq)$ is required.   **d.** $Na_2SO_4(s)$ is produced.

_____ **24.** Based on the activity series, the reaction that is most likely to occur from among the following is:
    a. $Cu(s) + HCl(aq) \rightarrow$ **c.** $Pb(s) + Na_2SO_4(aq) \rightarrow$
    b. $Zn(s) + HNO_3(aq) \rightarrow$ **d.** $Ag(s) + Cu(NO_3)_2(aq) \rightarrow$

_____ **25.** The spectator ions in the reaction $ZnCl_2(aq) + 2LiOH(aq) \rightarrow$
$2LiCl(aq) + Zn(OH)_2(s)$ are:

a. Zn^- and OH^-.

b. Zn^- and Cl^-.

c. Li^+ and OH^-.

d. Li^+ and Cl^-.

C. Problems

Solve the following problems in the space provided. Show your work.

26. Write a skeleton equation for the reaction in which aqueous sodium chloride reacts with aqueous silver nitrate to produce aqueous sodium nitrate and solid silver chloride.

27. Balance the following equations:

a. $CS_2(s) + O_2(g) \rightarrow CO_2(g) + SO_2(g)$

b. $HNO_3(aq) + Mg(OH)_2(aq) \rightarrow Mg(NO_3)_2(aq) + H_2O(l)$

c. $Fe_2O_3(s) + CO(g) \rightarrow Fe(s) + CO_2(g)$

28. Complete and balance each of the following reactions identified by type:

a. Combination reaction: $Li_2O(s) + H_2O(l) \rightarrow$

b. Decomposition reaction: $H_2O(l) \xrightarrow{\text{electricity}}$

c. Single-replacement reaction: $Al(s) + Fe(NO_3)_2(aq) \rightarrow$

d. Double-replacement reaction: $HNO_3(aq) + Ca(OH)_2(aq) \rightarrow$

e. Combustion reaction: $C_3H_8(g) + O_2(g) \rightarrow$

Name ______________________ Date ______________ Class ______________

29. Identify the spectator ions and write balanced net ionic equations for each of the following reactions:

a. $KOH(aq) + HCl(aq) \rightarrow KCl(aq) + H_2O(l)$

b. $Pb(NO_3)_2(aq) + KI(aq) \rightarrow PbI_2(s) + KNO_3(aq)$

c. $ZnI_2(aq) + NaOH(aq) \rightarrow NaI(aq) + Zn(OH)_2(s)$

D. Essay

Write a short essay for the following.

30. Distinguish between the single- and double-replacement reactions indicated below by completing each, identifying each as to type, and explaining, in words, what has occurred in each. (E is a metal.)

$AB + CD \rightarrow$

____

____

____

$E + FG \rightarrow$

____

____

____

SMALL-SCALE LAB: Precipitation Reactions: Formation of Solids

Laboratory Recordsheet   Use with Section 11.3

SAFETY

Wear safety glasses and follow standard safety procedures outlined in the Small-Scale Lab Manual.

PURPOSE

To observe, identify, and write balanced equations for precipitation reactions.

MATERIALS

- pencil
- paper
- ruler
- reaction surface
- chemicals shown in the grid below

PROCEDURE

Copy the grid on two sheets of paper. Make each square 2 cm on each side. Draw black X's on one of the grids. Place a reaction surface over the grid with black X's and add the chemicals as shown in Figure A. Use Figure A as a data table to record your observations for each solution. Draw a black X in each square of the grid.

	$AgNO_3$ (Ag^+)	$Pb(NO_3)_2$ (Pb^{2+})	$CaCl_2$ (Ca^{2+})
Na_2CO_3 (CO_3^{2-})	a	f	k
Na_3PO_4 (PO_4^{3-})	b	g	l
NaOH (OH^-)	c	h	m
Na_2SO_4 (SO_4^{2-})	d	i	n
NaCl (Cl^-)	e	j	o

ANALYSIS AND CONCLUSIONS

Using the experimental data, record the answers to the following.

1. Translate the following word equations into balanced chemical equations and explain how the equations represent what happens in grid spaces **a** and **g**.

   a. In grid space **a**, sodium carbonate reacts with silver nitrate to produce sodium nitrate and solid silver carbonate.

   _____

   _____

   _____

   b. In grid space **g**, sodium phosphate reacts with lead(II) nitrate to produce sodium nitrate and solid lead(II) phosphate.

   _____

   _____

2. Write a word equation to represent what happens in grid space **m**.

   _____

   _____

3. What happens in grid space **d**? Which other mixings gave similar results? Is it necessary to write an equation when no reaction occurs? Explain.

   _____

   _____

   _____

   _____

4. Write balanced equations for the other precipitation reactions you observed.

   _____

   _____

   _____

   _____

   _____

   _____

   _____

   _____

   _____

5. Write balanced net ionic equations for the precipitation reactions you observed.

_____

_____

_____

_____

_____

_____

_____

_____

_____

_____

_____

_____

YOU'RE THE CHEMIST

Use the space below to write what you observed in the small-scale activities in the *You're the Chemist* section.

_____

_____

_____

_____

_____

_____

_____

_____

_____

_____

_____

THE ARITHMETIC OF EQUATIONS

12.1

Section Review

Objectives

- Calculate the amount of reactants required or product formed in a nonchemical process
- Interpret balanced chemical equations in terms of interacting moles, representative particles, masses, and gas volume at STP

Vocabulary

- stoichiometry

Part A Completion

Use this completion exercise to check your understanding of the concepts and terms that are introduced in this section. Each blank can be completed with a term, short phrase, or number.

The coefficients of a balanced chemical equation indicate

the relative number of ___1___ of reactants and products. All

stoichiometric calculations begin with a ___2___. Only ___3___

and ___4___ are conserved in every reaction; moles, volumes,

and representative particles may not be.

In solving stoichiometric problems, conversion factors

relating moles of reactants to ___5___ of products are used.

If you assume ___6___, the balanced equation also tells you

about the volumes of gases.

1. _____

2. _____

3. _____

4. _____

5. _____

6. _____

Part B True-False

Classify each of these statements as always true, AT; sometimes true, ST; or never true, NT.

_____ 7. The coefficients in a balanced chemical equation can be used to form mole ratios relating reactants to products.

_____ 8. The coefficients in a balanced chemical equation tell the relative volumes of reactants and products, expressed in any suitable unit of volume.

_____ 9. To calculate the mass of a molecule in grams, you can use the molar mass and Avogadro's number.

_____ **10.** Because the mass of the reactants equals the mass of the products of a reaction, the number of moles will be conserved.

_____ **11.** If the ratio of molecules in the reaction $2A_2 + B_2 \rightarrow 2A_2B$ is 2:1:2, we can predict that 4 molecules of A_2 react with 2 molecules B_2 to produce 4 molecules of A_2B.

_____ **12.** One mole of any gas occupies a volume of 22.4 L.

Part C Matching

Match each description in Column B to the correct term in Column A.

Column A	**Column B**
_____ **13.** stoichiometry	**a.** Avogadro's number
_____ **14.** product	**b.** the calculations of quantities in chemical reactions
_____ **15.** coefficient	**c.** STP
_____ **16.** 6.02×10^{23}	**d.** a substance formed in a chemical reaction
_____ **17.** 0°C, 101.3 kPa	**e.** gives the relative number of molecules involved in a reaction

Part D Questions and Problems

Answer the following in the space provided. Show your work.

18. Interpret the following equation using moles, molecules, and volumes (assume STP). Compare the mass of the reactants to the mass of the product.

$$2N_2(g) + 3O_2(g) \rightarrow 2N_2O_3(g)$$

19. How many moles of chlorine gas will be required to react with sufficient iron to produce 14 moles of iron(III) chloride?

$$2Fe(s) + 3Cl_2(g) \rightarrow 2FeCl_3(g)$$

12.2 CHEMICAL CALCULATIONS

Section Review

Objectives

- Construct mole ratios from balanced chemical equations and apply these ratios in mole-mole stoichiometric calculations
- Calculate stoichiometric quantities from balanced chemical equations, using units of moles, mass, representative particles, and volumes of gases at STP

Key Equations

- mole-mole relationship used in every stoichiometric calculation:

$$aG \longrightarrow bW$$

(given quantity) (wanted quantity)

- $x \text{ mol } G \times \dfrac{b \text{ mol } W}{a \text{ mol } G} = \dfrac{xb}{a} \text{ mol } W$

    Given   Mole Ratio   Calculated

Part A Completion

Use this completion exercise to check your understanding of the concepts and terms that are introduced in this section. Each blank can be completed with a term, short phrase, or number.

Mole ratios from balanced equations may be used to solve

problems with other units such as numbers of ___1___ and ___2___

of gases at STP. The ___3___ from the balanced equation are used

to write conversion factors called ___4___. These conversion factors

are used to calculate the numbers of moles of ___5___ from a given

number of moles of ___6___. In mass-mass calculations, the molar

mass is used to convert mass to ___7___.

1. _____

2. _____

3. _____

4. _____

5. _____

6. _____

7. _____

Part B True-False

Classify each of these statements as always true, AT; sometimes true, ST; or never true, NT.

_____ **8.** In mass-mass calculations, the molar mass is used to convert mass to moles.

_____ **9.** The mole ratio 2 mol HF/1 mol SnF_2 can be used to determine the mass of SnF_2 produced according to the equation:
$$Sn(s) + 2HF(g) \rightarrow SnF_2(s) + H_2(g)$$

_____ **10.** In a volume-volume problem, the 22.4 L/mol factors always cancel out.

_____ **11.** In stoichiometric problems, volume is expressed in terms of liters.

_____ **12.** For a mass-mole problem, the first conversion from mass to moles is skipped.

_____ **13.** For a mass-mass problem, the first conversion is from moles to mass.

_____ **14.** Because mole ratios from balanced equations are exact numbers, they do not enter into the determination of significant figures.

Part C Matching

Match each conversion problem in Column A to the correct solution in Column B.

Column A	Column B

_____ **15.** moles $O_2 \rightarrow$ grams O_2

a. molecules $\times \dfrac{mol}{6.02 \times 10^{23} \text{ molecules}} \times \dfrac{18.0 \text{ g}}{mol}$

_____ **16.** liters $SO_2 \rightarrow$ grams SO_2 at STP

b. liters $\times \dfrac{mol}{22.4 \text{ L}} \times \dfrac{64.1 \text{ g}}{mol}$

_____ **17.** molecules He $\rightarrow$ liters He(g) at STP

c. mol $\times \dfrac{32.0 \text{ g}}{mol}$

_____ **18.** grams Sn $\rightarrow$ molecules Sn

d. molecules $\times \dfrac{mol}{6.02 \times 10^{23} \text{molecules}} \times \dfrac{22.4 \text{ L}}{mol}$

_____ **19.** molecules $H_2O \rightarrow$ grams H_2O

e. grams $\times \dfrac{mol}{119 \text{ g}} \times \dfrac{6.02 \times 10^{23} \text{ molecules}}{mol}$

Part D Questions and Problems

Answer the following questions in the space provided.

20. How many liters of carbon monoxide (at STP) are needed to react with 4.8 g of oxygen gas to produce carbon dioxide?

$$2CO(g) + O_2(g) \rightarrow 2CO_2(g)$$

21. What mass of ammonia, NH_3, is necessary to react with 2.1×10^{24} molecules of oxygen in the following reaction?

$$4NH_3(g) + 7O_2(g) \rightarrow 6H_2O(g) + 4NO_2(g)$$

Name _____ Date _____ Class _____

12.3 LIMITING REAGENT AND PERCENT YIELD

Section Review

Objectives

- Identify and use the limiting reagent in a reaction to calculate the maximum amount of product(s) produced and the amount of excess reagent
- Calculate theoretical yield, actual yield, or percent yield given the appropriate information

Vocabulary

- limiting reagent
- excess reagent
- theoretical yield
- actual yield
- percent yield

Key Equations

- $\text{percent yield} = \dfrac{\text{actual yield}}{\text{theoretical yield}} \times 100$

Part A Completion

Use this completion exercise to check your understanding of the concepts and terms that are introduced in this section. Each blank can be completed with a term, short phrase, or number.

Whenever quantities of two or more reactants are given in a stoichiometric problem, you must identify the __1__. This is the reagent that is completely __2__ in the reaction. The amount of limiting reagent determines the amount of __3__ that is formed.

When an equation is used to calculate the amount of product that will form during a reaction, the value obtained is the __4__. This is the __5__ amount of product that could be formed from a given amount of reactant. The amount of product that forms when the reaction is carried out in the laboratory is called the __6__.

1. _____

2. _____

3. _____

4. _____

5. _____

6. _____

Part B True-False

Classify each of these statements as always true, AT; sometimes true, ST; or never true, NT.

_____ 7. Normally, the actual yield in a chemical reaction will be equal to or less than the theoretical yield.

_____ 8. The actual yield of a chemical reaction can be calculated using mole ratios.

_____ 9. The amount of product can be determined from the amount of excess reagent.

_____ 10. The percent yield of a product is 100 percent.

_____ 11. If you had 100 steering wheels, 360 tires, and enough of every other part needed to assemble a car, the limiting reagent would be tires.

_____ 12. The theoretical yield is the maximum amount of product that could be formed in a chemical reaction.

Part C Matching

Match each description in Column B to the correct term in Column A.

Column A	Column B
_____ 13. actual yield	a. the ratio of the actual yield to the theoretical yield × 100
_____ 14. limiting reagent	b. the amount of product actually formed when a reaction is carried out in the laboratory
_____ 15. theoretical yield	c. the reactant that determines the amount of product that can be formed in a reaction
_____ 16. percent yield	d. the reactant that is not completely used up in a chemical reaction
_____ 17. excess reagent	e. the maximum amount of product that can be formed during a reaction

Part D Questions and Problems

Answer the following in the space provided.

18. **a.** What is the limiting reagent when 3.1 mol of SO_2 react with 2.7 mol of O_2 according to the equation:

$$2SO_2(g) + O_2(g) \rightarrow 2SO_3(g)$$

b. Calculate the maximum amount of product that can be formed and the amount of unreacted excess reagent.

12 STOICHIOMETRY

Practice Problems

In your notebook, solve the following problems.

SECTION 12.1 THE ARITHMETIC OF EQUATIONS

Use the 3-step problem-solving approach you learned in Chapter 1.

1. An apple pie needs 10 large apples, 2 crusts (top and bottom), and 1 tablespoon of cinnamon. Write a balanced equation that fits this situation. How many apples are needed to make 25 pies?

2. Two moles of potassium chloride and three moles of oxygen are produced from the decomposition of two moles of potassium chlorate, $KClO_3(s)$. Write the balanced equation. How many moles of oxygen are produced from 12 moles of potassium chlorate?

3. Using the equation from problem 2, how many moles of oxygen are produced from 14 moles of potassium chlorate?

4. Two molecules of hydrogen react with one molecule of oxygen to produce two molecules of water. How many molecules of water are produced from 2.0×10^{23} molecules of oxygen? How many moles of water are produced from 22.5 moles of oxygen?

SECTION 12.2 CHEMICAL CALCULATIONS

1. Calculate the number of moles of hydrogen chloride produced from 10 moles of hydrogen.
$$H_2(g) + Cl_2(g) \rightarrow 2HCl(g)$$

2. Calculate the number of moles of chlorine needed to form 14 moles of iron(III) chloride.
$$2Fe(s) + 3Cl_2(g) \rightarrow 2FeCl_3(s)$$

3. Calculate the number of grams of nitrogen dioxide that are produced from 4 moles of nitric oxide.
$$2NO(g) + O_2(g) \rightarrow 2NO_2(g)$$

4. Calculate the mass of oxygen produced from the decomposition of 75.0 g of potassium chlorate.
$$2KClO_3(s) \rightarrow 2KCl(s) + 3O_2(g)$$

5. Calculate the mass of silver needed to react with chlorine to produce 84 g of silver chloride. (*Hint:* Write a balanced equation first.)

6. How many liters of carbon monoxide at STP are needed to react with 4.80 g of oxygen gas to produce carbon dioxide?
$$2CO(g) + O_2(g) \rightarrow 2CO_2(g)$$

7. Calculate the number of liters of oxygen gas needed to produce 15.0 liters of dinitrogen trioxide. Assume all gases are at the same conditions of temperature and pressure.
$$2N_2(g) + 3O_2(g) \rightarrow 2N_2O_3(g)$$

8. A volume of 7.5 L of hydrogen gas at STP was produced from the single-replacement reaction of zinc with nitric acid. Calculate the mass of zinc needed for this reaction.

SECTION 12.3 LIMITING REAGENT AND PERCENT YIELD

1. How many moles of water can be made from 4 moles of oxygen gas and 16 moles of hydrogen gas? What is the limiting reagent?

2. Calculate the mass of water produced from the reaction of 24.0 g of H_2 and 160.0 g of O_2. What is the limiting reagent?

3. The burning of 18.0 g of carbon produces 55.0 g of carbon dioxide. What is the theoretical yield of CO_2? Calculate the percent yield of CO_2.

4. Calculate the percent yield of $Cl_2(g)$ in the electrolytic decomposition of hydrogen chloride if 25.8 g of HCl produces 13.6 g of chlorine gas.

5. One method for reclaiming silver metal from silver chloride results in a 94.6% yield. Calculate the actual mass of silver that can be produced in this reaction if 100.0 g of silver chloride is converted to silver metal.

$$2AgCl(s) \rightarrow 2Ag(s) + Cl_2(g)$$

6. What is the actual amount of magnesium oxide produced when excess carbon dioxide reacts with 42.8 g of magnesium metal? The percent yield of MgO(s) for this reaction is 81.7%.

$$2Mg(s) + CO_2(g) \rightarrow 2MgO(s) + C(s)$$

INTERPRETING GRAPHICS

12

Use with Section 12.3

Preparation of Salicylic Acid

Student #1

mass of flask	37.820 g
flask + $C_7H_6O_3$	39.961 g
volume of $C_4H_6O_3$	5.0 mL
mass of watch glass	22.744 g
watch glass + $C_9H_8O_4$	24.489 g

Student #2

mass of flask	37.979 g
flask + $C_7H_6O_3$	40.010 g
volume of $C_4H_6O_3$	5.0 mL
mass of watch glass	21.688 g
watch glass + $C_9H_8O_4$	24.197 g

Two students prepared aspirin according to the following reaction in which acetic anhydride, $C_4H_6O_3$, reacts with salicylic acid, $C_7H_6O_3$, to form aspirin, $C_9H_8O_4$, and acetic acid, $C_2H_4O_2$.

$$C_7H_6O_3 + C_4H_6O_3 \rightarrow C_9H_8O_4 + C_2H_4O_2$$

The procedure involved heating the reaction mixture in a water bath for 15 minutes at 75°C, not to exceed 80°C. The mixture was removed from the water bath, and distilled water was added to decompose any unreacted acetic anhydride. The mixture was then placed in an ice bath for 5 minutes to facilitate the formation of aspirin crystals. The aspirin crystals were collected using filtration. The aspirin crystals were dried and then transferred to a watch glass and massed.

Because their grades were partially based on accuracy, both students used their very best lab technique. Which student got the better grade and why?

  1. Determine the molar masses of the following:

   a. acetic anhydride, $C_4H_6O_3$ _____

   b. salicylic acid, $C_7H_6O_3$ _____

   c. aspirin, $C_9H_8O_4$ _____

2. How many moles of salicylic acid were added to the reaction mixture?

Student 1 _____ Student 2 _____

3. Given the density of acetic anhydride to be 1.05 g/mL, what was the mass of the acetic anhydride added to the reaction? How many moles of acetic acid were added?

Student 1 _____ Student 2 _____

_____ _____

4. According to the mole ratios in the given reaction, what is the limiting reagent in this reaction?

_____

5. What is the theoretical yield, in grams, of aspirin in each reaction?

Student 1 _____ Student 2 _____

6. What was the actual yield, in grams, of aspirin in each reaction?

Student 1 _____ Student 2 _____

7. What was the percent yield in each reaction?

Student 1 _____ Student 2 _____

8. Evaluate your answers. Which student got the better grade and why?

_____

_____

STOICHIOMETRY

12

Vocabulary Review

Match the correct vocabulary term to each numbered statement. Write the letter of the correct term on the line.

Column A

_____ 1. the starting materials in a chemical reaction

_____ 2. a conversion factor derived from the coefficients of a balanced chemical equation interpreted in terms of moles

_____ 3. the maximum amount of product that could be formed in a reaction

_____ 4. the amount of a substance that contains 6.02×10^{23} representative particles of that substance

_____ 5. the substance completely used up in a chemical reaction

_____ 6. the ratio of how much product is produced compared to how much is expected, expressed as a percentage

_____ 7. the calculations of quantities in a chemical reaction

_____ 8. the actual amount of product in a chemical reaction

_____ 9. the substance left over after a reaction takes place

_____ 10. a stoichiometric computation in which the mass of products is determined from the given mass of reactants

Column B

a. mole

b. stoichiometry

c. mass-mass calculation

d. reactants

e. excess reagent

f. theoretical yield

g. limiting reagent

h. mole ratio

i. actual yield

j. percent yield

12 STOICHIOMETRY

Chapter Quiz

Fill in the word(s) that will make each statement true.

1. The __1__ in a balanced chemical equation also reveal the mole ratios of the substances involved.

1. _____ *12.1*

2. The number of moles of a product can be calculated from a given number of moles of __2__ .

2. _____ *12.1*

3. In mass-mass calculations, the molar mass is used to convert mass to __3__ .

3. _____ *12.2*

4. In addition to mass, the only quantity conserved in every chemical reaction is __4__ .

4. _____ *12.2*

5. According to the equation:
$$2NO(g) + O_2(g) \rightarrow 2NO_2(g),$$
22.4 L of O_2 will react with __5__ L of NO at STP.

5. _____ *12.2*

Classify each of these statements as always true, AT; sometimes true, ST; or never true, NT.

_____ 6. The excess reagent determines the amount of product formed in a reaction.

12.3

_____ 7. In the reaction $2CO(g) + O_2(g) \rightarrow 2CO_2(g)$, using 4 moles of CO to react with 1 mole of O_2 will result in the production of 4 moles of CO_2.

12.3

_____ 8. To calculate the percent yield of a reaction, you use the following relationship:
$$\frac{\text{theoretical yield}}{\text{actual yield}} \times 100$$

12.3

_____ 9. The total mass of the excess reagent and the limiting reagent is equal to the total mass of the products.

12.3

_____ 10. The actual yield is equal to the theoretical yield.

12.3

STOICHIOMETRY

12

Chapter Test A

A. Matching

Match each description in Column B with the correct term in Column A. Write the letter of the correct description on the line.

Column A	**Column B**
_____ **1.** actual yield	**a.** the ratio of the actual yield to the theoretical yield, expressed as a percentage
_____ **2.** limiting reagent	**b.** the amount of product formed when a reaction is carried out in the laboratory
_____ **3.** theoretical yield	**c.** the reactant that determines the amount of product that can be formed in a reaction
_____ **4.** stoichiometry	**d.** the reactant that is not completely used up in a reaction
_____ **5.** percent yield	**e.** the calculated amount of product that might be formed during a reaction
_____ **6.** excess reagent	**f.** the calculation of quantities in chemical equations

B. Multiple Choice

Choose the best answer and write its letter on the line.

_____ **7.** Which of these expressions is an *incorrect* interpretation of the balanced equation?

$$2S(s) + 3O_2(g) \rightarrow 2SO_3(g)$$

a. 2 atoms S + 3 molecules $O_2 \rightarrow$ 2 molecules SO_3
b. 2 g S + 3 g $O_2 \rightarrow$ 2 g SO_3
c. 2 mol S + 3 mol $O_2 \rightarrow$ 2 mol SO_3
d. none of the above

_____ **8.** In a chemical reaction, the mass of the products
a. is less than the mass of the reactants.
b. is greater than the mass of the reactants.
c. is equal to the mass of the reactants.
d. has no relationship to the mass of the reactants.

_____ **9.** How many liters of oxygen are required to react completely with 1.2 liters of hydrogen to form water?

$$2H_2(g) + O_2(g) \rightarrow 2H_2(g)$$

a. 1.2 L   c. 2.4 L
b. 0.6 L   d. 4.8 L

_____ 10. How many molecules of NO_2 are produced when 2.0×10^{20} molecules of N_2O_4 are decomposed according to the following equation?

$$N_2O_4(g) \rightarrow 2NO_2(g)$$

    a. 4   **c.** 2.0×10^{20}
    b. 1.0×10^{20} **d.** 4.0×10^{20}

_____ 11. How many liters of $CO(g)$ at STP are produced when 68.0 g of $CaCO_3(s)$ is heated according to the following equation?

$$CaCO_3(s) \xrightarrow{\Delta} CaO(s) + CO_2(g)$$

    a. 0.679 L   **c.** 68.0 L
    b. 15.2 L   **d.** 30.4 L

_____ 12. A reaction that has been calculated to produce 60.0 g of $CuCl_2$ actually produces 50.0 g of $CuCl_2$. What is the percent yield?
    a. 0.833%   **c.** 83.3%
    b. 96.1%   **d.** 120%

_____ 13. When 0.2 mol of calcium is mixed with 880 g of water, 4.48 L of hydrogen gas forms (at STP). How would the amount of hydrogen produced change if the mass of water were decreased to 220 g?
    a. Only one half of the volume of hydrogen would be produced.
    b. The volume of hydrogen produced would be the same.
    c. The volume of hydrogen produced would double.
    d. No hydrogen would be produced.

_____ 14. The equation for the complete combustion of methane is

$$CH_4(g) + 2O_2(g) \rightarrow CO_2(g) + 2H_2O(l)$$

To calculate the number of grams of CO_2 produced by the reaction of 29.5 g of CH_4 with O_2, the first conversion factor to use is

    a. $\dfrac{1 \text{ mol } CH_4}{16.0 \text{ g } CH_4}$ **c.** $\dfrac{16.0 \text{ g } CH_4}{1 \text{ mol } CH_4}$

    b. $\dfrac{2 \text{ mol } O_2}{1 \text{ mol } CO_2}$ **d.** $\dfrac{29.5 \text{ g } CH_4}{2 \text{ mol } CO_2}$

_____ 15. In any chemical reaction, the quantities that are conserved are
    a. the number of moles and the volumes.
    b. the number of molecules and the volumes.
    c. mass and number of atoms.
    d. mass and moles.

Questions 16, 17, and 18 refer to the following equation:

$$3Cu(s) + 8HNO_3(aq) \rightarrow 3Cu(NO_3)_2(s) + 2NO(g) + 4H_2O(l)$$

_____ 16. Calculate the number of moles of water produced when 3.3 mol of $Cu(NO_3)_2$ are formed in the reaction.
    a. 4.4 mol   **c.** 4.9 mol
    b. 6.6 mol   **d.** 8.8 mol

_____ 17. How many grams of Cu would be needed to react with 2.0 mol HNO_3?
    a. 95.3 g   **c.** 47.6 g
    b. 63.5 g   **d.** 1.50 g

_____ **18.** If you could drop 12 atoms of copper into a beaker containing nitric acid, how many molecules of NO would be produced?

    a. 2   **c.** 8

    b. 4   **d.** 12

C. Problems

Solve the following problems in the space provided. Show your work.

19. What is the limiting reagent when 49.84 g of nitrogen react with 10.7 g of hydrogen according to this balanced equation?

$$N_2(g) + 3H_2(g) \rightarrow 2NH_3(g)$$

20. How many grams of CO are needed to react with an excess of Fe_2O_3 to produce 558 g Fe? The equation for the reaction is:

$$Fe_2O_3(s) + 3CO(g) \rightarrow 3CO_2(g) + 2Fe(s)$$

21. How many grams of butane (C_4H_{10}) must be burned in an excess of O_2 to produce 15.0 g of CO_2?

$$2C_4H_{10}(g) + 13O_2(g) \rightarrow 8CO_2(g) + 10H_2O(g)$$

22. a. If 4.0 g of H_2 are made to react with excess CO, how many grams of CH_3OH can theoretically be produced according to the following equation?

$$CO(g) + 2H_2(g) \rightarrow CH_3OH(l)$$

    b. If 28.0 g of CH_3OH are actually produced, what is the percent yield?

Name ______________________ Date ______________ Class ______________

D. Essay

Write a short essay for the following.

23. What is the importance of the coefficients in a balanced chemical equation?

____

____

____

____

____

____

____

E. Additional Problems

Solve the following problems in the space provided. Show your work.

24. A 5.00×10^2 g sample of $Al_2(SO_4)_3$ is made to react with 450 g of $Ca(OH)_2$. A total of 596 g of $CaSO_4$ is produced. The balanced equation is:

$$Al_2(SO_4)_3(aq) + 3Ca(OH)_2(aq) \rightarrow 2Al(OH)_3(s) + 3CaSO_4(s)$$

a. What is the limiting reagent in this reaction?

b. How many moles of excess reagent are unreacted?

25. How many liters of O_2 are needed to react completely with 10.0 L of H_2S at STP according to the following reaction?

$$2H_2S(g) + 3O_2(g) \rightarrow 2SO_2(g) + 2H_2O(g)$$

26. The decomposition of potassium chlorate gives oxygen gas according to the reaction:

$$2KClO_3(s) \rightarrow 2KCl(s) + 3O_2(g)$$

How many grams $KClO_3$ are needed to produce 5.00 L of O_2 at STP?

27. Suppose that the reaction described in question 26 produces 4.80 L of O_2 in the laboratory. What is the percent yield?

12 STOICHIOMETRY

Chapter Test B

A. Matching

Match each term in Column B with the correct description in Column A. Write the letter of the correct term on the line.

Column A	Column B
_____ 1. the substance that determines the amount of product that can be formed in a reaction	**a.** percent yield
_____ 2. the amount of product that forms when a reaction is carried out in the laboratory	**b.** limiting reagent
_____ 3. the calculation of quantities in chemical equations	**c.** theoretical yield
_____ 4. the ratio of the actual yield to the theoretical yield expressed as a percent	**d.** stoichiometry
_____ 5. the substance that is present in enough quantity to react with a limiting reagent	**e.** actual yield
_____ 6. the maximum amount of products that could be formed from given amounts of reactants	**f.** excess reagent

B. Multiple Choice

Choose the best answer and write its letter on the line.

_____ 7. In a chemical reaction
    a. mass is conserved.   **c.** moles are conserved.
    b. atoms are conserved.   **d.** both mass and atoms are conserved.

_____ 8. Which of the following is a correct interpretation of this balanced equation?

$$2Al(s) + 3Pb(NO_3)_2(aq) \rightarrow 2Al(NO_3)_3(aq) + 3Pb(s)$$

    a. 2 atoms Al + 3 molecules $Pb(NO_3)_2 \rightarrow$ 2 molecules $Al(NO_3)_3$ + 3 atoms of Pb
    b. 2 grams Al + 3 grams $Pb(NO_3)_2 \rightarrow$ 2 grams $Al(NO_3)_3$ + 3 grams Pb
    c. 2 moles Al + 3 moles $Pb(NO_3)_2 \rightarrow$ 2 moles $Al(NO_3)_3$ + 3 moles Pb
    d. both a and c

_____ 9. If 3.0 moles of HCl are consumed in the reaction below, how many moles of $FeCl_3$ are produced?

$$6HCl + Fe_2O_3 \rightarrow 2FeCl_3 + 3H_2O$$

    a. 0.50 mol   **c.** 2.0 mol
    b. 1.0 mol   **d.** 4.0 mol

_____ **10.** Given the equation $2H_2O \rightarrow 2H_2 + O_2$, how many moles of H_2O would
be required to produce 2.5 moles of O_2?
    a. 2.0 mol   **c.** 4.0 mol
    b. 2.5 mol   **d.** 5.0 mol

_____ **11.** If 3.00 mol of $CaCO_3$ undergo decomposition to form CaO and CO_2,
how many grams of CO_2 are produced?
    a. 3.00 g   **c.** 88.0 g
    b. 44.0 g   **d.** 132 g

_____ **12.** If $CuO + H_2 \rightarrow Cu + H_2O$, how many moles of H_2O are produced when
240 grams of CuO react?
    a. 1.0 mol   **c.** 18 mol
    b. 3.0 mol   **d.** 54 mol

_____ **13.** Given the balanced equation $16HCl + 2KMnO_4 \rightarrow 2KCl + 2MnCl_2 +$
$5Cl_2 + 8H_2O$, if 1.0 mol of $KMnO_4$ reacts, how many moles of H_2O are
produced?
    a. 0.50 mol   **c.** 4.0 mol
    b. 2.0 mol   **d.** 8.0 mol

_____ **14.** Based on the equation in question 13, how many grams of KCl are
produced when 1.0 mol of $KMnO_4$ reacts?
    a. 1.0 g   **c.** 150 g
    b. 75 g   **d.** 158 g

_____ **15.** If 110 grams of HCl are used in the reaction $6HCl + Fe_2O_3 \rightarrow 2FeCl_3 +$
$3H_2O$, how many moles of $FeCl_3$ are produced?
    a. 1.0 mol   **c.** 3.0 mol
    b. 2.0 mol   **d.** 6.0 mol

_____ **16.** In the reaction $Zn + H_2SO_4 \rightarrow ZnSO_4 + H_2$, how many grams of H_2SO_4
are required to produce 1.0 gram of H_2?
    a. 1.0 g   **c.** 49 g
    b. 2.0 g   **d.** 98 g

_____ **17.** If 18 grams of carbon react with oxygen to produce carbon dioxide,
how many molecules of oxygen would be required?
    a. 1.5 molecules   **c.** 9.0×10^{23} molecules
    b. 48 molecules   **d.** 3.2×10^{24} molecules

_____ **18.** Given the reaction $2NO(g) + O_2(g) \rightarrow 2NO_2(g)$, if 6.5 L of O_2 react at
STP, how many liters of NO_2 are produced?
    a. 6.5 L   **c.** 26 L
    b. 3.2 L   **d.** 13 L

_____ **19.** Given the reaction $Zn + 2HCl \rightarrow ZnCl_2 + H_2$, if 2.0 mol Zn and 5.0 mol HCl
are allowed to react
    a. Zn is the limiting reagent.   **c.** 1.0 mol of $ZnCl_2$ is produced.
    b. HCl is the limiting reagent.   **d.** 5.0 mol of H_2 is produced.

_____ **20.** Once the reaction in question 19 is completed, how many moles of excess reactant remain?

    a. 3.0 mol   **c.** 4.0 mol

    b. 1.0 mol   **d.** 2.0 mol

_____ **21.** Given the reaction $CaCO_3(s) \rightarrow CaO(s) + CO_2(g)$, if 50.0 g of $CaCO_3$ react to produce 20.0 g of CO_2, what is the percent yield of CO_2?

    a. 66.7%   **c.** 90.9%

    b. 40.0%   **d.** 250%

C. Problems

Solve the following problems in the space provided. Show your work.

22. Ammonia, NH_3, is a typical ingredient in household cleaners. It is produced through a combination reaction involving $N_2(g)$ and $H_2(g)$. If 12.0 mol of $H_2(g)$ react with excess $N_2(g)$, how many moles of ammonia are produced?

23. The compound tin(II) fluoride, or stannous fluoride, once was a common ingredient in toothpaste. It is produced according to the following reaction:

$$Sn(s) + 2HF(g) \rightarrow SnF_2(s) + H_2(g)$$

If 45.0 grams of HF react with Sn, how many grams of stannous fluoride are produced?

24. The combustion of methane, $CH_4(g)$, can be described by the following equation:

$$CH_4(g) + 2O_2(g) \rightarrow CO_2(g) + 2H_2O(g)$$

If 150 moles of carbon dioxide are produced, what mass, in grams, of methane is required?

Name _____ Date _____ Class _____

25. If aluminum reacts with oxygen according to the following equation:

$$4Al(s) + 3O_2(g) \rightarrow 2Al_2O_3(s)$$

what mass, in grams, of the product would be produced if 625 mL of oxygen react at STP?

26. Given the following reaction:

$$CaCO_3(s) \rightarrow CaO(s) + CO_2(g),$$

if 50.8 grams of $CaCO_3$ react to produce 26.4 grams of CaO, what is the percent yield of CaO?

D. Essay

Write a short essay for the following.

27. Based on the following general reaction, if 1.0 mole of A is allowed to react with 2.0 moles of B, which reactant is the limiting reactant and what amount of A_2B_3 can be produced?

$$2A + 3B \rightarrow A_2B_3$$

_____

_____

_____

_____

_____

_____

E. Additional Problems

Solve the following problems in the space provided. Show your work.

28. In photosynthesis, plants use energy from the sun in combination with carbon dioxide and water to form glucose ($C_6H_{12}O_6$) and oxygen. If 4.50 moles of water react with carbon dioxide, what mass of glucose is produced?

29. Acetylene gas (C_2H_2) is used in welding and produces an extremely hot flame according to the reaction:

$$2C_2H_2(g) + 5O_2(g) \rightarrow 4CO_2(g) + 2H_2O(g)$$

If 5.00×10^4 g of acetylene burn completely, how many grams of carbon dioxide are produced?

30. Given the following reaction:

$$3H_2SO_4(aq) + Ca_3(PO_4)_2(s) \rightarrow 3CaSO_4(s) + 2H_3PO_4(aq),$$

if 1.25×10^5 kg of $H_2S)_4$ react, how many kilograms of H_3PO_4 are produced?

31. Ammonia and copper(II) oxide react according to the following:

$$2NH_3(g) + 3CuO(s) \rightarrow N_2(g) + 3Cu(s) + 3H_2O(g)$$

If 57.0 g of ammonia are combined with 290.0 g of copper(II) oxide:

a. Identify the limiting reactant.

b. How much of the excess reactant remains, in moles?

c. What mass of nitrogen gas is produced, in grams?

32. If ammonia reacts according to the following equation, how many kilograms of NO could be produced from 10.0 kg of NH_3 if the percent yield of NO is 80.0%?

$$4NH_3(g) + 5O_2(g) \rightarrow 4NO(g) + 6H_2O(g)$$

Name _____ Date _____ Class _____

SMALL-SCALE LAB: Analysis of Baking Soda

Laboratory Recordsheet   Use with Section 12.2

SAFETY 🌀👤☠️🧪

Wear safety glasses and follow the standard safety procedure.

PURPOSE

To determine the mass of sodium hydrogen carbonate in a sample of baking soda, using stoichiometry.

MATERIALS

- baking soda
- 3 plastic cups
- pipets of HCl, NaOH, and thymol blue
- soda straw
- balance

PROCEDURE

Prepare and analyze a sample of baking soda. Take care to write down the results of each step.

A. Measure the mass of a clean, dry plastic cup.

_____

B. Using a soda straw as a scoop, fill one end with baking soda to a depth of about one centimeter. Add the sample to the cup and measure its mass again.

_____

C. Place two HCl pipets that are about three-fourths full into a clean cup and measure the mass of the system.

_____

D. Transfer the contents of both HCl pipets to the cup containing baking soda. Swirl until the fizzing stops. Wait 5–10 minutes to be sure the reaction is complete. Measure the mass of the two empty HCl pipets in their cup again.

_____

E. Add 5 drops of thymol blue to the plastic cup.

F. Place two full NaOH pipets in a clean cup and measure the mass of the system.

_____

G. Slowly add NaOH to the baking soda/HCl mixture until the pink color just disappears. Measure the mass of the NaOH pipets in their cup again.

_____

ANALYSIS

Using your experimental data, record the answers to the following questions.

1. Write and balance an equation for the reaction between baking soda ($NaHCO_3$) and hydrochloric acid.

   _____

   _____

2. Calculate the mass in grams of the baking soda used in the experiment.

   (Step A – Step B)

3. Calculate the total mmol of $1M$ HCl used in the experiment.

   (Step C – Step D) $\times$ 1.00 mmol/g

   Note: Every gram of HCl contains 1.00 mmol.

4. Calculate the total mmol of $0.5M$ NaOH used in the experiment.

   (Step F – Step G) $\times$ 0.500 mmol/mL

   Note: Every gram of NaOH contains 0.500 mmol.

5. Calculate the mmol of HCl that reacted with the baking soda.

   (Step 3 – Step 4)

   Note: The NaOH measures the amount of HCl that did not react.

6. Calculate the mass of the baking soda from the reaction data.

   (0.084 g/mmol $\times$ Step 5)

7. Calculate the percent error of the experiment.

$$\frac{(\text{Step 2} - \text{Step 6})}{\text{Step 2}} \times 100\%$$

YOU'RE THE CHEMIST

Use the space below to write your observations to the small-scale activities in the *You're the Chemist* section.

_____

_____

_____

_____

_____

_____

_____

_____

_____

QUICK LAB: Limiting Reagents

Laboratory Recordsheet   Use with Section 12.3

PURPOSE

To illustrate the concept of a limiting reagent in a chemical reaction.

MATERIALS

- graduated cylinder
- balance
- three 250-mL Erlenmeyer flasks
- three rubber balloons
- 4.2 g magnesium ribbon
- 300 mL 1.0M hydrochloric acid

PROCEDURE

1. Add 100 mL of the hydrochloric acid solution to each flask.

2. Weigh out 0.6 g, 1.2 g, and 2.4 g of magnesium ribbon, and place each sample into its own balloon.

3. Stretch the end of each balloon over the mouth of each flask. Do not allow the magnesium ribbon in the balloon to fall into the flask.

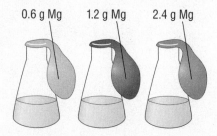

0.6 g Mg   1.2 g Mg   2.4 g Mg

4. Magnesium reacts with hydrochloric acid to form hydrogen gas. When you mix the magnesium with the hydrochloric acid in the next step, you will generate a certain volume of hydrogen gas. How do you think the volume of hydrogen produced in each flask will compare?

_____

_____

5. Lift up on each balloon and shake the magnesium metal down into each flask. Observe the volume of gas produced until the reaction in each flask is completed.

Name _____ Date _____ Class _____

ANALYSES AND CONCLUSIONS

1. How did the volumes of hydrogen gas produced, as measured by the size of the balloons, compare? Did the results agree with your prediction?

   _____

   _____

   _____

2. Write a balanced equation for the reaction between magnesium metal and hydrochloric acid.

   _____

3. The 100 mL of hydrochloric acid contained 0.10 mol HCl. Show by calculation why the balloon with 1.2 g Mg inflated to about twice the size of the balloon with 0.60 g Mg.

4. Show by calculation why the balloons with 1.2 g and 2.4 g Mg inflated to approximately the same volume. What was the limiting reagent when 2.4 g Mg was added to the acid?

13.1 THE NATURE OF GASES

Section Review

Objectives

- Describe the assumptions of the kinetic theory as it applies to gases
- Interpret gas pressure in terms of kinetic theory
- Define the relationship between Kelvin temperature and average kinetic energy

Vocabulary

- kinetic energy
- kinetic theory
- gas pressure
- vacuum
- atmospheric pressure
- barometer
- pascal (Pa)
- standard atmosphere (atm)

Part A Completion

Use this completion exercise to check your understanding of the concepts and terms that are introduced in this section. Each blank can be completed with a term, short phrase, or number.

The kinetic theory describes the __1__ of particles in matter
and the forces of attraction between them. The theory assumes
that the volume occupied by a gas is mostly __2__, that the
particles of gas are relatively __3__, move __4__ of each other,
and are in constant __5__ motion. The __6__ between
particles are perfectly elastic so that the total __7__ remains
constant. Gas pressure results from the simultaneous collisions
of billions of particles with an object. Barometers are used to
measure __8__ pressure. Standard conditions are defined
as a temperature of __9__ and a pressure of __10__.

1. _____

2. _____

3. _____

4. _____

5. _____

6. _____

7. _____

8. _____

9. _____

10. _____

Part B True-False

Classify each of these statements as always true, AT; sometimes true, ST; or never true, NT.

_____ 11. Atmospheric pressure is 760 mm Hg.

_____ 12. The SI unit of pressure is the pascal.

_____ **13.** Atmospheric pressure increases as you climb a mountain because the density of Earth's atmosphere decreases with altitude.

_____ **14.** When particles of a substance are heated, some of the energy is absorbed by the particle and stored in the form of potential energy.

_____ **15.** The Kelvin temperature of a substance is directly proportional to the total kinetic energy of the particles in the substance.

_____ **16.** At any given temperature, the particles of all substances have the same average kinetic energy.

Part C Matching

Match each description in Column B to the correct term in Column A.

Column A

_____ **17.** vacuum

_____ **18.** kinetic energy

_____ **19.** gas pressure

_____ **20.** atmospheric pressure

_____ **21.** barometer

Column B

a. an instrument used to measure atmospheric pressure

b. a space where no particles of matter exist

c. the energy an object has because of its motion

d. results from the force exerted by a gas per unit surface area of an object

e. results from the collisions of atoms and molecules in air with objects

Part D Questions and Problems

Answer the following in the space provided.

22. A gas is at a pressure of 4.30 atm. What is this pressure in kilopascals? In mm Hg?

23. Describe the motion of particles of a gas according to kinetic theory.

_____

_____

_____

_____

24. What simple evidence demonstrates that gas particles are in constant motion?

_____

13.2 THE NATURE OF LIQUIDS

Section Review

Objectives
- Identify factors that determine physical properties of a liquid
- Define *evaporation* in terms of kinetic energy
- Describe the equilibrium between a liquid and its vapor
- Identify the conditions under which boiling occurs

Vocabulary
- vaporization
- evaporation
- vapor pressure
- boiling point
- normal boiling point

Part A Completion

Use this completion exercise to check your understanding of the concepts and terms that are introduced in this section. Each blank can be completed with a term, short phrase, or number.

Liquids are much __1__ than gases. Liquids and solids are known as __2__ states of matter. The conversion of a liquid to a gas or vapor is called __3__. When a liquid that is not __4__ changes to a gas, the process is called evaporation. A liquid evaporates faster when heated; however, evaporation itself is a __5__ process. When a partially filled container of liquid is sealed, some of the particles at the __6__ of the liquid vaporize. These particles collide with the walls of the container, producing a force called __7__. The vapor pressure of a liquid can be determined by a device called a __8__. A liquid boils when its __9__ equals the external pressure. The normal boiling point of a liquid is the temperature at which the vapor pressure is equal to __10__.

1. _____
2. _____
3. _____
4. _____
5. _____
6. _____
7. _____
8. _____
9. _____
10. _____

Part B True-False

Classify each of these statements as always true, AT; sometimes true, ST; or never true, NT.

_____ 11. Particles in a liquid don't have enough kinetic energy to overcome the attractive forces between them and vaporize.

_____ **12.** When a liquid is in a closed container, there are more particles evaporating than condensing.

_____ **13.** The change of a substance directly from a solid to a gas or vapor is called condensation.

_____ **14.** The rates of evaporation and condensation are equal at equilibrium.

_____ **15.** Heating a liquid will increase the temperature of the liquid.

_____ **16.** During evaporation in an open container, the temperature of a liquid decreases.

Part C Matching

Match each description in Column B to the correct term in Column A.

Column A
_____ **17.** vapor pressure

_____ **18.** condensation

_____ **19.** normal boiling point

_____ **20.** liquid

_____ **21.** intermolecular attractions

Column B
a. a measure of the pressure exerted by a gas above a liquid

b. the forces between molecules

c. the boiling point of a liquid at a pressure of 101.3 kPa

d. a fluid with a fixed volume

e. the change of a gas or vapor directly to a liquid

Part D Questions and Problems

Answer the following in the space provided.

22. Describe what happens on a particle level when a liquid is at its boiling point.

_____

_____

23. Liquid A has a vapor pressure of 7.37 kPa at 40°C. Liquid B has a vapor pressure of 18.04 kPa at 40°C. Which liquid would evaporate faster at 40°C? Explain your answer.

_____

_____

24. Explain why evaporation leads to cooling of the liquid.

_____

_____

_____

Name _____ Date _____ Class _____

13.3 THE NATURE OF SOLIDS

Section Review

Objectives

- Evaluate how the way particles are organized explains the properties of solids
- Identify the factors that determine the shape of a crystal
- Explain how allotropes of an element are different

Vocabulary

- melting point
- crystal
- unit cell
- allotropes
- amorphous solid
- glass

Part A Completion

Use this completion exercise to check your understanding of the concepts and terms that are introduced in this section. Each blank can be completed with a term, short phrase, or number.

Solids tend to be dense and difficult to ___1___. They do not

flow or take the shape of their containers, like liquids do, because

the particles in solids vibrate around ___2___ points. When a solid

is heated until its particles vibrate so rapidly that they are no longer

held in fixed positions, the solid ___3___. The ___4___ is the

temperature at which a solid changes to a liquid. The melting and

___5___ of a substance are at the same temperature. In general,

ionic solids tend to have relatively ___6___ melting points, while

molecular solids tend to have relatively low melting points. Most

solids are ___7___. The particles are arranged in a pattern known

as a crystal ___8___. The smallest subunit of a crystal lattice

is the ___9___. Some solids lack an ordered internal structure

and are called ___10___ solids.

1. _____

2. _____

3. _____

4. _____

5. _____

6. _____

7. _____

8. _____

9. _____

10. _____

Part B True-False

Classify each of these statements as always true, AT; sometimes true, ST; or never true, NT.

_____ **11.** Glasses do not melt at a definite temperature, but soften gradually.

_____ **12.** Solid substances can exist in more than one form.

_____ **13.** Allotropes are two or more different elements that exist in the same
state with the same crystal system.

_____ **14.** When the atoms in a solid have a random arrangement, the solid is a
glass.

_____ **15.** The type of bonding that exists between the atoms in a crystal tends to
determine the melting point of the solid.

Part C Matching

Match each description in Column B to the correct term in Column A.

Column A   Column B

_____ **16.** crystal   **a.** describes a solid in which the particles are randomly
arranged

_____ **17.** unit cell   **b.** transparent fusion products of inorganic substances that
have cooled to a rigid state without crystallizing

_____ **18.** rhombohedral   **c.** the smallest group of particles within a crystal that retains
the geometric shape of the crystal

_____ **19.** amorphous   **d.** the temperature at which a solid changes to a liquid

_____ **20.** glasses   **e.** has a regular three-dimensional arrangement of particles

_____ **21.** solid   **f.** one of the seven crystal systems.

_____ **22.** melting point   **g.** dense state of matter that has a fixed shape and is not easily
compressed

Part D Questions and Problems

Answer the following in the space provided.

24. Explain what happens at the particle level when a solid melts.

_____

_____

_____

_____

Name _____   Date _____   Class _____

CHANGES OF STATE

Section Review

Objectives

- Identify the conditions necessary for sublimation
- Describe how equilibrium conditions are represented in a phase diagram

Vocabulary

- sublimation
- triple point
- phase diagram

Part A Completion

Use this completion exercise to check your understanding of the concepts and terms that are introduced in this section. Each blank can be completed with a term, short phrase, or number.

The change that occurs when a solid goes directly to the gas or vapor state without first becoming a liquid is ___1___.

This change can occur because solids, like liquids, have a ___2___. Substances that sublime include iodine and solid ___3___ (dry ice).

A graph that shows the relationship between the states of a substance is called a ___4___ diagram. On this diagram, a line between two phases shows the conditions at which the phases are in ___5___. The ___6___ is the only set of conditions at which solid, liquid, and gas phases coexist. The triple point for water is a temperature of ___7___ and a pressure of ___8___.

1. _____

2. _____

3. _____

4. _____

5. _____

6. _____

7. _____

8. _____

Part B True-False

Classify each of these statements as always true, AT; sometimes true, ST; or never true, NT.

_____   9. A phase diagram gives information on changes in mass of solids, liquids, and gases.

_____   10. Water could be made to boil at 105°C by increasing the pressure.

_____ **11.** The sublimation point of a substance refers to the temperature and pressure at which the substance exists in all three phases of matter.

_____ **12.** Below the triple point for water, decreasing the pressure will not change water vapor to ice.

_____ **13.** Water has more than one triple point.

_____ **14.** At 101.3 kPa, the normal boiling point and melting point of water are the same.

Part C Matching

Match each description in Column B to the correct term in Column A.

Column A	**Column B**
_____ **15.** melting	**a.** the change of a solid to a vapor without passing through the liquid state
_____ **16.** freeze drying	**b.** the change of a solid to the liquid state
_____ **17.** phase diagram	**c.** a method of removing water from food, using sublimation
_____ **18.** 0.016°C, 0.61 kPa	**d.** graph that shows the relationship among the states of a substance
_____ **19.** sublimation	**e.** defines the triple point for water
_____ **20.** 100°C at 101.3 kPa	**f.** normal boiling point for water

Part D Questions and Problems

Answer the following in the space provided.

21. Explain how some solids can vaporize and then condense back to a solid without passing through the liquid state. What is the process called?

_____

_____

22. When the physical state of a substance changes during a phase change, what happens to the temperature of the system?

_____

_____

13 STATES OF MATTER

Practice Problems

In your notebook, answer the following questions or solve the following problems.

SECTION 13.1 THE NATURE OF GASES

1. Explain why there is no gas pressure inside a vacuum.

2. How would the reading on a barometer change if you were to take one on a trip from Los Angeles to Lake Tahoe, which is at a much higher altitude?

3. The height of a column of mercury in a barometer is 754.3 mm. What is the atmospheric pressure in atm? In kPa?

4. How does the average kinetic energy of the helium atoms in a balloon change as the helium gas is heated from $-100.0°C$ to $73°C$?

SECTION 13.2 THE NATURE OF LIQUIDS

1. In general, how do the intermolecular attractions between particles in a gas compare with those between particles in a liquid?

2. An open beaker is about half filled with water. How can a dynamic equilibrium be established between the water and the vapor forming above its surface?

3. Explain how the following description is an analogy for evaporative cooling: If the fastest runner is removed from a race, the average speed of the remaining runners will be lower.

4. The normal boiling point of ethanol is $78.5°C$. The normal boiling point of water is $100°C$. At $75°C$, which liquid, ethanol or water, has the greater vapor pressure? Explain.

SECTION 13.3 THE NATURE OF SOLIDS

1. How does the crystalline structure of graphite compare with that of diamond?

2. Why is diamond classified as an allotrope of carbon?

3. Peanut brittle is a candy that is poured out while hot onto a surface. It is allowed to cool and harden into a sheet, which easily breaks into irregularly shaped pieces. The sugar in peanut brittle solidifies without reforming its crystal lattice. What type of solid is peanut brittle?

4. Which type of solid is likely to have the lowest melting point—an ionic solid or a molecular solid? Explain.

5. Give an example of a crystalline solid. What is a crystal?

Name ____________________ Date ______________ Class ______________

SECTION 13.4 CHANGES OF STATE

To answer the following questions, refer to the phase diagram shown in Figure 13.15 of your textbook.

1. How does the melting point of water change as the pressure increases?
2. What does the line separating the solid phase from the vapor phase represent?
3. What does the line separating the liquid phase from the vapor phase represent?
4. What is the vapor pressure of liquid water at 100°C?

INTERPRETING GRAPHICS

13

Use with Section 13.4

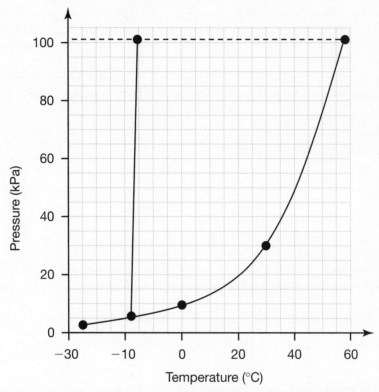

**Figure 1 Phase diagram for bromine (Br$_2$). Note that the scale on the
x-axis is distorted to emphasize some of the graph's features.**

*At standard temperature and pressure, bromine is a red liquid. Bromine sublimes
when the temperature is $-25°C$ and the pressure is 101.3 kPa.*

1. Label each region of the graph as solid, liquid, or vapor.

2. Label the triple point, normal melting point, and normal boiling point on the
   graph and estimate their temperature values. Include an estimate of the
   pressure for the triple point.

   Normal melting point = _____

   Normal boiling point = _____

   Triple point = _____

3. Use the letter *A* to label the line that gives the conditions for equilibrium
   between solid and liquid phases of bromine, the letter *B* to label the curve
   that gives the conditions for equilibrium between liquid and vapor phases of
   bromine, and the letter *C* to label the curve that gives the conditions for
   equilibrium between solid and vapor phases of bromine.

4. Describe how the melting point of bromine changes with the external pressure. Based on the slope of the melting-point curve in the phase diagram, would you characterize the solid phase of bromine as more dense or less dense than the liquid phase of bromine?

_____

_____

_____

5. What is the boiling point of bromine when the external pressure is 75 kPa?

_____

6. Explain the significance of the triple point.

_____

_____

_____

7. Place direction arrows labeled S, V, and M on the phase diagram to indicate where sublimation, vaporization, and melting occur, respectively.

Circle the correct word in the parentheses in each of the following sentences.

8. Bromine vapor at 15°C (condenses, sublimes) when the pressure is raised to 50 kPa.

9. Bromine liquid at 70 kPa (vaporizes, freezes) when the temperature is decreased to −15°C.

13 STATES OF MATTER

Vocabulary Review

Each clue describes a vocabulary term. Read the clues and write the letters of each term on the lines.

1. Clue: the energy an object has because of its motion.

   ___ ___ ___ ◯ ___ ___ ___ ___   ___ ___ ___ ___ ___ ___

2. Clue: results from the force exerted by a gas per unit surface area of an object.

   ___ ___ ___   ___ ◯ ___ ___ ___ ___ ___ ___

3. Clue: the process in which molecules of a liquid escape from the surface of a liquid that is not boiling.

   ___ ___ ___ ___ ___ ___ ___ ___ ___ ◯ ___

4. Clue: the temperature at which the vapor pressure of a liquid is just equal to the external pressure.

   ◯ ___ ___ ___ ___ ___ ___

5. Clue: sample in which particles are arranged in an orderly, repeating, three-dimensional pattern.

   ___ ◯ ___ ___ ___ ___ ___

6. Clue: two or more different molecular forms of the same element in the same physical state.

   ___ ___ ___ ___ ◯ ___ ___ ___ ◯ ___

7. Clue: the temperature at which a solid changes into a liquid.

   ◯ ___ ___ ___ ___ ___ ___   ___ ___ ___ ___ ___

8. Clue: the SI unit of pressure.

   ___ ◯ ___ ___ ___ ___

Write the letters found inside the circles on the lines below. Then unscramble them to find the name of a device for measuring the atmospheric pressure.

Scrambled Letters:

___ ___ ___ ___ ___ ___ ___ ___ ___

Solution:

___ ___ ___ ___ ___ ___ ___ ___ ___

13 STATES OF MATTER

Chapter Quiz

Fill in the word(s) that will make each statement true.

1. The ___1___ theory states that the tiny particles in matter are in constant motion.

   1. _____ *13.1*

2. Atmospheric pressure ___2___ with an increase in elevation.

   2. _____ *13.1*

3. An increase in the ___3___ of a substance corresponds to an increase in the average kinetic energy of its particles.

   3. _____ *13.1*

4. The energy an object has because of its motion is ___4___ energy.

   4. _____ *13.1*

5. In the kinetic theory, it is assumed that the collisions between gas particles are perfectly ___5___.

   5. _____ *13.1*

6. Liquids and solids are known as ___6___ states of matter.

   6. _____ *13.2*

7. During evaporation, only those molecules that possess a certain ___7___ can escape from the surface of a liquid.

   7. _____ *13.2*

8. At the boiling point, the vapor pressure of a liquid is equal to the ___8___.

   8. _____ *13.2*

9. The smallest group of particles in a crystal that retains the shape of a crystal is a(n) ___9___.

   9. _____ *13.3*

10. A solid that lacks an ordered internal structure is a(n) ___10___ solid.

   10. _____ *13.3*

Classify each of these statements as always true, AT; sometimes true, ST; or never true, NT.

_____ 11. The change of a substance to vapor is called vaporization.

   13.3, 13.4

_____ 12. At the triple point, solid, liquid, and gas can exist in equilibrium with one another.

   13.4

_____ 13. A phase diagram shows the temperature and pressure conditions at which a substance exists as a solid, liquid, and gas or vapor.

   13.4

13 STATES OF MATTER

Chapter Test A

A. Matching

Match each description in Column B with the correct term in Column A. Write the letter of the correct description on the line.

	Column A	Column B
_____	1. amorphous	**a.** an empty space with no particles of matter
_____	2. unit cell	**b.** the temperature at which a solid changes into a liquid
_____	3. crystal	**c.** a device used to measure atmospheric pressure
_____	4. normal boiling point	**d.** the pressure resulting from the collision of particles in air with objects
_____	5. barometer	**e.** the temperature at which the vapor pressure of a liquid is equal to the external pressure
_____	6. atmospheric pressure	**f.** the smallest group of particles within a crystal that retains the shape of the crystal
_____	7. melting point	**g.** a solid in which the particles are arranged in an orderly, repeating, three-dimensional pattern
_____	8. sublimation	**h.** a measure of the force exerted by a gas above a liquid
_____	9. boiling point	**i.** describes a solid that lacks an ordered internal structure
_____	10. kinetic theory	**j.** the temperature at which a liquid boils at a pressure of 101.3 kPa
_____	11. allotrope	**k.** one of two or more different molecular forms of the same element in the same physical state
_____	12. vapor pressure	**l.** the conversion of a liquid to a gas or vapor at a temperature below the boiling point
_____	13. evaporation	**m.** states that the tiny particles in all forms of matter are in constant motion
_____	14. vacuum	**n.** the change of a solid to a vapor without passing through the liquid state

Name _____ Date _____ Class _____

B. Multiple Choice

Choose the best answer and write its letter on the line.

_____ 15. The average kinetic energy of water molecules is greatest in
  a. steam at 200°C.   **c.** liquid water at 373 K.
  b. liquid water at 90°C.   **d.** ice at 0°C.

_____ 16. According to the kinetic theory of gases,
  a. the particles in a gas move rapidly.
  b. the particles in a gas are relatively far apart.
  c. the particles in a gas move independently of each other.
  d. all of the above are true.

_____ 17. The temperature at which the motion of particles theoretically ceases is
  a. 0°C.   **c.** −273 K.
  b. 273°C.   **d.** 0 K.

_____ 18. The average kinetic energy of particles of a substance
  a. is not affected by the temperature of the substance.
  b. increases as the temperature of the substance decreases.
  c. is directly proportional to the temperature of a substance.
  d. is equal to 0.

_____ 19. Which of these statements is *not* true, according to kinetic theory?
  a. There is no attraction between particles of a gas.
  b. Only particles of matter in the gaseous state are in constant motion.
  c. The particles of a gas collide with each other and with other objects.
  d. All collisions between particles of gas are perfectly elastic.

_____ 20. Standard conditions when working with gases are defined as
  a. 0 K and 101.3 kilopascals.   **c.** 0°C and 101.3 kilopascals.
  b. 0 K and 1 mm Hg.   **d.** 0°C and 1 mm Hg.

_____ 21. The pressure of a gas in a container is 76 mm Hg. This is equivalent to
  a. 0.1 atm.   **c.** 0.2 atm.
  b. 1 atm.   **d.** 0.76 atm.

_____ 22. A phase diagram gives information on
  a. volumes of gases.
  b. conditions at which a substance exists as a solid, liquid, and gas.
  c. volumes of liquids and solids.
  d. changes in mass of solids, liquids, and gases.

_____ 23. An increase in the temperature of a contained liquid
  a. causes the vapor pressure above the liquid to increase.
  b. decreases the vapor pressure above a liquid.
  c. causes fewer particles to escape the surface of the liquid.
  d. has no effect on the kinetic energy of the liquid.

_____ **24.** Water could be made to boil at 105°C by
  a. applying a great deal of energy.
  b. increasing the air pressure above the water.
  c. heating the water more gradually.
  d. decreasing the air pressure above the water.

_____ **25.** The direct change of a substance from a solid to a vapor is called:
  a. evaporation   **c.** condensation.
  b. sublimation.   **d.** vaporization.

_____ **26.** Most solids
  a. are amorphous.
  b. lack an orderly internal structure.
  c. are dense and not easily compressed.
  d. have low melting points.

_____ **27.** The escape of molecules from the surface of an uncontained liquid is
  a. boiling.   **c.** evaporation.
  b. sublimation.   **d.** condensation.

C. True-False

Classify each of these statements as always true, AT, sometimes true, ST, or never true, NT.

_____ **28.** The rates of evaporation and condensation are equal at equilibrium.

_____ **29.** The kinetic energy of all the particles in a given sample of matter is the same.

_____ **30.** The average kinetic energy of all the molecules in liquid water at 80°C is the same as the average kinetic energy of the molecules in oxygen gas at 80°C.

_____ **31.** Heating a liquid will increase the temperature of the liquid.

_____ **32.** The melting point and freezing point of a substance are the same.

D. Problems

Solve the following problems in the space provided. Show your work.

33. A gas is at a pressure of 3.70 atm. What is this pressure in kilopascals?

34. What is the pressure of the gas in problem 33, expressed in millimeters of mercury?

E. Essay

Write a short essay for the following.

35. Explain why the temperature of a gas does not depend on the number of particles in the sample of gas.

_____

_____

_____

_____

_____

F. Additional Problems

Solve the following problems in the space provided. Show your work.

36. A gas has a pressure of 610.0 mm Hg. What is the pressure in atmospheres?

37. What is the pressure of the gas in problem 36, expressed in kilopascals?

G. Additional Questions

Answer the following questions in the space provided.

38. A 100-g sample of water is heated from 50°C to 100°C. At 100°C, although the water is still being heated, the temperature of the water does not rise. Explain why.

_____

_____

_____

_____

39. Some types of bacteria are killed by being heated to a temperature of 150°C for 30 minutes. Explain why water heated under pressure can be used to kill these bacteria, although boiling water at atmospheric pressure does not kill them.

_____

_____

_____

_____

_____

_____

13 STATES OF MATTER

Chapter Test B

A. Matching

Match each term in Column B to the correct description in Column A. Write the letter of the correct term on the line.

<table>
<tr><td colspan="2">Column A</td><td>Column B</td></tr>
<tr><td>_____</td><td>1. an instrument used to measure atmospheric pressure</td><td>a. normal boiling point</td></tr>
<tr><td>_____</td><td>2. a measure of the force exerted by a gas above a liquid</td><td>b. pascal</td></tr>
<tr><td>_____</td><td>3. The tiny particles in all forms of matter are in constant motion.</td><td>c. kinetic energy</td></tr>
<tr><td>_____</td><td>4. the temperature at which a solid changes into a liquid</td><td>d. standard atmosphere</td></tr>
<tr><td>_____</td><td>5. the pressure required to support 760 mm of Hg at 25°C</td><td>e. melting point</td></tr>
<tr><td>_____</td><td>6. the change of a substance from a solid to a gas or vapor without passing through the liquid state</td><td>f. triple point</td></tr>
<tr><td>_____</td><td>7. the SI unit of pressure</td><td>g. evaporation</td></tr>
<tr><td>_____</td><td>8. the conversion of a liquid to a gas or vapor at a temperature below the liquid's boiling point</td><td>h. kinetic theory</td></tr>
<tr><td>_____</td><td>9. describes the only conditions of temperature and pressure at which all three phases of a substance can exist in equilibrium</td><td>i. allotropes</td></tr>
<tr><td>_____</td><td>10. the pressure that results from the collisions of particles in air with objects</td><td>j. barometer</td></tr>
<tr><td>_____</td><td>11. the temperature at which a liquid boils at a pressure of 101.3 kPa</td><td>k. sublimation</td></tr>
<tr><td>_____</td><td>12. the smallest group of particles within a crystal that retains the geometric shape of the crystal</td><td>l. atmospheric pressure</td></tr>
<tr><td>_____</td><td>13. the energy an object has because of its motion</td><td>m. unit cell</td></tr>
<tr><td>_____</td><td>14. two or more different molecular forms of the same element in the same physical state</td><td>n. vapor pressure</td></tr>
</table>

Name _____ Date _____ Class _____

B. Multiple Choice

Choose the best answer and write its letter on the line.

_____ **15.** According to the kinetic theory, gases consist of particles that
      a. occupy considerable volume.
      b. are relatively close together.
      c. exert attractive and repulsive forces on other particles.
      d. have motion that is constant, random, and rapid.

_____ **16.** As you climb a mountain, atmospheric pressure:
      a. increases.   **c.** remains the same.
      b. decreases.   **d.** varies randomly.

_____ **17.** Which of the following is true about atmospheric pressure?
      a. It is measured with a hydrometer.
      b. It varies widely, depending on the weather.
      c. It increases with altitude.
      d. It affects the boiling point of a liquid.

_____ **18.** At sea level in fair weather, atmospheric pressure is equal to
      a. 101.3 kPa.   **c.** 760 mm Hg.
      b. 1 standard atmosphere.   **d.** all of the above

_____ **19.** STP refers to:
      a. 100°C and 1 atm.   **c.** 0°C and 1 atm.
      b. 0°C and 1 kPa.   **d.** 100°C and 760 mm Hg.

_____ **20.** A pressure of 2.5 atm is equivalent to
      a. 41 kPa.   **c.** 3.0×10^2 mm Hg.
      b. 1900 mm Hg.   **d.** 2.5 kPa.

_____ **21.** Absolute zero is
      a. the temperature at which the motion of particles theoretically
          ceases.
      b. defined as 0°C.
      c. the triple point for water.
      d. all of the above

_____ **22.** At 80 K, the particles of a gas have
      a. twice the average kinetic energy of the same particles at 40 K.
      b. half the average kinetic energy of the same particles at 40 K.
      c. one fourth the average kinetic energy of the same particles at 20 K.
      d. none of the above

_____ **23.** Compared with gases, liquids:
      a. have stronger intermolecular attractions.
      b. have more space between their particles.
      c. are much less dense.
      d. are more easily compressed.

_____ 24. Evaporation is a type of
    a. boiling.
    b. vaporization.
    c. sublimation.
    d. condensation.

_____ 25. A decrease in the temperature of a contained liquid causes
    a. an increase in the vapor pressure.
    b. a decrease in the vapor pressure.
    c. more particles to evaporate.
    d. an increase in the average kinetic energy of the particles.

_____ 26. Water could be made to boil at 92°C by
    a. lowering the external air pressure.
    b. raising the external air pressure.
    c. increasing the pressure on the water.
    d. none of the above

_____ 27. In comparison with liquids and gases, solids are
    a. more dense.
    b. more easily compressed.
    c. less organized.
    d. more likely to flow.

_____ 28. Diamond and graphite are examples of
    a. phases.
    b. amorphous solids.
    c. allotropes.
    d. glasses.

_____ 29. The conditions at which the solid, liquid, and gaseous phases of a substance can exist in equilibrium with one another is called
    a. boiling point.
    b. freezing point.
    c. sublimation point.
    d. triple point.

_____ 30. Sublimation can occur because solids have
    a. a melting point.
    b. a vapor pressure.
    c. a boiling point.
    d. a triple point.

C. True-False

Classify each of these statements as always true, AT; sometimes true, ST; or never true, NT.

_____ 31. In an elastic collision, kinetic energy is transferred from one particle to another, but the total kinetic energy remains constant.

_____ 32. Atmospheric pressure is 101.3 kPa.

_____ 33. The Kelvin temperature of a substance is directly proportional to the average kinetic energy of the particles in that substance.

_____ 34. At any given temperature, the particles of all substances have the same average kinetic energy.

_____ 35. The temperature of a boiling liquid can rise above its boiling point.

_____ 36. Water boils at 100°C.

_____ 37. The melting and freezing points of a substance are the same temperature.

Name _____ Date _____ Class _____

D. Essay

Write a short essay for the following.

38. Distinguish between the boiling point and the normal boiling point of a liquid. Explain the impact of a change in atmospheric pressure on the relationship between the boiling point and the normal boiling point.

_____

_____

_____

_____

_____

_____

_____

_____

E. Additional Questions

Answer the following questions in the space provided.

39. Distinguish between gases, liquids, and solids in terms of the kinetic theory.

_____

_____

_____

_____

_____

_____

_____

_____

_____

Name ______________________ Date ______________ Class ______________

40. Explain why each of the following is true.

a. The temperature of a boiling liquid never rises above its boiling point.

____

____

____

____

____

b. The temperature of an ice and water mixture at 1 standard atmosphere remains at 0°C as long as both ice and liquid water are present, no matter what the surrounding temperature.

____

____

____

____

____

SMALL-SCALE LAB: The Behavior of Liquids and Solids

Laboratory Recordsheet   Use with Section 13.3

SAFETY 🦠🥼✋☠🔥🧪

Wear your safety glasses and follow standard safety procedures.

PURPOSE

To explore and explain some behaviors of liquids and solids.

MATERIALS

- plastic Petri dish
- water
- ice
- rubbing alcohol
- graph paper, 1-cm
- calcium chloride

PROCEDURE

1. In your notebook, make a copy of the table shown below. Add a column for your observations. In the experiments, you will place substances labeled A and B inside the Petri dish and substances labeled C on top of the dish.

2. For Experiment 1, place one drop of water in the Petri dish. Replace the cover and place a small piece of ice on top of the cover.

3. After a few minutes, observe the interior surface of the Petri dish cover and the contents of the dish. Record your observations. Clean and dry the Petri dish and cover.

4. Repeat Steps 2 and 3 for Experiment 2-5, using the materials listed in the table. For Experiment 4, place the Petri dish on the graph paper so that you can place the water and the calcium chloride about 3 cm apart.

Experiment	Substance A	Substance B	Substance C
1	drop of water		ice cube
2	drop of water		drop of water
3	drop of rubbing alcohol		drop of water
4	drop of water	piece of $CaCl_2$	
5		several pieces of $CaCl_2$	ice cube

ANALYZE

Using your experimental data, record the answers to the following questions beneath your data table.

1. Explain your observations in Experiment 1 in terms of the behavior of liquids.

   _____

   _____

   _____

2. Why is ice not needed for cloud formation in Experiment 2?

   _____

   _____

   _____

3. What difference do you observe about the behavior of water in the previous experiments? Explain.

   _____

   _____

   _____

4. What happens to solid calcium chloride in a humid environment?

   _____

   _____

   _____

5. Propose an explanation for no cloud formation in Experiment 5.

   _____

   _____

   _____

YOU'RE THE CHEMIST

Use the space below to write your observations to the small-scale activities in the
You're the Chemist section.

QUICK LAB: Sublimation

Laboratory Recordsheet   Use with Section 13.4

PURPOSE

To observe the sublimation of air freshener.

MATERIALS

- small pieces of solid air freshener
- small, shallow container
- 2 clear 8-oz plastic cups
- hot tap water
- ice
- 3 thick cardboard strips

PROCEDURE

1. Place a few pieces of air freshener in one of the cups. **CAUTION:** *Work in a well-ventilated room.*

2. Bend the cardboard strips and place them over the rim of the cup that has the air freshener pieces.

3. Place the second cup inside the first. The base of the second cup should not touch the air freshener. Adjust the cardboard as necessary. This assembly is your sublimator.

4. Fill the top cup with ice. Do not get any ice or water in the bottom cup.

5. Fill the shallow container about one-third full with hot tap water.

6. Carefully place your sublimator in the hot water. Observe what happens.

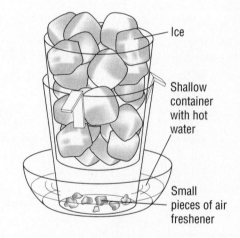

Ice

Shallow container with hot water

Small pieces of air freshener

ANALYSES AND CONCLUSIONS

1. Define *sublimation*.

_____

_____

Name ______________________ Date ________________ Class ______________

2. What do you think would happen if the water in the shallow container was at room temperature? If it were boiling?

____

____

3. Why is it possible to separate the substances in some mixtures by sublimation?

____

____

14.1 THE PROPERTIES OF GASES

Section Review

Objectives
- Explain why gases are easier to compress than solids or liquids are
- Describe the three factors that affect gas pressure

Vocabulary
- compressibility

Part A Completion

Use this completion exercise to check your understanding of the concepts and terms that are introduced in this section. Each blank can be completed with a term, short phrase, or number.

Gases are easily ___1___, or squeezed into a smaller volume

because of the ___2___ between particles in a gas. The four variables

used to describe a gas are pressure, (*P*), ___3___ (*V*), ___4___ (*T*),

and number of ___5___ (*n*).

You can use ___6___ theory to predict and explain how gases

will respond to a change in conditions. Doubling the amount of

gas in a rigid container ___7___ the pressure. You can raise the

pressure exerted by a contained gas by ___8___ its volume. As the

temperature of an enclosed gas decreases, the pressure ___9___.

1. _____

2. _____

3. _____

4. _____

5. _____

6. _____

7. _____

8. _____

9. _____

Part B True-False

Classify each of these statements as always true, AT; sometimes true, ST; or never true, NT.

_____ 10. According to kinetic theory, the volume of the particles in a gas is
small compared to the total volume of the gas.

_____ 11. Air will rush into a sealed container when the container is opened.

_____ 12. Gas flows from a region of lower pressure to a region of higher
pressure.

_____ 13. Adding air to an object will cause the object to inflate.

_____ 14. Four variables are used to describe a gas, *P*, *V*, *T*, and *n*, where
n = number of moles.

Part C Matching

Match each description in Column B to the correct term in Column A.

Column A   **Column B**

_____ **15.** collisions of particles   **a.** used to compress a gas in a cylinder

_____ **16.** 10 times the diameter of   **b.** the SI unit of pressure
                 a particle

_____ **17.** compressibility   **c.** result in pressure exerted by a gas

_____ **18.** piston   **d.** distance between particles in an enclosed gas at
                                                        room temperature

_____ **19.** kilopascals   **e.** a measure of how much the volume of matter
                                                        decreases under pressure

Part D Questions and Problems

Answer the following in the space provided.

20. Explain each assumption of the kinetic theory of gases in your own words.

_____

_____

_____

_____

_____

_____

_____

_____

_____

_____

_____

_____

_____

_____

_____

_____

14.2 THE GAS LAWS

Section Review

Objectives

- Describe the relationship among the temperature, volume, and pressure of a gas
- Use the combined gas law to solve problems

Vocabulary

- Boyle's law
- Charles's law
- Gay-Lussac's law
- combined gas law

Key Equations

- Boyle's law: $P_1 \times V_1 = P_2 \times V_2$

- Charles's law: $\dfrac{V_1}{T_1} = \dfrac{V_2}{T_2}$

- Gay-Lussac's law: $\dfrac{P_1}{T_1} = \dfrac{P_2}{T_2}$

- combined gas law: $\dfrac{P_1 \times V_1}{T_1} = \dfrac{P_2 \times V_2}{T_2}$

Part A Completion

Use this completion exercise to check your understanding of the concepts and terms that are introduced in this section. Each blank can be completed with a term, short phrase, or number.

The pressure and volume of a fixed mass of gas are __1__ related. If one decreases, the other __2__. This relationship is known as __3__ law. The volume of a fixed __4__ of a gas is directly proportional to its __5__ temperature. This relationship is known as __6__ law. __7__ law states that the pressure of a gas is __8__ proportional to the Kelvin temperature if the volume remains constant.

These three separate gas laws can be written as a single expression called the __9__ gas law. It can be used in situations in which only the __10__ of gas is constant.

1. _____

2. _____

3. _____

4. _____

5. _____

6. _____

7. _____

8. _____

9. _____

10. _____

Part B True-False

Classify each of these statements as always true, AT; sometimes true, ST; or never true, NT.

_____ **11.** According to Charles's law, $T_2 = \dfrac{V_1 \times V_2}{T_2}$.

_____ **12.** According to Boyle's law, when the volume of a gas at constant temperature increases, the pressure decreases.

_____ **13.** A balloon with a volume of 60 L at 100 kPa pressure will expand to a volume of 120 L at a pressure of 50 kPa.

_____ **14.** In an inverse relationship, the ratio of two variable quantities is constant.

_____ **15.** When using the combined gas law, pressure must always be in kilopascals but temperature can be in kelvins or degrees Celsius.

_____ **16.** When 20.0 L of O_2 is warmed from $-30.0°C$ to $85.0°C$ at constant pressure, the new volume is 29.5 L.

Part C Matching

Match each description in Column B to the correct term in Column A.

Column A	Column B
_____ **17.** Boyle's law	**a.** The volume of a fixed mass of gas is directly proportional to its Kelvin temperature if the pressure is kept constant
_____ **18.** combined gas law	**b.** $\dfrac{P_1 \times V_1}{T_1} = \dfrac{P_2 \times V_2}{T_2}$
_____ **19.** absolute zero	**c.** For a fixed mass of gas at constant temperature, the volume of gas varies inversely with pressure.
_____ **20.** Charles's law	**d.** The pressure of a gas is directly proportional to the Kelvin temperature if the volume remains constant.
_____ **21.** Gay-Lussac's law	**e.** $-273.15°C$

Part D Questions and Problems

Answer the following in the space provided.

22. A rigid container holds a gas at a pressure of 55 kPa and a temperature of $-100.0°C$. What will the pressure be when the temperature is increased to $200.0°C$?

23. What is the volume of a sample of CO_2 at STP that has a volume of 75.0 mL at $30.0°C$ and 91 kPa?

14.3 IDEAL GASES

Section Review

Objectives
- Compute the value of an unknown using the ideal gas law
- Compare and contrast real and ideal gases

Vocabulary
- ideal gas constant (R)
- ideal gas law

Key Equation
- Ideal gas law: $P \times V = n \times R \times T$ or $PV = nRT$

Part A Completion

Use this completion exercise to check your understanding of the concepts and terms that are introduced in this section. Each blank can be completed with a term, short phrase, or number.

The ideal gas law permits you to solve for the __1__ of a

contained gas when the pressure, volume, and temperature are

known. The ideal gas law is described by the formula __2__

where the variable __3__ represents the number of moles of

gas and the letter R is the __4__ . R is equal to __5__ .

A gas that conforms to the gas laws at all conditions of

temperature and pressure is an __6__ gas. No __7__ gas

behaves ideally at all temperatures and pressures. Deviations

from ideal behavior at high pressures can be explained by the

intermolecular __8__ between particles in a gas and the actual

__9__ of the particles.

1. _____

2. _____

3. _____

4. _____

5. _____

6. _____

7. _____

8. _____

9. _____

Part B True-False

Classify each of these statements as always true, AT; sometimes true, ST; or never true, NT.

_____ **10.** The ideal gas law allows you to solve for the number of moles of a contained gas when pressure, volume, and temperature are known.

_____ **11.** The ratio $(P \times V)/(R \times T)$ is equal to 1 for real gases.

_____ **12.** The behavior of a gas is most likely to approach ideal behavior at a high pressure and a low temperature.

_____ **13.** For an ideal gas, pressure and volume are directly proportional to each other when all other factors remain constant.

_____ **14.** The number of moles of gas is directly proportional to the number of particles.

Part C Matching

Match each description in Column B to the correct term in Column A.

Column A	**Column B**
_____ **15.** ideal gas law	**a.** $8.31 \times \dfrac{\text{L} \cdot \text{kPa}}{\text{K} \cdot \text{mol}}$
_____ **16.** real gas	**b.** a gas that follows the gas laws at all conditions of pressure and temperature
_____ **17.** ideal gas	**c.** a gas that can be liquefied by applying pressure
_____ **18.** ideal gas constant (R)	**d.** $PV = nRT$

Part D Questions and Problems

Answer the following in the space provided.

19. Calculate the number of moles of oxygen in a 12.5-L tank if the pressure is 25,325 kPa and the temperature is 22°C.

20. Calculate the mass of nitrogen dioxide present in a 275-mL container if the pressure is 240.0 kPa and the temperature is 28°C.

14.4 GASES: MIXTURES AND MOVEMENTS

Section Review

Objectives
- Relate the total pressure of a mixture of gases to the partial pressures of the component gases
- Explain how the molar mass of a gas affects the rate at which the gas diffuses and effuses

Vocabulary
- partial pressure
- Dalton's law of partial pressures
- diffusion
- effusion
- Graham's law of effusion

Key Equations
- Dalton's law of partial pressures: $P_{total} = P_1 + P_2 + P_3 + \ldots$

- Graham's law of effusion: $\dfrac{Rate_A}{Rate_B} = \sqrt{\dfrac{molar\ mass_B}{molar\ mass_A}}$

Part A Completion

Use this completion exercise to check your understanding of the concepts and terms that are introduced in this section. Each blank can be completed with a term, short phrase, or number.

According to Dalton's law of partial pressures, at constant volume and temperature, the __1__ pressure exerted by a mixture of gases is equal to the __2__ of the partial pressures of the component gases.

Molecules tend to move to areas of __3__ concentration until the concentration is __4__. This process is called __5__. During __6__ a gas escapes through a tiny __7__ in its container.

The rate of effusion of a gas is __8__ proportional to the square root of the gas's __9__. This relationship is described by __10__ of effusion.

1. _____
2. _____
3. _____
4. _____
5. _____
6. _____
7. _____
8. _____
9. _____
10. _____

Part B True-False

Classify each of these statements as always true, AT; sometimes true, ST; or never true, NT.

_____ **11.** The fraction of the pressure exerted by a gas in a mixture does not change as the temperature, pressure, or volume changes.

_____ **12.** The rate of diffusion of a gas is not influenced by its molar mass.

_____ **13.** Two objects with the same mass move at the same velocity.

_____ **14.** Diffusion is the tendency of molecules to move towards areas of lower concentration until the concentration is uniform throughout.

Part C Matching

Match each description in Column B to the correct term in Column A.

Column A	Column B
_____ **15.** partial pressure	**a.** the pressure exerted by each gas in a gaseous mixture
_____ **16.** effusion	**b.** the escape of a gas through a tiny hole in its container
_____ **17.** Graham's law of effusion	**c.** The rate of effusion of a gas is inversely proportional to the square root of its formula mass.

Part D Questions and Problems

Answer the following in the space provided.

18. Explain, using kinetic theory, why molecules of low molar diffuse more rapidly than molecules with a higher molar mass.

_____

_____

_____

_____

_____

_____

_____

THE BEHAVIOR OF GASES

14

Practice Problems

In your notebook, solve the following problems.

SECTION 14.1 THE PROPERTIES OF GASES

1. Using kinetic theory, explain why a tire is more likely to blow out during a trip in the summer than during one in the winter.

2. Use kinetic theory to explain why on a cold autumn morning a camper's air mattress may appear to be somewhat flatter than when it was blown up the afternoon before. Assume no leaks.

SECTION 14.2 THE GAS LAWS

1. The volume of a gas at 155.0 kPa changes from 22.0 L to 10.0 L. What is the new pressure if the temperature remains constant?

2. Is it possible for a balloon with an initial pressure of 200.0 kPa to naturally expand to four times its initial volume when the temperature remains constant and atmospheric pressure is 101.3 kPa?

3. Exactly 10.0 L of O_2 at $-25°C$ is heated to $100.0°C$. What is the new volume if the pressure is kept constant?

4. A gas at a pressure of 501 kPa and a temperature of 25°C occupies a volume of 5.2 L. When the gas is heated to 100.0°C the volume increases to 7.00 L. What is the new pressure?

5. A sample of O_2 with an initial temperature of 50.0°C and a volume of 105 L is cooled to $-25°C$. The new pressure is 105.4 kPa and the new volume is 55.0 L. What was the initial pressure of the sample?

SECTION 14.3 IDEAL GASES

1. A sample of argon gas is at a pressure of 1.24×10^4 kPa and a temperature of 24°C in a rigid 25-L tank. How many moles of argon does this tank contain?

2. A 35.0-L tank contains 7.00 mol of compressed air. If the pressure inside the tank is 500.0 kPa, what is the temperature of the compressed gas?

3. How many grams of helium does a 25.0-L balloon contain at 102.0 kPa and 24°C?

4. Calculate the volume that 2.25 mol of $O_2(g)$ will occupy at STP.

5. A sample of water vapor occupies a volume of 10.5 L at 200°C and 100.0 kPa. What volume will the water vapor occupy when it is cooled to 27°C if the pressure remains constant?

6. What is the volume occupied by 0.355 mole of nitrogen gas at STP?

7. What is the volume of a container that holds 25.0 g of carbon dioxide gas at STP?

SECTION 14.4 GASES: MIXTURES AND MOVEMENTS

1. A gaseous mixture consisting of nitrogen, argon, and oxygen is in a 3.5-L vessel at 25°C. Determine the number of moles of oxygen if the total pressure is 98.5 kPa and the partial pressures of nitrogen and argon are 22.0 kPa and 50.0 kPa, respectively.

2. Compare the effusion rates of O_2 (molar mass, 32.0 g/mol) and N_2 (molar mass, 28.0 g/mol).

INTERPRETING GRAPHICS

14

Use with Section 14.3

Determination of the Molar Mass of a Volatile Liquid

	Trial 1	Trial 2
Mass of flask + stopper	83.32 g	83.39 g
Mass of flask + stopper + condensed vapor	83.73 g	83.82 g
Temperature of boiling water	99.0°C	99.0°C
Barometric Pressure	773.5 mm Hg	812.0 mm Hg

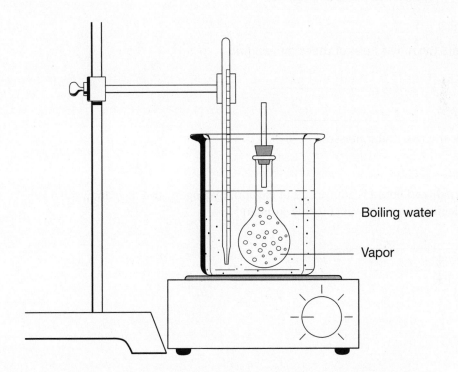

You can use the ideal gas law to determine the molar mass of a liquid. Using the setup shown, a student added a small volume of an unknown liquid to a round-bottom flask, which can hold 267 mL of water. The flask was then submerged in a hot-water bath to completely vaporize all of the liquid. As the vapor forms, any excess vapor escapes through the top of the flask. Next, the flask was cooled to condense the vapor in the flask. Then the mass of the flask and condensed vapor was determined. Use the data in the table to answer the following questions.

1. What is the mass of the condensed vapor?

 a. Trial 1 _____

 b. Trial 2 _____

Name ______________________ Date ________________ Class ________________

2. What is the volume of the vapor in each trial?

____

3. What is the temperature of the vapor in kelvins?

a. Trial 1 ____________________

b. Trial 2 ____________________

4. What is the pressure of the vapor in kPa?

a. Trial 1 ____________________

b. Trial 2 ____________________

5. Calculate the number of moles of condensed vapor.

a. Trial 1 ____________________

b. Trial 2 ____________________

6. Calculate the molar mass of the volatile liquid.

a. Trial 1 ____________________

b. Trial 2 ____________________

7. Average the two molar masses.

____

8. If the unknown liquid is composed of carbon, hydrogen, and oxygen, write one possible molecular formula for this substance.

____

THE BEHAVIOR OF GASES

Vocabulary Review

Match the correct vocabulary term to each numbered statement. Write the letter of the correct term on the line.

Column A

_____ **1.** At constant volume and temperature, the total pressure exerted by a mixture of gases is equal to the sum of the partial pressures of the component gases.

_____ **2.** The volume of a fixed mass of gas is directly proportional to its Kelvin temperature if the pressure is kept constant.

_____ **3.** The rate of effusion of a gas is inversely proportional to the square root of its molar mass.

_____ **4.** the contribution each gas in a mixture makes to the total pressure of that mixture

_____ **5.** a measure of how much the volume of matter decreases under pressure

_____ **6.** For a given mass of gas at constant temperature, the volume of the gas varies inversely with pressure.

_____ **7.** the tendency of molecules to move toward areas of lower concentration until the concentration is uniform throughout

_____ **8.** $\dfrac{P_1 \times V_1}{T_1} = \dfrac{P_2 \times V_2}{T_2}$

_____ **9.** the escape of a gas through a tiny hole in a container of gas

_____ **10.** 8.31 (L·kPa)/(K·mol)

Column B

a. combined gas law

b. ideal gas constant (R)

c. diffusion

d. compressibility

e. Boyle's law

f. partial pressure

g. Dalton's law of partial pressures

h. effusion

i. Charles's law

j. Graham's law of effusion

14 THE BEHAVIOR OF GASES

Chapter Quiz

Fill in the word(s) that will make each statement true.

1. Adding more gas to a closed container increases the number of __1__ of particles with the walls of the container.

    1. _____ *14.1*

2. Doubling the number of particles of a gas in a container __2__ the pressure, assuming that the temperature is constant.

    2. _____ *14.1*

3. According to kinetic theory, the particles of a gas have a volume that is __3__ compared to the total volume of the gas.

    3. _____ *14.1*

4. One difference between real gases and ideal gases is that __4__ gases may be liquefied when they are cooled and pressure is applied to them.

    4. _____ *14.3*

5. The tendency of a gas to move toward areas of lower concentrations until the concentration is uniform throughout is __5__ .

    5. _____ *14.4*

Solve the following problems in the space provided.

6. A rigid container of O_2 has a pressure of 388 kPa at a temperature of 713 K. What is the pressure at 273 K?

    14.2

7. A flexible gas storage container has a volume of 3.5×10^5 m^3 when the temperature is 27°C and the pressure is 115 kPa. What is the new volume of the container if the temperature drops to −10°C and the pressure drops to 99 kPa?

    14.2

8. A mixture of gases at a total pressure of 145.0 kPa contains N_2, CO_2, and O_2. The partial pressure of the N_2 is 28.5 kPa, and the partial pressure of the CO_2 is 76.0 kPa. What is the partial pressure of the O_2?

    14.4

THE BEHAVIOR OF GASES

14

Chapter Test A

A. Matching

Match each description in Column B with the correct term in Column A. Write the letter of the correct description on the line.

Column A

Column B

_____ **1.** ideal gas constant (*R*)

a. The volume of a fixed mass of gas is directly proportional to the Kelvin temperature if the volume is kept constant.

_____ **2.** Boyle's law

b. At constant volume and temperature, the total pressure exerted by a mixture of gases is equal to the sum of the partial pressures of the component gases.

_____ **3.** Dalton's law of partial pressures

c. $8.31 \dfrac{L \cdot kPa}{K \cdot mol}$

_____ **4.** ideal gas law

d. the contribution each gas in a mixture makes to the total pressure

_____ **5.** combined gas law

e. A gas tends to move to an area of lower concentration until the concentration is uniform throughout.

_____ **6.** Charles's law

f. $\dfrac{P_1 \times V_1}{T_1} = \dfrac{P_2 \times V_2}{T_2}$

_____ **7.** diffusion

g. $P \times V = n \times R \times T$

_____ **8.** partial pressure

h. For a given mass of gas at constant temperature, the volume of gas varies inversely with the pressure.

B. Multiple Choice

Choose the best answer and write its letter on the line.

_____ **9.** As the temperature of a fixed volume of gas increases, the pressure will
  a. vary inversely.   **c.** be unchanged.
  b. decrease.   **d.** increase.

_____ **10.** A breathing mixture used by deep-sea divers contains helium, oxygen, and carbon dioxide. What is the partial pressure of oxygen at 101.3 kPa total pressure if $P_{He} = 84.0$ kPa and $P_{CO_2} = 0.10$ kPa?
  a. 10.3 kPa   **c.** 34.4 kPa
  b. 17.2 kPa   **d.** 185.4 kPa

_____ 11. Increasing the volume of a given amount of gas at constant
temperature causes the pressure to decrease because
  a. the molecules are striking a larger area with the same force.
  b. there are fewer molecules.
  c. the molecules are moving more slowly.
  d. there are more molecules.

_____ 12. When a container is filled with 3.00 mol of H_2, 2.00 mol of O_2, and
1.00 mol of N_2, the pressure in the container is 465 kPa. The partial
pressure of O_2 is
  a. 78 kPa.   c. 155 kPa.
  b. 116 kPa.   d. 212 kPa.

_____ 13. A box with a volume of 22.4 L contains 1.0 mol of nitrogen and 2.0 mol
of hydrogen at 0°C. Which of the following statements is true?
  a. The total pressure in the box is 202.6 kPa.
  b. The partial pressure of N_2 and H_2 are equal.
  c. The total pressure is 101.3 kPa.
  d. The partial pressure of N_2 is 101.3 kPa.

_____ 14. The volume of a gas is doubled while the temperature is held constant.
The pressure of the gas
  a. remains unchanged.   c. is doubled.
  b. is reduced by one half.   d. depends on the kind of gas.

_____ 15. As the temperature of the gas in a balloon decreases
  a. the volume increases.
  b. the pressure increases.
  c. the average kinetic energy of the gas particles decreases.
  d. All of the above are true.

_____ 16. The volume of a gas is increased from 0.5 L to 4.0 L while the
temperature is held constant. The pressure of the gas
  a. increases by a factor of four.   c. increases by a factor of eight.
  b. decreases by a factor of eight. d. increases by a factor of two.

_____ 17. A gas occupies 40.0 mL at −123°C. What volume does it occupy at
27°C, assuming pressure is constant?
  a. 182 mL   c. 80.0 mL
  b. 8.80 mL   d. 20.0 mL

_____ 18. A gas occupies a volume of 0.2 L at 25 kPa. What volume will the gas
occupy at 2.5 kPa?
  a. 4 L   c. 2 L
  b. 20 L   d. 0.02 L

_____ 19. Which of these changes would *not* cause an increase in the pressure of
a contained gas?
  a. Another gas is added to the container.
  b. Additional amounts of the same gas are added to the container.
  c. The temperature is increased.
  d. The gas is moved to a larger container.

_____ **20.** If a balloon containing 1000 L of gas at 50°C and 101.3 kPa rises to an altitude where the pressure is 27.5 kPa and the temperature is 10°C, its volume there is

a. $1000 \text{ L} \times \dfrac{27.5 \text{ kPa}}{101.3 \text{ kPa}}$

c. $1000 \text{ L} \times \dfrac{27.5 \text{ kPa}}{101.3 \text{ kPa}} \times \dfrac{323 \text{ K}}{283 \text{ K}}$

b. $1000 \text{ L} \times \dfrac{283 \text{ K}}{323 \text{ K}} \times \dfrac{101.3 \text{ kPa}}{27.5 \text{ kPa}}$

d. $1000 \text{ L} \times \dfrac{50°C}{10°C} \times \dfrac{101.3 \text{ kPa}}{27.5 \text{ kPa}}$

C. Problems

Solve the following problems in the space provided. Show your work.

21. A gas has a pressure of 655 kPa at 227°C. What will its pressure be at 27°C if the volume does not change?

22. A 10-g mass of krypton occupies 15.0 L at a pressure of 156 kPa. Find the volume of the krypton when the pressure is increased to 215 kPa at the same temperature.

23. A gas occupies a volume of 180 mL at 35.0°C and 95.9 kPa. What is the volume of the gas at conditions of STP?

24. A gas has a volume of 550 mL at a temperature of −55.0°C. What volume will the gas occupy at 30.0°C, assuming constant pressure?

D. Essay

Write a short essay for the following.

25. What are some of the differences between a real gas and an ideal gas?

_____

_____

_____

_____

_____

_____

_____

_____

_____

_____

E. True-False

Classify each of these statements as always true, AT; sometimes true, ST; or never true, NT.

_____ **26.** Two small bicycle pumps are filled with different gases; one contains He, the other Ar. Using the same pressure, it will take longer to force out the He than the Ar.

_____ **27.** Theoretically, an ideal gas will contract in volume with increasing pressure and reduced temperature until absolute zero is reached.

_____ **28.** To obtain a value for the number of moles using the ideal gas law, one uses the conditions of STP.

_____ **29.** The kinetic energy of a moving body is directly proportional to the square of its velocity.

F. Additional Problems

Solve the following problems in the space provided. Show your work.

30. The gaseous product of a reaction is collected in a 25.0-L container at 27°C. The pressure in the container is 216 kPa, and the gas has a mass of 96.0 g. What is the molar mass of the gas?

31. The separation of uranium-235 from uranium-238 has been carried out using gaseous diffusion. Calculate the relative rates of diffusion of gaseous UF_6 containing these isotopes.

Molar mass of UF_6 containing uranium-235 = 349.0 amu.
Molar mass of UF_6 containing uranium-238 = 352.0 amu.

14 THE BEHAVIOR OF GASES

Chapter Test B

A. Matching

Match each term in Column B with the correct description in Column A. Write the letter of the correct term on the line.

Column A   **Column B**

_____ 1. At constant volume and temperature, the total   **a.** combined gas law
pressure exerted by a mixture of gases is equal to the
sum of the partial pressures of the component gases.

_____ 2. The volume of a fixed mass of gas is directly   **b.** ideal gas constant (R)
proportional to its Kelvin temperature if the pressure
is kept constant.

_____ 3. The rate of effusion of a gas is inversely proportional   **c.** diffusion
to the square root of its molar mass.

_____ 4. the contribution each gas in a mixture makes to the   **d.** compressibility
total pressure of that mixture

_____ 5. a measure of how much the volume of matter   **e.** Boyle's law
decreases under pressure

_____ 6. For a given mass of gas at constant temperature, the   **f.** partial pressure
volume of the gas varies inversely with pressure.

_____ 7. the tendency of particles to move toward areas of   **g.** Dalton's law of partial
lower concentration until the concentration is   pressures
uniform throughout

_____ 8. $\dfrac{P_1 \times V_1}{T_1} = \dfrac{P_2 \times V_2}{T_2}$ **h.** effusion

_____ 9. the escape of a gas through a tiny hole in a container   **i.** Charles's law
of gas

_____ 10. 8.31 (L·kPa)/(K·mol)   **j.** Graham's law of effusion

B. Multiple Choice

Choose the best answer and write its letter on the line.

_____ 11. Reducing the volume of a contained gas by one third, while holding
temperature constant, causes pressure to
   a. be decreased by two thirds.
   b. be increased by two thirds.
   c. be decreased by one third.
   d. be increased by one third.

Name _____ Date _____ Class _____

_____ 12. Which of the following would double the pressure on a contained gas at constant temperature?
   a. doubling the volume of the container
   b. halving the number of particles in the container
   c. doubling the number of particles in the container
   d. none of the above

_____ 13. A gas occupies a volume of 2.50 L at a pressure of 350.0 kPa. If the temperature remains constant, what volume would the gas occupy at 1750 kPa?
   a. 5.00 L
   b. 0.500 L
   c. 12.5 L
   d. 1.40×10^2 L

_____ 14. If the temperature of a gas in a closed container increases
   a. the pressure of the gas decreases.
   b. the average kinetic energy of the molecules decreases.
   c. the molecules collide with the walls of the container less frequently.
   d. the pressure of the gas increases.

_____ 15. Absolute zero is
   a. −273.15°C.
   b. the lowest possible temperature.
   c. the temperature at which the average kinetic energy of particles would theoretically be zero.
   d. all of the above

_____ 16. The graph of several pressure-volume readings on a contained gas at constant temperature would be
   a. a straight line.
   b. a curved line.
   c. a horizontal line.
   d. a vertical line.

_____ 17. At constant pressure, the volume of a fixed mass of gas and its Kelvin temperature are said to be
   a. directly related.
   b. inversely related.
   c. unrelated.
   d. constant.

_____ 18. The temperature of 6.24 L of a gas is increased from 25.0°C to 55.0°C at constant pressure. The new volume of the gas is
   a. 13.7 L.
   b. 5.67 L.
   c. 6.87 L.
   d. 2.84 L.

_____ 19. A temperature of −25°C is equivalent to:
   a. 248 K.
   b. 25 K.
   c. −25 K.
   d. 298 K.

_____ 20. A sample of chlorine gas has a pressure of 7.25 kPa at 20.0°C. What will its pressure be at 60.0°C if its volume remains constant?
   a. 2.42 kPa
   b. 8.24 kPa
   c. 21.8 kPa
   d. 6.38 kPa

_____ **21.** If a sample of oxygen occupies a volume of 2.15 L at a pressure of 58.0 kPa and a temperature of 25°C, what volume would this sample occupy at 101.3 kPa and 0°C?

    a. 1.35 L   **c.** 4.10 L
    b. 1.13 L   **d.** 3.44 L

_____ **22.** The volume (in L) that would be occupied by 5.00 mol of O_2 at STP is

    a. 0.411 L.   **c.** 41.6 L.
    b. 22.4 L.   **d.** 112 L.

_____ **23.** How many moles of H_2 would be contained in 4.0 L of the gas at 202.6 kPa and 127°C?

    a. 89.6 mol   **c.** 0.24 mol
    b. 6.38 mol   **d.** 0.77 mol

_____ **24.** A sample of H_2 is collected over water such that the combined hydrogen–water vapor sample is held at a pressure of 1 standard atmosphere. What is the partial pressure of the H_2 if that of the water vapor is 2.5 kPa?

    a. 103.8 kPa   **c.** 2.5 kPa
    b. 98.8 kPa   **d.** 101.3 kPa

_____ **25.** What is the mass, in grams, of 0.125 L of CO_2 at STP?

    a. 0.246 g   **c.** 181 g
    b. 2.80 g   **d.** 4.11 g

_____ **26.** Among the gases listed, which would have the fastest rate of effusion?

    a. NH_3 **c.** SO_2
    b. CH_4 **d.** NO_2

C. Problems

Solve the following problems in the space provided. Show your work.

27. A sample of hydrogen occupies a volume of 1.20 L at a pressure of 425 kPa. If the temperature of the gas is kept constant, what would the new volume of the gas be at 615 kPa?

28. A sample of nitrogen occupies a volume of 0.650 L at 20.0°C. What volume would the gas occupy at 40.0°C if the pressure remains constant?

29. The temperature of a sample of helium at 85.0 kPa is 37°C. If the volume of the gas remains constant, at what temperature (in °C) would the pressure of the gas be at 98.0 kPa?

30. If a sample of oxygen gas occupies a volume of 3.50 L at 57°C and 80.0 kPa, what volume would the gas occupy at STP?

31. How many grams of CO_2 would be contained in 8.0 L at 152 kPa and 27°C?

D. Essay

Write a short essay for the following.

32. If all gases behaved as ideal gases under all conditions of temperature and pressure, no solid or liquid forms of these substances could exist. Explain.

_____

_____

_____

_____

_____

_____

E. True-False

Classify each of these statements as always true, AT; sometimes true, ST; or never true, NT.

_____ **33.** Doubling the number of particles of gas in an inflated tire doubles the pressure of the gas in the tire.

_____ **34.** Halving the Kelvin temperature of a gas in a rigid container decreases the gas pressure by one half.

_____ **35.** The graph of a relationship between variables that is directly proportional is a straight line.

_____ **36.** At constant volume, if the Kelvin temperature of a gas is doubled, the pressure of the gas is halved.

F. Additional Problems

Solve the following problems in the space provided. Show your work.

37. A sample of oxygen gas occupies a volume of 1.25 L at −23°C. If the pressure remains constant, what is the new Celsius temperature of the gas if its volume decreases to 0.925 L?

38. How many moles of N_2 would be contained in a 10.0-L balloon at 50.6 kPa and −73°C?

QUICK LAB: Carbon Dioxide from Antacid Tablets

Laboratory Recordsheet   Use with Section 14.3

PURPOSE

To measure the amount of carbon dioxide gas given off when antacid tablets dissolve in water.

MATERIALS

- 6 effervescent antacid tablets
- 3 rubber balloons (spherical)
- plastic medicine dropper
- water
- clock or watch
- metric tape measure
- graph paper

PROCEDURE

1. Break six antacid tablets into small pieces. Keep the pieces from each tablet in a separate pile. Put the pieces from one tablet into the first balloon. Put the pieces from two tablets into a second balloon. Put the pieces from three tablets into a third balloon. **CAUTION:** *If you are allergic to latex, do not handle the balloons.*

2. After you use the medicine dropper to squirt about 5 mL of cold water into each balloon, immediately tie off each balloon.

3. Shake the balloons to mix the contents. Allow the contents to warm to room temperature.

4. Carefully measure and record the circumference of each balloon several times during the next 20 minutes.

5. Use the maximum circumference of each balloon to calculate the volume of each balloon. Assume that the balloons are spherical. (*Hint:* Volume of a sphere $= \dfrac{4\pi r^3}{3}$ and $r = $ circumference$/2\pi$)

ANALYSES AND CONCLUSIONS

1. Make a graph of balloon volume versus number of tablets. Use your graph to describe the relationship between the number of tablets used and the volume of the balloon.

   _____

2. Assume that the balloon is filled with carbon dioxide gas at 20°C and standard pressure. Calculate the mass and the number of moles of CO_2 in each balloon at maximum inflation.

3. If a typical antacid tablet contains 2.0 g of sodium hydrogen carbonate, how many moles of CO_2 should one tablet yield? Compare this theoretical value with your results.

SMALL-SCALE LAB: Diffusion

Laboratory Recordsheet   Use with Section 14.4

SAFETY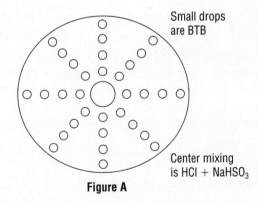

Wear safety glasses and follow the standard safety procedures.

PURPOSE

To infer diffusion of a gas by observing color changes during chemical reactions.

MATERIALS

- clear plastic cup or Petri dish
- reaction surface
- dropper bottles containing bromthymol blue, hydrochloric acid, and sodium hydrogen sulfite
- ruler
- cotton swab
- NaOH, NH_4Cl, KI, and $NaNO_2$ (optional)

PROCEDURE

1. Use the plastic cup or Petri dish to draw the large circle shown in Figure A on a sheet of paper.

2. Place a reaction surface over the grid and add small drops of bromthymol blue (BTB) in the pattern shown by the small circles. Make sure the drops do not touch one another.

3. Mix one drop of each of hydrochloric acid (HCl) and sodium hydrogen sulfite ($NaHSO_3$) in the center of the pattern.

4. Place the cup or Petri dish over the grid and observe what happens.

5. If you plan to do You're The Chemist Activity 1, don't dispose of your materials yet.

Small drops are BTB

Center mixing is HCl + NaHSO₃

Figure A

ANALYSES AND CONCLUSIONS

Using your experimental data, record the answers to the following questions below your data table.

1. Describe in detail the changes you observed in the drops of BTB over time. Draw pictures to illustrate the changes.

2. Draw a series of pictures showing how one of the BTB drops might look over time if you could view the drop from the side.

3. The BTB changed even though you added nothing to it. If the mixture in the center circle produced a gas, would this explain the change in the drops of BTB? Use kinetic theory to explain your answer.

   _____

   _____

   _____

   _____

   _____

4. Translate the following word equation into a balanced chemical equation: Sodium hydrogen sulfite reacts with hydrochloric acid to produce sulfur dioxide gas, water, and sodium chloride.

   _____

   _____

YOU'RE THE CHEMIST

Use the space below to write your observations to the small-scale activities in the *You're the Chemist* section.

Name _____ Date _____ Class _____

15.1 WATER AND ITS PROPERTIES

Section Review

Objectives
- Explain the high surface tension and low vapor pressure of water in terms of the structure of the water molecule and hydrogen bonding
- Describe the structure of ice

Vocabulary
- surface tension
- surfactant

Part A Completion

Use this completion exercise to check your understanding of the concepts and terms that are introduced in this section. Each blank can be completed with a term, short phrase, or number.

Each O—H bond in a water molecule is highly ___1___. Oxygen

acquires a partial ___2___ charge, while hydrogen acquires a

partial ___3___ charge. Because the H—O—H bond angle is 105°,

the water molecule as a whole is ___4___.

    Water molecules are attracted to each other by intermolecular

___5___ bonds. This bonding accounts for many properties

of water, such as its ___6___ vapor pressure and ___7___

boiling point. Hydrogen bonding is also responsible for the high

___8___ tension of water. Liquids tend to minimize their surface

area and form ___9___ droplets because of their surface tension.

The surface tension of water can be reduced by adding a ___10___.

    ___11___ floats in liquid water. This is because it is less

___12___ than water. Ice has a rigid open structure, which is also

due to ___13___.

1. _____

2. _____

3. _____

4. _____

5. _____

6. _____

7. _____

8. _____

9. _____

10. _____

11. _____

12. _____

13. _____

Part B True-False

Classify each of these statements as always true, AT; sometimes true, ST; or never true, NT.

_____ 14. Hydrogen bonding is responsible for the polar nature of the water molecule.

_____ 15. The water molecule is a straight molecule.

_____ 16. Detergents lower the surface tension of water by interfering with the formation of hydrogen bonds.

_____ 17. Ice is more dense than water.

_____ 18. Water becomes more dense as it is cooled.

Part C Matching

Match each description in Column B to the correct term in Column A.

Column A	**Column B**
_____ 19. surface tension	**a.** inward force that tends to minimize the surface area of a liquid
_____ 20. surfactant	**b.** intermolecular attraction between a hydrogen atom and a highly electronegative atom such as oxygen, on an adjacent molecule
_____ 21. hydrogen bond	**c.** a wetting agent

Part D Question

Answer the following in the space provided.

22. State whether each of the following properties of water is higher or lower than compounds of similar size and molecular mass.

   a. vapor pressure

   _____

   b. surface tension

   _____

15.2 HOMOGENEOUS AQUEOUS SYSTEMS

Section Review

Objectives

• Distinguish between a solvent and a solute
• Describe what happens in the solution process
• Explain why all ionic compounds are electrolytes
• Demonstrate how to write the formula for a hydrate

Vocabulary

• aqueous solution
• solvent
• solute

• solvation
• electrolyte
• nonelectrolyte

• strong electrolyte
• weak electrolyte
• hydrate

Key Equation

• Percent $H_2O = \dfrac{\text{mass of water}}{\text{mass of hydrate}} \times 100\%$

Part A Completion

Use this completion exercise to check your understanding of the concepts and terms that are introduced in this section. Each blank can be completed with a term, short phrase, or number.

Water is a polar liquid and an excellent __1__ for many

substances. Aqueous solutions are __2__ mixtures of ions or

molecules in water. The solubility of a solute depends on solute-

solvent interactions. A good rule to remember is __3__.

Substances that dissolve as ions are known as __4__. A

solute that is completely ionized in solution is a __5__

electrolyte. A weak electrolyte is only __6__ ionized. A solution

of an electrolyte will __7__ an electric current, whereas a

solution of a __8__ is nonconducting.

Many crystals are __9__; they contain water of hydration.

In the process called __10__, the water of hydration is lost from a

hydrate that is exposed to air.

1. _____
2. _____
3. _____
4. _____
5. _____
6. _____
7. _____
8. _____
9. _____
10. _____

Part B True-False

Classify each of these statements as always true, AT; sometimes true, ST; or never true, NT.

_____ **11.** Carbon tetrafluoride is a nonelectrolyte.

_____ **12.** Hydrates are crystals that contain a fixed quantity of water within their structure.

_____ **13.** Covalent solutes are very soluble in water.

_____ **14.** Solutions are always homogeneous.

Part C Matching

Match each description in Column B to the correct term in Column A.

Column A	Column B
_____ **15.** aqueous solutions	**a.** the dissolved particles in a solution
_____ **16.** solute	**b.** compounds that conduct electric current in aqueous solution
_____ **17.** solvation	**c.** compounds able to remove moisture from air
_____ **18.** electrolyte	**d.** water samples containing dissolved substances
_____ **19.** nonelectrolytes	**e.** drying agents
_____ **20.** hydrate	**f.** compounds that do not conduct electric current in aqueous solution
_____ **21.** hygroscopic	**g.** a compound that contains water of hydration
_____ **22.** dessicants	**h.** process that occurs when a solute dissolves

Part D Questions and Problems

Answer the following questions or solve the following problems in the space provided. Show your work.

23. Calculate the percent by mass of water in Glauber's salt ($Na_2SO_4 \cdot 10H_2O$).

24. Which of the following substances dissolves to a significant extent in water?

   a. C_6H_6 **c.** Na_2SO_4

   b. NaCl   **d.** N_2

Name _____ Date _____ Class _____

15.3 HETEROGENEOUS AQUEOUS SYSTEMS

Section Review

Objectives
- Distinguish between a suspension and a solution
- Identify the distinguishing characteristic of a colloid

Vocabulary
- suspension
- colloid
- Tyndall effect
- Brownian motion
- emulsion

Part A Completion

Use this completion exercise to check your understanding of the concepts and terms that are introduced in this section. Each blank can be completed with a term, short phrase, or number.

The component particles of a suspension are much __1__ than those of a solution. Gravity or __2__ will separate the suspended particles from a suspension. The particles in a colloid generally do not settle out under gravity, and they pass through ordinary filter paper unchanged. __3__ are good at scattering light, as are suspensions, as evidenced by the __4__. Colloidal dispersions also exhibit __5__ motion. The particles in solutions are small __6__ or __7__. They cannot be trapped by filter paper, nor do they exhibit the Tyndall effect.

__8__ are colloidal dispersions of liquids in liquids.

Emulsifying agents maintain the __9__ of an emulsion and allow the formation of __10__ between liquids that do not ordinarily mix.

1. _____

2. _____

3. _____

4. _____

5. _____

6. _____

7. _____

8. _____

9. _____

10. _____

Part B True-False

Classify each of these statements as always true, AT; sometimes true, ST; or never true, NT.

_____ 11. The scattering of light by colloidal particles is called Brownian motion.

_____ 12. Heterogeneous aqueous systems can be separated by filtration.

_____ **13.** Emulsifying agents are essential to forming and maintaining emulsions.

_____ **14.** Colloids are dispersions of liquids in liquids.

_____ **15.** The random motion of particles is known as the Tyndall effect.

Part C Matching

Match each description in Column B to the correct term in Column A.

Column A	**Column B**
_____ **16.** suspensions	**a.** chaotic movement of colloidal particles
_____ **17.** colloids	**b.** heterogeneous mixtures containing particles intermediate in size between those of suspensions and solutions
_____ **18.** Tyndall effect	**c.** substance necessary to the formation and stability of an emulsion
_____ **19.** Brownian motion	**d.** scattering of visible light by colloidal particles
_____ **20.** emulsions	**e.** mixtures from which particles settle on standing
_____ **21.** emulsifying agent	**f.** dispersions of liquids in liquids

Part D Questions and Problems

Answer the following questions in the space provided.

22. What is the typical particle size in a colloidal dispersion?

    a. greater than 1000 nm

    b. 1 nm to 1000 nm

    c. less than 1 nm

    d. There are no particles in a colloidal dispersion.

23. What is the typical particle size in a suspension?

    a. greater than 1000 nm

    b. 1 nm to 1000 nm

    c. less than 1 nm

    d. There are no particles in a suspension.

15

WATER AND AQUEOUS SYSTEMS

Practice Problems

In your notebook, answer the following questions or solve the following problems.

SECTION 15.1 WATER AND ITS PROPERTIES

1. In your own words, explain hydrogen bonds.

2. Draw a diagram of the hydrogen bonding between three water molecules.

3. Explain why the density of ice at 0°C is less than the density of liquid water at 0°C.

SECTION 15.2 HOMOGENEOUS AQUEOUS SOLUTIONS

1. Identify the solute and solvent in a dilute aqueous solution of potassium chloride.

2. Write an equation showing how ammonia is ionized when it dissolves in water.

3. Give an example of a polar molecular compound that dissolves in water and is a nonelectrolyte.

4. Explain the meaning of the term *hygroscopic*.

5. Which of the following compounds are soluble in water? Which are insoluble?

    a. $CaCl_2$

    b. N_2

    c. HBr

    d. $NH_4C_2H_3O_2$

6. Write equations to show how the following compounds dissociate in water.

    a. NH_4NO_3

    b. KOH

7. Write the formulas for the following hydrates.

    a. Calcium sulfate dihydrate

    b. Cobalt(II) chloride hexahydrate

8. Find the percent by mass of water in $NiCl_2 \cdot 6H_2O$.

SECTION 15.3 HETEROGENEOUS AQUEOUS SYSTEMS

1. Distinguish colloids and suspensions from solutions by discussing their properties.

2. What is Brownian motion?

3. Classify each of the following mixtures as a colloid, suspension, or solution.

   a. fog

   b. milk

   c. sodium chloride dissolved in water

   d. cornstarch in water

   e. potting soil shaken with water

   f. soap suds

   g. a mixture of sucrose and water

Name _____ Date _____ Class _____

15 WATER AND AQUEOUS SYSTEMS

Vocabulary Review

Each clue describes a vocabulary term. Read the clues and write the letters of each term on the lines.

1. Clue: hygroscopic substances used as drying agents.

   __ __ __ __ __ ◯ ◯ __ ◯ __

2. Clue: a relatively strong intermolecular force responsible for water's high surface tension.

   __ __ __ __ __ __ ◯ __   __ ◯ __ __ __ __ __

3. Clue: a mixture from which particles settle out upon standing.

   __ __ __ ◯ __ __ __ __ __ __

4. Clue: a solution in which the solvent is water.

   __ ◯ ◯ ◯ __ __   __ __ ◯ __ ◯ __ __

5. Clue: the dissolving medium in a solution.

   __ __ __ ◯ __ __ __

6. Clue: a wetting agent that interferes with hydrogen bonding in water.

   __ __ ◯ __ ◯ __ __ __ __ __

7. Clue: a substance that completely dissociates into its ions in solution.

   __ __ ◯ __ __ __ ◯ __ __ __ __ __ __ __ __

8. Clue: the water loosely held in a crystal structure.

   ◯ ◯ __ __ __ __ __ __ __ ◯ __ __ __ ◯ __ __

9. Clue: the chaotic movement of particles in a solution.

   __ ◯ __ ◯ __ __ __ __   __ __ ◯ ◯ __ __

Write the letters found inside the circles on the lines below. Then unscramble them to find the three states of a substance essential for life on Earth.

Scrambled Letters:

__ __ __ __ __ __ __ __ __ __ __ __ __

__ __ __ __ __ __ __ __ __ __ __

Solution:

1. __ __ __ __ __   __ __ __ __ __

2. __ __ __

3. __ __ __ __ __ __   __ __ __ __ __ __

15 WATER AND AQUEOUS SYSTEMS

Chapter Quiz

Choose the best answer and write its letter on the line.

_____ 1. The attractions between adjacent water molecules are called: 15.1
   a. hydrogen bonds.   c. nonpolar covalent bonds.
   b. ionic bonds.   d. polar covalent bonds.

_____ 2. Surface tension is: 15.1
   a. the inward force that tends to minimize the surface area of a liquid.
   b. increased by detergents.
   c. decreased by hydrogen bonding.
   d. all of the above

_____ 3. Which of the following is an example of a strong electrolyte? 15.2
   a. acetic acid   c. NaCl
   b. sucrose   d. H_2O

_____ 4. Which of the following mixtures do *not* exhibit the Tyndall effect? 15.3
   a. colloids   c. emulsions
   b. solutions   d. suspensions

Fill in the word(s) that will make each statement true.

5. In a solution, the dissolved particles are known as the _____. 15.2

6. In a solution, the dissolving medium is called the _____. 15.2

7. Water samples containing dissolved substances are called _____. 15.2

8. The expression "_____" sums up the dissolving of polar 15.2
   or nonpolar solvents and solutes.

15 WATER AND AQUEOUS SYSTEMS

Chapter Test A

A. Completion

Fill in the word(s) that will make each statement true.

1. A compound that does not conduct an electric current in aqueous solution or when molten is called a(n) ___1___.

   1. _____

2. A substance is said to be ___2___ when it is able to remove sufficient water from the air to dissolve completely and form a solution.

   2. _____

3. A mixture from which some of the particles will settle slowly upon standing is a(n) ___3___.

   3. _____

4. The dissolving medium of a solution is called the ___4___.

   4. _____

5. A hydrate will ___5___ if its vapor pressure is higher than the vapor pressure of the water vapor in the air.

   5. _____

6. The chaotic movements of colloidal particles are known as ___6___.

   6. _____

7. ___7___ are colloidal dispersions of liquids in liquids.

   7. _____

8. A(n) ___8___ contains water molecules that form part of its crystal structure.

   8. _____

9. The scattering of visible light in all directions by colloids or suspensions is called the ___9___.

   9. _____

10. ___10___ is the inward force or pull that tends to minimize the surface area of a liquid.

   10. _____

B. Multiple Choice

Choose the best answer and write its letter on the line.

_____ 11. The high surface tension of water is due to the:
   a. small size of water molecules.
   b. low mass of water molecules.
   c. hydrogen bonding between water molecules.
   d. covalent bonds in water molecules.

_____ 12. Salts and other compounds that remove moisture from air are said to be:
   a. efflorescent.   c. colloidal.
   b. surfactant.   d. hygroscopic.

_____ **13.** A water molecule is best represented by:

a.
$$\delta-$$
$$O$$
$$\delta+ \diagup \diagdown \delta+$$
$$H \quad H$$

c.
$$\delta+$$
$$O$$
$$\delta- \diagup \diagdown \delta-$$
$$H \quad H$$

b. H—O—H

d. H—H—O

_____ **14.** The density of ice is less than the density of water because:
   a. ice has a lower molecular mass than water.
   b. the same mass occupies a smaller volume.
   c. the molecules are more closely packed.
   d. hydrogen bonding in ice produces an open framework.

_____ **15.** A solution is a mixture:
   a. from which the solute cannot be filtered.
   b. that is colloidal.
   c. that is heterogeneous.
   d. in which a solid solute is always dissolved in a liquid solvent.

_____ **16.** Which of the following is *not* an electrolyte?
   a. cane sugar(aq)   **c.** KCl(aq)
   b. HCl(aq)   **d.** $(NH_4)_2SO_4$(aq)

_____ **17.** An electric current is conducted by:
   a. a solution of NaCl.   **c.** solid NaCl.
   b. a sugar solution.   **d.** solid sugar.

_____ **18.** How many water molecules are in two formula units of barium hydroxide octahydrate, $Ba(OH)_2 \cdot 8H_2O$?
   a. 2   **c.** 16
   b. 8   **d.** 20

_____ **19.** Which of these would you expect to be soluble in the nonpolar solvent carbon disulfide, CS_2?
   a. $MgCl_2$ **c.** CBr_4
   b. $CaCO_3$ **d.** H_2O

_____ **20.** Gelatin would best be classed as:
   a. a colloidal dispersion.   **c.** a heterogeneous mixture.
   b. a suspension.   **d.** an aqueous solution.

_____ **21.** A typical kind of emulsion is:
   a. muddy water.   **c.** sea water.
   b. mayonnaise.   **d.** smoke.

_____ **22.** When sodium chloride is mixed with water, it forms:
   a. a dispersion.   **c.** a solution.
   b. an emulsion.   **d.** a suspension.

C. True-False

Classify each of these statements as always true, AT; sometimes true, ST; or never true, NT.

_____ **23.** Ionic solutes are very soluble in water.

_____ **24.** Liquids decrease in density as they cool.

_____ **25.** Hydrates are hygroscopic.

_____ **26.** Rubbing alcohol, C_3H_7OH, is an electrolyte.

D. Problem

Solve the following problem in the space provided. Show your work.

27. What is the percent by mass of water in the hydrate $CoCl_2 \cdot 6H_2O$?

Name ____________ Date ____________ Class ____________

E. Essay

Write a short essay for the following.

28. Describe the process of solvation of ionic solids in water.

Name _____ Date _____ Class _____

 15 WATER AND AQUEOUS SYSTEMS

Chapter Test B

A. Completion

Fill in the word(s) that will make each statement true.

1. Salts and other compounds that remove moisture from air are said to be

   _____.

2. When a solute dissolves, the process is referred to as _____.

3. When salt is dissolved in water, the salt particles are referred to as the

   _____.

4. In terms of their effect on the surface tension of water, wetting agents such as

   soaps and detergents are called _____.

5. Another name for drying agents is _____.

6. Mixtures containing particles that are intermediate in size between those of

   suspensions and true solutions are called _____.

7. Water samples containing dissolved substances are called

   _____ solutions.

8. Surface tension is explained by the ability of water to form

   _____ bonds.

9. Compounds that do not conduct an electric current in either aqueous solution

   or when molten are referred to as _____.

10. When a hydrate loses its water of hydration, it is said to

    _____.

B. Multiple Choice

Choose the best answer and write its letter on the line.

_____ 11. A liquid that has strong intermolecular attractions has:
- **a.** a high surface tension.
- **b.** an intermediate surface tension.
- **c.** a low surface tension.
- **d.** no surface tension.

_____ **12.** Ice floats on liquid water because its density is:
  a. lower than that of liquid water.
  b. the same as that of liquid water.
  c. higher than that of liquid water.
  d. none of the above

_____ **13.** If salt is dissolved in water, water serves as the:
  a. solute.   **c.** dissolved medium.
  b. solvent.   **d.** none of the above

_____ **14.** Which of the following would be expected to dissolve very readily in water?
  a. CH_4 **c.** NaOH
  b. H_2 **d.** CBr_4

_____ **15.** Which of the following would be expected to dissolve readily in the nonpolar solvent CCl_4?
  a. table salt   **c.** grease
  b. KNO_3 **d.** $Ca(OH)_2$

_____ **16.** The electrolyte among the following is:
  a. KCl.   **c.** NH_4OH.
  b. $Mg(NO_3)_2$.   **d.** all of the above

_____ **17.** Mixtures from which some of the particles will settle slowly upon standing are referred to as:
  a. homogeneous.   **c.** suspensions.
  b. solutions.   **d.** colloids.

_____ **18.** The scattering of a beam of light as it passes through a colloid is referred to as:
  a. efflorescence.   **c.** the Tyndall effect.
  b. Brownian motion.   **d.** deliquescence.

_____ **19.** Smoke is an example of a(n):
  a. solution.   **c.** colloid.
  b. suspension.   **d.** emulsion.

_____ **20.** Which of the following is true about hygroscopic substances?
  a. They have low vapor pressures.
  b. They remove moisture from the air.
  c. They can be used as drying agents.
  d. all of the above

_____ **21.** What is the percent by mass of water in $MgSO_4 \cdot 7H_2O$?
  a. 51.1%   **c.** 56.0%
  b. 195%   **d.** 21.0%

C. True-False

Classify each of these statements as always true, AT; sometimes true, ST; or never true, NT.

_____ **22.** Detergents are used in washing clothes because they reduce the surface tension of water.

_____ **23.** Solids can float in their own liquids.

_____ **24.** As a general rule, like dissolves like.

_____ **25.** All ionic compounds are electrolytes.

_____ **26.** The strength of an aqueous electrolyte is determined by the extent to which the solute particles dissociate.

_____ **27.** In general, the particles in a colloid are larger than those in a suspension.

_____ **28.** Brownian motion is caused by the water molecules of the medium colliding with the small, dispersed colloidal particles dissolved in that medium.

_____ **29.** Soaps and detergents are good emulsifying agents.

D. Problem

Solve the following problems in the space provided. Show your work.

30. Determine the percent by mass of water in $Na_2SO_4 \cdot 10H_2O$.

Name ______________________ Date __________________ Class __________________

E. Essay

Write a short essay for the following.

31. Using at least two of the concepts presented in this chapter, explain how soaps and detergents work in removing oil and grease from clothing.

Name _____   Date _____   Class _____

QUICK LAB: Surfactants

Laboratory Recordsheet   Use with Section 15.1

PURPOSE

To observe the unusual surface property of water that result from hydrogen bonding.

MATERIALS

- shallow dish or petri dish
- water
- paper clip
- rubber band, approximately 2 inches in diameter
- micropipets or droppers (2)
- vegetable oil
- liquid dish detergent

PROCEDURE

1. Thoroughly clean and dry the dish.

2. Fill the dish almost full with water. Dry your hands.

3. Being careful not to break the surface, gently place the paper clip on the water. Observe what happens.

4. Repeat Steps 1 and 2.

5. Gently place the open rubber band on the water.

6. Slowly add oil, drop by drop, onto the water encircled by the rubber band until that water is covered with a layer of oil. Observe for 15 seconds.

7. Allow one drop of dish detergent to fall onto the center of the oil layer. Observe the system for 15 seconds.

ANALYSES AND CONCLUSIONS

1. What happened to the paper clip in step 3? Explain.

   _____

   _____

   _____

Name ______________________ Date ________________ Class ________________

2. If a paper clip becomes wet, does it float? Explain your answer.

3. What shape did the rubber band take when the water inside it was covered with oil? Why did it take the observed shape?

4. Describe what happened when dish detergent was dropped onto the layer of oil.

SMALL-SCALE LAB: Electrolytes

Laboratory Recordsheet   Use with Section 15.2

SAFETY 🌀🧍🧤

Wear safety glasses and follow the standard safety procedures outlined in the Small-Scale Lab Manual.

PURPOSE

To classify compounds as electrolytes by testing their conductivity in aqueous solution.

MATERIALS

- pencil
- paper
- ruler
- reaction surface
- conductivity tester
- chemicals shown in grid below
- water
- micropipet or dropper
- conductivity probe (optional)

PROCEDURE

On a separate sheet of paper, draw a grid similar to the one below. Make each square 2 cm on each side. Place a reaction surface over the grid and place a few grains of each solid in the indicated places. Test each solid for conductivity. Then add 1 drop of water to each solid and test the wet mixture for conductivity. Be sure to clean and dry the conductivity leads between each test. Use the grid as a data table to record your observations.

$NaCl(s)$	$MgSO_4(s)$
$Na_2CO_3(s)$	Sugar ($C_{12}H_{22}O_{11}$)
$NaHCO_3(s)$	Cornstarch ($C_6H_{22}O_6)_n$
$KCl(s)$	$KI(s)$

Name _____ Date _____ Class _____

ANALYSIS

Using your experimental data, record the answers to the following questions.

1. Electrolytes are compounds that conduct electricity in aqueous solution. Which compounds in your table are electrolytes? Which are nonelectrolytes?

_____

_____

_____

2. Do any of these electrolytes conduct electricity in the solid form? Why?

_____

_____

_____

3. Are these ionic or covalent compounds? Classify each compound in the grid as ionic or covalent. For a compound to be an electrolyte, what must happen when it dissolves in water?

_____

_____

_____

_____

YOU'RE THE CHEMIST

Use the space below to write about the small-scale activities in the *You're the Chemist* section.

_____

_____

_____

_____

_____

_____

_____

_____

_____

_____

PROPERTIES OF SOLUTIONS

16.1

Section Review

Objectives

- Identify the factors that determine the rate at which a solute dissolves
- Identify the units usually used to express the solubility of a solute
- Calculate the solubility of a gas in a liquid under various pressure conditions
- Identify the factors that determine the mass of solute that will dissolve in a given mass of a solvent

Vocabulary

- saturated solution
- solubility
- unsaturated solution
- miscible
- immiscible
- supersaturated solution
- Henry's law

Key Equation

- Henry's law: $\dfrac{S_1}{P_1} = \dfrac{S_2}{P_2}$

Part A Completion

Use this completion exercise to check your understanding of the concepts and terms that are introduced in this section. Each blank can be completed with a term, short phrase, or number.

Changes in the temperature of a system and __**1**__ of a

solute alter the __**2**__ at which a solute dissolves. The extent

to which a gas dissolves in a liquid is proportional to the __**3**__

of the gas in accordance with __**4**__ law. The solubility of a gas

decreases with increasing __**5**__. A solution that contains the

maximum amount of solute at a given temperature is said to be

__**6**__. Two liquids that are mutually soluble in each other are

said to be __**7**__. Generally the __**8**__ of a solid in water

__**9**__ with increasing temperature, but there are exceptions. A(n)

__**10**__ solution holds more solute than is theoretically possible.

1. _____

2. _____

3. _____

4. _____

5. _____

6. _____

7. _____

8. _____

9. _____

10. _____

Part B True-False

Classify each of these statements as always true, AT; sometimes true, ST; or never true, NT.

_____ **11.** The rate at which a solute dissolves can be increased by grinding.

_____ **12.** As the temperature of a solvent decreases, the solubility of a solute increases.

_____ **13.** Stirring a solute when adding it to a solvent should increase the rate of its dissolving.

_____ **14.** Henry's law states that the solubility of a gas in a liquid is a function of temperature.

_____ **15.** Two liquids that dissolve in each other are miscible.

Part C Matching

Match each description in Column B to the correct term in Column A.

Column A	**Column B**
_____ **16.** saturated solution	**a.** the amount of a substance that dissolves in a given quantity of solvent at a given temperature
_____ **17.** solubility	**b.** The solubility of a gas in a liquid is directly proportional to the pressure of the gas above the liquid.
_____ **18.** unsaturated solution	**c.** solution that contains the maximum amount of solute for a given amount of solvent at a constant temperature
_____ **19.** miscible	**d.** a solution containing more solute than it can theoretically hold at a given temperature
_____ **20.** immiscible	**e.** description of two liquids that dissolve in each other
_____ **21.** supersaturated solution	**f.** a solution that contains less solute than possible at a given temperature
_____ **22.** Henry's law	**g.** description of two liquids that do not dissolve in each other

Part D Problem

Solve the following problem in the space provided. Show your work.

23. The solubility of a gas in water is 1.6 g/L at 1.0 atm of pressure. What is the solubility of the same gas at 2.5 atm? Assume the temperature to be constant.

CONCENTRATIONS OF SOLUTIONS

16.2

Section Review

Objectives

- Solve problems involving the molarity of a solution
- Describe the effect of dilution on the total moles of solute in solution
- Define what is meant by percent by volume [%(v/v)] and percent by mass [%(m/m)]

Vocabulary

- concentration
- concentrated solution
- dilute solution
- molarity (M)

Key Equations

- Molarity (M) = $\dfrac{\text{moles of solute}}{\text{liters of solution}}$

- $M_1 \times V_1 = M_2 \times V_2$

- Percent by volume [%(v/v)] = $\dfrac{\text{volume of solute}}{\text{volume of solution}} \times 100\%$

- Percent by mass [%(m/m)] = $\dfrac{\text{mass of solute}}{\text{mass of solution}} \times 100\%$

Part A Completion

Use this completion exercise to check your understanding of the concepts and terms that are introduced in this section. Each blank can be completed with a term, short phrase, or number.

The relative amounts of solute and __1__ in a __2__ can

be described qualitatively as __3__ or concentrated. Quantitative

units of concentration include molar concentration, percent by

volume, and percent by mass.

Molarity, the most important unit of concentration in

chemistry, is expressed as __4__ of solute per __5__ of solution.

Solutions of different concentrations can be prepared by

__6__ a stock solution. In dilution, the moles of __7__ remain

the same, while the amount of __8__ changes.

1. _____

2. _____

3. _____

4. _____

5. _____

6. _____

7. _____

8. _____

Part B True-False

Classify each of these statements as always true, AT; sometimes true, ST; or never true, NT.

_____ **9.** One hundred mL of 1.0M sodium hydroxide solution is more
concentrated than 1.0 L of 5M sodium hydroxide solution.

_____ **10.** The amount of sodium hydroxide in 100 mL of 1.0M NaOH is less than
that in 1.0 L of 5M NaOH solution.

_____ **11.** Fifty mL of a 32% solution (v/v) of ethyl alcohol in water would
contain 42 mL of water.

_____ **12.** A dilute solution is a quantitative expression of concentration.

Part C Matching

Match each description in Column B to the correct term in Column A.

Column A

_____ **13.** concentration

_____ **14.** dilute solution

_____ **15.** concentrated solution

_____ **16.** molarity

_____ **17.** percent solution

Column B

a. number of moles of solute dissolved in 1 L of solution

b. measure of the amount of solute that is dissolved in a
given quantity of solvent

c. solution that contains a low concentration of solute

d. concentration expressed as volume of solute over
volume of solution × 100%

e. solution that contains a high concentration of solute

Part D Problem

Solve the following problem in the space provided. Show your work.

18. What mass of sucrose, $C_{12}H_{22}O_{11}$, is needed to make 300.0 mL of a
0.50M solution?

Name _____ Date _____ Class _____

COLLIGATIVE PROPERTIES OF SOLUTIONS
16.3

Section Review

Objectives

- Identify the three colligative properties of solutions
- Describe why the vapor pressure, freezing point, and boiling point of a solution differ from those properties of the pure solvent.

Vocabulary

- colligative properties
- freezing-point depression
- boiling-point elevation

Part A Completion

Use this completion exercise to check your understanding of the concepts and terms that are introduced in this section. Each blank can be completed with a term, short phrase, or number.

In a solution, the effects of a nonvolatile __1__ on the

properties of the solvent are called ___2___ . They include __3__

point and vapor pressure ___4___ , and boiling point ___5___ . In

each case, the magnitude of the effect is ___6___ proportional to

the number of solute molecules or ions present in the ___7___ .

Colligative properties are a function of the number of solute

___8___ in solution. For example, one mole of sodium chloride

produces ___9___ as many particles in solution as one mole of

sucrose and, thus, will depress the freezing point of water __10__

as much.

1. _____
2. _____
3. _____
4. _____
5. _____
6. _____
7. _____
8. _____
9. _____
10. _____

Part B True-False

Classify each of these statements as always true, AT; sometimes true, ST; or never true, NT.

_____ 11. When added to 1000 g of water, 2 moles of a solute will increase the boiling point by 0.512°C.

_____ 12. One mole of solute A will depress the freezing point of 1000 g of water the same as one mole of solute B.

_____ **13.** Addition of a nonvolatile solute will lower the boiling point of a solvent.

_____ **14.** Addition of a nonvolatile solute will lower the freezing point of a solvent.

Part C Matching

Match each description in Column B to the correct term in Column A.

Column A

_____ **15.** colligative properties

_____ **16.** freezing-point depression

_____ **17.** boiling-point elevation

_____ **18.** vapor pressure

Column B

a. difference between the freezing point of a solution and the freezing point of the pure solvent

b. pressure exerted by a vapor that is in equilibrium with its liquid in a closed system

c. difference between the boiling point of a solution and the boiling point of the pure solvent

d. properties of solutions that depend only on the number of particles in solution

Part D Questions and Problems

Answer the following questions in the space provided.

19. How many moles of solute particles are produced by adding one mole of each of the following to water?

a. sodium nitrate

b. glucose

c. aluminum chloride

d. potassium iodide

20. An equal number of moles of NaCl and K_2CO_3 are dissolved in equal volumes of water. Which solution has the higher

a. boiling point?

b. vapor pressure?

c. freezing point?

16.4 CALCULATIONS INVOLVING COLLIGATIVE PROPERTIES

Section Review

Objectives

- Calculate the molality and mole fraction of a solution
- Describe how the freezing-point depression and boiling-point elevation are related to molality

Vocabulary

- molality (m)
- mole fraction
- molal freezing-point depression constant (K_f)
- molal boiling-point elevation constant (K_b)

Key Equations

- $\text{Molality} = \dfrac{\text{moles of solute}}{\text{kilogram of solvent}}$

- mole fractions: $X_A = \dfrac{n_A}{n_A + n_B}$ $X_B = \dfrac{n_B}{n_A + n_B}$

  where n_A = moles of solute
     n_B = moles of solvent

- $\Delta T_b = K_b \times m$
- $\Delta T_f = K_f \times m$

Part A Completion

Use this completion exercise to check your understanding of the concepts and terms that are introduced in this section. Each blank can be completed with a term, short phrase, or number.

Molality is an expression of concentration involving the ratio

of ___1___ particles to ___2___ particles. Molality is expressed as

moles of solute per ___3___ of solvent.

Another expression of concentration is ___4___, in which

concentrations are expressed as the ratio of moles of solute to the

total number of moles of solvent and solute. Each solvent has a

characteristic ___5___ elevation constant and molal freezing-point

___6___ constant. The elevation in boiling point of a solution can

be calculated by multiplying the ___7___ concentration of the

solution by the boiling-point ___8___ constant of the solvent.

1. _____

2. _____

3. _____

4. _____

5. _____

6. _____

7. _____

8. _____

Part B True-False

Classify each of these statements as always true, AT; sometimes true, ST; or never true, NT.

_____ **9.** It is possible to calculate the molar mass of a solute if you know the K_b or K_f of a solvent.

_____ **10.** Molal concentration is the same as molar concentration.

_____ **11.** The depression in freezing point of a solution is proportional to the molal concentration of solute.

_____ **12.** The sum of X_A and X_B for any solution is always 1.

Part C Matching

Match each description in Column B to the correct term in Column A.

Column A	**Column B**
_____ **13.** molality	**a.** a constant for a given solvent equal to the change in boiling point for a $1m$ solution
_____ **14.** mole fraction	**b.** number of moles of solute dissolved in 1 kilogram of solvent
_____ **15.** molal freezing-point depression constant	**c.** mass of one mole of a substance
_____ **16.** molal boiling-point elevation constant	**d.** a constant for a given solvent equal to the change in freezing point for a $1m$ solution
_____ **17.** molar mass	**e.** ratio of moles of solute in solution to the total number of moles of solute and solvent

Part D Problem

Solve the following problem in the space provided. Show your work.

18. What is the freezing point of a solution that contains 2.0 mol of $CaCl_2$ in 800.0 g of water? K_f for water $= 1.86°C/m$

16 SOLUTIONS

Practice Problems

In your notebook, solve the following problems.

SECTION 16.1 PROPERTIES OF SOLUTIONS

1. The solubility of CO_2 in water at 1.22 atm is 0.54 g/L. What is the solubility of carbon dioxide at 1.86 atm? Assume that temperature is constant.

2. What mass of KCl will produce a saturated solution in 500.0 g of water at 20°C? The solubility of KCl at 20°C is 34.0 g/100 g H_2O.

3. A saturated solution of silver nitrate is prepared in 100.0 g of water at 20°C. The solution is then heated to 50.0°C. How much more silver nitrate must now be added to obtain a saturated solution? (Use Table 16.1.)

SECTION 16.2 CONCENTRATIONS OF SOLUTIONS

1. Calculate the molarity of each of the following solutions.

   a. 0.40 mol of NaCl dissolved in 1.6 L of solution

   b. 20.2 g of potassium nitrate, KNO_3, in enough water to make 250.0 mL of solution

2. Calculate the number of grams of solute needed to prepare each of the following solutions.

   a. 2500.0 mL of a 3.0*M* solution of potassium hydroxide, KOH

   b. 2.0 liters of 2.0*M* nitric acid, HNO_3, solution

3. What is the molarity of a solution that contains 212.5 g of sodium nitrate ($NaNO_3$) in 3.0 liters of solution?

4. You must prepare 300.0 mL of 0.750*M* NaBr solution using 2.00*M* NaBr stock solution. How many milliliters of stock solution should you use?

5. In order to dilute 1.0 L of a 6.00*M* solution of NaOH to 0.500*M* solution, how much water must you add?

6. What is the concentration in percent by volume, %(v/v), of the following solutions?

   a. 60.0 mL of methanol in a total volume of 500.0 mL

   b. 25.0 mL of rubbing alcohol (C_3H_7OH) diluted to a volume of 200.0 mL with water

7. How many grams of solute are needed to prepare each of the following solutions?

   a. 1.00 L of a 3.00% (m/m) NaCl solution?

   b. 2.00 L of 5.00% (m/m) KNO_3 solution?

SECTION 16.3 COLLIGATIVE PROPERTIES OF SOLUTIONS

1. What are colligative properties of solutions? Give examples of three colligative properties.

2. How many particles in solution are produced by each formula unit of potassium carbonate, K_2CO_3?

3. How may moles of particles would 3 mol Na_2SO_4 give in solution?

4. What is the boiling point of a solution that contains 2 mol of magnesium chloride in 100.0 g of water?

5. What kind of property is vapor-pressure lowering?

6. An equal number of moles of NaCl and $CaCl_2$ are dissolved in equal volumes of water. Which solution has the lower

   a. freezing point?

   b. vapor pressure?

   c. boiling point?

SECTION 16.4 CALCULATIONS INVOLVING COLLIGATIVE PROPERTIES

1. Calculate the mole fraction of solute in each of the following solutions.

   a. 3.0 moles of lithium bromide, LiBr, dissolved in 6.0 moles of water

   b. 125.0 g of potassium nitrate, KNO_3, dissolved in 800.0 g of water

2. How many grams of sodium chloride must dissolve in 750.0 g of water to make a 0.50 molal solution?

3. How many grams of lithium sulfide must be dissolved in 1600.0 g of water to make a 2.0 molal solution?

4. Find the molality of each of the following solutions.

   a. 2.3 moles of glucose dissolved in 500.0 g of water

   b. 131 g of $Ba(NO_3)_2$ dissolved in 750.0 g of water

5. Find the boiling points of the following solutions.

   a. 2.00m solution of sodium chloride, NaCl

   b. 1.50m solution of calcium chloride, $CaCl_2$

6. Find the freezing points of the following solutions.

   a. 0.35 moles of sodium chloride, NaCl, dissolved in 900.0 g of water

   b. 126.0 g of table sugar, $C_{12}H_{22}O_{11}$, dissolved in 2500.0 g of water

INTERPRETING GRAPHICS

16

Use with Section 16.1

Solubilities of Some Substances in Water at Various Temperatures					
		Solubility (g/100 g of H_2O)			
Substance	Formula	0°C	20°C	50°C	100°C
Barium hydroxide	$Ba(OH)_2$	1.67	31.89	—	—
Barium sulfate	$BaSO_4$	0.00019	0.00025	0.00034	—
Calcium hydroxide	$Ca(OH)_2$	0.189	0.173	—	0.07
Lead(II) chloride	$PbCl_2$	0.60	0.99	1.70	—
Lithium carbonate	Li_2CO_3	1.5	1.3	1.1	0.70
Potassium chlorate	$KClO_3$	4.0	7.4	19.3	56.0
Potassium chloride	KCl	27.6	34.0	42.6	57.6
Sodium chloride	$NaCl$	35.7	36.0	37.0	39.2
Sodium nitrate	$NaNO_3$	74	88.0	114.0	182
Sodium sulfate	Na_2SO_4	4.76	62	50.0	41.0
Silver nitrate	$AgNO_3$	122	222.0	455.0	733
Lithium bromide	$LiBr$	143.0	166	203	266.0
Cane sugar (sucrose)	$C_{12}H_{22}O_{11}$	179	230.9	260.4	487

A portion of Table 16.1 from your textbook has been reproduced above. Use the table to answer the following questions.

1. Saturated solutions of each of the following compounds are made at 20°C. Circle the letter(s) of the solution(s) that will form a precipitate upon heating.

   a. NaCl

   b. Na_2SO_4

   c. Li_2CO_3

   d. sucrose

2. A saturated solution of potassium chloride is prepared in 100.0 g of water at 20°C. If the solution is heated to 50°C, how much more KCl must be added to obtain a saturated solution?

3. A saturated solution of sucrose in 1000.0 g of boiling water is cooled to 20°C. What mass of rock candy will be formed?

4. Using data from the table, plot the solubility curves of KCl, LiBr and Na_2SO_4 on the graph below. Be sure to label each curve. Use the graph to answer the following questions.

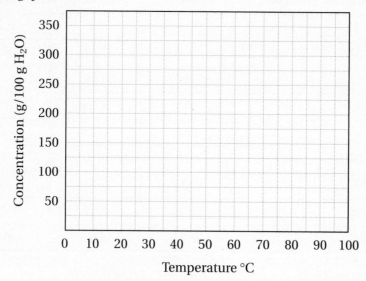

a. Which of the compounds is most soluble at 25°C?

_____

_____

b. Which of the compounds has the lowest solubility at 90°C?

_____

_____

16 VOCABULARY REVIEW

From each group of terms, choose the term that does not belong and then explain your choice.

1. saturated, unsaturated, molarity, supersaturated

   _____

   _____

2. miscible, immiscible, concentration

   _____

   _____

3. molarity, mole fraction, molality, Henry's law

   _____

   _____

4. solubility of a gas, Henry's law, pressure, colligative properties

   _____

   _____

5. colligative properties, saturated solution, freezing-point depression, molality

   _____

   _____

6. molal freezing-point depression constant (K_f), colligative properties, ice cream, molarity

   _____

   _____

7. surface area, mole fraction, temperature, stirring

   _____

   _____

8. dilute solution, concentrated solution, $M_1 \times V_1 = M_2 \times V_2$, boiling-point elevation

   _____

   _____

16 **SOLUTIONS**

Chapter Quiz

Choose the best answer and write its letter on the line.

_____ 1. At a given temperature, the solubility of a gas in a liquid is: *16.1*
a. proportional to the square root of the pressure of the gas above the liquid.
b. directly proportional to the pressure of the gas above the liquid.
c. inversely proportional to the pressure of the gas above the liquid.
d. unrelated to the pressure of the gas above the liquid.

_____ 2. If the addition of a crystal to an aqueous solution causes a great deal of   *16.1*
dissolved solid to come out of solution, the original solution was:
a. a colloid.   c. saturated.
b. unsaturated.   d. supersaturated.

_____ 3. In general, as the temperature of a solution composed of a gas in a   *16.1*
liquid is decreased, the solubility of the gas:
a. increases.   c. remains the same.
b. decreases.   d. none of the above

_____ 4. What is the molarity of a solution that contains 8 moles of solute in   *16.2*
2 L of solution?
a. $4M$ c. $6M$
b. $8M$ d. $0.25M$

_____ 5. To 225 mL of a $0.80M$ solution of KI, a student adds enough water to   *16.2*
make 1 L of a more dilute KI solution. What is the molarity of the new
solution?
a. $180M$ c. 137 g
b. $0.18M$ d. 100 g

_____ 6. How many milliliters of alcohol are in 167 mL of an 85.0% (v/v) alcohol   *16.2*
solution?
a. 252 mL   c. 142 mL
b. 228 mL   d. 145 mL

_____ 7. Colligative properties depend on: *16.3*
a. the nature of the solute.
b. the nature of the solvent.
c. the number of particles dissolved in a given mass of solvent.
d. none of the above

_____ 8. What is the freezing point of an aqueous $0.500m$ NaBr solution?   *16.4*
(K_f for water = 1.86°C/m)
a. −0.93°C   c. −3.72°C
b. −1.86°C   d. −9.30°C

16 SOLUTIONS

Chapter Test A

A. Matching

Match each description in Column B to the correct term in Column A. Write the letter of the correct description on the line.

Column A

_____ 1. saturated solution

_____ 2. colligative properties

_____ 3. miscible

_____ 4. molarity

_____ 5. unsaturated solution

_____ 6. immiscible

_____ 7. concentrated solution

_____ 8. Henry's law

_____ 9. supersaturated solution

_____ 10. dilute solution

Column B

a. At a given temperature, the solubility of a gas in a liquid is directly proportional to the pressure of the gas above the liquid.

b. a solution containing the maximum amount of solute that can be dissolved at a given temperature

c. the number of moles of solute dissolved in 1 L of solution

d. describes liquids that are insoluble in each other

e. contains only a small amount of the maximum amount of solute that can be dissolved at a given temperature

f. contains less solute than can theoretically be dissolved

g. describes liquids that dissolve in each other

h. contains more solute than can theoretically be held at a given temperature

i. depend upon the number of particles of solute in solution

j. a solution with a large amount of solute compared to solvent

B. Multiple Choice

Choose the best answer and write its letter on the line.

_____ 11. Increasing the temperature of a liquid–solid solution will:
   a. always increase the rate at which a crystalline solute dissolves.
   b. often increase the amount of crystalline solute that dissolves.
   c. both a and b
   d. neither a nor b

_____ 12. Which of the following operations usually makes a substance dissolve
faster in a solvent?
a. agitation   c. crushing the substance to a powder
b. raising the temperature   d. all of the above

_____ 13. To increase the solubility of a gas at constant temperature and 202 kPa
pressure from 0.85 g/L to 5.1 g/L, the pressure would have to be
increased to:
a. 1212 kPa.   c. 606 kPa.
b. 505 kPa.   d. 17.2 kPa.

_____ 14. If the pressure of a gas above a liquid is decreased (at constant
temperature), the solubility of the gas in the liquid:
a. remains unchanged.
b. increases.
c. decreases.
d. would change but in an unpredictable direction.

_____ 15. An ionic compound has a solubility of 30 g per 100 mL of water at
room temperature. A solution containing 70 g of the compound in
250 mL of water at the same temperature is:
a. saturated.   c. unsaturated.
b. supersaturated.   d. a suspension.

_____ 16. How many mL of alcohol are in 240 mL of 95.0% (v/v) alcohol
solution?
a. 12 mL   c. 145 mL
b. 228 mL   d. 142 mL

_____ 17. If more solvent is added to a solution:
a. the molarity decreases.
b. the solution becomes less dilute.
c. the percent (v/v) increases.
d. all of the above

_____ 18. What is the molarity of a 200-mL solution in which 0.2 mole of sodium
bromide is dissolved?
a. 0.20M c. 0.40M
b. 1.0M d. 4.0M

_____ 19. What is the percent (m/m) of a water solution that contains 60 g of
calcium chloride, $CaCl_2$, and that has a mass of 400 g?
a. 15%   c. 24%
b. 1.35%   d. 6.7%

_____ 20. Which of the following is *not* a colligative property of a solution?
a. boiling-point elevation   c. vapor-pressure lowering
b. solubility   d. freezing-point depression

_____ **21.** If one mole of each of these solutes is added to the same amount of
water, which solution has the highest boiling point?
  a. copper(II) chloride, $CuCl_2$
  b. glucose, $C_6H_{12}O_6$
  c. magnesium acetate, $Mg(C_2H_3O_2)_2$
  d. aluminum sulfate, $Al_2(SO_4)_3$

C. True-False

Classify each of these statements as always true, AT; sometimes true, ST; or never true NT.

_____ **22.** The solubility of a solute can be increased by cooling the solvent.

_____ **23.** Grinding a solute increases the rate at which it dissolves.

_____ **24.** As an open bottle of a carbonated beverage warms, the concentration
of dissolved carbon dioxide decreases.

_____ **25.** One hundred mL of a $5.0M$ sodium chloride solution is more
concentrated than 1.0 L of a $1.0M$ sodium chloride solution.

_____ **26.** The amount of sodium chloride in 100 mL of a $5.0M$ NaCl solution is
greater than that in 1.0 L of a $1.0M$ NaCl solution.

_____ **27.** As the temperature of a solvent increases, the solubility of a gaseous
solute increases.

_____ **28.** Fifty mL of a 16% solution (v/v) of ethyl alcohol in water contains
16 mL of water.

_____ **29.** An unsaturated solution contains less solute than required for
equilibrium.

_____ **30.** A saturated solution has a large amount of solute compared to solvent.

_____ **31.** If a crystal of a substance dissolves when added to an aqueous
solution, the original solution containing that substance was
supersaturated.

D. Problems

Solve the following problems in the space provided. Show your work.

32. How would you prepare 250 mL of $0.60M$ $Al_2(SO_4)_3$ solution from a $2.0M$ $Al_2(SO_4)_3$
stock solution?

33. Calculate the molarity of a solution prepared by dissolving 95.5 g of KNO_3 in enough water to make 750 mL of solution.

34. A gas has a solubility in water of 16.9 g/L at 15°C and 505 kPa of pressure. What is its solubility in water at 15°C and 606 kPa of pressure?

E. Essay

Write a short essay for the following.

35. Explain on a particle basis how the addition of a solute affects the boiling point, freezing point, and vapor pressure of the solvent.

_____

_____

_____

_____

_____

_____

_____

_____

_____

F. Additional Problems

Solve the following problems in the space provided. Show your work.

36. Calculate the boiling point of a solution that contains 0.900 mol of K_3PO_4 dissolved in 2750 g of water. (K_b for water = 0.512°C/m.)

37. Calculate the molality of a solution prepared by dissolving 175 g of KNO_3 in 1250 g of water.

SOLUTIONS

16

Chapter Test B

A. Matching

Match each term in Column B to the correct description in Column A. Write the letter of the correct term on the line.

Column A	Column B

_____ **1.** the number of moles of a solute dissolved in 1 L of solution

a. colligative properties

_____ **2.** the difference in temperature between the boiling points of a solution and of the pure solvent

b. Henry's law

_____ **3.** describes two liquids that dissolve in each other

c. boiling-point elevation

_____ **4.** the number of moles of solute dissolved in 1 kg of solvent

d. supersaturated solution

_____ **5.** a solution that contains more solute than it can theoretically hold at a given temperature

e. molality

_____ **6.** those properties of solutions that depend on the number of particles dissolved in a given mass of solvent

f. saturated solution

_____ **7.** a solution that contains the maximum amount of solute for a given amount of solvent at constant temperature

g. molarity

_____ **8.** the difference in temperature between the freezing points of a solution and of the pure solvent

h. miscible

_____ **9.** a measure of the amount of solute that is dissolved in a given quantity of solvent

i. freezing-point depression

_____ **10.** At a given temperature, the solubility of a gas in a liquid is directly proportional to the pressure of the gas above the liquid.

j. concentration

B. Multiple Choice

Choose the best answer and write its letter on the line.

_____ 11. The rate at which a solute dissolves in a given solvent is determined by:
   a. the extent to which the solution is agitated.
   b. the temperature of the solution.
   c. the size of the solute particles.
   d. all of the above

_____ 12. A glass of iced tea containing excess sugar at the bottom is said to be:
   a. saturated.   c. supersaturated.
   b. unsaturated.   d. homogeneous.

_____ 13. If the solubility of $AgNO_3$ at 40°C is 311 g per 100 g of water, what mass of this solute can be dissolved in 350 g of water at the same temperature?
   a. 0.89 g   c. 1.1 g
   b. 1100 g   d. 110 000 g

_____ 14. In general, as the temperature of a solvent increases, the solubility of any gas dissolved in that solvent:
   a. increases.   c. remains the same.
   b. decreases.   d. cannot be predicted.

_____ 15. Which of the following would increase the solubility of a gas in a liquid?
   a. stirring the solution
   b. increasing the temperature of the solvent
   c. increasing the pressure of the gas above the solution
   d. adding more solvent

_____ 16. If the solubility of a gas in water is 1.22 g/L at 2.75 atm, what is its solubility (in g/L) at 1.0 atm?
   a. 0.44 g/L   c. 2.25 g/L
   b. 3.97 g/L   d. 3.36 g/L

_____ 17. The most concentrated solution from among those listed is:
   a. 100 mL 0.25M KCl.   c. 75 mL 0.23M KNO_3.
   b. 150 mL 0.18M NaOH.   d. 200 mL 0.15M $NaNO_3$.

_____ 18. The molarity of a solution that contains 14 g KOH per 150 mL of solution is:
   a. 93M.   c. 0.093M.
   b. 1.7M.   d. 11M.

_____ 19. How many moles of solute are present in 1.25 L of a 0.75M $NaNO_3$ solution?
   a. 1.7 mol   c. 0.75 mol
   b. 0.60 mol   d. 0.94 mol

_____ 20. What volume of 1.25M HCl would be required to prepare 180 mL of a 0.500M HCl solution?
   a. 450 mL   c. 0.014 mL
   b. 72 mL   d. 2.2×10^{-3} mL

_____ **21.** What is the percent (m/m) of a solution containing 25 g of NaCl in
175 g of solution?

    a. 700%   **c.** 7.0%

    b. 0.14%   **d.** 14%

_____ **22.** Which of the following results from the presence of a solute in a given
solvent?

    a. The vapor pressure of the solution is lower than that of the pure
solvent.

    b. The boiling point of the solution is lower than that of the pure
solvent.

    c. The freezing point of the solution is higher than that of the pure
solvent.

    d. all of the above

_____ **23.** What is the molality of a solution prepared by dissolving 13.0 g of
$Ba(NO_3)_2$ in 450 g of water?

    a. 0.029 molal   **c.** 0.11 molal

    b. 29 molal   **d.** 1.1×10^{-4} molal

_____ **24.** The mole fraction of ethanol in a solution containing 1.50 moles of
ethanol and 3.25 mol of water is:

    a. 0.316   **c.** 0.462

    b. 0.217   **d.** 0.681

_____ **25.** The addition of antifreeze to water in a car radiator causes the freezing
point of the mixture to:

    a. increase.   **c.** remain the same.

    b. decrease.   **d.** vary unpredictably.

_____ **26.** What is the molality of an aqueous solution of a molecular solute if the
boiling point of the solution is 101.4°C?

    a. 2.70 molal   **c.** 1.04 molal

    b. 0.515 molal   **d.** 0.556 molal

C. True-False

Classify each of these statements as always true, AT; sometimes true, ST; or never true NT.

_____ **27.** Whether a solute dissolves in a given solvent is determined by the
nature of the two substances.

_____ **28.** Stirring a solution at constant temperature increases the amount of
solute that can be dissolved.

_____ **29.** At constant temperature, more powdered sugar will dissolve in a cup
of coffee than will sugar that is in the form of cubes.

_____ **30.** Oil and water are completely miscible.

_____ **31.** Increasing the temperature increases the solubility of a given
substance.

_____ **32.** A 2.5*M* solution of KNO_3 contains 2.5 moles solute particles per 1 kg of solvent.

_____ **33.** The number of moles of solute in a given solution decreases as the solution is diluted.

_____ **34.** A solution has a lower vapor pressure than that of the pure solvent.

_____ **35.** The boiling point of a solution is lower than that of the pure solvent.

_____ **36.** The freezing point of a 1.0 molal solution of $MgCl_2$ is 5.58°C lower than that of pure water.

D. Problems

Solve the following problems in the space provided. Show your work.

37. If a saturated solution of $AgNO_3$ at 20°C contains 216 g $AgNO_3$ per 100.0 g of water, what mass of water could contain 725 g of this solute at the same temperature?

38. At 10°C, the solubility of a gas in water is 2.45 g/L at 0.750 atm. What pressure would be required to produce an aqueous solution containing 6.25 g/L of this gas at 10°C?

39. Calculate the molarity of a solution that contains 50.0 g of $Mg(NO_3)_2$ per 225 mL of solution.

40. What mass of $AgNO_3$ would be required to prepare a 0.250 molal solution in 125 g of water?

E. Essay

Write a short essay for the following

41. Often during the winter, salt is sprinkled on bridges and sidewalks. Explain the purpose for doing so and the reasons why salt is effective for this purpose.

_____

_____

_____

_____

_____

_____

_____

F. Additional Problems

Solve the following problems in the space provided. Show your work.

42. What mass of H_2SO_4 would be required to prepare 750 mL of a 0.15M H_2SO_4 solution?

43. Determine the freezing point of a solution made by adding 27.5 g of methanol (CH_3OH) to 250.0 g of water.

44. What is the boiling point of an aqueous solution that contains 62.5 g of Ba(NO₃)₂ in 750.0 g of water?

QUICK LAB: Solutions and Colloids

Laboratory Recordsheet   Use with Section 16.3

PURPOSE

To classify mixtures as solutions or colloids using the Tyndall effect.

MATERIALS

- sodium hydrogen carbonate
- cornstarch
- stirring rod
- distilled water (or tap water)
- flashlight

- masking tape
- 3 jars with parallel sides
- teaspoon
- cup

PROCEDURE

1. In a cup, make a paste by mixing $\frac{1}{2}$ teaspoon cornstarch with 4 teaspoons water.

2. Fill one of the jars with water. Add $\frac{1}{2}$ teaspoon sodium hydrogen carbonate to a second jar and fill with water. Stir to mix. Add the cornstarch paste to the third jar and fill with water. Stir to mix.

3. Turn out the lights in the room. Shine the beam of light from the flashlight at each of the jars and record your observations.

ANALYSES AND CONCLUSIONS

1. In which of the jars was it possible to see the path of the beam of light?

   _____

   _____

   _____

2. What made the light beam visible?

   _____

   _____

   _____

3. If a system that made the light beam visible was filtered, would the light beam be visible in the filtrate? Explain.

_____

_____

_____

4. Predict what you would observe if you were to replace the sodium hydrogen carbonate with sucrose (cane sugar) or sodium chloride (table salt).

_____

_____

_____

5. Predict what you would observe if you were to replace the cornstarch with flour or diluted milk.

_____

_____

_____

6. Explain how you could use this method to distinguish a colloid from a suspension.

_____

_____

_____

SMALL-SCALE LAB: Making a Solution

Laboratory Recordsheet   Use with Section 16.4

SAFETY

Wear safety glasses and follow the standard safety procedures outlined in the Small-Scale Lab Manual.

PURPOSE

To make a solution and use carefully measured data to calculate the solution's concentration.

MATERIALS

- solid NaCl
- water
- 50-mL volumetric flask
- balance

PROCEDURE

Measure the mass of a clean, dry volumetric flask. Add enough solid NaCl to approximately fill one tenth of the volume of the flask. Measure the mass of the flask again. Half fill the flask with water and shake it gently until all the NaCl dissolves. Fill the flask with water to the 50-mL mark and measure the mass again.

ANALYSES AND CONCLUSIONS

Using your experimental data, record the answers to the following questions.

1. Percent by mass tells how many grams of solute are present in 100 g of solution.

$$\% \text{ by mass} = \frac{\text{mass of solute}}{\text{mass of solute} + \text{solvent}} \times 100\%$$

   a. Calculate the mass of the solute (NaCl).

   b. Calculate the mass of the solvent (water).

   c. Calculate the percent by mass of NaCl in the solution.

Name _____ Date _____ Class _____

2. Mole fraction tells how many moles of solute are present for every 1 mol of total solution.

$$\text{Mole fraction} = \frac{\text{mol NaCl}}{\text{mol NaCl} + \text{mol H}_2\text{O}}$$

   a. Calculate the moles of NaCl solute. (Molar mass NaCl = 58.5 g/mol)

   b. Calculate the moles of water. (Molar mass H_2O = 18 g/mol)

   c. Calculate the mole fraction of your solution.

3. Molality (m) tells how many moles of solute are present in 1 kg of solvent.

$$m = \frac{\text{mol NaCl}}{\text{kg H}_2\text{O}}$$

Calculate the molality of your solution.

4. Molarity (M) tells how many moles of solute are dissolved in 1 L of solution.

$$M = \frac{\text{mol NaCl}}{\text{L solution}}$$

   a. Calculate the liters of solution. (1000 mL = 1 L)

   b. Calculate the molarity of the NaCl solution.

5. Density tells how many grams of solution are present in 1 mL of solution.

$$\text{Density} = \frac{\text{g solution}}{\text{mL solution}}$$

Calculate the density of the solution.

Name ______________________ Date ________________ Class ________________

YOU'RE THE CHEMIST

Use the space below to record your observations of the small-scale activities in the *You're the Chemist* section.

17.1 THE FLOW OF ENERGY— HEAT AND WORK

Section Review

Objectives

- Explain the relationship between energy, heat, and work
- Distinguish between exothermic and endothermic processes
- Distinguish between heat capacity and specific heat

Vocabulary

- thermochemistry
- chemical potential energy
- heat
- system
- surroundings
- law of conservation of energy
- endothermic process
- exothermic process
- heat capacity
- specific heat

Key Equations and Relationships

- 1 Calorie = 1 kilocalorie = 1000 calories

- 1 J = 0.2390 cal and 4.184 J = 1 cal

- $C = \dfrac{q}{m \times \Delta T} = \dfrac{\text{heat (joules or calories)}}{\text{mass (g)} \times \text{change in temperature (°C)}}$

Part A Completion

Use this completion exercise to check your understanding of the concepts and terms that are introduced in this section. Each blank can be completed with a term, short phrase, or number.

The energy that flows from a warm object to a cool object is called ___1___. The energy stored within the structural units of chemical substances is called chemical ___2___. The study of heat transfer during chemical reactions and changes of state is called ___3___. One of the units used to measure heat flow is the ___4___, defined as the amount of heat needed to raise 1 g of water 1°C. The SI unit of heat and energy is the ___5___, which is equal to 0.2390 cal. The ___6___ of a substance is the amount of heat it takes to change the temperature of 1 g of the substance 1°C. Substances like ___7___, with low heat capacities, take a shorter time to heat up than substances with high heat capacities, such as ___8___.

1. _____

2. _____

3. _____

4. _____

5. _____

6. _____

7. _____

8. _____

Part B True-False

Classify each of these statements as always true, AT; sometimes true, ST; or never true, NT.

_____ 9. The joule is the SI unit of force.

_____ 10. Endothermic processes absorb heat from the surroundings.

_____ 11. The law of conservation of energy states that in a chemical process, energy is sometimes created and sometimes destroyed.

_____ 12. A system that loses heat to its surrounding is said to be exothermic, and the value of q is negative.

_____ 13. A calorie is defined as the quantity of heat needed to raise the temperature of 1 gram of pure water 1°C.

Part C Matching

Match each description in Column B to the correct term in Column A.

Column A	Column B
_____ 14. heat	**a.** a process that absorbs heat from the surroundings
_____ 15. exothermic process	**b.** the amount of heat required to change the temperature of an object by exactly 1°C
_____ 16. heat capacity	**c.** energy that transfers from one object to another because of a temperature difference between them
_____ 17. system	**d.** the part of the universe being studied
_____ 18. endothermic process	**e.** a process that loses heat to the surroundings

Part D Questions and Problems

Answer the following in the space provided.

19. Distinguish among the various forms of energy: chemical potential energy, work, and heat.

_____

_____

_____

20. The temperature of a piece of unknown metal with a mass of 18.0 g increases from 25.0°C to 40°C when the metal absorbs 124.2 J of heat. What is the specific heat of the unknown metal? Compare your answer to the values listed in Table 17.2 of your textbook. What is the identity of the unknown metal?

17.2 MEASURING AND EXPRESSING ENTHALPY CHANGES

Section Review

Objectives

- Construct equations that show the enthalpy changes for chemical and physical processes
- Calculate enthalpy changes in chemical and physical processes

Vocabulary

- calorimetry
- calorimeter
- enthalpy, (H)
- thermochemical equation
- heat of reaction
- heat of combustion

Key Equation

- $q_{sys} = \Delta H = -q_{surr} = -m \times C \times \Delta T$, where $\Delta T = T_f - T_i$

Part A Completion

Use this completion exercise to check your understanding of the concepts and terms that are introduced in this section. Each blank can be completed with a term, short phrase, or number.

A ___1___ is a device used to measure the absorption or release of heat in chemical and physical processes. For systems at constant pressure, the heat changes that occur are the same as changes in ___2___ , symbolized as ___3___ . To measure the enthalpy change for a reaction in aqueous solution, it is necessary to measure the ___4___ and ___5___ temperatures of the system and the ___6___ of the water in the system.

1. _____
2. _____
3. _____
4. _____
5. _____
6. _____

Part B True-False

Classify each of these statements as always true, AT; sometimes true, ST; or never true, NT.

_____ 7. When a substance dissolves in water, heat is released.

_____ 8. The sign of ΔH is negative for an exothermic reaction.

_____ 9. If 129 kJ of heat is required to decompose 2 moles of $NaHCO_3$, then 258 kJ is required to decompose 4 moles of $NaHCO_3$.

_____ **10.** The physical state of the reactants and products in a thermochemical reaction are not important when calculating ΔH of the reaction.

_____ **11.** In endothermic reactions, the potential energy of the product(s) is higher than the potential energy of the reactants.

_____ **12.** The equation $CaO(s) + H_2O(l) \rightarrow Ca(OH)_2(s)$ $\Delta H = 65.2$ kJ is an example of a thermochemical equation.

Part C Matching

Match each description in Column B to the correct term in Column A.

Column A

_____ **13.** enthalpy (*H*)

_____ **14.** heat of combustion

_____ **15.** thermochemical equation

_____ **16.** calorimetry

_____ **17.** bomb calorimeter

Column B

a. the heat of reaction for the complete burning of 1 mole of a substance

b. a chemical equation that includes the enthalpy change (ΔH)

c. the accurate and precise measurement of heat changes for chemical and physical processes

d. an insulated device containing a sealed vessel that is used to measure the heat released during a combustion reaction

e. the amount of heat that a system has at a constant pressure

Part D Questions and Problems

Answer the following in the space provided.

18. When 2 moles of nitric oxide, NO, burn in air to produce 2 moles of nitrogen dioxide, 113.04 kJ of heat is produced. Write a balanced thermochemical equation for this reaction.

19. Calculate the amount of heat produced when 34.8 g of methane, CH_4, burns in an excess of oxygen, according to the following equation.

$$CH_4(g) + 2O_2(g) \rightarrow CO_2(g) + 2H_2O(l) \qquad \Delta H = -890.2 \text{ kJ}$$

17.3 HEAT IN CHANGES OF STATE

Section Review

Objectives

- Classify, by type, the enthalpy changes that occur during melting, freezing, boiling, and condensing
- Calculate the enthalpy changes that occur during melting, freezing, boiling, and condensing
- Explain what thermochemical changes can occur when a solution forms

Vocabulary

- molar heat of fusion
- molar heat of solidification
- molar heat of vaporization
- molar heat of condensation
- molar heat of solution

Part A Completion

Use this completion exercise to check your understanding of the concepts and terms that are introduced in this section. Each blank can be completed with a term, short phrase, or number.

The heat absorbed by 1 mole of a substance in melting from a solid to a liquid at a constant temperature is called the ___1___ . The heat lost when 1 mole of a liquid solidifies at a constant temperature is called the ___2___ . The quantity of heat absorbed by a melting solid is ___3___ to the quantity of heat lost when the liquid solidifies. The heat of fusion for methanol is ___4___ .

When liquids absorb heat at their boiling points, they become vapors. The amount of heat necessary to vaporize one mole of a given liquid is called its ___5___ . ___6___ is the exact opposite of vaporization. The amount of heat released when one mole of vapor condenses is called its ___7___ .

1. _____

2. _____

3. _____

4. _____

5. _____

6. _____

7. _____

Name _____ Date _____ Class _____

Part B True-False

Classify each of these statements as always true, AT; sometimes true, ST; or never true, NT.

_____ 8. $\Delta H_{fus} = -\Delta H_{solid}$

_____ 9. Melting and vaporization are exothermic processes.

_____ 10. In order to convert 1 mole of $H_2O(l)$ to 1 mol of $H_2O(g)$, 40.7 kJ must be supplied.

_____ 11. When ice melts, the temperature of the ice increases until the entire sample becomes liquid.

_____ 12. When ammonium nitrate dissolves in water, the solution gets cold. This is an example of an exothermic reaction.

Part C Matching

Match each description in Column B to the correct term in Column A.

Column A

_____ 13. molar heat of fusion

_____ 14. molar heat of solidification

_____ 15. molar heat of vaporization

_____ 16. ΔH_{vap}

_____ 17. molar heat of solution

Column B

a. the heat absorbed by 1 mole of a substance in melting from a solid to a liquid

b. the amount of heat necessary to vaporize 1 mole of a liquid

c. $= -\Delta H_{cond}$

d. the heat change caused by dissolution of 1 mole of substance

e. the heat lost when 1 mole of a liquid solidifies at a constant temperature

Part D Questions and Problems

Answer the following in the space provided.

18. State whether the following physical and chemical changes are endothermic or exothermic.

a. melting _____ **d.** fusion _____

b. vaporization _____ **e.** freezing _____

c. condensation _____ **f.** combustion _____

19. How much heat is absorbed when 28.3 g of $H_2O(s)$ at 0°C is converted to liquid at 0°C?

20. How much heat is absorbed when 5.53 mol of NH_4NO_3 solid is dissolved in water? ($\Delta H_{soln} = 25.7$ kJ/mol)

Name _____ Date _____ Class _____

Section Review

Objectives

- Apply Hess's law of heat summation to find enthalpy changes for chemical and physical processes
- Calculate enthalpy changes using standard heats of formation

Vocabulary

- Hess's law of heat summation
- standard heat of formation

Key Equation

- $\Delta H^0 = \Delta H_f^0 \text{ (products)} - \Delta H_f^0 \text{ (reactants)}$

Part A Completion

Use this completion exercise to check your understanding of the concepts and terms that are introduced in this section. Each blank can be completed with a term, short phrase, or number.

Hess's law of heat summation states that for a chemical equation that can be written as the __1__ of two or more steps, the __2__ change for the final equation equals the sum of the enthalpy changes for the individual steps. Hess's law makes it possible to measure the heat of a reaction __3__. When a reaction is reversed, the sign of ΔH must be __4__.

Sometimes it is hard to measure the heat for a reaction. In such cases, the __5__ is used to calculate heats of reaction at standard conditions. The standard heat of formation of a compound is the __6__ in enthalpy that accompanies the formation of __7__ mole of a compound from its elements. The symbol used for standard heat of formation is __8__. The standard heat of formation of a free element in its standard state is __9__. The standard heat of reaction is determined by __10__ the ΔH_f^0 of all the reactants from the ΔH_f^0 of all the products.

1. _____
2. _____
3. _____
4. _____
5. _____
6. _____
7. _____
8. _____
9. _____
10. _____

Part B True-False

Classify each of these statements as always true, AT; sometimes true, ST; or never true, NT.

_____ 11. The standard heat of formation for a substance is determined at 100°C.

_____ 12. Hess's law of heat summation is not related to the law of conservation of energy.

_____ 13. When using Hess's law of heat summation, intermediate reactions are summed and terms are canceled, as in algebra, to arrive at a final equation.

_____ 14. The ΔH_f^0 for $I_2(g)$ is zero.

_____ 15. The ΔH_f^0 for $H_2O(l)$ and $H_2O(s)$ are the same.

Part C Matching

Match each description in Column B to the correct term in Column A.

Column A	Column B
_____ 16. standard heat of formation	a. symbol for the standard heat of formation
_____ 17. Hess's law of heat summation	b. the change in enthalpy that accompanies the formation of 1 mole of a compound from its elements
_____ 18. ΔH_f^0	c. in going from a particular set of reactants to a particular set of products, the enthalpy change is the same whether the reaction takes place in one step or in a series of steps
_____ 19. ΔH^0 for $Br_2(g) \rightarrow Br_2(l)$	d. -30.91 kJ
_____ 20. zero	e. ΔH_f^0 of $Cl_2(g)$

Part D Questions and Problems

Answer the following in the space provided.

21. Determine the heat of reaction for the following reaction.
$$CuO(s) + H_2(g) \rightarrow Cu(s) + H_2O(g)$$
Use the following thermochemical equations.
1) $CuO(s) \rightarrow Cu(s) + \frac{1}{2}O_2(g)$ $\Delta H = 155$ kJ
2) $H_2O(g) \rightarrow H_2(g) + \frac{1}{2}O_2(g)$ $\Delta H = 242$ kJ

22. Calculate the change in enthalpy for the following reaction using standard heats of formation. (Refer to Table 17.4 in your textbook.)
$$Fe_2O_3(s) + 3CO(g) \rightarrow 2Fe(s) + 3CO_2(g)$$

17 THERMOCHEMISTRY

Practice Problems

In your notebook, solve the following problems.

SECTION 17.1 THE FLOW OF ENERGY—HEAT AND WORK

Use the three-step problem-solving approach you learned in Chapter 1.

1. How many kilojoules of energy are in a donut that contains 200.0 Calories?

2. What is the specific heat of a substance that has a mass of 25.0 g and requires 525.0 calories to raise its temperature by 15.0°C?

3. Suppose 100.0 g of $H_2O(s)$ absorbs 1255.0 J of heat. What is the corresponding temperature change? The specific heat capacity of $H_2O(s)$ is 2.1 J/g•°C.

4. How many joules of heat energy are required to raise the temperature of 100.0 g of aluminum by 120.0°C? The specific heat capacity of aluminum is 0.90 J/g•°C.

SECTION 17.2 MEASURING AND EXPRESSING ENTHALPY CHANGES

1. A student mixed 75.0 mL of water containing 0.75 mol HCl at 25°C with 75.0 mL of water containing 0.75 mol of NaOH at 25°C in a foam cup calorimeter. The temperature of the resulting solution increased to 35°C. How much heat in kilojoules was released by this reaction?

$$C_{water} = 4.18 \text{ J/g•°C}$$

2. Calculate the amount of heat evolved when 15.0 g of $Ca(OH)_2$ forms from the reaction of $CaO(s) + H_2O(l)$.

$$CaO(s) + H_2O(l) \rightarrow Ca(OH)_2(s) \quad \Delta H = -65.2 \text{ kJ}$$

3. Calculate the amount of heat produced when 52.4 g of methane, CH_4, burns in an excess of air, according to the following equation.

$$CH_4(g) + 2O_2(g) \rightarrow CO_2(g) + 2H_2O(l) \quad \Delta H = -890.2 \text{ kJ}$$

4. Balance the following equation, then calculate the enthalpy change for the reaction given that the standard heat of combustion of $NH_3(g)$ is -226 kJ/mol.

$$NH_3(g) + O_2(g) \rightarrow NO(g) + H_2O(g)$$

SECTION 17.3 HEAT IN CHANGES OF STATE

1. Calculate the amount of heat needed to melt 35.0 g of ice at 0°C. Express your answer in kilojoules.

2. Calculate the amount of heat needed to convert 190.0 g of liquid water at 18°C to steam at 100.0°C.

3. How much heat (kJ) is released when 2.543 mol NaOH(s) is dissolved in water?

$$NaOH(s) \xrightarrow{H_2O(l)} Na^+(aq) + OH^-(aq) \quad \Delta H_{soln} = -445.1 \text{ kJ/mol}$$

4. Calculate the amount of heat needed to convert 96 g of ice at $-24°C$ to water at $28°C$. The specific heat capacity of $H_2O(s)$ is 2.1 J/g·°C.

SECTION 17.4 CALCULATING HEATS OF REACTION

1. What is the standard heat of reaction for the combustion of hydrogen sulfide? Refer to Table 17.4 in your textbook.

$$2H_2S(g) + 3O_2(g) \rightarrow 2H_2O(g) + 2SO_2(g)$$

2. Calculate the enthalpy change (in kJ) for the following reaction. State whether the reaction is exothermic or endothermic. Refer to Table 17.4 in your textbook.

$$CaO(s) + CO_2(g) \rightarrow CaCO_3(s)$$

3. What is the enthalpy change for the formation of hydrazine, $N_2H_4(l)$, from its elements?

$$N_2(g) + 2H_2(g) \rightarrow N_2H_4(l)$$

Use the following reactions and enthalpy changes:

$$N_2H_4(l) + O_2(g) \rightarrow N_2(g) + 2H_2O(l) \quad \Delta H = -622.2 \text{ kJ}$$
$$H_2(g) + \tfrac{1}{2}O_2(g) \rightarrow H_2O(l) \quad \Delta H = -285.8 \text{ kJ}$$

INTERPRETING GRAPHICS

17

Use with Section 17.2

A student performed an experiment to determine the specific heat of an unknown metal. The data she collected is organized in the table below. Use this information to answer the following questions.

Quantity	Trial 1	Trial 2
1. Mass of test tube + metal	118.19 g	118.21 g
2. Mass of test tube	67.86 g	67.86 g
3. Mass of metal	50.33 g	50.35 g
4. Mass of calorimeter	7.037 g	3.818 g
5. Mass of calorimeter + water	46.137 g	43.270 g
6. Mass of water	39.100 g	39.452 g
7. Initial temperature of metal	100.0°C	100.0°C
8. Initial temperature of water	22.0°C	21.0°C
9. Final temperature of water	27.0°C	26.5°C

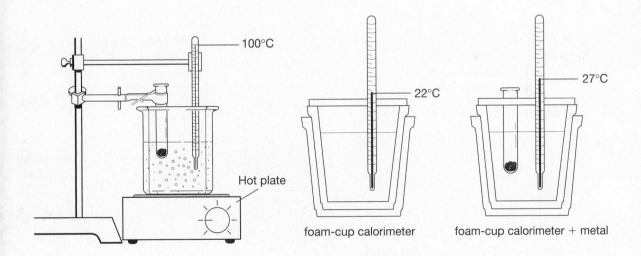

foam-cup calorimeter   foam-cup calorimeter + metal

Name ______________________ Date ________________ Class ________________

1. What was the final temperature of the metal?
   a. Trial 1

   b. Trial 2

2. What was the ΔT for the metal?
   a. Trial 1

   b. Trial 2

3. What was the ΔT for the water?
   a. Trial 1

   b. Trial 2

4. Calculate the heat change for the water. (Specific heat capacity for water is 4.184 J/g•C.)
   a. Trial 1

   b. Trial 2

5. Calculate the heat change for the metal.
   a. Trial 1

   b. Trial 2

6. Calculate the specific heat of the metal.
   a. Trial 1

   b. Trial 2

7. What metal might this have been?
   a. aluminum b. silver c. iron d. mercury

THERMOCHEMISTRY

Vocabulary Review

Match the correct vocabulary term to each numbered statement. Write the letter of the correct term on the line.

Column A	Column B
_____ 1. the quantity of heat that raises the temperature of 1 g of pure water by 1°C	**a.** calorie
_____ 2. the capacity to do work or to supply heat	**b.** joule
_____ 3. a device used to measure the amount of heat absorbed or released during chemical or physical processes	**c.** exothermic
_____ 4. the heat content of a substance	**d.** molar heat of solution
_____ 5. the SI unit of energy	**e.** molar heat of fusion
_____ 6. the heat absorbed by 1 mole of a substance in melting from a solid to a liquid at a constant temperature	**f.** calorimeter
_____ 7. If two or more thermochemical equations are added to give a final equation, their heat changes can be added to determine the final heat change.	**g.** enthalpy
_____ 8. the heat absorbed or released by the dissolution of 1 mole of substance	**h.** energy
_____ 9. a chemical change in which heat is absorbed	**i.** Hess's law of heat summation
_____ 10. a process that loses heat to the surroundings	**j.** endothermic reaction

17 THERMOCHEMISTRY

Chapter Quiz

Choose the best answer and write its letter on the line.

_____ 1. Thermochemistry is the study of   17.1
   a. reaction rates.   c. combustion reactions.
   b. heat transfer during reactions.   d. stoichiometry relationships.

_____ 2. A sample of glass that has a mass of 6.0 g gives off 12 J of heat. If the   17.1
   temperature of the sample changes by 4.0°C during this change, what
   is the specific heat of the glass?
   a. 2.0 J/g•°C   c. 0.50 J/g•°C
   b. 1.1 J/g•°C   d. 0.45 J/g•°C

_____ 3. The accurate and precise measurement of heat flow for chemical   17.1
   and physical processes is called:
   a. calorimetry.   c. thermochemistry.
   b. stoichiometry.   d. thermometry.

_____ 4. Two water solutions that have a density of 1.00 g/mL are mixed, and a   17.2
   reaction occurs. The temperature rises from 25.0°C to 27.0°C. Given
   that the heat capacity is 4.18 J/g•°C and that the total mass of the
   water is 75.0 g, what is the heat change for the reaction?
   a. 6.27 J   c. 314 J
   b. 125 J   d. 627 J

_____ 5. If 4.0 mol of a substance releases 12 kJ when it decomposes, what is   17.2
   ΔH for the process, in terms of kJ per mole of reactant?
   a. 3.0 kJ   c. 0.33 kJ
   b. −3.0 kJ   d. −0.33 kJ

_____ 6. The heat absorbed by 1 mol of a substance in melting from a solid to a   17.3
   liquid at constant temperature is symbolized by which of these symbols?
   a. ΔH_{fus} c. ΔH_{vap}
   b. ΔH_{solid} d. ΔH_{soln}

Fill in the word(s) that will make each statement true.

7. When a chemical equation is reversed, the sign of ΔH _____.   17.3

8. The value of ΔH_f^0 of any free element in the standard state is   17.4
   set at _____.

9. The standard heat of reaction is equal to ΔH_f^0 of the products   17.4
   _____ ΔH_f^0 of the reactants.

17 THERMOCHEMISTRY

Chapter Test A

A. Matching

Match the correct description to each numbered term. Write the letter of the correct description on the line.

Column A

_____ 1. heat capacity

_____ 2. law of conservation of energy

_____ 3. heat of reaction

_____ 4. energy

_____ 5. calorimeter

_____ 6. specific heat

_____ 7. heat

_____ 8. standard heat of formation

_____ 9. calorie

_____ 10. exothermic process

Column B

a. the quantity of heat that raises the temperature of 1 g of pure water 1°C

b. the change in enthalpy that accompanies the formation of 1 mole of a compound from its elements, with all substances in their standard states at 25°C

c. energy that always flows from a warmer object to a cooler object

d. a process that loses heat to the surroundings

e. the amount of heat required to change the temperature of an object by exactly 1°C

f. the capacity to do work or to supply heat

g. the heat absorbed or released by a chemical reaction

h. the amount of heat required to raise the temperature of 1 gram of a substance 1°C

i. In any chemical or physical process, energy is neither created nor destroyed.

j. a device used to measure the amount of heat absorbed or released during chemical or

B. Multiple Choice

Choose the best answer and write its letter on the line.

_____ 11. The SI unit of energy is
   a. heat capacity.
   b. calorie.
   c. joule.
   d. enthalpy.

_____ 12. How many calories are required to raise the temperature of 75.0 g of water from 20°C to 50°C?

    a. 1.50×10^3 cal   **c.** 3750 cal

    b. 2250 cal   **d.** 75.0 cal

_____ 13. If 1 Calorie = 4.18 kJ, how many kJ of energy can be released by an apple containing 125 Cal?

    a. 0.0334 kJ   **c.** 522 kJ

    b. 29.9 kJ   **d.** 5.22×10^5 kJ

_____ 14. The temperature of a 6.0-g sample of glass changed from 20°C to 45°C when it absorbed 550 J of heat. What is the specific heat of this glass sample?

    a. 3.7 J/g•°C   **c.** 2300 J/g•°C

    b. 0.27 J/g•°C   **d.** 130 J/g•°C

_____ 15. The enthalpy of a system is the same as its:

    a. specific heat.   **c.** heat of combustion.

    b. heat of reaction.   **d.** heat content.

_____ 16. When your body is warmed by an electric blanket during the winter, this process is said to be

    a. endothermic.   **c.** isothermic.

    b. exothermic.   **d.** none of the above

_____ 17. A student mixes two water solutions with an initial temperature of 25.0°C to form a final solution with a mass of 65.0 g at 30.0°C. What is the heat change, in kJ, for this reaction?

    a. 325 kJ   **c.** 1.36 kJ

    b. 272 kJ   **d.** 1.95 kJ

_____ 18. Given the equation $2Mg(s) + O_2(g) \rightarrow 2MgO(s) + 72.3$ kJ, which of the following is true?

    a. The reaction is endothermic.   **c.** $\Delta H = +72.3$ kJ

    b. $\Delta H = -72.3$ kJ   **d.** The reaction absorbs heat.

_____ 19. Given the equation in question 18, how much heat is involved in the production of 5.0 mol of MgO?

    a. 36 kJ   **c.** 360 kJ

    b. 72 kJ   **d.** 180 kJ

_____ 20. Given the equation $Si(s) + 2Cl_2(g) \rightarrow SiCl_2(g) \rightarrow SiCl_2(l) + 687$ kJ, how much heat is produced when 106 g of Cl_2 react?

    a. 7.28×10^4 kJ   **c.** 360 kJ

    b. 513 kJ   **d.** 180 kJ

_____ 21. Which of the following statements is true?

    a. $\Delta H_{fus} = \Delta H_{solid}$ **c.** ΔH_{fus} is always negative.

    b. $\Delta H_{fus} = -\Delta H_{solid}$ **d.** ΔH_{solid} is always positive.

_____ 22. How much heat, in kJ, is required to melt 54.0 g of ice at 0°C into water at 0°C if ΔH_{fus} for water = 6.01 kJ/mol?

    a. 0.111 kJ   **c.** 18.0 kJ

    b. 325 kJ   **d.** 8.99 kJ

_____ 23. How much heat is required to convert 9.00 g of water at 100°C into steam at 100°C, if ΔH_{vap} for water = 40.7 kJ/mol?

    a. 20.4 kJ   **c.** 18.0 kJ

    b. 366 kJ   **d.** 81.4 kJ

_____ 24. If the molar heat of solution of NH_4NO_3 is 25.7 kJ/mol, how much heat (in kJ) would be required to dissolve 20.0 g of NH_4NO_3 in water?

    a. 103 kJ   **c.** 0.250 kJ

    b. 514 kJ   **d.** 6.43 kJ

_____ 25. Calculate the enthalpy change, ΔH in kJ, for the reaction

$$H_2O(s) \rightarrow H_2(g) + \tfrac{1}{2}O_2(g)$$

Use the following:

$H_2(g) + \tfrac{1}{2}O_2(g) \rightarrow H_2O(l)$ $\Delta H = -285.9$ kJ

$H_2O(s) \rightarrow H_2O(l)$ $\Delta H = +6.0$ kJ

    a. −291.9 kJ   **c.** −279.9 k

    b. +291.9 kJ   **d.** +279.9 kJ

C. Essay

Write a short essay for the following.

26. Distinguish between endothermic and exothermic processes. Give at least three examples of each that you encounter in everyday life.

_____

_____

_____

_____

_____

_____

_____

_____

D. Problems

Solve the following problems in the space provided. Show your work.

27. Determine the specific heat of a material if a 12-g sample absorbed 96 J as it was heated from 20°C to 40°C.

28. If 22.0 mL of water containing 0.030 mol of HCl is mixed with 38.0 mL of water containing 0.030 mol of NaOH in a calorimeter such that the initial temperature of each solution was 27.0°C and the final temperature of the mixture is 35.0°C, how much heat (in kJ) is released in the reaction? Assume that the densities of the solutions are 1.00 g/mL.

29. Given the equation $3CO(g) + Fe_2O_3(s) \rightarrow 2Fe(s) + 3CO_2(g) + 24.7$ kJ, how much heat is released when 56.0 g of CO react?

30. How many grams of water at 0°C can be frozen into ice at 0°C if 55.0 kJ of heat is removed? ΔH_{solid} for water $= -6.01$ kJ/mol

31. What is the enthalpy change, ΔH in kJ, for the following reaction?

$2Mg(s) + SiCl_4(l) \rightarrow Si(s) + 2MgCl_2(s)$

Use the following:

$Si(s) + 2Cl_2(g) \rightarrow SiCl_4(l) \qquad \Delta H = -687$ kJ
$Mg(s) + Cl_2(g) \rightarrow MgCl_2(s) \qquad \Delta H = -641$ kJ

32. What is the standard heat of reaction (ΔH^0) for the combustion of ethane, $C_2H_6(g)$, to form carbon dioxide gas and water? Write the final balanced equation for the reaction.

Standard heats of reaction:

$C_2H_6 = -84.68$ kJ
$O_2(g) = 0.0$ kJ
$CO_2(g) = -393.5$ kJ
$H_2O(l) = -285.5$ kJ

Name _____ Date _____ Class _____

Chapter Test B

A. Matching

Match the correct vocabulary term to each numbered statement. Write the letter of the correct term on the line.

Column A	Column B
_____ 1. the accurate and precise measurement of heat flow for chemical and physical processes	**a.** thermochemical equation
_____ 2. the heat of reaction for the complete burning of 1 mole of a substance	**b.** joule
_____ 3. the study of the heat transfers that occur during chemical reactions and physical changes of state	**c.** endothermic process
_____ 4. a process that absorbs heat from the surroundings	**d.** Hess's law of heat summation
_____ 5. the heat content of a substance	**e.** chemical potential energy
_____ 6. If two or more thermochemical equations are added to give a final equation, their heat changes can be added to determine the final heat change.	**f.** heat of combustion
_____ 7. the energy stored in the chemical bonds of a substance	**g.** calorimetry
_____ 8. the heat absorbed by 1 mole of a substance in melting from a solid to a liquid at a constant temperature	**h.** thermochemistry
_____ 9. the SI unit of energy	**i.** molar heat of fusion
_____ 10. a chemical equation that includes the enthalpy change	**j.** enthalpy

B. Multiple Choice

Choose the best answer and write its letter on the line.

_____ 11. The quantity of heat that raises the temperature of 1 gram of pure water 1°C is
   a. heat capacity.   **c.** a calorie.
   b. joule.   **d.** heat of combustion.

_____ 12. The amount of heat required to change the temperature of an object by exactly 1°C is the object's
   a. heat of combustion.   **c.** enthalpy.
   b. heat capacity.   **d.** heat of formation.

_____ 13. The number of calories required to raise the temperature of 55.0 g of water from 25°C to 45°C is
   a. 1.10×10^3 cal.   **c.** 2480 cal.
   b. 1380 cal.   **d.** 55.0 cal.

_____ 14. If 1 Calorie = 4.18 kJ, how many kJ of energy can be released by a banana containing 150 Cal?
   a. 6.3×10^5 kJ   **c.** 36 kJ
   b. 0.028 kJ   **d.** 630 kJ

_____ 15. The temperature of an 8.0-g sample of metal changed from 25°C to 50°C when it absorbed 420 J of heat. What is the specific heat of this sample?
   a. 130 J/g·°C   **c.** 1300 J/g·°C
   b. 2.1 J/g·°C   **d.** 0.48 J/g·°C

_____ 16. As perspiration evaporates from your skin, your body is cooled. With respect to your body, this process is said to be
   a. endothermic.   **c.** isothermic.
   b. exothermic.   **d.** none of the above.

_____ 17. A student mixes two water solutions beginning at 22.0°C to form a final solution with a mass of 58.0 g at 28.5°C. What is the heat change, in kJ, for this reaction?
   a. 37.3 kJ   **c.** 27.2 kJ
   b. 242 kJ   **d.** 1.58 kJ

_____ 18. Given the equation $I_2(s) + 62.4$ kJ $\rightarrow I_2(g)$, which of the following is true?
   a. The reaction is exothermic.
   b. $\Delta H = +62.4$ kJ
   c. $\Delta H = -62.4$ kJ
   d. The reaction releases heat.

_____ 19. Given the equation in question 18, how much heat is involved in the production of 3.5 mol $I_2(g)$?
   a. 110 kJ   **c.** 220 kJ
   b. 62 kJ   **d.** 3.5 kJ

_____ 20. Given the equation $C_3H_8(g) + 5O_2(g) \rightarrow 3CO_2(g) + 4H_2O(g) + 2220$ kJ, how much heat is produced when 80.0 g of O_2 react?
   a. 1110 kJ   **c.** 2.50 kJ
   b. 5.55×10^3 kJ   **d.** 1.78×10^5 kJ

_____ 21. Which of the following statements is true?
   a. $\Delta H_{vap} = \Delta H_{cond}$ **c.** ΔH_{vap} is always negative.
   b. $\Delta H_{vap} = -\Delta H_{cond}$ **d.** ΔH_{cond} is always positive.

_____ **22.** How much heat, in kJ, is released when 108 g of water at 0°C freezes to ice at 0°C if ΔH_{solid} for water = −6.01 kJ/mol?
    a. 18.0 kJ   **c.** 649 kJ
    b. 6.00 kJ   **d.** 36.1 kJ

_____ **23.** How much heat is released in the condensation of 27.0 g of steam at 100°C to water at 100°C if ΔH_{cond} for water = −40.7 kJ/mol?
    a. 1.51 kJ   **c.** 61.0 kJ
    b. 1.10 3 10^3 kJ   **d.** 27.1 kJ

_____ **24.** If the molar heat of solution of NaOH is −445.1 kJ/mol, how much heat (in kJ) will be released if 80.00 g of NaOH are dissolved in water?
    a. 22.6 kJ   **c.** 5.564 kJ
    b. 890.2 kJ   **d.** 35610 kJ

_____ **25.** Calculate the enthalpy change, ΔH in kJ, for the reaction
$NO(g) + \frac{1}{2}O_2(g) \rightarrow NO_2(g)$
Use the following:

$\frac{1}{2}N_2(g) + \frac{1}{2}O_2(g) \rightarrow NO(g)$	$\Delta H = +90.25$ kJ
$\frac{1}{2}N_2(g) + O_2(g) \rightarrow NO_2(g)$	$\Delta H = +33.18$ kJ

    a. −123.43 kJ   **c.** 57.07 kJ
    b. +123.43 kJ   **d.** −57.07 kJ

C. Essay

Write a short essay for the following.

26. Explain why a burn from steam is generally more serious than a burn from very hot water.

_____

_____

_____

_____

_____

_____

D. Problems

Solve the following problems in the space provided. Show your work.

27. Determine the specific heat of a material if an 18-g sample absorbed 75 J as it was heated from 15°C to 40°C.

28. If 27.0 mL of water containing 0.035 mol HCl is mixed with 28.0 mL of water containing 0.035 mol NaOH in a calorimeter such that the initial temperature of each solution was 24.0°C and the final temperature of the mixture is 33.0°C, how much heat (in kJ) is released in the reaction? Assume that the densities of the solutions are 1.00 g/mL.

29. Given the equation $C_2H_4(g) + 3O_2(g) \rightarrow 2CO_2(g) + 2H_2O(l) + 1411$ kJ, how much heat is released when 8.00 g of O_2 react?

30. How many grams of ice at 0°C can be melted into water at 0°C by the addition of 75.0 kJ of heat? ΔH_{fus} for water = 6.01 kJ/mol

31. What is the enthalpy change, ΔH in kJ, for the following reaction:

$2C(s) + O_2(g) \rightarrow 2CO(g)$

Given the following:

$C(s) + O_2(g) \rightarrow CO_2(g)$ $\Delta H = -393.5$ kJ
$2CO(g) + O_2(g) \rightarrow 2CO_2(g)$ $\Delta H = -565.7$ kJ

32. What is the heat of reaction (ΔH) for the combustion of benzene, $C_6H_6(l)$, to form carbon dioxide gas and water? Write the final balanced equation for the reaction.

Standard heats of formation:

$C_6H_6 = +48.50$ kJ
$O_2(g) = 0.0$ kJ
$CO_2(g) = -393.5$ kJ
$H_2O(l) = -285.8$ kJ

QUICK LAB: Heat of Fusion of Ice

Laboratory Recordsheet   Use with Section 17.3

PURPOSE

To estimate the heat of fusion of ice.

MATERIALS

- ice
- foam cup
- 100-mL graduated cylinder
- thermometer
- hot water
- temperature probe (optional)

PROCEDURE

1. Fill the graduated cylinder with hot tap water and let stand for 1 minute. Pour the water into the sink.

2. Use the graduated cylinder to measure 70 mL of hot water. Pour the water into the foam cup. Measure the temperature of the water.

3. Add an ice cube to the cup of water. Gently swirl the cup. Measure the temperature of the water as soon as the ice cube has completely melted.

4. Pour the water from the cup into the graduated cylinder and measure the volume.

ANALYSES AND CONCLUSIONS

1. Calculate the mass of the ice. (*Hint:* The mass of ice melted is the same as the increase in the volume of the water.) Convert this to moles.

   _____

   _____

   _____

2. Calculate the heat of fusion of ice (in kJ/mol) by dividing the heat transferred from the water by the moles of the ice melted.

   _____

   _____

   _____

3. Compare your experimental value for the heat of fusion of ice with the accepted value of 6.01 kJ/mol. Account for any error.

_____

_____

_____

4. How might you revise the procedure to achieve more accurate results?

_____

_____

_____

_____

Name _____ Date _____ Class _____

SMALL-SCALE LAB: Heat of Combustion
of a Candle

Laboratory Recordsheet   Use with Section 17.4

SAFETY

Wear safety glasses and follow the standard safety procedures outlined on page 7 of this manual. Keep the burning candle away from combustible materials.

PURPOSE

To observe a burning candle and calculate the heat associated with the combustion reaction.

MATERIALS

- candle
- aluminum foil
- safety matches

- ruler
- balance
- temperature probe (optional)

PROCEDURE

Measure and record the length of a candle in centimeters. Place the candle on a small piece of aluminum foil and measure the mass of the foil-candle system. Note the time as you light the candle. Let the candle burn for five minutes. While you wait, begin answering the ANALYSIS questions. After about five minutes, extinguish the candle and record the time. Measure the mass of the foil-candle system again. Do not try to measure the mass while the candle is burning.

ANALYSIS

Using your experimental data, answer the following questions.

1. Observe the candle burn and draw a picture of what you see.

2. Examine the flame closely. Is it the wax or the wick that burns?

   _____

3. If you said the wax, how does the wax burn without touching the flame? If you said the wick, what is the function of the wax?

   _____

   _____

4. If you could measure the temperature near the flame, you would find that the air is much hotter above the flame than it is beside it. Why? Explain.

   _____

   _____

5. Scientists have often wondered if a candle would burn well in zero gravity. How would zero gravity change the shape of the flame?

   _____

   _____

6. How much length and mass did the candle lose? Are these data more consistent with the wax or the wick burning?

   _____

   _____

7. Keeping in mind that *wick* is also a verb, explain how a candle works.

   _____

   _____

8. The formula for candle wax can be approximated as $C_{20}H_{42}$. Write and balance an equation for the complete combustion of the candle wax.

9. Calculate the number of moles of candle wax burned in the experiment.

10. Calculate the heat of combustion of candle wax in kJ/mol. The standard heat of formation of candle wax ($C_{20}H_{42}$) is -2230 kJ/mol. The standard heats of formation of carbon dioxide and water are -394 kJ/mol and -242 kJ/mol, respectively. The heat of combustion of candle wax equals the sum of the heats of formations of the products minus the sum of the heats of formation of the reactants.

11. Calculate the amount of heat (in kJ) released in your reaction. (*Hint:* Multiply the number of moles of candle wax burned in the experiment by the heat of combustion of candle wax.)

YOU'RE THE CHEMIST

Use the space below to write your observations to the small-scale activities in the *You're the Chemist* section.

_____

_____

_____

_____

_____

_____

18.1 RATES OF REACTION

Section Review

Objectives

- Describe how to express the rate of a chemical reaction
- Identify four factors that influence the rate of a chemical reaction

Vocabulary

- rate
- collision theory
- activation energy
- activated complex
- transition state
- inhibitor

Part A Completion

Use this completion exercise to check your understanding of the concepts and terms that are introduced in this section. Each blank can be completed with a term, short phrase, or number.

____1____ measure the speed of any change that occurs within

a time interval. Collision theory states that particles ___2___ when

they collide, provided that they have enough ___3___.

The rate at which a chemical reaction occurs is determined

by an ___4___ energy barrier. The activation energy is the ___5___

energy that reactants must have to be converted to ___6___. The

higher the activation energy barrier, the ___7___ the reaction.

Chemists help reactants overcome the activation barrier in a

number of ways. Two effective methods are to increase the ___8___

at which the reaction is done or use a ___9___. Rates of reaction

can also be increased by ___10___ the concentration of reactants.

1. _____

2. _____

3. _____

4. _____

5. _____

6. _____

7. _____

8. _____

9. _____

10. _____

Part B True-False

Classify each of these statements as always true, AT; sometimes true, ST; or never true, NT.

_____ **11.** An increase in temperature will increase the rate of a reaction.

_____ **12.** A catalyst is considered as a reactant in a chemical reaction.

_____ **13.** The speed of a reaction can be increased by increasing reactant concentration or decreasing particle size.

_____ **14.** An enzyme is a biological catalyst.

Part C Matching

Match each description in Column B to the correct term in Column A.

Column A

_____ **15.** rate

_____ **16.** collision theory

_____ **17.** activation energy

_____ **18.** transition state

_____ **19.** activated complex

_____ **20.** inhibitor

Column B

a. synonym for an activated complex

b. speed of a change that occurs over time

c. substance that interferes with the action of a catalyst

d. Particles can react to form products when they collide, provided they have enough kinetic energy.

e. an unstable arrangement of atoms that forms momentarily at the peak of the activation energy barrier

f. minimum energy that particles must have in order to react

Part D Questions and Problems

Answer the following question and solve the following problem in the space provided.

21. An ice machine can produce 120 kg of ice in 24 hours. Express the rate of ice production in kg/h.

22. Which of the following will increase the rate of a reaction?
   a. increase particle size
   b. increase temperature
   c. decrease concentration
   d. add a catalyst

18.2 REVERSIBLE REACTIONS AND EQUILIBRIUM

Section Review

Objectives

- Describe how the amounts of reactants and products change in a chemical system at equilibrium
- Identify three stresses that can change the equilibrium position of a chemical system
- Explain what the value of K_{eq} indicates about the position of equilibrium

Vocabulary

- reversible reaction
- chemical equilibrium
- equilibrium position
- Le Châtelier's principle
- equilibrium constant (K_{eq})

Key Equation

- $K_{eq} = \dfrac{[C]^c \times [D]^d}{[A]^a \times [B]^b}$

  When $aA + bB \rightleftharpoons cC + dD$

Part A Completion

Use this completion exercise to check your understanding of the concepts and terms that are introduced in this section. Each blank can be completed with a term, short phrase, or number.

In principle, all reactions are ___1___. That is, reactants go to ___2___ in the ___3___ direction, and products go to ___4___ in the ___5___ direction.

The point at which the rate of conversion of ___6___ to ___7___ and vice versa is equal is the ___8___ position. The ___9___ of a reversible reaction, K_{eq}, is useful for determining the position of equilibrium. It is essentially a measure of the ___10___ of products to reactants at equilibrium. The direction of change in the position of equilibrium may be predicted by applying ___11___ principle.

1. _____

2. _____

3. _____

4. _____

5. _____

6. _____

7. _____

8. _____

9. _____

10. _____

11. _____

Part B True-False

Classify each of these statements as always true, AT; sometimes true, ST; or never true, NT.

_____ **12.** The concentrations of reactants and products in a system at dynamic equilibrium are always changing.

_____ **13.** A change in the pressure on a system can cause a shift in the equilibrium position.

_____ **14.** For a chemical equilibrium to be established, the chemical reaction must be irreversible.

_____ **15.** The K_{eq} for a certain reaction was 2×10^{-7}. For this reaction at equilibrium, the concentration of the reactants is greater than the concentration of the products.

Part C Matching

Match each description in Column B to the correct term in Column A.

Column A	**Column B**
_____ **16.** reversible reaction	**a.** state of balance in which forward and reverse reactions take place at the same rate
_____ **17.** chemical equilibrium	**b.** relative concentrations of reactants and products of a reaction that has reached equilibrium
_____ **18.** equilibrium position	**c.** When stress is applied to a system at equilibrium, the system changes to relieve the stress.
_____ **19.** Le Châtelier's principle	**d.** reaction in which conversion of reactants to products and products to reactants occur simultaneously
_____ **20.** equilibrium constant	**e.** ratio of product concentrations to reactant concentrations with each raised to a power given by the number of moles of the substance in the balanced equation

Part D Problem

Solve the following problem in the space provided. Show your work.

21.
$$2SO_3(g) \rightarrow 2SO_2(g) + O_2(g)$$

Calculate K_{eq} for this reaction if the equilibrium concentrations are:
$[SO_2] = 0.42M$, $[O_2] = 0.21M$, $[SO_3] = 0.072M$

18.3 SOLUBILITY EQUILIBRIUM

Section Review

Objectives

- Describe the relationship between the solubility product constant and the solubility of a compound
- Predict whether precipitation will occur when the two salt solutions are mixed

Vocabulary

- solubility product constant (K_{sp})
- common ion
- common ion effect

Part A Completion

Use this completion exercise to check your understanding of the concepts and terms that are introduced in this section. Each blank can be completed with a term, short phrase, or number.

The ___1___ is the equilibrium constant for the equilibrium

between an ionic solid and its ions in solution. The term ___2___

refers to the lowering of the solubility of a substance by the ___3___

of a common ion. If the ion-product concentration of two ions in

solution is greater than the K_{sp} of the compound formed from the

two ions, a(n) ___4___ will form.

1. _____

2. _____

3. _____

4. _____

Part B Matching

Match each description in Column B to the correct term in Column A.

Column A	Column B

_____ **5.** solubility product constant (K_{sp})

a. an equilibrium constant that can be applied to the solubility of electrolytes

_____ **6.** common ion

b. a decrease in the solubility of a substance caused by the addition of a common ion

_____ **7.** common ion effect

c. an ion that is common to both salts in a solution

Part C Problem

Answer the following in the space provided.

8. Will a precipitate form when 0.00070 mol Na_2CO_3 is mixed with 0.0015 mol $Ba(OH)_2$ in one liter of solution? Assume that these two salts both dissolve completely. Refer to Table 18.2 in your textbook.

18.4 ENTROPY AND FREE ENERGY

Section Review

Objectives

- Identify two characteristics of spontaneous reactions
- Describe the role of entropy in chemical reactions
- Identify two factors that determine the spontaneity of a reaction
- Define Gibbs free-energy change

Vocabulary

- free energy
- spontaneous reaction
- nonspontaneous reactions
- entropy
- law of disorder
- Gibbs free-energy change

Key Equation

- $\Delta G = \Delta H - T\Delta S$

Part A Completion

Use this completion exercise to check your understanding of the concepts and terms that are introduced in this section. Each blank can be completed with a term, short phrase, or number.

Reactions that actually occur as written are called __1__

reactions. Equations for other reactions may be written, but the

reactions are __2__. All spontaneous reactions release __3__

that becomes available to do __4__. This energy is called __5__.

It is the natural tendency for all things to go to lower __6__

and toward __7__ disorder. In addition to the change in heat

energy, __8__ is a factor that determines whether a reaction

is spontaneous.

Entropy is a measure of the __9__ of a system. The __10__

states that processes move in the direction of __11__ disorder.

1. _____

2. _____

3. _____

4. _____

5. _____

6. _____

7. _____

8. _____

9. _____

10. _____

11. _____

Part B True-False

Classify each of these statements as always true, AT; sometimes true, ST; or never true, NT.

_____ **12.** An exothermic reaction is a spontaneous reaction.

_____ **13.** The numerical value of ΔG is negative in spontaneous processes because the system loses free energy.

_____ **14.** Some spontaneous reactions appear to be nonspontaneous because their rate of reaction is slow.

_____ **15.** Spontaneous reactions release free energy.

_____ **16.** Entropy will increase in a spontaneous reaction.

Part C Matching

Match each description in Column B to the correct term in Column A.

Column A

_____ **17.** free energy

_____ **18.** spontaneous reactions

_____ **19.** nonspontaneous reactions

_____ **20.** entropy

_____ **21.** law of disorder

_____ **22.** Gibbs free-energy change

Column B

a. measure of the disorder of a system

b. maximum amount of energy that can be coupled to another process to do work

c. energy in a reaction that is available to do work

d. It is the natural tendency of systems to move in the direction of maximum disorder.

e. reactions that do not give products under the specified conditions

f. reactions that favor formation of products under the specified conditions

Part D Questions

Answer the following in the space provided.

23. In each of the following pairs, choose the system with the higher entropy.

a. a heap of loose stamps or stamps in an album _____

b. ice cubes in their tray or ice cubes in a bucket _____

c. 10 mL of water at 100°C or 10 mL of steam at 100°C _____

d. the people watching the parade or a parade _____

24. Which combination of factors will always give a spontaneous reaction?

a. heat absorbed, entropy increases

b. heat released, entropy increases

c. heat released, entropy decreases

d. heat absorbed, entropy decreases

25. Which combination described in question 24 will never give a spontaneous reaction?

THE PROGRESS OF CHEMICAL REACTIONS

18.5

Section Review

Objectives

- Describe the general relationship between the value of the specific rate constant, k, and the speed of a chemical reaction
- Interpret the hills and valleys in a reaction progress curve

Vocabulary

- rate law
- specific rate constant
- first-order reaction
- elementary reaction
- reaction mechanism
- intermediate

Key Equation

- rate = $k[A]^a[B]^b$

Part A Completion

Use this completion exercise to check your understanding of the concepts and terms that are introduced in this section. Each blank can be completed with a term, short phrase, or number.

The ___1___ of a reaction is dependent in part on the

___2___ of the reactants. An equation that relates reaction

rate to reactant concentration is called a ___3___. In a rate law

equation, k is known as the ___4___.

The power to which a reaction concentration is raised is called

the ___5___ of the reaction in that reactant. A reaction whose rate

is directly proportional to the concentration of one reactant is

called a ___6___ reaction. A reaction that is first order for each of

two reactants is ___7___ overall. The actual order of a reaction is

determined by ___8___.

A single-step reaction is called an ___9___. A series of elementary

reactions combine to form the ___10___ of a complex reaction.

1. _____

3. _____

4. _____

5. _____

6. _____

7. _____

8. _____

9. _____

10. _____

Name _____ Date _____ Class _____

Part B True-False

Classify each of these statements as always true, AT; sometimes true, ST; or never true, NT.

_____ **11.** The rate order of a reaction can be determined from the balanced equation.

_____ **12.** There is at least one intermediate product in a chemical reaction.

_____ **13.** There is at least one activated complex in a chemical reaction.

_____ **14.** An elementary reaction is a one-step reaction.

Part C Matching

Match each description in Column B to the correct term in Column A.

Column A	Column B
_____ **15.** rate law	**a.** a single-step reaction
_____ **16.** specific rate constant	**b.** reaction in which the rate is directly proportional to the concentration of one reactant
_____ **17.** first-order reaction	**c.** a product of a reaction that becomes a reactant in another step of the reaction
_____ **18.** elementary reaction	**d.** expression relating the rate of a reaction to the concentration of the reactants
_____ **19.** reaction mechanism	**e.** series of elementary reactions that take place during a complex reaction
_____ **20.** intermediate	**f.** proportionality constant relating the concentrations of reactants to the reaction rate

Part D Question

Answer the following question in the space provided.

21. Below is the reaction progress curve for a complex reaction. Describe the reaction represented by the curve (number of steps and the significance of points *A, B, C,* and *D*).

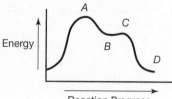

_____

_____

_____

_____

REACTION RATES AND EQUILIBRIUM

18

Practice Problems

In your notebook, solve the following problems.

SECTION 18.1 RATES OF REACTION

1. List three ways that reaction rates can generally be increased.

2. Ethyl acetate ($C_4H_8O_2$) reacts with a solution of sodium hydroxide (NaOH) in water to form sodium acetate ($C_2H_3O_2Na$) and ethyl alcohol (C_2H_6O). Suppose at 25°C two moles of ethyl acetate react completely in four hours. How would you express the rate of reaction?

3. How would the following actions likely change the rate of the reaction in problem 2?

    a. the temperature is lowered to 4°C.

    b. the concentration of sodium hydroxide in water is increased.

4. Ethyl acetate and water are not miscible; thus, the reaction in problem 2 only occurs at the interface of the two liquids. What would be the effect on the reaction rate of adding a solvent to make the reaction homogeneous?

SECTION 18.2 REVERSIBLE REACTIONS AND EQUILIBRIUM

1. Write the expression for the equilibrium constant for this reaction:
$$2N_2O_5(g) \rightleftharpoons 4NO_2(g) + O_2(g)$$

2. Calculate the equilibrium constant for the reaction in problem 1 if the equilibrium concentrations are $[N_2O_5] = 0.50$ mol/L, $[NO_2] = 0.80$ mol/L, $[O_2] = 0.20$ mol/L.

3. How would the equilibrium position for the equation in problem 1 be affected by

    a. an addition of O_2 to the reaction vessel?

    b. a decrease in the pressure?

4. The equilibrium constant for the reaction of nitrogen dioxide to form dinitrogen tetroxide is 5.6.
$$2NO_2\ (g) \rightleftharpoons N_2O_4\ (g)$$
In a one-liter container, the amount of N_2O_4, at equilibrium, is 0.66 mol. What is the equilibrium concentration of NO_2?

5. Write the equilibrium constant expression for each of the following reactions.

    a. $4NO(g) + 2O_2(g) \rightleftharpoons 2N_2O_4\ (g)$

    b. $2NO(g) + Br_2(g) \rightleftharpoons 2NOBr(g)$

    c. $CO(g) + 2H_2(g) \rightleftharpoons CH_3OH(g)$

    d. $SO_2(g) + NO_2(g) \rightleftharpoons SO_3(g) + NO(g)$

6. What effect would an increase in pressure have on the equilibrium position of each reaction in problem 5?

7. Which value of K_{eq} indicates most favorably for product formation, $K_{eq} = 1 \times 10^{12}$, $K_{eq} = 1.5$, or $K_{eq} = 5.6 \times 10^{-4}$?

8. Hydrogen sulfide gas decomposes into its elements and establishes an equilibrium at 1400 °C.

$$2H_2S(g) \rightleftharpoons 2H_2(g) + S_2(g)$$

A liter of this gas mixture at equilibrium contains 0.18 mol H_2S, 0.014 mol H_2, and 0.035 mol S_2. Calculate the equilibrium constant, K_{eq}, for this reaction.

SECTION 18.3 SOLUBILITY EQUILIBRIUM

1. Write the solubility product expression for **a.** $Ca(OH)_2$ and **b.** Ag_2CO_3.

2. What is the concentration of silver ions in a saturated solution of silver carbonate? The K_{sp} of Ag_2CO_3 is 8.1×10^{-12}.

3. The equilibrium concentration of hydroxide ions in a saturated solution of iron(II) hydroxide is $1.2 \times 10^{-5} M$ at a certain temperature. Calculate the K_{sp} of $Fe(OH)_2$ at this temperature.

4. Strontium carbonate has a $K_{sp} = 9.3 \times 10^{-10}$ at 25°C. What is the concentration of strontium ions in a saturated solution of $SrCO_3$?

5. What is the equilibrium concentration of silver ions at 25°C in a 1.0-L saturated solution of silver carbonate to which 0.20 mol of Na_2CO_3 has been added? The K_{sp} of Ag_2CO_3 is 8.1×10^{-12} at 25°C.

6. Will a precipitate of $PbSO_4$ form when 400.0 mL of $0.0050M$ $MgSO_4$ is mixed with 600.0 mL of $0.0020M$ $Pb(NO_3)_2$? The K_{sp} of $PbSO_4 = 6.3 \times 10^{-7}$.

7. Will precipitation of $CaCO_3$ occur when 500.0 mL of $4.2 \times 10^{-3} M$ $CaCl_2$ is mixed with 500.0 mL of $2.6 \times 10^{-3} M$ Na_2CO_3? The K_{sp} of $CaCO_3$ is 4.5×10^{-9}.

8. Which of these compounds would not decrease the solubility of $Mg(OH)_2$ when added to a saturated solution of the compound?

$$NaOH, MgCl_2, NaCl, KOH$$

SECTION 18.4 ENTROPY AND FREE ENERGY

1. When gently warmed, the element iodine will sublime:

$$I_2(s) \rightarrow I_2(g)$$

Is this process accompanied by an increase or decrease in entropy?

2. Does entropy increase or decrease when air is cooled and liquefied (changed from a gas to a liquid)?

3. Is the degree of disorder increasing or decreasing in these reactions?

   a. $H_2(g) + Br_2(l) \rightarrow 2HBr(g)$

   b. $CuSO_4 \cdot 5H_2O(s) \rightarrow CuSO_4(s) + 5H_2O(g)$

   c. $2XeO_3(s) \rightarrow 2Xe(g) + 3O_2(g)$

4. Classify each of these systems as always spontaneous (A), never spontaneous (N), or depends on the relative magnitude of the heat and entropy changes (D).

   a. entropy decreases, heat is released

   b. entropy decreases, heat is absorbed

   c. entropy increases, heat is absorbed

   d. entropy increases, heat is released

SECTION 18.5 THE PROGRESS OF CHEMICAL REACTIONS

1. A first-order reaction has an initial reaction rate of 2.4 mol/(L·s). What is the rate when one eighth the starting materials remain?

2. It has been experimentally determined that the rate law for the reaction between mercury(II) chloride and sodium oxalate is third-order overall and first-order with respect to $HgCl_2$. Write the rate law for this reaction.

$$2HgCl_2 + Na_2C_2O_4 \rightarrow 2NaCl + 2CO_2 + Hg_2Cl_2$$

3. A combination reaction gave the following data. What is the rate law for this reaction?

$$J + K \rightarrow M$$

Initial Concentration (mol/L)		Initial Rate (mol/L·s)
[J]	[K]	
0.30	0.50	0.080
0.60	0.50	0.160
0.60	0.25	0.080

4. Iodide ion catalyzes the decomposition of hydrogen peroxide. The reaction is first-order in H_2O_2. What is the value of the rate constant, k, if the initial rate is 0.00842 mol/(L·s)?

The initial concentration of H_2O_2 is 0.500 mol/L.

$$2H_2O_2 \rightarrow 2H_2O + O_2$$

5. A proposed reaction mechanism has two intermediates. How many elementary reactions are in this mechanism?

6. The reaction $A + B \rightarrow C$ is first-order in A and B, second-order overall. Complete the following table:

Initial Concentration (mol/L)		Initial Rate (mol/L·s)
[A]	[B]	
0.50	0.50	0.020
0.50		0.040
0.25	1.0	

7. The condensation of acetic acid ($C_2H_4O_2$) with methanol (CH_4O) to form methyl acetate ($C_3H_6O_2$) and water is catalyzed by HCl.

$$C_2H_4O_2 + CH_4O \overset{HCl}{\rightleftharpoons} C_3H_8O_3 \overset{HCl}{\rightleftharpoons} C_3H_6O_2 + H_2O$$

   a. How many elementary reactions are there in this condensation?

   b. Write the formula for the reaction intermediate(s).

   c. Write the rate law for this condensation.

INTERPRETING GRAPHICS

18

Use with Section 18.4

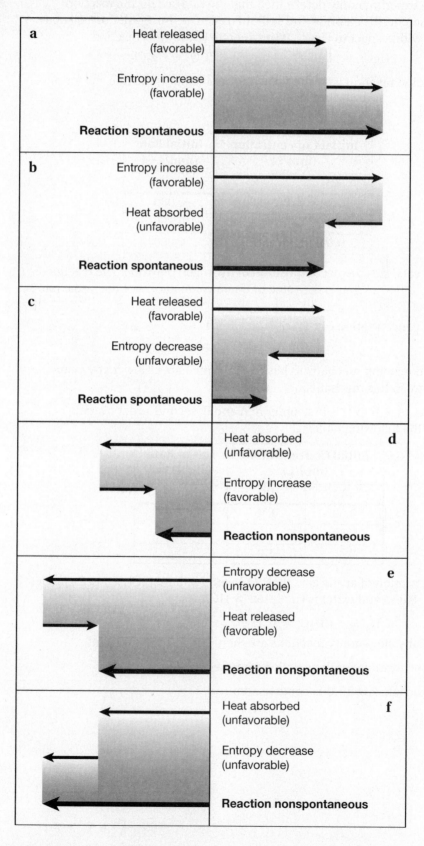

Name _____ Date _____ Class _____

The lettered diagrams on the previous page are from Figure 18.25 in your textbook. Use them to answer the following questions.

1. For each example, state whether ΔG is positive or negative.

   a. _____

   b. _____

   c. _____

   d. _____

   e _____

   f. _____

2. For example b, is $|T\Delta S|$ greater or less than $|\Delta G|$?

   _____

3. For example d, is $|T\Delta S|$ greater or less than $|\Delta G|$?

   _____

4. Which example would provide the most energy for work?

   _____

5. Could example d be made to be spontaneous by an increase in temperature?

   _____

18 REACTION RATES AND EQUILIBRIUM

Vocabulary Review

Match the correct vocabulary term to each numbered statement. Write the letter of the correct term on the line.

Column A	Column B
_____ 1. the disorder of a system	**a.** activation energy
_____ 2. a substance that interferes with the action of a catalyst	**b.** solubility product constant
_____ 3. reactions that favor the formation of products at the specified conditions	**c.** chemical equilibrium
_____ 4. the minimum energy colliding particles must have in order to react	**d.** free energy
_____ 5. equals the product of the concentrations of the ions, each raised to a power equal to the coefficient of the ion in the dissociation equation	**e.** entropy
_____ 6. the arrangement of atoms at the peak of the activation-energy barrier	**f.** activated complex
_____ 7. a reaction in which the rate is directly proportional to the concentration of one of the reactants	**g.** inhibitor
_____ 8. energy that is available to do work	**h.** equilibrium constant
_____ 9. when the forward and reverse reactions are taking place at the same rate	**i.** spontaneous reactions
_____ 10. the ratio of product concentrations to reactant concentrations, with each concentration raised to a power given by the number of moles of that substance in the balanced equation	**j.** first-order reaction

18 REACTION RATES AND EQUILIBRIUM

Chapter Quiz

Choose the best answer and write its letter on the line.

_____ 1. At chemical equilibrium, the rates of the forward reaction and reverse reactions are: *18.2*
   a. equal to 0.
   b. equal to each other.
   c. at a maximum.
   d. at a minimum.

_____ 2. A catalyst works by: *18.1*
   a. changing the pressure of the system.
   b. changing the temperature of the reactants.
   c. shifting the equilibrium position toward the products.
   d. lowering the activation energy barrier.

_____ 3. The rate of a chemical reaction normally: *18.1*
   a. increases as reactant concentration increases.
   b. is slowed down by a catalyst.
   c. decreases as temperature increases.
   d. decreases as reactant concentration increases.

_____ 4. Activation energy is: *18.1*
   a. heat released or absorbed in a reaction.
   b. the minimum energy colliding particles must have in order to react.
   c. the energy given off when reactants collide.
   d. generally very high for a reaction that takes place rapidly.

_____ 5. Spontaneous reactions: *18.4*
   a. are always exothermic.
   b. always take place at a rapid rate.
   c. always result in increased disorder of the system.
   d. naturally favor the formation of products.

_____ 6. Given the reaction at equilibrium *18.3*

$$Zn(OH)_2(s) \rightleftharpoons Zn^{2+}(aq) + 2OH^-(aq)$$

what is the expression for the solubility product constant, K_{sp}, for this reaction?

   a. $K_{sp} [Zn^{2+}] \times [2OH^-]$

   c. $K_{sp} = \dfrac{[Zn^{2+}] \times [OH^-]}{[Zn(OH)_2]}$

   b. $K_{sp} = [Zn^{2+}] \times [OH^-]^2$

   d. $K_{sp} = \dfrac{[Zn(OH)_2]}{[Zn^{2+}] \times [OH^-]}$

Classify each of these statements as always true, AT; sometimes true, ST; or never true, NT.

_____ 7. The value of K_{eq} for a spontaneous reaction less than 1. *18.4*

_____ 8. The Gibbs free energy for a spontaneous process is negative. *18.4*

_____ 9. In a first-order reaction involving several reactants, the reaction rate is directly proportional to the concentration of each of the reactants. *18.5*

REACTION RATES AND EQUILIBRIUM

18

Chapter Test A

A. Matching

Match each description in Column B to the correct term in Column A. Write the letter of the correct description on the line.

Column A   **Column B**

_____ 1. activated complex   **a.** the number of particles that react in a given time to form products

_____ 2. reaction rate   **b.** energy available to do work

_____ 3. Le Châtelier's principle   **c.** favoring the formation of products

_____ 4. spontaneous reaction   **d.** the minimum energy colliding particles must have in order to react

_____ 5. elementary reaction   **e.** the forward and reverse reactions take place at the same rate

_____ 6. chemical equilibrium   **f.** a substance that interferes with the action of a catalyst

_____ 7. entropy   **g.** Reactants are converted to products in a single step.

_____ 8. activation energy   **h.** the measure of disorder

_____ 9. inhibitor   **i.** the arrangement of atoms at the peak of the activation energy barrier

_____ 10. free energy   **j.** If a stress is applied to a system in dynamic equilibrium, the system changes to relieve the stress.

B. Multiple Choice

Choose the best answer and write its letter on the line.

_____ 11. In which of the following physical states does a given substance have the highest entropy?
   a. solid   **c.** liquid
   b. gas   **d.** all of the above

_____ 12. A reaction that requires free energy:
   a. must be endothermic.
   b. is nonspontaneous.
   c. must correspond to a decrease in entropy.
   d. is spontaneous.

_____ 13. When 0.1M HCl is added to the following system at equilibrium:

$$AgCl(s) \rightleftharpoons Ag^+(aq) + Cl^-(aq)$$

the point of equilibrium will shift to the
   a. right and the concentration of $Ag^+(aq)$ will decrease.
   b. right and the concentration of $Ag^+(aq)$ will increase.
   c. left and the concentration of $Ag^+(aq)$ will decrease.
   d. left and the concentration of $Ag^+(aq)$ will increase.

_____ 14. In which of these systems is the entropy decreasing?
   a. air escaping from a tire   c. salt dissolving in water
   b. snow melting   d. a gas condensing to a liquid

_____ 15. All spontaneous processes:
   a. are exothermic.   c. involve an increase in entropy.
   b. are endothermic   d. release free energy.

_____ 16. If a catalyst is used in a reaction:
   a. the energy of activation increases.
   b. the reaction rate does not change.
   c. the reaction rate increases.
   d. the equilibrium shifts.

_____ 17. Which of the following affects the rate of a chemical reaction?
   a. the presence of a catalyst   c. the concentration of reactants
   b. the temperature   d. all of the above

_____ 18. What is the expression for K_{eq} for this reaction?

$$2H_2O(g) \rightleftharpoons 2H_2(g) + O_2(g)$$

   a. $K_{eq} = \dfrac{[2H_2O]}{[H_2] \times [O_2]}$ c. $K_{eq} = \dfrac{[2H_2] \times [O_2]}{[2H_2O]}$

   b. $K_{eq} = \dfrac{[H_2]^2 \times [O_2]}{[H_2O]^2}$ d. $K_{eq} = \dfrac{[H_2O]^2}{[H_2]^2 \times [O_2]}$

_____ 19. In an equilibrium reaction with a K_{eq} of 1×10^8
   a. reactants are favored.   c. products are favored.
   b. the reaction is nonspontaneous. d. the reaction is exothermic.

_____ 20. What is the effect of adding more CO_2 to the following equilibrium reaction?

$$CO_2 + H_2O \rightleftharpoons H_2CO_3$$

   a. More H_2CO_3 is produced.
   b. More H_2O is produced.
   c. The equilibrium is pushed in the direction of reactants.
   d. no change

_____ 21. Doing which of the following generally increases the entropy of a substance?
   a. freezing it   c. condensing it
   b. dissolving it in water   d. all of the above

_____ 22. The K_{eq} of a reaction is 4×10^{-7}. At equilibrium:
   a. the reactants are favored.
   b. the products are favored.
   c. the reactants and products are present in equal amounts.
   d. the rate of the reverse reaction is greater than the rate of the forward reaction.

_____ 23. Two opposing reactions (A + B ⇌ C + D) occurring simultaneously at the same rate is an example of:

    a. reversibility.   **c.** neither a nor b

    b. chemical equilibrium.   **d.** both a and b

C. Problems

Solve the following problems in the space provided. Show your work.

24. Calculate the value of K_{eq} for this reaction at equilibrium.

$$2NOCl(g) \rightleftharpoons 2NO(g) + Cl_2(g)$$

An analysis of the equilibrium mixture in a 1-L flask gives the following results: NOCl, 0.30 mol; NO, 1.2 mol; Cl_2, 0.60 mol.

25. Carbon monoxide and hydrogen are combined in the commercial preparation of methyl alcohol.

$$CO(g) + 2H_2(g) \rightleftharpoons CH_3OH(g)$$

At a certain set of conditions, the equilibrium mixture contains 0.020 mol/L of CO, 0.60 mol/L of H_2, and the equilibrium constant is 2.2×10^2. What is the concentration of CH_3OH in the equilibrium mixture?

26. Predict the changes in the equilibrium position for this reaction when the following changes are made:

$$2A(g) + B(g) \rightleftharpoons 4C(g) + heat$$

    a. decrease the concentration of C

    b. add more heat

    c. increase the concentration of A

    d. increase the pressure

In each case, state whether the change causes a shift that favors the formation of reactants or of products.

    a. _____

    b. _____

    c. _____

    d. _____

Name _____ Date _____ Class _____

D. Essay

Write a short essay for the following.

27. Characterize spontaneous and nonspontaneous reactions. Then explain why a spontaneous reaction may appear to be nonspontaneous.

_____

_____

_____

_____

E. Additional Problem

Solve the following in the space provided. Show your work.

28. The rate law for the following reaction is: Rate $= k[A]^a [B]^b$.

$$aA + bB \rightarrow cC + dD$$

From the data in the following chart, find the order of the reaction with respect to A and B, as well as the overall order.

Initial Concentration of A (mol/L)	Initial Concentration of B (mol/L)	Initial Rate [mol/(L·s)]
0.50	0.05	2×10^{-3}
0.10	0.05	4×10^{-3}
0.20	0.05	8×10^{-3}
0.01	0.05	1×10^{-3}
0.01	0.10	8×10^{-3}
0.01	0.20	64×10^{-3}

_____

_____

_____

_____

18 REACTION RATES AND EQUILIBRIUM

Chapter Test B

A. Matching

Match each term in Column B to the correct description in Column A. Write the letter of the correct term on the line.

Column A   Column B

_____ 1. when the forward and reverse reactions are taking   **a.** Le Châtelier's principle
place at the same rate

_____ 2. Things move in the direction of maximum disorder   **b.** activated complex
or randomness.

_____ 3. the minimum energy colliding particles must have   **c.** entropy
in order to react

_____ 4. the ratio of product concentrations to reactant   **d.** collision theory
concentrations, with each concentration raised
to a power given by the number of moles of that
substance in the balanced equation

_____ 5. the product of the concentrations of the ions, each   **e.** free energy
raised to a power equal to the coefficient of the ion
in the dissociation equation

_____ 6. the disorder of a system   **f.** solubility product
constant

_____ 7. Atoms, ions, and molecules can form a chemical   **g.** law of disorder
bond between them when they collide, provided
the particles have enough kinetic energy.

_____ 8. energy that is available to do work   **h.** activation energy

_____ 9. the arrangement of atoms at the peak of the   **i.** equilibrium constant
activation energy barrier

_____ 10. If a stress is applied to a system in a dynamic   **j.** chemical equilibrium
equilibrium, the system changes to relieve the stress.

Name _____ Date _____ Class _____

B. Multiple Choice

Choose the best answer and write its letter on the line.

_____ 11. According to collision theory, in order for a chemical reaction to occur, the reactant atoms must:
  a. make contact with each other.
  b. have a minimum level of kinetic energy.
  c. form an activated complex.
  d. all of the above

_____ 12. In general, increasing temperature causes the rate of most chemical reactions to:
  a. increase.   c. remain the same.
  b. decrease.   d. vary unpredictably.

_____ 13. Which of the following is true concerning the impact of increasing temperature on reaction rates?
  a. The number of collisions between reactant atoms is increased.
  b. The energy of each reactant atom is increased.
  c. The percentage of collisions with sufficient energy to cross the activation energy barrier is increased.
  d. all of the above

_____ 14. What would decrease the rate of most chemical reactions?
  a. increasing the concentration of reactant atoms
  b. increasing the size of the reactant particles
  c. adding an appropriate catalyst
  d. all of the above

_____ 15. Catalysts alter the rate of a chemical reaction by:
  a. increasing the number of collisions between reactant atoms.
  b. increasing the kinetic energy of each reactant atom.
  c. lowering the activation energy barrier.
  d. being consumed in the reaction.

_____ 16. Which of the following is true concerning a reaction that has reached chemical equilibrium?
  a. The forward reaction is occurring faster than the reverse reaction.
  b. The reverse reaction is occurring faster than the forward reaction.
  c. The forward reaction is occurring as fast as the reverse reaction.
  d. The mass of products is equal to the mass of reactants.

_____ 17. Given the following system at equilibrium:
$$N_2(g) + 3H_2(g) \rightleftharpoons 2NH_3(g)$$
what would be the effect of removing $NH_3(g)$ as it is formed?
  a. The equilibrium would shift to the left.
  b. More $N_2(g)$ would be produced.
  c. More $H_2(g)$ would be produced.
  d. The equilibrium would shift to the right.

_____ **18.** Given the following system at equilibrium:
$$H_2O(l) + heat \rightleftharpoons H_2O(g)$$
how would a decrease in temperature affect the system?
a. The equilibrium would shift to the right.
b. More $H_2O(l)$ would be produced.
c. More $H_2O(g)$ would be produced.
d. The levels of reactants and products would remain the same.

_____ **19.** Which of the following would increase the yield of $CO(g)$ in the following equilibrium system?
$$C(s) + H_2O(g) + heat \rightleftharpoons CO(g) + H_2(g)$$
a. decreasing temperature   **c.** adding $H_2(g)$
b. increasing pressure   **d.** adding $H_2O(g)$

_____ **20.** Spontaneous reactions:
a. favor the formation of products.
b. give substantial amounts of reactants at equilibrium.
c. absorb free energy.
d. have high reaction rates.

_____ **21.** Which of the following has the greatest entropy?
a. ice   **c.** water vapor
b. water   **d.** cannot be predicted

_____ **22.** The type of reaction most likely to be spontaneous is one in which:
a. both enthalpy and entropy are decreased.
b. enthalpy is decreased, while entropy is increased.
c. both enthalpy and entropy are increased.
d. enthalpy is increased, while entropy is decreased.

_____ **23.** What is the expression for K_{eq} for the following reaction?
$$H_2(g) + Cl_2(g) \rightleftharpoons 2HCl(g)$$
a. $K_{eq} = \dfrac{[H_2] \times [Cl_2]}{[2HCl]}$ **c.** $K_{eq} = \dfrac{[HCl]^2}{[H_2] \times [Cl_2]}$

b. $K_{eq} = \dfrac{[2HCl]}{[H_2] \times [Cl_2]}$ **d.** $K_{eq} = \dfrac{[H_2] \times [Cl_2]}{[HCl]^2}$

_____ **24.** If the equilibrium concentrations for the system in question 23 are as follows, find the value of K_{eq}.
$[H_2] = 0.450$ mol/L, $[Cl_2] = 0.450$ mol/L, $[HCl] = 6.25$ mol/L
a. 1.62×10^{-2} **c.** 5.18×10^{-3}
b. 193   **d.** 61.7

Name _____ Date _____ Class _____

C. Problems

Solve the following problems in the space provided. Show your work.

25. Given the following system at equilibrium:

$$4HCl(g) + O_2(g) \rightleftharpoons 2H_2O(g) + 2Cl_2(g) + heat$$

determine the effect of each of the following changes on the equilibrium position of the system (shifts right or left) and on the amount of $Cl_2(g)$ that would result (increases or decreases):

	Equilibrium Position	Amount of $Cl_2(g)$
a. increasing temperature		
b. decreasing pressure		
c. adding $O_2(g)$		
d. removing $H_2O(g)$		
e. increasing pressure		
f. adding $H_2O(g)$		

26. At equilibrium, the concentrations of the components of the reaction in problem 25 are as follows:

[HCl] = 1.2×10^{-3} mol/L, [O_2] = 3.8×10^{-4} mol/L,
[H_2O] = 5.8×10^{-2} mol/L, and [Cl_2] = 5.8×10^{-2} mol/L

Determine the value of K_{eq} for this system.

27. Which compound, PbF_2 ($K_{sp} = 3.6 \times 10^{-8}$) or AgBr ($K_{sp} = 5.0 \times 10^{-13}$) has the higher solubility?

D. Essay

Write a short essay for the following.

28. Explain how and why an equilibrium system reacts to each of the following stresses:

a. the addition of more reactant

_____

_____

_____

_____

b. an increase in temperature

_____

_____

_____

_____

c. an increase in pressure (for a gaseous system with an unequal number of molecules)

_____

_____

_____

E. Additional Problem

Solve the following problems in the space provided. Show your work.

29. Given:

$$N_2(g) + 3H_2(g) \rightleftharpoons 2NH_3(g) \text{ with } K_{eq} = 6.59 \times 10^{-3} \text{ at } 450°C$$

If $[NH_3] = 1.23 \times 10^{-4}$ mol/L and $[H_2] = 2.75 \times 10^{-6}$ mol/L at equilibrium, what is the concentration of N_2 at equilibrium?

Name _____ Date _____ Class _____

QUICK LAB: Does Steel Burn?

Laboratory Recordsheet   Use with Section 18.1

PURPOSE

To determine whether steel will burn.

MATERIALS

- # 0000 steel wool pad
- tissue paper
- tongs
- Bunsen burner
- heat-resistant pad
- pencil and paper

PROCEDURE

1. Roll a small piece of steel wool into a very tight, pea-sized ball. Use the tissue paper to protect your fingers from small steel fibers while handling the steel wool.

2. Holding the ball with tongs, heat the steel wool in the blue-tip flame of the burner for no longer than 10 seconds. In this and subsequent steps, place pieces of heated steel wool on the heat-resistant pad to cool. Observe all appropriate safety precautions when working with the burner and the heated materials. Record your observations.

3. Gently roll a second piece of steel wool into a loose, pea-sized ball. Holding the loose ball with the tongs, heat the wool in the burner flame for no longer than 10 seconds. Record your observations.

4. Pull a few individual fibers of steel wool from the pad. Hold one end of the loose fibers with the tongs and heat them in the flame of the burner for no longer than 10 seconds. Again record your observations.

ANALYSES AND CONCLUSIONS

1. What differences did you observe when the tight ball, the loose ball, and the loose fibers were heated in the flame? Give a reason for any differences you observed.

   _____

   _____

   _____

2. Write the balanced equation for any chemical reaction you may have observed. (Assume that the steel wool is composed mainly of iron.)

_____

_____

3. How do your results differ from those observed in the rusting of an automobile body?

_____

_____

_____

4. Explain why steel wool is a hazard in shops where there are hot plates, open flames, or sparking motors.

_____

_____

_____

Name _____ Date _____ Class _____

SMALL-SCALE LAB: Enthalpy and Entropy

Laboratory Recordsheet   Use with Section 18.4

SAFETY

Wear safety glasses and follow the standard safety procedures outlined in the Small-Scale Lab Manual.

PURPOSE

To observe and measure energy changes during the formation of a solution and to describe and explain these changes in terms of entropy and enthalpy.

MATERIALS

- alcohol thermometer
- four 1-oz plastic cups
- plastic spoon
- solid chemicals shown in the table

- crushed ice
- water
- stirring rod

PROCEDURE

Place two level spoonfuls of water in a plastic cup and measure the temperature (T_1) of the water. Add one level spoonful of solid NaCl to the cup, stir gently, and measure the highest or lowest temperature (T_2). Record this information in the table. Repeat the experiment two more times, using NH_4Cl and $CaCl_2$. Record the temperatures.

Mixture	T_1	T_2	ΔT
a. $NaCl(s) + H_2O(l)$			
b. $NH_4Cl(s) + H_2O(l)$			
c. $CaCl_2(s) + H_2O(l)$			

Figure A

ANALYSES AND CONCLUSIONS

Using your experimental data, record the answers to the following questions.

1. Calculate ΔT for each mixture. $\Delta T = T_2 - T_1$.

_____

_____

_____

2. An exothermic process gives off heat (warms up). An endothermic process absorbs heat (cools off). Which solutions are endothermic and which are exothermic? What is the sign of ΔH in each case?

_____

_____

3. Which solution(s) had little or no change in temperature?

_____

_____

4. When sodium chloride dissolves in water, the ions dissociate.

$$NaCl(s) \longrightarrow Na^+(aq) + Cl^-(aq)$$

Write ionic equations, similar to the one above, that describe how NH_4Cl and $CaCl_2$ each dissociate as they dissolve in water. Include heat as a reactant or product in each equation.

_____

_____

5. Which solids in this experiment rapidly dissolved in water? Does the dissolving process usually occur with an increase or decrease in entropy? What is the sign of ΔS in each case?

_____

_____

6. Consider the equation $\Delta G = \Delta H - T\Delta S$. For each dissolving process, substitute the sign of ΔS and ΔH into the equation and determine the sign of ΔG. For which process might ΔG be either positive or negative?

_____

_____

YOU'RE THE CHEMIST

Use the space below to record your observations of the small-scale activities in the *You're the Chemist* section.

_____

_____

_____

_____

_____

_____

19.1 ACID-BASE THEORIES

Section Review

Objectives

- Define the properties of acids and bases
- Compare and contrast acids and bases as defined by the theories of Arrhenius, Brønsted-Lowry, and Lewis

Vocabulary

- monoprotic acids
- diprotic acids
- triprotic acids
- conjugate acid

- conjugate base
- conjugate acid–base pair
- hydronium ion (H_3O^+)

- amphoteric
- Lewis acid
- Lewis base

Part A Completion

Use this completion exercise to check your understanding of the concepts and terms that are introduced in this section. Each blank can be completed with a term, short phrase, or number.

Compounds can be classified as acids or bases according to __1__ different theories. An __2__ acid yields hydrogen ions in aqueous solution. An Arrhenius base yields __3__ in aqueous solution. A Brønsted-Lowry acid is a __4__ donor. A Brønsted-Lowry base is a proton __5__. In the Lewis theory, an acid is an __6__ acceptor. A Lewis base is an electron-pair __7__.

An acid with one ionizable hydrogen atom is called a __8__ acid, while an acid with two ionizable hydrogen atoms is called a __9__ acid.

A __10__ is a pair of substances related by the gain or loss of a hydrogen ion. A substance that can act as both an acid and a base is called __11__.

1. _____
2. _____
3. _____
4. _____
5. _____
6. _____
7 _____
8. _____
9. _____
10. _____
11. _____

Part B True-False

Classify each of these statements as always true, AT; sometimes true, ST; or never true, NT.

_____ **12.** Hydrochloric acid is a strong acid that is diprotic.

_____ **13.** The ammonium ion, NH_4^+, is a Brønsted-Lowry base.

_____ **14.** A Brønsted-Lowry base is a hydrogen-ion acceptor.

_____ **15.** A compound can act as both an acid and a base.

_____ **16.** PBr_3 is a Lewis base.

Part C Matching

Match each description in Column B to the correct term in Column A.

Column A	Column B
_____ **17.** monoprotic acids	**a.** tastes sour and will change the color of an acid-base indicator
_____ **18.** triprotic acids	**b.** an electron-pair donor
_____ **19.** acid properties	**c.** a water molecule that gains a hydrogen ion
_____ **20.** base properties	**d.** acids that contain three ionizable hydrogens
_____ **21.** conjugate base	**e.** particle that remains when an acid has donated a hydrogen ion
_____ **22.** conjugate acid	**f.** an electron-pair acceptor
_____ **23.** hydronium ion (H_3O^+)	**g.** acids that contain one ionizable hydrogen
_____ **24.** Lewis acid	**h.** tastes bitter and feels slippery
_____ **25.** Lewis base	**i.** particle formed when a base gains a hydrogen ion

Part D Problem

Answer the following in the space provided.

26. Identify the Lewis acid and Lewis base in the following reaction. Explain.

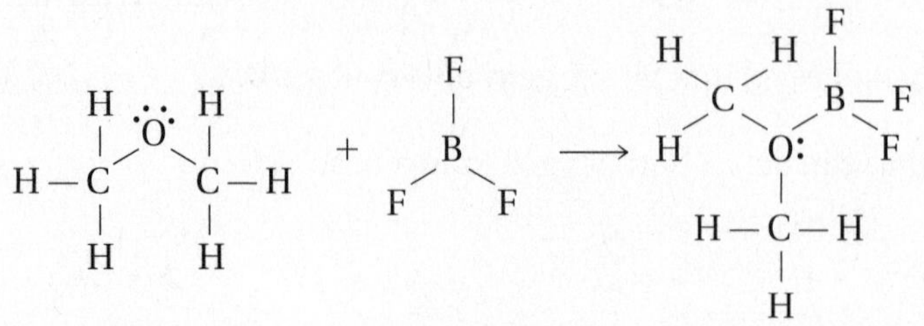

dimethyl ether   boron trifluoride

Section Review

Objectives

- Classify a solution as neutral, acidic, or basic, given the hydrogen-ion or hydroxide-ion concentration
- Convert hydrogen-ion concentrations into values of pH and hydroxide-ion concentrations into values of pOH
- Describe the purpose of pH indicators

Vocabulary

- self-ionization
- neutral solution
- ion-product constant for water (K_w)
- acidic solution
- basic solution
- alkaline solutions
- pH

Key Equations

- $K_w = [H^+] \times [OH^-] = 1.0 \times 10^{-14} M^2$
- $pH = -\log [H^+]$
- $pOH = -\log [OH^-]$
- $pH + pOH = 14$

Part A Completion

Use this completion exercise to check your understanding of the concepts and terms that are introduced in this section. Each blank can be completed with a term, short phrase, or number.

Water molecules can __**1**__ to form hydrogen ions (H^+) and hydroxide ions (OH^-). The concentrations of these ions in pure water at 25°C are both equal to __**2**__ mol/L.

The pH scale, which has a range from __**3**__, is used to denote the __**4**__ concentration of a solution. On this scale, 0 is strongly __**5**__, 14 is strongly __**6**__, and 7 is __**7**__. Pure water at 25°C has a pH of __**8**__.

The __**9**__ constant for water has a value of 1.0×10^{-14}.

Thus, the product of the concentrations of __**10**__ ions and __**11**__ ions in aqueous solution will always equal 1.0×10^{-14}.

1. _____
2. _____
3. _____
4. _____
5. _____
6. _____
7. _____
8. _____
9. _____
10. _____
11. _____

Part B True-False

Classify each of these statements as always true, AT; sometimes true, ST; or never true, NT.

_____ **12.** In an acidic solution, $[H^+]$ is greater than $[OH^-]$.

_____ **13.** pH indicators can give accurate pH readings for solutions.

_____ **14.** If the $[H^+]$ in a solution increases, the $[OH^-]$ must decrease.

_____ **15.** The $[OH^-]$ is less than $10^{-7}M$ in a basic solution.

_____ **16.** The definition of pH is the negative logarithm of the hydroxide-ion concentration.

Part C Matching

Match each description in Column B to the correct term in Column A.

Column A	Column B
_____ **17.** alkaline solutions	**a.** aqueous solution in which $[H^+]$ and $[OH^-]$ are equal
_____ **18.** pH	**b.** product of hydrogen ion and hydroxide ion concentrations for water
_____ **19.** self-ionization	**c.** base solutions
_____ **20.** neutral solution	**d.** solution in which $[H^+]$ is less than $[OH^-]$
_____ **21.** ion-product constant for water (K_w)	**e.** reaction in which two water molecules produce ions
_____ **22.** acidic solution	**f.** the negative logarithm of the hydrogen-ion concentration
_____ **23.** basic solution	**g.** solution in which $[H^+]$ is greater than $[OH^-]$

Part D Problems

Answer the following in the space provided.

24. Calculate the hydroxide-ion concentration, $[OH^-]$, for an aqueous solution in which $[H^+]$ is 1×10^{-10} mol/L. Is this solution acidic, basic, or neutral?

25. Determine the hydrogen-ion concentrations for aqueous solutions that have the following pH values.

    a. 3   **b.** 6   **c.** 10

Name _____ Date _____ Class _____

19.3 STRENGTHS OF ACIDS AND BASES

Section Review

Objectives

- Define strong acids and weak acids
- Calculate an acid dissociation constant (K_a) from concentration and pH measurements
- Order acids by strength according to their acid dissociation constants (K_a)
- Order bases by strength according to their base dissociation constants (K_b)

Vocabulary

- strong acids
- weak acids
- acid dissociation constant (K_a)
- strong bases
- weak bases
- base dissociation constant (K_b)

Part A Completion

Use this completion exercise to check your understanding of the concepts and terms that are introduced in this section. Each blank can be completed with a term, short phrase, or number.

The strength of an acid or a base is determined by the ___1___

of the substance in solution. The acid dissociation constant,

___2___ , is a quantitative measure of acid strength. A strong acid

has a much ___3___ K_a than a weak acid. The K_a of an acid is

determined from measured ___4___ values.

Hydrochloric acid and sulfuric acid are ___5___ ionized in

solution and are ___6___ acids. Ethanoic acid, which is only about

1 percent ionized, is a ___7___ acid. Magnesium hydroxide and

calcium hydroxide are strong ___8___ .

Weak bases react with ___9___ to form the hydroxide ion and

the conjugate ___10___ of the base. Concentration in solution does

not affect whether an acid or a base is ___11___ or weak.

1. _____
2. _____
3. _____
4. _____
5. _____
6. _____
7. _____
8. _____
9. _____
10. _____
11. _____

Part B True-False

Classify each of these statements as always true, AT; sometimes true, ST; or never true, NT.

_____ **12.** Acids are completely dissociated in aqueous solution.

_____ **13.** Diprotic acids lose both hydrogens at the same time.

_____ **14.** Acid dissociation constants for weak acids can be calculated from experimental data.

_____ **15.** Bases react with water to form hydroxide ions.

Part C Matching

Match each description in Column B to the correct term in Column A.

Column A

_____ **16.** strong acids

_____ **17.** weak acids

_____ **18.** acid dissociation constant (K_a)

_____ **19.** strong bases

_____ **20.** weak bases

_____ **21.** base dissociation constant (K_b)

Column B

a. ratio of the concentration of the dissociated (or ionized) form of an acid to the concentration of the undissociated acid

b. bases that dissociate completely into metal ions and hydroxide ions in aqueous solution

c. acids that ionize completely in aqueous solution

d. bases that do not dissociate completely in aqueous solution

e. acids that are only partially ionized in aqueous solution

f. ratio of concentration of conjugate acid times concentration of hydroxide ion to the concentration of conjugate base

Part D Problem

Answer the following in the space provided.

22. A 0.35M solution of a strong acid, HX, has a [H^+] of 4.1×10^{-2}. What is the value of K_a for this acid?

19.4 NEUTRALIZATION REACTIONS

Section Review

Objectives

- Explain how acid–base titration is used to calculate the concentration of an acid or a base
- Explain the concept of equivalence in neutralization reactions

Vocabulary

- neutralization reactions
- titration
- equivalence point
- end point
- standard solution

Key Equations

- Acid + Base → Salt + Water
- Gram equivalent mass = $\dfrac{\text{molar mass}}{\text{number of ionizable hydrogens}}$
- Normality (N) = equiv/L
- $N_1 \times V_1 = N_2 \times V_2$
- $N_A \times V_A = N_B \times V_B$

Part A Completion

Use this completion exercise to check your understanding of the concepts and terms that are introduced in this section. Each blank can be completed with a term, short phrase, or number.

In the reaction of a(n) __1__ with a base, hydrogen ions

and __2__ ions react to produce __3__ . This reaction, called

__4__ , is usually carried out by __5__ . The __6__ in a

titration is the point at which the solution is neutral. At the

__7__ point of a titration, the number of equivalents of acid

equals the number of equivalents of base.

1. _____

2. _____

3. _____

4. _____

5. _____

6. _____

7. _____

Part B True-False

Classify each of these statements as always true, AT; sometimes true, ST; or never true, NT.

_____ **8.** A solution of known concentration is called a standard solution.

_____ **9.** The end point of a titration of a strong base with a strong acid occurs when $[H^+] = [OH^-]$.

_____ **10.** The point of neutralization is the end point of titration.

_____ **11.** The reaction of an acid and a base produces only water.

Part C Matching

Match each description in Column B to the correct term in Column A.

Column A

_____ **12.** titration

_____ **13.** neutralization reactions

_____ **14.** equivalence point

_____ **15.** standard solution

_____ **16.** end point

Column B

a. when the number of moles of hydrogen ions equals the number of moles of hydroxide ions

b. a solution of known concentration

c. a process for determining the concentration of a solution by adding a known amount of a standard solution

d. point of neutralization

e. reactions between acids and bases to produce a salt and water

Part D Problem

Answer the following in the space provided.

17. Complete and balance the equations for the following acid–base reactions.

    a. $H_3PO_4 + Al(OH)_3$

_____

    b. $HI + Ca(OH)_2$

_____

SALTS IN SOLUTION
19.5

Section Review

Objectives

- Define when a solution of a salt is acidic or basic
- Demonstrate with equations how buffers resist changes in pH

Vocabulary

- salt hydrolysis
- buffers
- buffer capacity

Part A Completion

Use this completion exercise to check your understanding of the concepts and terms that are introduced in this section. Each blank can be completed with a term, short phrase, or number.

A ___**1**___ forms when an acid is neutralized by a base. Salts

can be neutral, ___**2**___, or ___**3**___ in solutions. Salts of strong

acid–strong base reactions produce ___**4**___ solutions with water.

Salts formed from the neutralization of weak acids or weak bases

___**5**___ water. They produce solutions that are acidic or basic.

For example, the pH of a solution at the equivalence point is

greater than 7 for a ___**6**___ base-___**7**___ acid titration. Solutions

that resist changes in pH are called ___**8**___ solutions. The buffer

___**9**___ is the amount of acid or base that can be added to a buffer

without changing the pH greatly.

1. _____

2. _____

3. _____

4. _____

5. _____

6. _____

7. _____

8. _____

9. _____

Part B True-False

Classify each of these statements as always true, AT; sometimes true, ST; or never true, NT.

_____ **10.** An aqueous solution of NH_4Cl is basic.

_____ **11.** HCl–NaCl would be a good buffer system.

_____ **12.** A buffer is a solution of a weak acid and one of its salts.

_____ **13.** A strong acid and a weak base produce an acidic solution.

Part C Matching

Match each description in Column B to the correct term in Column A.

Column A

_____ **14.** salt hydrolysis

_____ **15.** buffer

_____ **16.** buffer capacity

_____ **17.** NH_4Cl

Column B

a. the cations or anions of a dissociated salt remove hydrogen ions from or donate hydrogen ions to water

b. the amount of acid or base that can be added to a buffer solution before a significant change in pH can occur

c. the salt produced by the titration of ammonia with hydrochloric acid.

d. a solution in which the pH remains relatively constant when small amounts of acid or base are added

Part D Question

Answer the following in the space provided.

18. Predict whether an aqueous solution of each salt will be acidic, basic, or neutral.

   a. NH_4Cl

   b. Na_2CO_3

   c. NH_4NO_3

19 ACIDS, BASES, AND SALTS

Practice Problems

In your notebook, solve the following problems.

SECTION 19.1 ACID–BASE THEORIES

1. Identify the hydrogen ion donor(s) and hydrogen ion acceptor(s) for ionization of H_2SO_4 in water. Label the conjugate acid–base pairs.

2. Identify all of the ions that may be formed when H_3PO_4 ionizes in water.

3. Classify the following acids as monoprotic, diprotic, or triprotic.

   a. HCOOH   **b.** HBr   **c.** H_2SO_3 **d.** H_3ClO_4

4. What would you expect to happen when lithium metal is added to water? Show the chemical reaction.

5. In the following chemical reaction, identify the Lewis acid and base.
$$BF_3 + F^- \rightleftharpoons BF_4^-$$

6. Describe some distinctive properties of acids.

7. Describe some distinctive properties of bases.

SECTION 19.2 HYDROGEN IONS AND ACIDITY

1. A solution has a hydrogen ion concentration of $1 \times 10^{-6}M$. What is its pH?

2. What is the pH of a solution if the $[H^+] = 7.2 \times 10^{-9}M$?

3. What is the pOH of a solution if the $[OH^-] = 3.5 \times 10^{-2}M$?

4. What is the pOH of a solution that has a pH of 3.4?

5. Classify each solution as acidic, basic, or neutral.

   a. $[H^+] = 2.5 \times 10^{-9}M$ **d.** $[H^+] = 1 \times 10^{-7}M$

   b. pOH = 12.0   **e.** pH = 0.8

   c. $[OH^-] = 9.8 \times 10^{-11}M$

6. Calculate the pH of each solution.

   a. $[H^+] = 1 \times 10^{-5}M$ **c.** $[OH^-] = 2.2 \times 10^{-7}M$

   b. $[H^+] = 4.4 \times 10^{-11}M$ **d.** pOH = 1.4

7. Classify the solutions in problem 6 as acidic or basic.

8. Why is there a minus sign in the definition of pH?

9. A solution has a pOH of 12.4. What is the pH of this solution?

10. What is the pH of a solution with $[H^-] = 1 \times 10^{-3}M$?

SECTION 19.3 STRENGTHS OF ACIDS AND BASES

1. Rank $1M$ of these compounds in order of increasing hydrogen ion concentration: weak acid, strong acid, strong base, weak base.

2. Write the expression for the acid dissociation constant of the strong acid hydrofluoric acid, HF.

3. Write the expression for the base dissociation constant for hydrazine, N_2H_4, a weak base. Hydrazine reacts with water to form the $N_2H_5^+$ ion.

4. Use Table 19.8 in your textbook to rank these acids from weakest to strongest: HOOCCOOH, HCO_3^-, $H_2PO_4^-$, HCOOH.

5. Write the equilibrium equation and the acid dissociation constant for the following weak acids.

   a. H_2S b. NH_4^+ c. C_6H_5COOH

6. Match each solution with its correct description.

   a. dilute, weak acid   (1) $18M\ H_2SO_4(aq)$

   b. dilute, strong base   (2) $0.5M\ NaOH(aq)$

   c. concentrated, strong acid (3) $15M\ NH_3(aq)$

   d. dilute, strong acid   (4) $0.1M\ HC_2H_3O_2(aq)$

   e. concentrated, weak base   (5) $0.1M\ HCl(aq)$

7. Write the base dissociation constant expression for the weak base analine, $C_6H_5NH_2$.

$$C_6H_5NH_2(aq) + H_2O(l) \rightleftharpoons C_6H_5NH_3^+(aq) + OH^-(aq)$$

8. A $0.10M$ solution of formic acid has an equilibrium $[H^+] = 4.2 \times 10^{-3}M$.

$$HCOOH(aq) \rightarrow H^+(aq) + HCOO^-(aq)$$

   What is the K_a of formic acid?

9. The K_a of benzoic acid, C_6H_5COOH, is 6.3×10^{-5}. What is the equilibrium $[H^+]$ in a $0.20M$ solution of benzoic acid?

10. A $0.10M$ solution of hydrocyanic acid, HCN, has an equilibrium hydrogen ion concentration of $6.3 \times 10^{-6}M$. What is the K_a of hydrocyanic acid?

SECTION 19.4 NEUTRALIZATION REACTIONS

1. What is the molarity of a sodium hydroxide solution if 38 mL of the solution is titrated to the end point with 14 mL of $0.75M$ sulfuric acid?

2. If 24.6 mL of a $Ca(OH)_2$ solution is needed to neutralize 14.2 mL of $0.0140M$ $HC_2H_3O_2$, what is the concentration of the calcium hydroxide solution?

3. A 12.4 mL solution of H_2SO_4 is completely neutralized by 19.8 mL of $0.0100M$ $Ca(OH)_2$. What is the concentration of the H_2SO_4 solution?

4. What volume of $0.12M$ $Ba(OH)_3$ is needed to neutralize 12.2 mL of $0.25M$ HCl?

5. A 55.0-mg sample of $Al(OH)_3$ is reacted with $0.200M$ HCl. How many milliters of the acid are needed to neutralize the $Al(OH)_3$?

SECTION 19.5 SALTS IN SOLUTION

1. A buffer solution is prepared by mixing together equal quantities of formic acid, $HCHO_2$, and sodium formate, $NaCHO_2$. Write equations that show what happens when first acid, and then base, is added to this buffer solution.

2. Complete the following rules.

   a. strong acid + strong base →   c. weak acid + strong base →

   b. strong acid + weak base →

INTERPRETING GRAPHICS

19

Use with Section 19.5

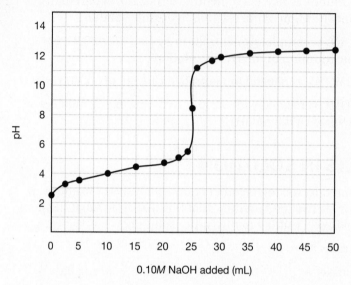

Figure 1 The pH curve for the titration of a benzoic acid (C_6H_5COOH) solution with a standard solution of 0.10M sodium hydroxide (NaOH).

The plot shown in Figure 1 shows how the pH of a benzoic acid solution of unknown concentration changes as a function of the volume of 0.10M NaOH added. The starting volume of benzoic acid solution was 25 mL. Use this titration curve to answer the following questions.

1. Write the chemical equation for the reaction of benzoic acid (C_6H_5COOH) with NaOH. Note that the acidic hydrogen atom in benzoic acid is shown in bold. How many moles of benzoic acid are neutralized per mole of NaOH added?

_____

_____

2. Estimate the pH of the solution at the equivalence point of the titration. Is the solution acidic, neutral, or basic at the equivalence point?

_____

_____

3. Based on your estimate of the pH at the equivalence point, characterize benzoic acid as a weak acid or a strong acid. Explain your answer.

_____

_____

4. How many moles of NaOH were needed to reach the equivalence point?

_____

5. Define the equivalence point in this reaction. What are [NaOH], [C_6H_5COOH], and [C_6H_5COONa] at the equivalence point?

_____

_____

6. What is the concentration of benzoic acid in the original "unknown" solution?

7. Refer to Figure 19.8 in your textbook. Which of the acid–base indicators shown would be most appropriate for this particular titration? Label the titration curve in Figure 1 to indicate the range of pH values for which your chosen indicator is most effective.

_____

_____

_____

8. At the equivalence point, the pH of the solution is determined by the hydrolysis of the sodium benzoate salt, C_6H_5COONa. Write the chemical equation showing the hydrolysis of water by the benzoate ion ($C_6H_5COO^-$). How does this equation support your answer to question 2?

_____

_____

9. Use your answer to question 8 to write the base dissociation constant (K_b) expression for the reaction of benzoate ion with water.

10. Based on your estimate of the pH at the equivalence point and using the expression for K_b, determine the numerical value of K_b for the benzoate ion ($C_6H_5COO^-$).

19 ACIDS, BASES, AND SALTS

Vocabulary Review

From each group of terms, choose the term that does not belong and then explain your choice.

1. basic, neutral, acidic, hydronium ion

_____

_____

2. acidic solution, hydroxide ion, basic solution, alkaline solution

_____

_____

3. Arrhenius, Brønsted-Lowry, Lewis, amphoteric

_____

_____

4. conjugate acid, Brønsted-Lowry, Lewis acid, conjugate base

_____

_____

5. weak bases, weak acids, strong acids, dissociation constant

_____

_____

Choose the term from the following list that best matches each description.

equivalence point   neutral

hydrolyzing salts   buffer

_____ **6.** compounds derived from the reaction of a strong base with a weak acid or from the reaction of a strong acid with a weak base

_____ **7.** a term used to describe the pH of a solution that results when one equivalent of a strong acid is mixed with one equivalent of a strong base

_____ **8.** the point of neutralization in a titration

_____ **9.** a solution that consists of a weak acid and one of its salts, or a solution of a weak base and one of its salts

19 ACIDS, BASES, AND SALTS

Chapter Quiz

Choose the best answer and write its letter on the line.

_____ 1. A solution in which the hydroxide-ion concentration is 1×10^{-2} is   19.2
    a. acidic.   **c.** neutral.
    b. basic.   **d.** none of the above

_____ 2. What is the pH of a solution in which $[OH^-] = 1 \times 10^{-5}$?   19.2
    a. 5.0   **c.** −5.0
    b. 9.0   **d.** −9.0

_____ 3. If the $[H^+]$ in a solution is 1×10^{-3} mol/L, then the $[OH^-]$ is   19.2
    a. 1×10^{-11} mol/L.   **c.** 1×10^{-13} mol/L.
    b. 1×10^{-17} mol/L.   **d.** cannot be determined

_____ 4. In the reaction: 19.1
$$CO_3{}^{2-} + H_2O \rightleftharpoons HCO_3{}^- + OH^-$$
the carbonate ion is acting as a(n)
    a. Arrhenius base.   **c.** Brønsted-Lowry base.
    b. Arrhenius acid.   **d.** Brønsted-Lowry acid.

_____ 5. Identify the Brønsted-Lowry base and conjugate base in this reaction.   19.1
$$H_2S + H_2O \rightleftharpoons H_3O^+ + HS^-$$
    a. H_2S and H_2O **c.** HS^- and H_2O
    b. H_2S and H_3O^+ **d.** HS^- and H_3O^+

_____ 6. For the reaction $HX \rightleftharpoons H^+ + X^-$, the equilibrium concentrations   19.3
are as follows.
$$[HX] = 1 \times 10^{-1}; [H^+] , [X^-] = 1 \times 10^{-5}$$
K_a would be:
    a. 1×10^9.   **c.** 1×10^{-7}.
    b. 1×10^{-11}.   **d.** 1×10^{-9}.

_____ 7. The reaction that takes place when an acid is added to an ethanoic   19.5
acid-ethanoate (CH_3COOH/CH_3COO^-) buffer is
    a. $CH_3COO^- + H^+ \rightleftharpoons CH_4 + CO_2$
    b. $CH_3COOH + H^+ \rightleftharpoons CH_3COO^- + H^+$
    c. $CH_3COO^- + H^+ \rightleftharpoons CH_3COOH$
    d. $CH_3COOH + OH^- \rightleftharpoons CH_3COO^- + H_2O$

_____ 8. Which salt hydrolyzes water to form a solution that is acidic?   19.5
    a. LiBr   **c.** NaBr
    b. NH_4Br **d.** KBr

19 ACIDS, BASES, AND SALTS

Chapter Test A

A. Matching

Match each term in Column B with the correct description in Column A. Write the letter of the correct term on the line.

Column A

Column B

_____ 1. acid dissociation constant

    a. acidic solution

_____ 2. [H^+] greater than [OH^-]

    b. conjugate acid–base pair

_____ 3. The cations or anions of a dissociated salt remove hydrogen ions from or donate hydrogen ions to water.

    c. amphoteric

_____ 4. point of neutralization of the titration

    d. alkaline solution

_____ 5. H_3O^+

    e. K_w

_____ 6. [OH^-] and [H^+] = 1×10^{-7}

    f. end point

_____ 7. [OH^-] greater than [H^+]

    g. neutral solution

_____ 8. ion-product constant for water

    h. hydronium ion

_____ 9. describes a substance that can act as both an acid and a base

    i. K_a

_____ 10. two substances that are related by the loss or gain of a single hydrogen ion

    j. salt hydrolysis

B. Multiple Choice

Choose the best answer and write its letter on the line.

_____ 11. A solution in which the hydroxide-ion concentration is $1 \times 10^{-5}M$ is
    a. acidic.
    b. basic.
    c. neutral.
    d. none of the above

_____ 12. In a neutral solution, the [H^+] is
    a. 10^{-14}.
    b. zero.
    c. 1×10^7M.
    d. equal to [OH^-].

_____ 13. The products of the self-ionization of water are
    a. $H_3O_7^+$ and H_2O.
    b. HO^- and OH^+.
    c. OH^+ and H^-.
    d. OH^- and H^+.

_____ 14. Which of these solutions is most basic?
     a. $[H^+] = 1 \times 10^{-11}$ **c.** $[H^+] = 1 \times 10^{-2}$
     b. $[OH^-] = 1 \times 10^{-4}$ **d.** $[OH^-] = 1 \times 10^{-13}$

_____ 15. The formula of the hydrogen ion is often written as
     a. H_2O^+.   **c.** H^+.
     b. OH^+.   **d.** H_3O^-.

_____ 16. What is the pH of a solution in which the $[H^+] = 1 \times 10^{-12}$?
     a. -1.0 **c.** 2.0
     b. -2.0 **d.** 12.0

_____ 17. What is the pH of a 0.01M hydrochloric acid solution?
     a. 10^{-2} **c.** 2.0
     b. 12.0   **d.** 10^{-12}

_____ 18. The K_a of carbonic acid is 4.3×10^{-7}.
$$H_2CO_3 \rightleftharpoons H^+ + HCO_3^-$$
This means that H_2CO_3 is a
     a. good hydrogen-ion acceptor.
     b. poor hydrogen-ion acceptor
     c. good hydrogen-ion donor.
     d. poor hydrogen-ion donor.

_____ 19. Which of the following pairs consist of a weak acid and a strong base?
     a. ethanoic acid, sodium hydroxide
     b. ethanoic acid, calcium hydroxide
     c. sulfuric acid, sodium hydroxide
     d. ethanoic acid, ammonia

_____ 20. In the reaction $NH_4^+ + H_2O \rightleftharpoons NH_3 + H_3O^+$, water is acting as a(n)
     a. Arrhenius acid.   **c.** Brønsted-Lowry acid.
     b. Brønsted-Lowry base.   **d.** Arrhenius base.

_____ 21. A solution with a pH of 5.0
     a. is basic.
     b. has a hydrogen-ion concentration of 5.0M.
     c. is neutral.
     d. has a hydroxide-ion concentration of $1 \times 10^{-9}M$.

_____ 22. With solutions of strong acids and strong bases, the word *strong* refers to
     a. molality.   **c.** solubility.
     b. molarity.   **d.** degree of ionization.

_____ 23. The hydrolysis of water by the salt of a weak base and a strong acid should produce a solution that is
     a. weakly basic.   **c.** strongly basic.
     b. neutral.   **d.** acidic.

_____ 24. Which of these is an Arrhenius base?
     a. KOH   **c.** $H_2PO_4^-$
     b. NH_3 **d.** CH_3COOH

_____ **25.** Which of these acids is monoprotic?

    a. CH_3COOH **c.** H_2SO_4

    b. H_2CO_3 **d.** H_3PO_4

_____ **26.** A solution that contains one mole of $Ca(OH)_2$ and one mole of H_2SO_4 is

    a. $CaSO_4 + H_3O^+ + H_2O$.   **c.** $CaH_2 + H_3SO_4$.

    b. $CaSO_4 + H_3O^+ + OH^-$.   **d.** $CaSO_4 + 2H_2O$.

_____ **27.** According to the Brønsted-Lowry theory, water

    a. acts as a base when it accepts a hydrogen ion.

    b. can be neither an acid nor a base.

    c. acts as an acid by accepting hydrogen ions.

    d. can accept but not donate hydrogen ions.

_____ **28.** What are the Brønsted-Lowry acids in this equilibrium reaction?

$$CN^- + H_2O \rightleftharpoons HCN + OH^-$$

    a. H_2O, OH^- **c.** H_2O, HCN

    b. CN^-, OH^- **d.** CN^-, H_2O

_____ **29.** A solution of one of the following compounds is acidic because one of its ions undergoes hydrolysis. The compound is

    a. KCl.   **c.** CH_3COOK.

    b. NH_4Cl.   **d.** NH_3.

C. Problems

Solve the following problems in the space provided. Show your work.

30. Calculate the pH for the following solutions. State whether each solution is acidic, basic, or neutral.

    a. $[H^+] = 1 \times 10^{-9}$

    b. $[OH^-] = 1 \times 10^{-10}$

    c. $[H^+] = 1 \times 10^{-7}$

31. Calculate the hydrogen-ion concentration $[H^+]$ for an aqueous solution in which $[OH^-]$ is 1×10^{-12} mol/L. Is this solution acidic, basic, or neutral?

Name ______________________________ Date ____________________ Class ____________________

32. Write the expression for K_a for each acid. Assume that only one hydrogen is ionized in each case.

a. H_2SO_3

b. HNO_3

33. Write complete and balanced equations for each of the following acid–base reactions.

a. $HBr + Mg(OH)_2 \rightarrow$

b. $H_2SO_4 + Al(OH)_3 \rightarrow$

34. Predict whether an aqueous solution of each salt will be acidic, basic, or neutral.

a. Na_2CO_3

b. KNO_3

c. $(NH_4)SO_4$

d. $Mg(C_2H_3O_2)_2$

D. Essay

Write a short essay for the following.

35. Compare and contrast the properties of acids and bases.

____

____

____

____

____

____

____

____

19 ACIDS, BASES, AND SALTS

Chapter Test B

A. Matching

Match each term in Column B with the correct description in Column A. Write the letter of the correct term on the line.

Column A   **Column B**

_____ 1. a substance that can donate a pair of electrons to form a   **a.** the ion-product
            covalent bond   constant for water

_____ 2. a compound that produces hydroxide ions when   **b.** Lewis base
            dissolved in water

_____ 3. the particle formed when a weak base gains a hydrogen   **c.** acid
            ion

_____ 4. 1.0×10^{-14} $(mol/L)^2$ **d.** conjugate acid

_____ 5. a substance that can accept a pair of electrons to form a   **e.** neutralization
            covalent bond   reaction

_____ 6. a compound that produces hydrogen ions when   **f.** Lewis acid
            dissolved in water

_____ 7. H_2SO_4 **g.** base

_____ 8. when the number of moles of hydrogen ions equals the   **h.** diprotic acid
            number of moles of hydroxide ions in titration

_____ 9. describes a substance that can act as both an acid and a   **i.** amphoteric
            base

_____ 10. the process of adding a known amount of solution of   **j.** titration
            known concentration to determine the concentration of
            another solution

_____ 11. reactions in which an acid and a base react in an   **k.** equivalence point
            aqueous solution to produce a salt and water

B. Multiple Choice

Choose the best answer and write its letter on the line.

_____ 12. Which of the following is true about acids?
            a. Acids give foods a bitter taste.
            b. Aqueous solutions of acids conduct electricity.
            c. Acids have a pH value greater than 7.
            d. all of the above

_____ 13. The products of the neutralization reaction between $HNO_2(aq)$ and $Ca(OH)_2(aq)$ are
    a. $CaNO_3 + H_2O$.
    b. $Ca(NO_3)_2 + H_2O$.
    c. $CaNO_3 + 2H_2O$.
    d. $Ca(NO_3)_2 + 2H_2O$.

_____ 14. A solution in which the $[H^+]$ is 1.0×10^{-4} mol/L is said to be
    a. acidic.
    b. basic.
    c. neutral.
    d. none of the above

_____ 15. What is the pH of the solution in question 14?
    a. 1.00
    b. 4.00
    c. 10.00
    d. 14.00

_____ 16. A solution with a pH of 9 has a $[OH^-]$ concentration of
    a. 1.0×10^{-14} mol/L.
    b. 1.0×10^{-9} mol/L.
    c. 1.0×10^{-5} mol/L.
    d. 1.0×10^{-7} mol/L.

_____ 17. Among the following, which solution is the most acidic?
    a. $[H^+] = 1 \times 10^{-5}$ mol/L
    b. pH = 3
    c. $[OH^-] = 1 \times 10^{-7}$ mol/L
    d. pH = 10

_____ 18. The monoprotic acid from among the following is
    a. H_2CO_3.
    b. H_2SO_4.
    c. H_3PO_4.
    d. HCl.

_____ 19. The Brønsted-Lowry theory defines an acid as a(n)
    a. hydrogen ion donor.
    b. hydrogen ion acceptor.
    c. electron-pair donor.
    d. electron-pair acceptor.

_____ 20. Which of the following is true about neutralization reactions?
    a. They involve strong acids and strong bases.
    b. They result in the production of a salt and water.
    c. They are all double-replacement reactions.
    d. all of the above

_____ 21. In the reaction: $HCl(g) + NH_3(aq) \rightarrow NH_4^+(aq) + Cl^-(aq)$, $HCl(g)$ is acting as a(n):
    a. Brønsted-Lowry acid.
    b. Brønsted-Lowry base.
    c. Lewis acid.
    d. Lewis base.

_____ 22. The conjugate acid in the reaction described in question 21 is
    a. $HCl(g)$.
    b. $NH_3(aq)$.
    c. $NH_4^+(aq)$.
    d. $Cl^-(aq)$.

_____ 23. Which of the following is true about indicators?
    a. They are weak acids or bases.
    b. They are as accurate as a pH meter.
    c. They maintain their colors across the range of pH values for which they are used.
    d. all of the above

_____ **24.** What is the Lewis acid in the following reaction?

$$NH_3 + BI_3 \rightarrow I_3BNH_3$$

    a. NH_3 **c.** I_3BNH_3
    b. BI_3 **d.** none of these

_____ **25.** Among the following K_a values, which represents the strongest acid?

    a. $K_a = 1.2 \times 10^{-3}$ **c.** $K_a = 8.7 \times 10^{-8}$
    b. $K_a = 3.4 \times 10^{-5}$ **d.** $K_a = 5.8 \times 10^{-10}$

_____ **26.** How many moles of $Mg(OH)_2(aq)$ would be required to neutralize 3.0 mol $HCl(aq)$?

    a. 1.5 mol   **c.** 6.0 mol
    b. 3.0 mol   **d.** 2.0 mol

C. Problems

Solve the following problems in the space provided. Show your work.

27. Calculate the $[OH^-]$ for an aqueous solution in which $[H^+] = 1.0 \times 10^{-9}$ mol/L. Is the solution acidic, basic, or neutral?

28. For each of the following, fill in the concentration of the requested ion, the pH, and the type of solution (acid, base, or neutral).

	Concentration	pH	Solution Type
a. $[H^+] = 1 \times 10^{-3}$	$[OH^-] =$		
b. $[OH^-] = 1 \times 10^{-8}$	$[H^+] =$		
c. $[H^+] = [OH^-]$	$[H^+] =$		

29. Write the expression for K_a for each of the following acids. Assume that only one hydrogen is ionized.

    a. HI

    b. H_2SO_4

30. Write complete and balanced equations for each of the following neutralization reactions:

    a. $HF(aq) + KOH(aq) \rightarrow$

    b. $H_2SO_4(aq) + LiOH(aq) \rightarrow$

31. How many moles of sulfuric acid would be required to neutralize 0.35 mol of KOH?

32. If the K_{sp} for a CuCl solution is 3.2×10^{-7}, what is the concentration of Cu and of Cl ions at equilibrium?

D. Essay

Write a short essay for the following.

33. Distinguish between the Brønsted-Lowry and Lewis theories of acids and bases.

_____

_____

_____

E. Additional Problems

Solve the following problems in the space provided. Show your work.

34. Determine the pH of a solution whose $[H^+] = 3.4 \times 10^{-4}$ mol/L. Is the solution acidic, basic, or neutral?

35. Use the Brønsted-Lowry definitions of acids and bases to identify the acid, base, conjugate acid, and conjugate base in each of the following reactions.

   a. $HF(aq) + H_2O(l) \rightleftharpoons H_3O^+(aq) + F^-(aq)$

   b. $HCl(g) + H_2O(l) \rightleftharpoons H_3O^+(aq) + Cl^-(aq)$

   c. $HC_2H_3O_2(aq) + H_2O(l) \rightleftharpoons H_3O^+(aq) + C_2H_3O_2^-(aq)$

	Acid	Base	Conjugate Acid	Conjugate Base
a.				
b.				
c.				

36. Identify the Lewis acids and bases in the following reactions:

	Lewis Acid	Lewis Base
a. $H^+ + I^- \rightarrow HI$		
b. $NH_3 + BCl_3 \rightarrow Cl_3BNH_3$		

37. A $0.1000M$ solution of ethanoic acid ($HC_2H_3O_2$) is only partially ionized so that $[H^+] = 2.25 \times 10^{-3}M$. What is the acid dissociation constant for this acid?

QUICK LAB: Indicators from Natural Sources

Laboratory Recordsheet   Use with Section 19.2

PURPOSE

To measure the pH of various household materials by using a natural indicator to make an indicator chart.

MATERIALS

- knife
- red cabbage leaves
- 1-cup measure
- hot water
- 2 jars
- clean white cloth
- teaspoon
- tape
- 3 sheets of plain white paper
- pencil
- ruler
- 10 clear plastic cups
- white vinegar (CH_3COOH)
- baking soda ($NaHCO_3$)
- household ammonia
- dropper
- various household items listed in Step 5

PROCEDURE

1. Put $\frac{1}{2}$ cup of finely chopped red cabbage leaves in a jar and add $\frac{1}{2}$ cup of hot water. Stir and crush the leaves with a spoon. Continue the extraction until the water is distinctly colored.

2. Strain the extract through a piece of cloth into a clean jar. This liquid is your natural indicator.

3. Tape three sheets of paper end to end. Draw a line along the center and label it at 5 cm intervals with the numbers 1 to 14. This is your pH scale.

4. Pour your indicator to about 1 cm depth into each of three plastic cups. To one cup, add several drops of vinegar, to the second add a pinch of baking soda, and to the third add several drops of ammonia. The resulting colors indicate pH values of about 3, 9, and 11, respectively. Place these colored positions on your pH scale.

5. Repeat Step 4 for household items such as table salt, borax, milk, lemon juice, laundry detergent, dish detergent, milk of magnesia, mouthwash, toothpaste, shampoo, and carbonated beverages.

ANALYSES AND CONCLUSIONS

1. What was the color of the indicator at acidic, neutral, and basic conditions?

   _____

   _____

   _____

2. What chemical changes were responsible for the color changes?

   _____

   _____

   _____

3. Label the materials you tested as acidic, basic, or neutral.

   _____

   _____

   _____

   _____

   _____

4. Which group contains items used for cleaning or for personal hygiene?

   _____

   _____

SMALL-SCALE LAB: Ionization Constants of Weak Acids

Laboratory Recordsheet   Use with Section 19.4

SAFETY

Wear safety glasses and follow the standard safety procedures outlined on page 7 of this manual.

PURPOSE

To measure ionization constants of weak acids such as bromocresol green (BCG).

MATERIALS

- pencil
- ruler
- chemicals shown in Figure A
- paper
- reaction surface

PROCEDURE

1. On a separate sheet of paper, draw a grid similar to Figure A. Make each square 2 cm on each side. Draw a black X in each square of the grid.

2. Place a reaction surface over the grid and place one drop of BCG in each square.

3. Place one drop of pH buffer in each square corresponding to its pH value.

4. Use Figure A as a data table to record your observations for each solution.

1 drop pH buffer + 1 drop BCG

pH

1	2	3
4	5	6
7	8	9
10	11	12

Figure A

ANALYSIS

Using your experimental data, record the answers to the following questions.

1. What is the color of the lowest pH solutions?

   _____

2. What is the color of the highest pH solutions?

   _____

3. At which pH does the bromocresol green change from one color to the other? At which pH does an intermediate color exist?

   _____

An acid–base indicator is usually a weak acid with a characteristic color. Because bromocresol green is an acid, it is convenient to represent its rather complex formula as HBCG. HBCG ionizes in water according to the following chemical equation.

$$HBCG + H_2O = BCG^- + H_3O^+$$

   (yellow)   (blue)

The K_a expression is $K_a = \dfrac{[BCG^-] \times [H_3O^+]}{[HBCG]}$

When $[BCG^-] = [HBCG]$, $K_a = [H_3O^+]$

4. What color is the conjugate acid of BCG^-?

   _____

   _____

5. What color is the conjugate base of HBCG?

   _____

6. What color is an equal mixture of the conjugate acid and the conjugate base of bromocresol green? At what pH does this equal mixture occur?

   _____

YOU'RE THE CHEMIST

Use the space below to write your observations to the small-scale activities in the *You're the Chemist* section.

_____

_____

_____

_____

_____

_____

_____

20.1 THE MEANING OF OXIDATION AND REDUCTION

Section Review

Objectives

- Define *oxidation* and *reduction* in terms of the loss or gain of oxygen or hydrogen and the loss or gain of electrons
- State the characteristics of a redox reaction and identify the oxidizing agent and reducing agent

Vocabulary

- oxidation-reduction reactions
- redox reactions
- oxidation
- reduction
- reducing agent
- oxidizing agent

Part A Completion

Use this completion exercise to check your understanding of the concepts and terms that are introduced in this section. Each blank can be completed with a term, short phrase, or number.

Oxidation–reduction, or ___1___ , reactions are an important

category of chemical reactions. Oxidation is considered to be any

shift of electrons ___2___ from an atom. Reduction includes any

shift of electrons ___3___ an atom. An oxidation reaction is always

accompanied by a ___4___ reaction. The substance that does the

oxidizing (the ___5___ agent) is ___6___ . The substance that does

the reducing (the ___7___ agent) is ___8___ .

1. _____

2. _____

3. _____

4. _____

5. _____

6. _____

7. _____

8. _____

Part B True-False

Classify each of these statements as always true, AT; sometimes true, ST; or never true, NT.

_____ 9. Reduction is the complete or partial gain of electrons by a substance.

_____ 10. In the reaction $2Na + Cl_2 \rightarrow 2NaCl$, sodium is the reducing agent.

_____ 11. In the reaction $2Na + Cl_2 \rightarrow 2NaCl$, sodium is being reduced.

_____ **12.** To protect an iron ship hull, you should attach a metal that is easily
reduced.

Part C Matching

Match each description in Column B to the correct term in Column A.

Column A	Column B

_____ **13.** combustion

_____ **14.** oxidation

_____ **15.** oxidizing agent

_____ **16.** corrosion

_____ **17.** zinc

_____ **18.** gold

a. a metal that loses electrons easily

b. complete or partial loss of electrons or gain of oxygen

c. oxidation of metals to metallic ions by oxygen and water in the environment

d. a metal that resists corrosion

e. a chemical change in which oxygen reacts with another substance, often producing energy in the form of heat and light

f. a substance that accepts electrons in a redox reaction

Part D Questions and Problems

Answer the following in the space provided.

19. Define *oxidation* and *reduction* in terms of the loss or gain of electrons.

_____

_____

_____

20. In the equation given, identify the substance oxidized, the substance reduced, the oxidizing agent, and the reducing agent.

$$Zn + Cu^{2+} \rightarrow Zn^{2+} + Cu$$

_____

_____

21. Explain how putting a block of zinc or aluminum on the iron hull of a large ship will protect the ship from corrosion.

_____

_____

_____

Name _____ Date _____ Class _____

20.2 OXIDATION NUMBERS

Section Review

Objectives

• Determine the oxidation number of an atom of any element in a pure substance
• Define *oxidation* and *reduction* in terms of a change in oxidation number, and identify atoms being oxidized or reduced in redox reactions

Vocabulary

• oxidation number

Part A Completion

Use this completion exercise to check your understanding of the concepts and terms that are introduced in this section. Each blank can be completed with a term, short phrase, or number.

The oxidation number of an element in an uncombined state is __1__. The oxidation number of a monatomic ion is the same in magnitude and __2__ as its ionic __3__. The sum of the oxidation numbers of the elements in a neutral compound is __4__. In a polyatomic ion, however, the sum is equal to the __5__. Oxidation numbers help you keep track of __6__ – transfer in redox reactions. An oxidation number increase is __7__, while a __8__ is reduction.

1. _____

2. _____

3. _____

4. _____

5. _____

6. _____

7. _____

8. _____

Part B True-False

Classify each of these statements as always true, AT; sometimes true, ST; or never true, NT.

_____ 9. Oxygen is more electronegative than chlorine.

_____ 10. The oxidation number of each oxygen atom in most compounds is −2.

_____ 11. The oxidation number of Cl in $KClO_3$ is −1.

_____ 12. The oxidation number of each hydrogen atom in most compounds is −1.

_____ 13. The oxidation number for copper in a copper penny is +2.

_____ **14.** In the reaction $C + H_2O \rightarrow CO + H_2$, the oxidation number of the hydrogen doesn't change.

_____ **15.** In the reaction $C + H_2O \rightarrow CO + H_2$, the oxidation number of the carbon increases.

_____ **16.** An increase in the oxidation number of an atom indicates oxidation.

Part C Matching

Match the oxidation number of nitrogen in each formula in Column B to the correct oxidation number in Column A.

Column A	Column B
_____ **17.** -3	**a.** N_2
_____ **18.** -2	**b.** HNO_3
_____ **19.** -1	**c.** NO
_____ **20.** 0	**d.** NH_2OH
_____ **21.** $+1$	**e.** NH_3
_____ **22.** $+2$	**f.** N_2O_3
_____ **23.** $+3$	**g.** N_2O
_____ **24.** $+4$	**h.** N_2H_4
_____ **25.** $+5$	**i.** NO_2

Part D Questions and Problems

Answer the following in the space provided.

26. Define *oxidation* and *reduction* in terms of a change in oxidation number.

_____

_____

27. Use the change in oxidation number to determine which elements are oxidized and which are reduced in these reactions. (Note: It is not necessary to use balanced equations.)

a. $HNO_3 + HBr \rightarrow NO + Br_2 + H_2O$ _____

b. $KMnO_4 + HCl \rightarrow MnCl_2 + Cl_2 + H_2O + KCl$ _____

c. $Sb + HNO_3 \rightarrow Sb_2O_5 + NO + H_2O$ _____

d. $C + H_2SO_4 \rightarrow CO_2 + SO_2 + H_2O$ _____

BALANCING REDOX REACTIONS

20.3

Section Review

Objectives

- Balance a redox equation using the oxidation-number-change method
- Balance a redox equation by breaking a redox equation into oxidation and reduction half-reactions and then using the half-reaction method

Vocabulary

- oxidation-number-change method
- half-reaction
- half-reaction method

Part A Completion

Use this completion exercise to check your understanding of the concepts and terms that are introduced is this section. Each blank can be completed with a term, short phrase, or number.

One method for balancing redox equations involves determining the change in ___**1**___ of the substances that are oxidized and reduced. Coefficients are then used to make the increase in oxidation number equal to the decrease.

The ___**2**___ method is another way to write a ___**3**___ equation for a redox reaction. In this method, the net ___**4**___ equation is divided into ___**5**___ half-reactions. Each half-reaction is balanced independently. Finally, the half-reactions are ___**6**___.

The half-reaction method is particularly useful in balancing

equations for ___**7**___ reactions.

1. _____

2. _____

3. _____

4. _____

5. _____

6. _____

7. _____

Part B True-False

Classify each of these statements as always true, AT; sometimes true, ST; or never true, NT.

_____ 8. The reduction half-reaction in the reaction $MnO_4^- + Cl^- \rightarrow Mn^{2+} + Cl_2$ involves $MnO_4^- \rightarrow Mn^{2+}$

_____ **9.** In an oxidation half-reaction, electrons occur on the right side of the equation.

_____ **10.** Electrons never appear in a balanced redox reaction.

_____ **11.** $2e^- + 2Cl^- \rightarrow Cl_2$ is a balanced half-reaction.

_____ **12.** To balance the oxygen in a half reaction involving $MnO_4^- \rightarrow Mn^{2+}$, $2H_2O$ will be added to the product side of the equation.

_____ **13.** In the equation $2FeBr_2 + Br_2 \rightarrow 2FeBr_3$, the oxidation number of the iron doesn't change.

Part C Matching

Match each description in Column B to the correct term in Column A.

Column A	Column B
_____ **14.** half-reaction method	**a.** ions that are present but do not participate in or change during the reaction
_____ **15.** spectator ions	**b.** $Fe^{2+} \rightarrow Fe^{3+} + e^-$
_____ **16.** anions	**c.** balancing a redox equation by first balancing the oxidation and reduction half-reactions
_____ **17.** oxidation half-reaction	**d.** balancing a redox equation by comparing the increase and decrease in oxidation numbers
_____ **18.** half-reaction	**e.** equation showing either the reduction or the oxidation of a species in an oxidation-reduction reaction
_____ **19.** oxidation-number-change method	**f.** ions that can serve as reducing agents
_____ **20.** reduction half-reaction	**g.** $2e^- + Br_2 \rightarrow 2Br^-$

Part D Questions and Problems

Answer the following in the space provided.

21. Balance these redox equations using the oxidation-number-change method.

    a. $HNO_3(aq) + HI(g) \rightarrow NO(g) + I_2(s) + H_2O$

    b. $HNO_3(aq) + I_2(s) \rightarrow HIO_3(aq) + NO_2(g) + H_2O(l)$

_____

_____

22. Balance these redox equations using the half-reaction method.

    a. $H_2S(aq) + HNO_3(aq) \rightarrow S(s) + NO(g) + H_2O(l)$

    b. $Fe^{2+} + Cr_2O_7^{2-} \rightarrow Fe^{3+} + Cr^{3+}$

20 OXIDATION-REDUCTION REACTIONS

Practice Problems

In your notebook, solve the following problems.

SECTION 20.1 THE MEANING OF OXIDATION AND REDUCTION

Determine what is oxidized and what is reduced in each reaction. Identify the oxidizing agent and the reducing agent.

1. $2Sr + O_2 \rightarrow 2SrO$

2. $2Li + S \rightarrow 2Li_2S$

3. $2Cs + Br_2 \rightarrow 2CsBr$

4. $3Mg + N_2 \rightarrow Mg_3N_2$

5. $4Fe + 3O_2 \rightarrow 2Fe_2O_3$

6. $Cl_2 + 2NaBr \rightarrow 2NaCl + Br_2$

7. $Si + 2F_2 \rightarrow SiF_4$

8. $2Ca + O_2 \rightarrow 2CaO$

9. $Mg + 2HCl \rightarrow MgCl_2 + H_2$

10. $2Na + 2H_2O \rightarrow 2NaOH + H_2$

SECTION 20.2 OXIDATION NUMBERS

1. Give the oxidation number of each kind of atom or ion.

   a. Sn c. S^{2-} e. Se g. Sn^{4+}

   b. K^+ d. Fe^{3+} f. Mg^{2+} h. Br^-

2. Calculate the oxidation number of chromium in each of the following formulas.

   a. Cr_2O_3 b. $H_2Cr_2O_7$ c. $CrSO_4$ d. CrO_4^{2-}

3. Use the changes in oxidation number to determine which elements are oxidized and which are reduced in these reactions. (Note: It is not necessary to use balanced reactions.)

   a. $C + H_2SO_4 \rightarrow CO_2 + SO_2 + H_2O$

   b. $HNO_3 + HI \rightarrow NO + I_2 + H_2O$

   c. $KMnO_4 + HCl \rightarrow MnCl_2 + Cl_2 + H_2O + KCl$

   d. $Sb + HNO_3 \rightarrow Sb_2O_5 + NO + H_2O$

4. For each reaction in problem 3 above, identify the oxidizing agent and reducing agent.

SECTION 20.3 BALANCING REDOX EQUATIONS

1. Balance these equations using the oxidation-number-change method.

   a. $C + H_2SO_4 \rightarrow CO_2 + SO_2 + H_2O$

   b. $H_2S + HNO_3 \rightarrow S + NO + H_2O$

   c. $HNO_3 + HI \rightarrow NO + I_2 + H_2O$

   d. $Sb + HNO_3 \rightarrow Sb_2O_5 + NO + H_2O$

   e. $KMnO_4 + HCl \rightarrow MnCl_2 + Cl_2 + H_2O + KCl$

   f. $KIO_4 + KI + HCl \rightarrow KCl + I_2 + H_2O$

   g. $Zn + Cr_2O_7^{2-} + H^+ \rightarrow Zn^{2+} + Cr^{3+} + H_2O$

2. Write half-reactions for the oxidation and reduction processes for each of the following reactions.

   a. $Fe^{2+} + MnO_4^- \rightarrow Fe^{3+} + Mn^{2+}$ (acidic solution)

   b. $Sn^{2+} + IO_3^- \rightarrow Sn^{4+} + I^-$ (acidic solution)

   c. $S^{2-} + NO_3^- \rightarrow S + NO$ (acidic solution)

   d. $Mn^{2+} + H_2O_2 \rightarrow MnO_2 + H_2O$ (basic solution)

3. Balance these reactions using the half-reaction method.

   a. $Zn + HgO \rightarrow ZnO_2^{2-} + Hg$ (basic solution)

   b. $Fe^{2+} + MnO_4^- \rightarrow Fe^{3+} + Mn^{2+}$ (acidic solution)

   c. $Sn^{2+} + IO_3^- \rightarrow Sn^{4-} + I^-$ (acidic solution)

   d. $S^{2-} + NO_3^- \rightarrow S + NO$ (acidic solution)

   e. $Mn^{2+} + H_2O_2 \rightarrow MnO_2 + H_2O$ (basic solution)

   f. $CrO_2 + ClO^- \rightarrow CrO_4^{2-} + Cl^-$ (basic solution)

20 INTERPRETING GRAPHICS

Use with Section 20.3

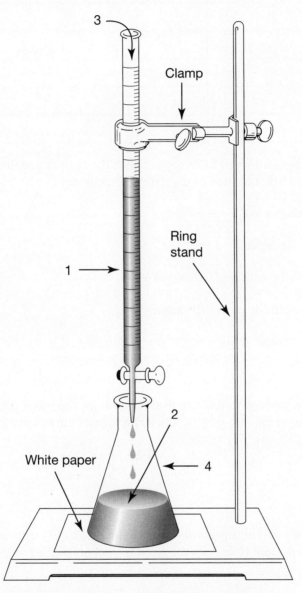

Figure 1 Titration of iron(II) ion (Fe^{2+}) with a standard solution of 0.0200M potassium permanganate ($KMnO_4$).

To determine the relative amount of iron in a sample of iron ore, a chemist dissolved 2.938 g of the ore in 50.0 mL of dilute sulfuric acid (H_2SO_4) in a reaction flask. The colorless solution was then titrated to the end point with potassium permanganate. The half-reactions for the oxidation and reduction processes that occur during this titration are:

$$Fe^{2+} \rightarrow Fe^{3+}$$
$$MnO_4^- \rightarrow Mn^{2+}$$

Use the data in Table 1 and what you have learned about oxidation-reduction reactions to answer the following questions.

Table 1 Analysis of an Unknown Iron-Containing Ore

Initial Volume of $KMnO_4$	48.65 mL
Final Volume of $KMnO_4$	23.35 mL
Volume of MnO_4^-	
Moles MnO_4^-	
Moles Iron(II), Fe^{2+}	
Mass of Iron	
% of Iron in Ore	

1. Match each component from the following list with the correct number shown in Figure 1. The same number may be used more than once.

   _____ **a.** oxidizing agent

   _____ **b.** reducing agent

   _____ **c.** standard solution of 0.0200M $KMnO_4$

   _____ **d.** acidic solution of iron(II) ion, Fe^{2+}

   _____ **e.** reaction flask

   _____ **f.** buret

2. Use the half-reaction method to balance the equation for the redox reaction between permanganate ion and iron(II) ion. Write the net ionic equation only.

3. Explain what the *end point* of this particular titration means in terms of the reacting species in solution. How does the chemist recognize the end point when it occurs?

   _____

   _____

   _____

4. Use the stoichiometry of the balanced equation given in your answer to question 2 and the fact that the molar mass of Fe is 55.85 g to complete Table 1 above. Use the space below to show your work.

20 OXIDATION-REDUCTION REACTIONS

Vocabulary Review

Select the term from the following list that best matches each description.

half-reaction   oxidation-reduction reaction
half-reaction method   oxidizing agent
oxidation   redox reaction
oxidation number   reducing agent
oxidation-number-change method   reduction

1. the substance in a redox reaction that accepts electrons

   _____

2. a method of balancing a redox equation by comparing the increases and
   decreases in oxidation numbers

   _____

3. a process that involves a complete or partial gain of electrons or the loss of
   oxygen; it results in a decrease in the oxidation number of an atom

   _____

4. a method for balancing a redox equation by balancing the oxidation and
   reduction half-reactions

   _____

5. a positive or negative number assigned to a combined atom according to a
   set of arbitrary rules

   _____

6. a substance in a redox reaction that donates electrons

   _____

7. an equation showing either the reduction or the oxidation of a species in an
   oxidation-reduction reaction

   _____

8. a reaction that involves the transfer of electrons between reactants during a
   chemical change

   _____

9. a process that involves complete or partial loss of electrons or a gain of
   oxygen; it results in an increase in the oxidation number of an atom

   _____

10. another name for an oxidation-reduction reaction

   _____

Name _____ Date _____ Class _____

OXIDATION-REDUCTION REACTIONS

20

Chapter Quiz

Choose the best answer and write its letter on the line.

_____ 1. The oxidation number of sulfur in each of the following is +6 *except* for
    a. SO_3.   **c.** SO_4^{2-}.
    b. $S_2O_3^{2-}$.   **d.** Na_2SO_4.

20.2

_____ 2. Reduction is
    a. a gain of electrons.   **c.** a gain of oxygen.
    b. a loss of electrons.   **d.** both a and c

20.1

_____ 3. Identify the oxidizing agent in the following reaction.
$$2Na + S \rightarrow Na_2S$$
    a. Na   **c.** Na_2S
    b. S   **d.** Na^+

20.1

_____ 4. From the unbalanced equations below, identify the one that does *not* represent a redox reaction.
    a. $HNO_3(aq) + H_3PO_3(aq) \rightarrow NO(g) + H_3PO_4(aq) + H_2O(l)$
    b. $H_2SO_4(aq) + NaOH(aq) \rightarrow H_2O(l) + Na_2SO_4(aq)$
    c. $C(s) + O_2(g) \rightarrow CO_2(g)$
    d. $H_2O_2(aq) + PbS(s) \rightarrow PbSO_4(s) + H_2O(l)$

20.1

_____ 5. Identify the oxidation half-reaction among the following.
    a. $Fe^{2+} \rightarrow Fe^{3+} + e^-$ **c.** $O_2 + 4H^+ + 4e^- \rightarrow 2H_2O$
    b. $Cl_2 + 2e^- \rightarrow 2Cl^-$ **d.** $Fe^{3+} + e^- \rightarrow Fe^{2+}$

20.3

_____ 6. What will the coefficient of HNO_3 be when the following equation is completely balanced using the smallest whole-number coefficients?
$$HNO_3 + MnCl_2 + HCl \rightarrow NO + MnCl_4 + H_2O$$
    a. 2   **c.** 6
    b. 3   **d.** 5

20.3

_____ 7. When the half-reactions $I_2 + 2e^- \rightarrow 2I^-$ and $Na \rightarrow Na^+ + e^-$ are correctly combined, the balanced redox equation is
    a. $Na + I + e^- \rightarrow Na^+ + 2I^-$
    b. $Na + I_2 \rightarrow Na^+ + 2I^-$
    c. $2Na + I_2 \rightarrow 2Na^+ + 2I^-$
    d. $Na + I_2 + 2e^- \rightarrow Na^+ + 2I^- + e^-$

20.3

_____ 8. What is the reduction half-reaction for the following unbalanced redox equation?
$$Cr_2O_7^{2-} + NH_4^+ \rightarrow Cr_2O_3 + N_2$$
    a. $NH_4^+ \rightarrow N_2$ **c.** $Cr_2O_3 \rightarrow Cr_2O_7^{2-}$
    b. $N_2 \rightarrow NH_4^+$ **d.** $Cr_2O_7^{2-} \rightarrow Cr_2O_3$

20.3

528 *Core Teaching Resources*

OXIDATION-REDUCTION REACTIONS

20

Chapter Test A

A. Matching

Match each term in Column B with the correct description in Column A.

Column A	Column B
_____ 1. a positive or negative number assigned to an atom according to a set of arbitrary rules	**a.** half-reaction
_____ 2. the substance in a redox reaction that accepts electrons	**b.** oxidation-number-change method
_____ 3. chemical change that occurs when electrons are transferred between reactants	**c.** oxidation
_____ 4. an equation showing either the reduction or the oxidation of a species in a redox reaction	**d.** oxidation number
_____ 5. complete or partial gain of electrons or loss of oxygen	**e.** half-reaction method
_____ 6. ion that does not change oxidation number or composition during a reaction	**f.** oxidation-reduction reaction
_____ 7. balances redox reactions by balancing oxidation and reduction half-reactions	**g.** spectator ion
_____ 8. balances a redox reaction by comparing the increases and decreases in oxidation numbers	**h.** reducing agent
_____ 9. complete or partial loss of electrons or gain of oxygen	**i.** reduction
_____ 10. the substance in a redox reaction that donates electrons	**j.** oxidizing agent

B. Multiple Choice

Choose the best answer and write its letter on the line.

_____ 11. Identify the oxidizing agent in the following reaction.

$$2Na + 2H_2O \rightarrow 2NaOH + H_2$$

    a. Na   **c.** NaOH
    b. H_2O **d.** H_2

_____ 12. Identify the reducing agent in the following reaction.

$$CH_4 + 2O_2 \rightarrow CO_2 + 2H_2O$$

    a. H_2O **b.** O_2
    b. CO_2 **d.** CH_4

_____ **13.** Nitrogen has the same oxidation number in all of the following *except*
    a. NO_3^-.
    b. N_2O_5.
    c. NH_4Cl.
    d. $Ca(NO_3)_2$.

_____ **14.** Determine what happens in this reaction.
$$S + Cl_2 \rightarrow SCl_2$$
    (*Hint:* Chlorine is the more electronegative element.)
    a. Sulfur is reduced.
    b. Chlorine is reduced.
    c. Chlorine is oxidized.
    d. Sulfur is the oxidizing agent.

_____ **15.** $Zn \rightarrow Zn^{2+}$ represents
    a. oxidation.
    b. reduction.
    c. both a and b
    d. neither a nor b

_____ **16.** $Sn^{4+} \rightarrow Sn^{2+}$ represents
    a. oxidation.
    b. reduction.
    c. hydrolysis.
    d. none of the above

_____ **17.** What happens to chlorine (in ClO_3^-) in the following redox reaction?
$$ClO_3^- + I^- \rightarrow Cl^- + I_2$$
    a. It is oxidized.
    b. Its oxidation number changes from +6 to −1.
    c. Its oxidation-number change is −6.
    d. Its oxidation-number change is +6.

_____ **18.** Identify the atom that increases in oxidation number in the following redox reaction.
$$2MnO_2 + 2K_2CO_3 + O_2 \rightarrow 2KMnO_4 + 2CO_2$$
    a. C
    b. K
    c. Mn
    d. O

_____ **19.** Identify the reducing agent in this reaction.
$$I^- + MnO_4^- \rightarrow I_2 + MnO_2$$
    a. I^-
    b. MnO_4^-
    c. I_2
    d. MnO_2

_____ **20.** What is the increase in oxidation number for the atom that is oxidized in the following balanced redox equation?
$$Cr_2O_7^{2-} + 8H^+ + 3SO_3^{2-} \rightarrow Cr^{3+} + 3SO_4^{2-} + 8H_2O$$
    a. +2
    b. +6
    c. −3
    d. −6

_____ **21.** To balance the oxygen and hydrogen for a redox reaction that takes place in basic solution, it is necessary to use
    a. H_2O and H^+.
    b. H_2O only.
    c. H_2O and OH^-.
    d. OH^- only.

_____ **22.** Which of the following is an oxidation half-reaction?
    a. $Zn^{2+} + 2e^- \rightarrow Zn$
    b. $NO + 2H_2O \rightarrow NO_3^- + 4H^+ + 3e^-$
    c. $Na^+ + e^- \rightarrow Na$
    d. $2H^+ + 2e^- \rightarrow H_2$

_____ **23.** What is the reduction half-reaction for the following unbalanced redox equation?

$$Cr_2O_7{}^{2-} + Fe^{2+} \rightarrow Cr^{3+} + Fe^{3+}$$

a. $Cr^{3+} \rightarrow Cr_2O_7{}^{2-}$ c. $Fe^{3+} \rightarrow Fe^{2+}$
b. $Fe^{2+} \rightarrow Fe^{3+}$ d. $Cr_2O_7{}^{2-} \rightarrow Cr^{3+}$

_____ **24.** Which atom is reduced in the following unbalanced redox equations?

$$K_2Cr_2O_7 + H_2O + S \rightarrow KOH + Cr_2O_3 + SO_2$$

a. S   c. Cr
b. O   d. K

_____ **25.** Identify a true statement about how to protect an iron object from corrosion.
   a. Increase the amount of salt and/or acid in the water.
   b. Place a gold or silver bar in contact with the iron.
   c. Place a better reducing agent in contact with the iron.
   d. Place a metal more easily reduced in contact with the iron.

_____ **26.** Identify from the unbalanced equations below the one that does *not* represent a redox reaction.
   a. $H_2O_2(aq) + MnO_4{}^-(aq) \rightarrow O_2(g) + Mn^{2+}(aq)$
   b. $H_2(g) + N_2(g) \rightarrow NH_3(g)$
   c. $NaCl(aq) + AgNO_3(aq) \rightarrow NaNO_3(aq) + AgCl(s)$
   d. $Cu(s) + AgNO_3(aq) \rightarrow Cu(NO_3)_2(aq) + Ag(s)$

C. Questions

Answer the following questions in the space provided.

27. Determine which substance is oxidized and which substance is reduced in each reaction. Identify the oxidizing agent and reducing agent in each case.
   a. $2Na + Br_2 \rightarrow 2NaBr$

   b. $2K + S \rightarrow K_2S$

28. Combine these two half-reactions to form a balanced redox equation.

$$Br_2 + 2e^- \rightarrow 2Br^- \text{ and } Cr \rightarrow Cr^{3+} + 3e^-$$

29. Determine the oxidation number of each element in these substances.

    a. Li_3AlF_6

    b. Na_2O

    c. S_8

30. Balance the following redox equation, using either the oxidation-number-change method or the half-reaction method. Show all your work. (In using the half-reaction method, assume that the reaction occurs in aqueous acid solution.)

$$Fe_2O_3 + CO \rightarrow Fe + CO_2 \text{ (acid solution)}$$

D. Essay

31. How are oxidation numbers determined and used?

_____

_____

_____

_____

_____

_____

_____

20 OXIDATION-REDUCTION REACTIONS

Chapter Test B

A. Matching

Match each term in Column B with the correct description in Column A. Write the letter of the correct term on the line.

Column A	Column B

_____ 1. the substance in a redox reaction that accepts electrons

_____ 2. the complete or partial gain of electrons or the loss of oxygen

_____ 3. those ions that do not change oxidation number or composition during a reaction

_____ 4. a positive or negative number assigned to an atom according to a set of arbitrary rules

_____ 5. the complete or partial loss of electrons or the gain of oxygen

_____ 6. the balancing of a redox reaction by comparing the increases and decreases in oxidation numbers

_____ 7. the chemical changes that occur when electrons are transferred between reactants

_____ 8. a method of balancing redox reactions by balancing the oxidation and reduction half-reactions

_____ 9. the substance in a redox reaction that donates electrons

_____ 10. another name for an oxidation-reduction reaction

a. oxidation-number-change method

b. reducing agent

c. oxidation-reduction reactions

d. spectator ions

e. oxidizing agent

f. reduction

g. oxidation number

h. half-reaction method

i. oxidation

j. redox reaction

B. Multiple Choice

Choose the best answer and write its letter on the line.

_____ 11. Which of the following is true about oxidation reactions?
   a. Oxidation reactions are the principal source of energy on Earth.
   b. All oxidation reactions are accompanied by reduction reactions.
   c. The burning of wood in a fireplace and the metabolization of food by your body are oxidation reactions.
   d. all of the above

_____ 12. What is the oxidized substance in the following reaction?
$$Fe + 2HCl \rightarrow FeCl_2 + H_2$$
    a. Fe   **c.** $FeCl_2$
    b. HCl   **d.** H_2

_____ 13. The reducing agent in the reaction described in question 12 is
    a. Fe.   **c.** $FeCl_2$.
    b. HCl.   **d.** H_2.

_____ 14. What is occurring in the following reaction?
$$H_2 + Cl_2 \rightarrow 2HCl$$
    a. H_2 is being reduced.
    b. Cl_2 is being oxidized.
    c. H_2 is gaining two electrons.
    d. Cl_2 is acting as an oxidizing agent.

_____ 15. What is the oxidation number of sulfur in H_2SO_3?
    a. +1   **c.** +3
    b. +2   **d.** +4

_____ 16. What is the usual oxidation number of oxygen in a compound?
    a. −1   **c.** +1
    b. −2   **d.** +2

_____ 17. In the unbalanced equation below, what element is being reduced?
$$MnO_2 + HCl \rightarrow H_2O + MnCl_2 + Cl_2$$
    a. Mn   **c.** H
    b. O   **d.** Cl

_____ 18. Which of the following is an oxidation reaction?
    a. $Co^{3+} \rightarrow Co^{2+}$ **c.** $AuCl_4^- \rightarrow AuCl_2^-$
    b. $Cl_2 \rightarrow ClO_3^-$ **d.** $Mn^{7+} \rightarrow Mn^{2+}$

_____ 19. Among the following, which is an oxidation-reduction reaction?
    a. $Na_2S + CaCO_3 \rightarrow CaS + Na_2CO_3$
    b. $2HNO_3 + Mg(OH)_2 \rightarrow Mg(NO_3)_2 + 2H_2O$
    c. $H_2 + F_2 \rightarrow 2HF$
    d. $3Ba(OH)_2 + 2H_3PO_4 \rightarrow Ba_3(PO_4)_2 + 6H_2O$

_____ 20. Which of the following is true concerning the reaction below?
$$H_2S + HNO_3 \rightarrow S + NO + H_2O$$
    a. S is reduced.   **c.** N is reduced.
    b. H is oxidized.   **d.** O is oxidized.

_____ 21. When the equation in question 20 is balanced, what is the coefficient
for H_2O?
    a. 2   **c.** 3
    b. 4   **d.** 6

_____ 22. In the equation $PbO_2 + 4HCl \rightarrow 2H_2O + PbCl_2 + Cl_2$, how many electrons are transferred?

a. 1
b. 2
c. 3
d. 4

_____ 23. The element oxidized in the reaction described in question 22 is
a. Pb.
b. O.
c. H.
d. Cl.

_____ 24. In the unbalanced equation given below, what is the element that is gaining electrons?

$$HCl + MnO_2 \rightarrow MnCl_2 + H_2O + Cl_2$$

a. H
b. Cl
c. Mn
d. O

_____ 25. When the equation in question 24 is balanced, what is the coefficient for HCl?
a. 1
b. 2
c. 3
d. 4

_____ 26. Which of the following is true concerning redox reactions?
a. Double-replacement reactions are always redox reactions.
b. Single-replacement reactions may be redox reactions.
c. Acid-base reactions are always redox reactions.
d. all of the above

_____ 27. Identify a *false* statement about how to protect iron from corrosion.
a. Coat the surface with oil, paint, or plastic.
b. Attach a metal that is more easily reduced.
c. Exclude air and water.
d. Attach a metal that is a better reducing agent.

_____ 28. From the unbalanced equations below, identify the one that does *not* represent a redox reaction.
a. $H_2CO_3(aq) \rightarrow CO_2(g) + H_2O(l)$
b. $C(s) + H_2O(g) \rightarrow CO(g) + H_2(g)$
c. $S_2O_3{}^{2-}(aq) + I_2(s) \rightarrow S_4O_6{}^{2-}(aq) + I^-(aq)$
d. $FeBr_2(aq) + Br_2(l) \rightarrow FeBr_3(aq)$

Name ______________________ Date ________________ Class ________________

C. Questions

Answer the following questions in the space provided.

29. For each of the following reactions, identify the element oxidized, the element reduced, the oxidizing agent, and the reducing agent.

	Oxidized	Reduced	Oxidizing Agent	Reducing Agent
a. $K + I_2 \rightarrow 2KI$				
b. $2Na + 2H_2O \rightarrow 2NaOH + H_2$				
c. $H_2 + CuO \rightarrow Cu + H_2O$				
d. $Cu(NO_3)_2 + Mg \rightarrow Mg(NO_3)_2 + Cu$				

30. Determine the oxidation number of each element in the following.

a. K_2SO_4

b. $Cu(NO_3)_2$

c. $HAsO_3$

d. MnO_4^-

31. Use the oxidation-number-change method to balance the equations given below. Show all your work.

a. $HNO_3 + Ag \rightarrow AgNO_3 + NO + H_2O$

b. $Br_2 + SO_2 + H_2O \rightarrow H_2SO_4 + HBr$

Name ____________________ Date ____________________ Class ____________________

32. Use the half-reaction method to balance the equations given below. Show all your work.

a. $HNO_2 + HI \rightarrow I_2 + NO + H_2O$

b. $K_2Cr_2O_7 + FeCl_2 + HCl \rightarrow CrCl_3 + KCl + FeCl_3 + H_2O$

D. Essay

33. Explain why oxidation cannot occur without reduction, and vice versa.

____

____

____

____

____

QUICK LAB: Bleach It! Oxidize the Color Away

Laboratory Recordsheet   Use with Section 20.3

PURPOSE

To test the effect of oxidizing agents on stains and dyes.

MATERIALS

- spot plate
- medicine dropper
- water
- colorimeter (optional)

Oxidizing agents

- liquid chlorine bleach (5% (m/v) sodium hypochlorite)
- powder bleach
- oxalic acid solution (1% (m/v))
- sodium thiosulfate solution (hypo) (0.2M $Na_2S_2O_3$)
- hydrogen peroxide (3% (v/v) H_2O_2)

Samples

- iodine solution (1% I_2 in 2% (m/v) KI)
- potassium permanganate solution (0.05M $KMnO_4$)
- grape juice
- rusty water
- piece of colored fabric
- colored flower petals
- grass stain on piece of white fabric

PROCEDURE

1. Place samples on a spot plate. Use 4 drops of each liquid or a small piece of each solid.

2. Describe the color and appearance of each sample in Step 1.

3. Add a few drops of the first oxidizing agent to each sample.

4. Describe any immediate change in appearance and any further change after 15 minutes.

5. Repeat Steps 2–4 with each oxidizing agent.

Name ______________________ Date ________________ Class ________________

ANALYSES AND CONCLUSIONS

1. Make a grid and record your observations.

2. Compare the oxidizing power of the oxidizing agents.

____

____

____

____

____

____

3. How do you know that chemical changes have occurred?

____

____

____

SMALL-SCALE LAB: Half-Reactions

Laboratory Recordsheet   Use with Section 20.3

SAFETY

Wear safety glasses and follow the standard safety procedures outlined on page 7 of this manual.

PURPOSE

To observe redox reactions and to write half-reactions that describe them.

MATERIALS

- pencil
- paper
- ruler
- reaction surface
- chemicals shown in Figure A

PROCEDURE

On a separate sheet of paper, draw a grid similar to Figure A. Make each square 2 cm on each side. Place a reaction surface over the grids and add one drop of each acid solution to one piece of each metal shown in Figure A. Use Figure A as a data table to record your observations for each solution.

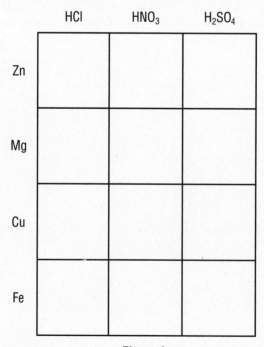

Figure A

Name _____ Date _____ Class _____

ANALYZE

Using your experimental data, record the answers to the following questions.

1. Which metal is the most reactive? On what observation do you base your answer? Which metal did not react with any of the acids? List the metals in order of decreasing reactivity.

   _____

   _____

   _____

   _____

   _____

2. What is the chemical formula of the gas produced in each reaction?

   _____

   _____

3. An active metal reacts with an acid to produce hydrogen gas and a salt. Write equations and net ionic equations to describe the reactions you observed. Are all of these redox reactions? Explain.

   _____

   _____

   _____

   _____

   _____

   _____

   _____

   _____

4. The half-reaction for the oxidation of Zn is

$$Zn(s) \longrightarrow Zn^{2+}(aq) + 2e^-$$

   Write the oxidation half-reaction for the other metals that react.

   _____

   _____

5. The half-reaction for the reduction of H^+ from the acid is

$$2H^+ + 2e^- \longrightarrow H_2(g)$$

Notice that this half-reaction is the same for all the acids. Demonstrate how adding this half-reaction to each oxidation half-reaction results in the overall net ionic equations.

YOU'RE THE CHEMIST

Use the space below to write your observations to the small-scale activities in the *You're the Chemist* section.

_____

_____

_____

_____

_____

_____

_____

_____

_____

_____

_____

_____

_____

_____

_____

_____

_____

_____

_____

_____

21.1 ELECTROCHEMICAL CELLS

Section Review

Objectives

- Use the activity series to identify which metal in a pair is more easily oxidized
- Identify the source of electrical energy in a voltaic cell
- Describe current technologies that use electrochemical processes to produce electrical energy

Vocabulary

- electrochemical process
- electrochemical cell
- voltaic cells
- half-cell

- salt bridge
- electrode
- anode
- cathode

- dry cell
- battery
- fuel cells

Part A Completion

Use this completion exercise to check your understanding of the concepts and terms that are introduced in this section. Each blank can be completed with a term, short phrase, or number.

Chemical processes can release or absorb energy. Any

conversion between chemical energy and electrical is known as an

___1___ . These processes always involve spontaneous redox

reactions in which a transfer of ___2___ occurs. Electrochemical

cells that generate electrical energy are known as ___3___ .

The half-cells of an electrochemical cell are separated by a

porous plate or ___4___ . This barrier prevents the contents of the

two half-cells from mixing, but permits the passage of ___5___

between the half-cells. Electrons are transferred through an external

circuit from the ___6___ , the electrode where oxidation occurs, to

the ___7___ , the electrode where reduction occurs.

1. _____

2. _____

3. _____

4. _____

5. _____

6. _____

7. _____

Name _____ Date _____ Class _____

Part B True-False

Classify each of these statements as always true, AT; sometimes true, ST; or never true, NT.

_____ 8. Nickel is below mercury in the activity series of metals.

_____ 9. The reduction half-reaction in a voltaic cell occurs at the cathode.

_____ 10. In a flashlight battery, the anode is the graphite rod.

_____ 11. A salt bridge is part of a voltaic cell.

Part C Matching

Match each description in Column B to the correct term in Column A.

Column A

_____ 12. dry cell

_____ 13. voltaic cells

_____ 14. cathode

_____ 15. battery

_____ 16. fuel cell

_____ 17. electrochemical cell

_____ 18. anode

Column B

a. the electrode at which oxidation occurs

b. a group of voltaic cells that are connected together

c. a voltaic cell in which a fuel substance undergoes oxidation to continuously produce electrical energy

d. the electrode at which reduction occurs

e. any device that converts chemical energy into electrical energy or electrical energy into chemical energy

f. electrochemical cells used to convert chemical energy into electrical energy

g. a commercial voltaic cell in which the electrolyte is a moist paste

Part D Problem

Answer the following in the space provided.

19. Describe the voltaic cell represented as

    $Mg(s) \mid MgSO_4(aq) \parallel PbSO_4(aq) \mid Pb(s)$

    Sketch a diagram of the cell similar to the one shown in Figure 21.3 of your textbook. Label the cathode and anode, and indicate the direction of electron flow.

21.2 HALF-CELLS AND CELL POTENTIALS

Section Review

Objectives

- Identify the origin of the electrical potential of a cell
- Explain the value of the standard reduction potential of the hydrogen half-cell
- Describe how the standard reduction potential of a half-cell is determined
- Interpret the meaning of a positive standard cell potential

Vocabulary

- electrical potential
- reduction potential
- cell potential
- standard cell potential
- standard hydrogen electrode

Key Equation

$$E^0_{cell} = E^0_{red} - E^0_{oxid}$$

Part A Completion

Use this completion exercise to check your understanding of the concepts and terms that are introduced in this section. Each blank can be completed with a term, short phrase, or number.

The measure of a voltaic cell's ability to produce an electric
current is called its ___1___, which is usually measured in volts. The
electrical potential of a cell results from a competition for ___2___
between the two half-cells. The difference between the reduction
potentials of the two half-cells is called the ___3___.

In comparing standard cell potentials for half-reactions, the
___4___ serves as a reference and is assigned a value of ___5___.
A negative value for the standard reduction potential means that
the tendency for this half-cell to be reduced is ___6___ than the
tendency for hydrogen ions to be reduced. If the calculated
standard cell potential for a given redox reaction is positive, then
the reaction is ___7___.

1. _____
2. _____
3. _____
4. _____
5. _____
6. _____
7. _____

Part B True-False

Classify each of these statements as always true, AT; sometimes true, ST; or never true, NT.

_____ **8.** The half-cell that has a greater tendency to acquire electrons will be the one in which oxidation occurs.

_____ **9.** In an electrochemical cell, the hydrogen half-cell is the reduction half-cell.

_____ **10.** A positive value for a standard reduction potential means hydrogen ions have a greater tendency to be reduced than the ions in this half-cell.

_____ **11.** If the cell potential for a given redox reaction is negative, the reaction is spontaneous.

Part C Matching

Match each description in Column B to the correct term in Column A.

Column A   ### Column B

_____ **12.** electrical potential

a. the difference between the reduction potentials of the two half-cells

_____ **13.** reduction potential

b. the measure of a cell's ability to produce an electric current

_____ **14.** spontaneous reaction

c. the standard reduction potential of the hydrogen electrode

_____ **15.** 0.00 V

d. the tendency of a given half-reaction to occur as a reduction

_____ **16.** cell potential

e. standard reduction potential for the oxidation half-cell

_____ **17.** E^0_{oxid}

f. a reaction having a positive cell potential

Part D Problem

Answer the following in the space provided.

18. Compute the standard cell potential of a $Mg \mid Mg^{2+} \parallel Cl_2 \mid Cl^-$ cell, using standard electrode potentials.

21.3 ELECTROLYTIC CELLS

Section Review

Objectives

- Distinguish between electrolytic and voltaic cells
- Describe the process of electrolysis of water
- Describe the process of electrolysis of brine
- Explain how electrolysis is used in metal processing

Vocabulary

- electrolysis
- electrolytic cell

Part A Completion

Use this completion exercise to check your understanding of the concepts and terms that are introduced in this section. Each blank can be completed with a term, short phrase, or number.

The process in which electrical energy is used to make a
nonspontaneous redox reaction go forward is called ___1___. The
apparatus in which this process is carried out is called an ___2___.
In this type of cell, as in voltaic cells, ___3___ flow from the anode
to the cathode through an external circuit. In an electrolytic cell,
electrons are driven by an outside power source such as a ___4___.

In the electrolysis of water, a small amount of ___5___ must
be added to enable the water to conduct electricity. The products
of the electrolysis of water are ___6___ and ___7___. During the
electrolysis of brine, chloride ions are oxidized to produce chlorine
gas at the anode, and water is reduced to produce ___8___ at the cathode.

1. _____

2. _____

3. _____

4. _____

5. _____

6. _____

7. _____

8. _____

Part B True-False

Classify each of these statements as always true, AT; sometimes true, ST; or never true, NT.

_____ **9.** During the electrolysis of brine, sodium metal is produced at the cathode.

_____ **10.** An electrolytic cell drives a nonspontaneous reaction to completion.

_____ **11.** When a current is applied via two electrodes in water, oxygen and hydrogen are produced.

_____ **12.** An object that is to be electroplated needs to be the cathode of the electrolytic cell.

Part C Matching

Match each description in Column B to the correct term in Column A.

Column A   ### Column B

_____ **13.** electrolysis   **a.** an electrolytic method for obtaining ultrapure metals

_____ **14.** electrolytic cell   **b.** the process in which electrical energy is used to make a nonspontaneous reaction go forward

_____ **15.** brine   **c.** the deposition of a thin layer of metal on an object in an electrolytic cell

_____ **16.** electroplating   **d.** an electrochemical cell used to cause a chemical change through the application of electrical energy

_____ **17.** electrorefining   **e.** a concentrated solution of sodium chloride

Part D Questions and Problems

Answer the following in the space provided.

18. Distinguish between electrolytic and voltaic cells and list some applications of each.

_____

_____

_____

19. Sketch an electrolytic cell that could be used to silverplate a teaspoon. Label the anode, cathode, and the direction of electron flow. Write the anode and cathode reactions that occur.

ELECTROCHEMISTRY

21

Practice Problems

Use Table 21.2 to solve the following problems in your notebook.

SECTION 21.2 HALF-CELLS AND CELL POTENTIALS

1. Determine the cell reaction, the standard cell potential (E^0_{cell}) and the half-cell that acts as the cathode for the voltaic cells composed of the following half-cells.

   a. $Mg^{2+}(aq) + 2e^- \rightarrow Mg(s)$

   $Cl_2(g) + 2e^- \rightarrow 2Cl^-(aq)$

   b. $Ni^{2+}(aq) + 2e^- \rightarrow Ni(s)$

   $Ag^+(aq) + e^- \rightarrow Ag(s)$

   c. $MnO_4^-(aq) + 8H^+(aq) + 5e^- \rightarrow Mn^{2+}(aq) + 4H_2O(l)$

   $Cd^{2+}(aq) + 2e^- \rightarrow Cd(s)$

   d. $Br_2(l) + 2e^- \rightarrow 2Br^-(aq)$

   $Na^+(aq) + e^- \rightarrow Na(s)$

   e. $2H^+(aq) + 2e^- \rightarrow H_2(g)$

   $MnO_2(s) + 4H^+(aq) + 2e^- \rightarrow Mn^{2+}(aq) + 2H_2O(l)$

2. Calculate E^0_{cell} to determine whether the following redox reactions are spontaneous as written.

   a. $Sn^{2+}(aq) + Ba(s) \rightarrow Sn(s) + Ba^{2+}(aq)$

   b. $2Ag^+(aq) + 2Cl^-(aq) \rightarrow 2Ag(s) + Cl_2(g)$

   c. $Zn(s) + F_2(g) \rightarrow 2F^-(aq) + Zn^{2+}(aq)$

   d. $2Li(s) + Co^{2+}(aq) \rightarrow 2Li^+(aq) + Co(s)$

   e. $2I^-(aq) + K^+(aq) \rightarrow I_2(s) + K(s)$

21 INTERPRETING GRAPHICS
Use with Section 21.3

Electrolysis is sometimes used to purify metals from mixtures. In this process, a slab or bar of impure metal containing many types of metallic elements is made the anode of an electrolytic cell. When external electrical energy is supplied to the cell, metallic elements in the anode are oxidized to cations that dissolve in solution. Then the cations are reduced to the pure metal at the surface of the cathode. A schematic diagram of an electrolytic cell used to purify copper is shown below. If the voltage supply is carefully regulated, less reactive metals are not oxidized at the anode, but instead collect as "mud" at the bottom of the cell below the anode. Metals more reactive than copper are oxidized at the anode, but are not reduced at the cathode; therefore, they remain dissolved as ions in the electrolyte solution ($CuSO_4$).

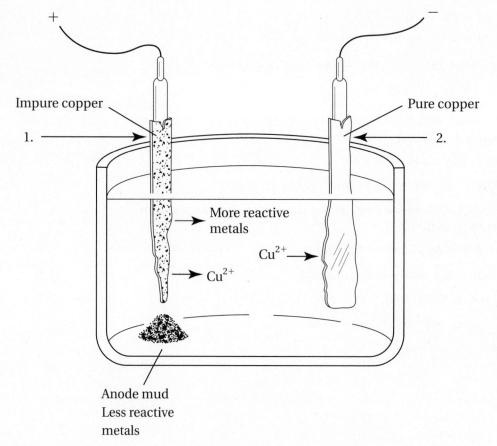

Figure 1 Purification of copper by electrolysis at 25°C, 101.3 kPa, in 1M $CuSO_4$.

Identify the anode and cathode in the diagram. Write your answers on the lines.

1. _____   2. _____

3. What name is given to the technique used to obtain pure copper by electrolysis?

_____

4. The apparatus depicted in Figure 1 is not complete. The electrolytic cell must be connected to a DC source (a battery).

   a. To which electrodes of the battery, positive (+) or negative (−), should the anode and cathode of the electrolytic cell be connected?

_____

   b. Describe the connections in terms of the anode and cathode of the battery.

_____

_____

_____

5. At which of the electrodes, numbered 1 and 2 in Figure 1, is oxidation occurring? Reduction? Label the electrodes in the diagram.

_____

_____

6. Using arrows, annotate the diagram in Figure 1 to show the flow of electrons out of or into the electrodes.

_____

The E^0_{red} values for several metals are shown below.

$E^0_{Zn^{2+}} = -0.76\,V$ $E^0_{Cu^{2+}} = +0.34\,V$ $E^0_{Au^{3+}} = +1.50\,V$

$E^0_{Fe^{2+}} = -0.44\,V$ $E^0_{Ag^{+}} = +0.80\,V$ $E^0_{Pt^{2+}} = +1.18\,V$

Assume that all of these metals are present in the impure metal anode. Use these data to answer the following questions.

7. What voltage should be applied to the electrolytic cell to purify copper in the manner described above?

_____

_____

_____

_____

8. If the voltage from the DC source is maintained at 0.40 V:

   a. Which metals will be found in the anode mud when the electrolysis is complete?

_____

   b. Which cations will be found dissolved in the electrolyte solution?

_____

   c. Which metal(s) will plate out at the cathode?

_____

21 **ELECTROCHEMISTRY**

Vocabulary Review

Each clue describes a vocabulary term. Read the clues and write the letters of each term on the lines.

1. Clue: an electrochemical cell used to convert chemical energy into electrical energy.

   __ __ __ __ __ Ⓞ __ __ __ __ Ⓞ

2. Clue: a cell in which a fuel undergoes oxidation to produce electrical energy.

   __ Ⓞ __ __ __ __ __ __

3. Clue: any device that converts chemical energy into electrical energy or electrical energy into chemical energy.

   __ __ __ __ __ __ __ __ __ Ⓞ __ __ __ __

   __ __ __ __

4. Clue: the interconversion of chemical energy and electrical energy.

   __ __ __ __ __ __ __ __ __ __ Ⓞ __ __ __ __

   __ __ __ __ __ __ __

5. Clue: the electrode at which reduction occurs.

   __ Ⓞ __ __ __ __ __

6. Clue: a measure of the tendency of a given half-reaction to occur as a reduction in an electrochemical cell.

   __ __ __ Ⓞ __ __ __ __ __

   __ __ __ __ Ⓞ __ __ __ __

Write the letters found inside the circles on the lines below. Then unscramble them to find the name of one metal commercially produced by electrolysis.

Scrambled letters:

__ __ __ __ __ __ __ __

Solution:

__ __ __ __ __ __ __ __

ELECTROCHEMISTRY

21

Chapter Quiz

Classify each of these statements as always true, AT; sometimes true, ST; or never true, NT.

_____ 1. In a lead storage battery, the sulfuric acid concentration increases during discharge.   *21.1*

_____ 2. The oxidation half-reaction in a voltaic cell occurs at the anode.   *21.1*

_____ 3. In a flashlight battery, the zinc metal case is the cathode.   *21.1*

_____ 4. A strip of zinc metal, when dipped into a solution of copper sulfate, becomes copper plated. (Zinc is more easily oxidized than copper.)   *21.1*

_____ 5. Batteries can be recharged.   *21.1*

_____ 6. Voltaic cells were named for electromotive force (emf), which is measured in volts.   *21.1*

_____ 7. A salt bridge allows for the passage of electrons from one half-cell to another half-cell.   *21.1*

_____ 8. In a voltaic cell, a wire carries the electrons in the external circuit from the anode to the cathode.   *21.1*

_____ 9. In a voltaic cell, the anode is the negative electrode.   *21.1*

_____ 10. Fuel cells use methane as fuel.   *21.1*

_____ 11. The standard hydrogen electrode is assigned a reduction potential of 1.00 V.   *21.2*

_____ 12. The anode in an electrolytic cell is the positive electrode.   *21.3*

_____ 13. The electrolysis of brine produces chlorine gas at the cathode.   *21.3*

_____ 14. The standard cell potential is the measured cell potential when the ion concentrations are $1M$, any gases are at a pressure of 101 kPa, and the temperature is 25°C.   *21.2*

_____ 15. $E^0_{cell} = E^0_{red} + E^0_{oxid}$ *21.2*

_____ 16. A standard reduction potential for a half-cell is negative if the tendency for reduction to occur is less than the tendency of hydrogen ions to be reduced to hydrogen gas.   *21.2*

_____ 17. A redox reaction is spontaneous if the standard cell potential is positive.   *21.2*

_____ 18. Electroplating is the deposition of a thin layer of a metal on an object in a voltaic cell.   *21.3*

21 ELECTROCHEMISTRY

Chapter Test A

A. Matching

Match each term in Column B to the correct description in Column A.

Column A	Column B

_____ 1. a conductor in a circuit that carries electrons to or from a substance other than a metal

a. anode

_____ 2. one part of a voltaic cell, in which either oxidation or reduction occurs

b. electrode

_____ 3. a voltaic cell in which the electrolyte is a paste

c. cathode

_____ 4. the electrode at which reduction occurs

d. dry cell

_____ 5. a voltaic cell in which a fuel undergoes oxidation and from which electrical energy is obtained continuously

e. battery

_____ 6. an electrochemical cell that is used to convert chemical energy into electrical energy

f. electrolysis

_____ 7. a tube containing a conducting solution

g. voltaic cell

_____ 8. a group of cells that are connected together

h. half-cell

_____ 9. the process in which electrical energy is used to bring about a chemical change

i. salt bridge

_____ 10. the electrode at which oxidation occurs

j. fuel cell

B. Multiple Choice

Choose the best answer and write its letter on the line.

_____ 11. In the electrolysis of brine, the substance produced at the cathode is
    a. chlorine.   **c.** sodium.
    b. oxygen.   **d.** hydrogen.

_____ 12. Which of the following describes a dry cell?
    a. It can be recharged many times.
    b. The graphite rod does not undergo reduction, even though it is the cathode.
    c. It contains concentrated sulfuric acid.
    d. all of the above

_____ 13. A clean strip of copper is dipped into a solution of magnesium sulfate. Magnesium is above the copper in the activity series of metals. Predict what you will observe.
   a. The copper strip becomes magnesium-plated.
   b. Copper dissolves and the solution turns blue.
   c. No reaction occurs.
   d. Bubbles of hydrogen gas appear on the copper.

_____ 14. A clean iron nail is dipped into a solution of silver nitrate. Iron is above silver in the activity series of metals. Predict what you will observe.
   a. The iron will be reduced.
   b. Bubbles of nitrogen gas will form on the iron nail.
   c. The iron nail will become silver-plated.
   d. No reaction occurs.

_____ 15. In a fully charged lead storage battery, the cathode grid is packed with
   a. spongy lead.   c. lead(IV) oxide.
   b. lead sulfate.   d. sulfuric acid.

_____ 16. Which of the following is true about fuel cells?
   a. They can be designed so that they emit no pollutants.
   b. They are inexpensive.
   c. They have never been built or used.
   d. They produce energy in short bursts only.

_____ 17. Which of the following is true for an electrolytic cell?
   a. It changes electrical energy into chemical energy.
   b. It is the type of cell used in electroplating.
   c. It uses an electric current to make a nonspontaneous reaction go.
   d. all of the above

_____ 18. When a lead storage battery discharges
   a. the concentration of lead sulfate in the battery decreases.
   b. the concentration of sulfuric acid increases.
   c. the concentration of sulfuric acid decreases.
   d. none of the above

_____ 19. A zinc-copper cell is constructed:

$$Zn \mid Zn^{2+} \ (1M) \parallel Cu^{2+} \ (1M) \mid Cu$$

What occurs to the mass of the copper electrode as the reaction proceeds? (Zinc is above copper in the activity series of metals.)
   a. It increases.   c. It decreases.
   b. It remains the same.

_____ 20. In the cell reaction described in question 19, the negative electrode is
   a. $Zn(s)$.   c. $Zn^{2+}(aq)$.
   b. $Cu^{2+}(aq)$.   d. $Cu(s)$.

_____ 21. Which half-reaction occurs at the negative electrode in an electrolytic cell in which an object is being plated with silver?
   a. $Ag + 1e^- \rightarrow Ag^+$ c. $Ag^+ + 1e^- \rightarrow Ag$
   b. $Ag \rightarrow Ag^+ + 1e^-$ d. $Ag^+ \rightarrow Ag + 1e^-$

_____ **22.** Which metal will react spontaneously with $Cu^{2+}(aq)$ at 25°C?
    a. Ag   **c.** Mg
    b. Au   **d.** Hg

_____ **23.** Which reaction occurs when bromine is added to an aqueous solution of iodide ions?
    a. $2I^- + Br_2 \rightarrow I_2 + 2Br^-$ **c.** $2I^- + 2Br^- \rightarrow I_2 + Br_2$
    b. $I_2 + 2Br \rightarrow Br_2 + 2I^-$ **d.** $I_2 + Br_2 \rightarrow 2I^- + 2Br^-$

_____ **24.** Which ion can be most easily reduced?
    a. Cu^{2+} **c.** Fe^{2+}
    b. Zn^{2+} **d.** Ca^{2+}

_____ **25.** Oxygen and copper are produced during the electrolysis of a CuO solution. Which reaction occurs at the negative electrode?
    a. Oxygen ions are reduced.   **c.** Copper ions are reduced.
    b. Oxygen atoms are oxidized.   **d.** Copper atoms are oxidized.

C. True-False

Classify each of these statements as always true, AT; sometimes true, ST; or never true, NT.

_____ **26.** During the electrolysis of brine, chlorine gas is produced at the cathode.

_____ **27.** Copper is above gold in the activity series of metals because copper is less reactive and less easily oxidized.

_____ **28.** The oxidation half-reaction in a voltaic cell occurs at the anode.

_____ **29.** Cell potential is the sum of the reduction potential of the half-cell where reduction occurs and the reduction potential of the half-cell where oxidation occurs.

_____ **30.** In an electrolytic cell, oxidation occurs at the cathode, and reduction occurs at the anode.

D. Question

Answer the following question in the space provided.

31. Draw a voltaic cell. Label the cathode, anode, salt bridge, and direction of the flow of electrons.

E. Essay

Write a short essay for the following.

32. State the sign of the electrodes and the reaction that occurs at each electrode for both voltaic and electrolytic cells.

_____

_____

_____

_____

F. Additional Questions

Answer the following questions in the space provided.

33. The standard reduction potential for the cobalt half-cell is −0.28 V. What is the significance of the negative value? (Refer to the standard hydrogen half-cell in your answer.)

_____

_____

_____

_____

34. What is meant by the reduction potential of a half-cell?

_____

_____

35. Are the following redox reactions spontaneous as written? (Use the information in the Reference Section. Show your work.)

a. $Ni(s) + Zn^{2+}(aq) \rightarrow Ni^{2+}(aq) + Zn(s)$

b. $3Co(s) + 2Al^{3+}(aq) \rightarrow 3Co^{2+}(aq) + 2Al(s)$

Reference Section

Reduction Potentials at 25°C		
Electrode	**Half-Reaction**	**$E^0(V)$**
Al^{3+}/Al	$Al^{3+} + 3e^- \rightarrow Al$	−1.66
Zn^{2+}/Zn	$Zn^{2+} + 2e^- \rightarrow Zn$	−0.76
Co^{2+}/Co	$Co^{2+} + 2e^- \rightarrow Zn$	−0.28
Ni^{2+}/Ni	$Ni^{2+} + 2e^- \rightarrow Ni$	−0.25

21 ELECTROCHEMISTRY

Chapter Test B

A. Matching

Match each term in Column B to the correct description in Column A.

Column A   **Column B**

_____ **1.** the ability of a voltaic cell to produce an electric current   **a.** fuel cells

_____ **2.** any device that converts chemical energy into electrical   **b.** salt bridge
energy or electrical energy into chemical energy

_____ **3.** the process in which electrical energy in used to bring   **c.** battery
about a chemical change

_____ **4.** the electrode at which oxidation occurs   **d.** electrochemical cell

_____ **5.** a group of voltaic cells that are connected together   **e.** cathode

_____ **6.** electrochemical cells that are used to convert chemical   **f.** electrolysis
energy into electrical energy

_____ **7.** a voltaic cell in which the electrolyte is a paste   **g.** voltaic cells

_____ **8.** the electrode at which reduction occurs   **h.** electrical potential

_____ **9.** a tube containing a conducting solution that lets ions   **i.** anode
pass from one compartment of a voltaic cell to another

_____ **10.** voltaic cells in which a fuel undergoes oxidation and from   **j.** dry cell
which electrical energy is obtained continuously

B. Multiple Choice

Choose the best answer and write its letter on the line. Refer to the Reference Section on p. 561 for the reduction potentials as needed.

_____ **11.** Which of the following is true concerning the reaction given below?

$$Zn(s) + 2H^+(aq) \rightarrow Zn^{2+}(aq) + H_2(g)$$

a. $Zn(s)$ is being reduced.
b. $H^+(aq)$ is being oxidized.
c. Electrons are being transferred from $Zn(s)$ to $H^+(aq)$.
d. all of the above

_____ **12.** If Al is above Co in the activity series of metals, which of the following
will occur if a strip of Al is dipped into a solution of $Co(NO_3)_2$?
a. A redox reaction takes place.   **c.** The Al strip becomes coated with Co.
b. The Al strip dissolves.   **d.** all of the above

_____ **13.** In an electrochemical cell, the anode is
   a. the electrode at which reduction occurs.
   b. the electrode at which electrons are produced.
   c. the positive electrode.
   d. all of the above

_____ **14.** If Mg is above Ni in the activity series of metals, which of the following
   will occur if a strip of Mg is dipped into a solution of $Ni(NO_3)_2$?
   a. No reaction occurs.   **c.** The Mg is oxidized.
   b. The Ni^{2+} loses electrons.   **d.** none of the above

_____ **15.** Which of the following is true concerning the electrochemical cell
   represented by the following?

$$Mn(s) \mid Mn(NO_3)_2(aq) \parallel PbSO_4(aq) \mid Pb(s)$$

   a. Pb is oxidized.
   b. Mn is reduced.
   c. A strip of Pb is dipped into a solution of $Mn(NO_3)_2$.
   d. Electrons are lost at the Mn electrode.

_____ **16.** Which of the following is true about a dry cell?
   a. It is a voltaic cell in which the electrolyte is a paste.
   b. Zn serves as the cathode.
   c. Graphite serves as the anode.
   d. all of the above

_____ **17.** In a lead storage battery
   a. the anode is packed with spongy lead, and the cathode is packed
       with lead(IV) oxide.
   b. the electrodes are immersed in sulfuric acid.
   c. the system can be recharged by the passage of electric current
       through the cell.
   d. all of the above

_____ **18.** If the metals Ca, Zn, Fe, and Cu are listed in that order in the activity
   series of metals, the one that would be most readily oxidized is
   a. Ca.   **c.** Fe.
   b. Zn.   **d.** Cu.

_____ **19.** Among the metals listed in question 18, the one that would be most
   readily reduced is
   a. Ca.   **c.** Fe.
   b. Zn.   **d.** Cu.

_____ **20.** In a hydrogen-oxygen fuel cell
   a. oxygen is fed into the anode compartment.
   b. hydrogen is fed into the cathode compartment.
   c. the net reaction is the oxidation of hydrogen to form water.
   d. all of the above

_____ **21.** The standard reference electrode that is used with other electrodes to
   measure their reduction potentials consists of
   a. Zn.   **c.** Cu.
   b. H_2.   **d.** Ag.

_____ **22.** Which of the following is true concerning standard reduction
potentials?
  a. A positive value indicates that the tendency for a specified
  substance to be reduced is less than that of H^+.
  b. A negative value indicates that the tendency for a specified
  substance to be reduced is more than that of H^+.
  c. The half-reactions at the top of the standard reduction potential
  table have the greatest tendency to occur as oxidations.
  d. all of the above

_____ **23.** The standard cell potential of a cell composed of the half-cells
$$Zn \mid Zn^{2+} \parallel Pb^{2+} \mid Pb \text{ is}$$
  a. +0.89 V.   **c.** −0.89 V.
  b. +0.63 V.   **d.** −0.63 V.

_____ **24.** In the voltaic cell described in question 23, the anode is
  a. Zn.   **c.** Pb^{2+}.
  b. Zn^{2+}.   **d.** Pb.

_____ **25.** Among the following reactions, which would be expected to occur
spontaneously?
  a. $Cu(s) + Mg^{2+}(aq) \rightarrow Cu^{2+}(aq) + Mg(s)$
  b. $2Na(s) + Pb^{2+}(aq) \rightarrow 2Na^+(aq) + Pb(s)$
  c. $2Ag(s) + Zn^{2+}(aq) \rightarrow 2Ag^+(aq) + Zn(s)$
  d. all of the above

_____ **26.** Which of the following is true about an electrolytic cell?
  a. Electrons flow from the cathode to the anode in the external
  circuit.
  b. Oxidation occurs at the cathode.
  c. The redox reaction involved in such a cell is nonspontaneous.
  d. all of the above

_____ **27.** The net products that result from the electrolysis of water are
  a. H_2 and OH^-.   **c.** H^+ and OH^-.
  b. O_2 and H^+.   **d.** H_2 and O_2.

C. True-False

Classify each of these statements as always true, AT; sometimes true, ST; or never true, NT.

_____ **28.** Given any two elements in the activity series of metals, the one that
appears above the other undergoes reduction.

_____ **29.** The salt bridge in a voltaic cell provides a pathway for the electrons to
flow from one electrode to the other.

_____ **30.** A flashlight battery is an example of a dry cell.

_____ **31.** The specific gravity of the sulfuric acid contained in a lead storage
battery is an indication of the condition of that battery.

_____ **32.** Half-cell potentials cannot be measured.

_____ **33.** The standard cell potential for a voltaic cell consisting of some
combination of Zn, Zn^{2+}, F_2 and F^- would be a positive value.

D. Questions

Answer the following questions in the space provided.

34. Given the following voltaic cell, draw the cell and label the cathode, anode, salt bridge, and direction of flow of the electrons.

$$Cu(s) \mid Cu(NO_3)_2(aq) \parallel AgNO_3(aq) \mid Ag(s)$$

35. Based on the information given in question 34, write the two half-reactions, as well as the final net reaction for the Cu-Ag voltaic cell. Use the information provided in the Reference Section to calculate the standard cell potential for this voltaic cell.

E. Essay

Write a short essay for the following.

36. Give at least three similarities and three differences between voltaic and electrolytic cells.

_____

_____

_____

_____

_____

_____

Reference Section

Reduction Potentials at 25°C	
Electrode	**E^0(V)**
N^+/Na	-2.71 V
Mg^{2+}/Mg	-2.37 V
Al^{3+}/Al	-1.66 V
Zn^{2+}/Zn	-0.76 V
Pb^{2+}/Pb	-0.13 V
Cu^{2+}/Cu	$+0.34$ V
Ag^+/Ag	$+0.80$ V
F_2/F	$+2.87$ V

F. Additional Questions

Answer the following questions in the space provided.

37. Write the half-cell reactions and the net reaction for the following voltaic cell. Calculate the standard cell potential for the cell.

$$Al(s) \mid Al^{3+}(aq) \parallel Pb^{2+}(aq) \mid Pb(s)$$

38. Determine which of the following redox reactions will occur spontaneously and calculate the standard cell potential in each case.

a. $2Na(s) + Cu^{2+}(aq) \rightarrow 2Na^{+}(aq) + Cu(s)$

b. $2Ag(s) + Mg^{2+}(aq) \rightarrow 2Ag^{+}(aq) + Mg(s)$

c. $2Al(s) + 3Zn^{2+}(aq) \rightarrow 2Al^{3+}(aq) + 3Zn(s)$

39. Given the hypothetical elements W, X, Y, and Z, along with their corresponding ions W^{2+}, X^{2+}, Y^{2+}, and Z^{2+}, use the information provided below to determine the order in which these elements should be listed in the activity series of metals.

Reaction 1: $X^{2+} + Z \rightarrow X + Z^{2+}$ (reacts spontaneously)
Reaction 2: $W + X^{2+} \rightarrow$ (does not react)
Reaction 3: $Y + Z^{2+} \rightarrow Y^{2+} + Z$ (reacts spontaneously)

QUICK LAB: Electrochemical Analysis of Metals

Laboratory Recordsheet   Use with Section 21.3

PURPOSE

To electrochemically oxidize metals and identify them.

MATERIALS

- 9-volt battery
- sodium sulfate solution
- copper penny
- nickel coin
- iron nail
- filter paper
- aluminum foil
- reaction surface

PROCEDURE

1. Stack the following in order on a reaction surface: a 3-cm square of aluminum foil, a 2-cm square of filter paper, 1 drop of Na_2SO_4 solution, and a penny. The penny should be roughly centered on the filter paper, which should be roughly centered on the foil.

2. Apply the negative (−) terminal of the 9-volt battery to the aluminum foil and the positive (+) terminal to the penny for no more than three seconds.

3. Remove the penny and observe the filter paper.

4. Repeat Steps 1–3, replacing the penny with the nickel coin.

5. Repeat Steps 1–3, replacing the penny with the iron nail.

ANALYSES AND CONCLUSIONS

1. What colors formed on the filter paper for each object?

_____

_____

_____

2. For each metal object you tested, the battery oxidized the metal to form metal cations with a 2+ charge. Write a half-reaction for each metal oxidation you observed. Did these reactions take place at the anode or the cathode?

_____

_____

_____

3. Explain in your own words why the colors formed in the filter paper.

_____

_____

_____

_____

4. The aluminum foil serves as the cathode, where the reduction of water takes place. Write the half-reaction for the reduction of water.

_____

_____

_____

_____

5. Combine the half-reaction for the oxidation of copper with the half-reaction for the reduction of water to form an overall equation.

_____

_____

_____

_____

SMALL-SCALE LAB: Electrolysis of Water

Laboratory Recordsheet   Use with Section 21.3

SAFETY

Wear safety glasses and follow the standard safety procedures outlined on page 7 of this manual.

PURPOSE

To electrolyze solutions and interpret your observations in terms of chemical reactions and equations.

MATERIALS

- pencil
- paper
- ruler
- reaction surface
- electrolysis device
- chemicals shown in Figure A

PROCEDURE

On a separate sheet of paper, draw a grid similar to Figure A. Make each square 2 cm on each side. Place a reaction surface over the grid and add one drop of each solution shown in Figure A. Apply the leads of the electrolysis device to each solution. Be sure to clean the leads between each experiment. Look carefully at the cathode (negative lead) and the anode (positive lead). Use Figure A as a data table to record your observations for each solution.

H_2O	Na_2SO_4	Na_2SO_4 + BTB

Figure A

ANALYZE

Using your experimental data, answer the following questions.

1. Explain why pure water does not conduct electricity and does not undergo electrolysis.

_____

_____

2. Explain why water with sodium sulfate conducts electricity and undergoes electrolysis.

_____

_____

3. The cathode (negative lead) provides electrons to water, and the following half-reaction occurs.

$$2H_2O + 2e^- \longrightarrow H_2(g) + 2OH^-$$

Explain how your observations correspond to the products shown in this reaction.

_____

_____

_____

4. The anode (positive lead) takes away electrons from water, and the following half-reaction occurs.

$$H_2O \longrightarrow \tfrac{1}{2} O_2(g) + 2H^+ + 2e^-$$

Explain how your observations correspond to the products shown in this reaction.

_____

_____

5. Add the two half-reactions to obtain the overall reaction for the electrolysis of water. Simplify the result by adding the OH^- and H^+ to get HOH, and then canceling anything that appears on both sides of the equation.

YOU'RE THE CHEMIST

Use the space below to write your observations to the small-scale activities in the *You're the Chemist* section.

_____

_____

_____

_____

_____

_____

_____

22.1 HYDROCARBONS

Section Review

Objectives

- Describe the relationship between number of valence electrons and bonding in carbon
- Define and describe *alkanes*
- Relate the polarity of hydrocarbons to their solubility

Vocabulary

- hydrocarbons
- alkanes
- straight-chain alkanes
- homologous series
- condensed structural formulas
- substituent
- alkyl group
- branched-chain alkane

Part A Completion

Use this completion exercise to check your understanding of the concepts and terms that are introduced in this section. Each blank can be completed with a term, short phrase, or number.

The branch of chemistry that deals with __1__ compounds is called __2__ chemistry. Organic compounds that contain only carbon and hydrogen are __3__ . Carbon always forms __4__ covalent bonds.

Alkanes contain only carbon-carbon __5__ bonds. The carbons can be arranged in a __6__ chain or in a chain that has __7__ . A hydrocarbon substituent is called an __8__ group. The first step in naming branched-chain alkanes is to find the __9__ chain of carbons in the molecule. This chain is the __10__ structure.

1. _____
2. _____
3. _____
4. _____
5. _____
6. _____
7. _____
8. _____
9. _____
10. _____

Part B True-False

Classify each of these statements as always true, AT; sometimes true, ST; or never true, NT.

_____ 11. Because a carbon atom contains 6 valence electrons, it forms 3 covalent bonds.

_____ **12.** Straight-chain alkanes contain 10 carbon atoms.

_____ **13.** A substituent can take the place of a hydrogen atom on a parent hydrocarbon molecule.

_____ **14.** Hydrocarbon structural formulas are numbered from right to left.

_____ **15.** When naming branched-chain hydrocarbons, the names of the substituent alkyl groups are listed in alphabetical order.

Part C Matching

Match each description in Column B to the correct term in Column A.

Column A	Column B
_____ **16.** hydrocarbons	**a.** hydrocarbons that contain only single covalent bonds
_____ **17.** alkanes	**b.** a hydrocarbon substituent
_____ **18.** straight-chain alkanes	**c.** alkanes that contain one or more alkyl substituents
_____ **19.** substituent	**d.** organic compounds that contain only carbon and hydrogen
_____ **20.** alkyl group	**e.** alkanes that contain any number of carbons one after another in a chain
_____ **21.** branched-chain alkanes	**f.** atom or group of atoms that take the place of a hydrogen atom in a hydrocarbon molecule

Part D Questions and Problems

Answer the following in the space provided.

22. Name this compound, using the IUPAC system.

$$CH_3 - \overset{\overset{\displaystyle CH_3}{|}}{\underset{\underset{\displaystyle CH_3}{|}}{C}} - CH_2 - CH_3$$

_____

23. a. What is the total number of single bonds in a molecule of pentane, C_5H_{12}?

   b. What is the total number of single bonds in a molecule of 2,2-dimethylpropane?

24. Write the structural formula for 3-ethyl-2,2,5-trimethyloctane.

Name _____ Date _____ Class _____

22.2 UNSATURATED HYDROCARBONS

Section Review

Objectives

- Describe the difference between unsaturated and saturated hydrocarbons
- Distinguish the structures of alkenes and alkynes

Vocabulary

- saturated compounds
- unsaturated compounds
- alkenes
- alkynes
- aliphatic hydrocarbons

Part A Completion

Use this completion exercise to check your understanding of the concepts and terms that are introduced in this section. Each blank can be completed with a term, short phrase, or number.

Alkenes are __1__ hydrocarbons. That is, they contain one

or more carbon-carbon __2__ bonds. Alkynes are also

unsaturated compounds. They contain one or more carbon-

carbon __3__ bonds. Rotation is restricted about the multiple

bonds of alkenes and alkynes.

Alkenes are named by finding the __4__ chain in the

molecule that contains a __5__ bond. The root name of the

corresponding __6__ is used, plus the ending __7__. Atoms

are numbered so that the carbon atoms of the __8__ have the

lowest possible numbers. Alkynes are named in the same way,

except that the ending __9__ is added to the alkane root.

1. _____

2. _____

3. _____

4. _____

5. _____

6. _____

7. _____

8. _____

9. _____

Part B True-False

Classify each of these statements as always true, AT; sometimes true, ST; or never true, NT.

_____ 10. An alkane with one or more alkyl groups is called an alkyne.

_____ 11. Hydrocarbons are saturated.

_____ 12. Parent alkene chains are numbered so that the carbons of the double bond have the lowest possible numbers.

_____ 13. Unsaturated hydrocarbons contain double bonds.

Part C Matching

Match each description in Column B to the correct term in Column A.

Column A

_____ 14. unsaturated compounds

_____ 15. saturated compounds

_____ 16. alkenes

_____ 17. alkynes

Column B

a. contain at least one carbon-carbon double bond

b. contain at least one carbon-carbon triple bond

c. organic compounds that contain double or triple carbon-carbon bonds

d. hydrocarbons that contain the maximum number of hydrogen atoms per carbon atom

Part D Questions and Problems

Answer the following in the space provided.

18. Name this compound using the IUPAC system.

$$CH_3-CH_2 \quad CH_3$$
$$\mspace | \qquad |$$
$$CH_2-C=CH-CH_3$$

_____

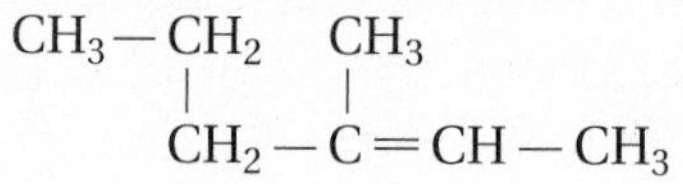

19. Name this compound, using the IUPAC system.

$$CH_3-CH-CH-CH-CH-CH_2-CH_2-CH_2-CH_3$$
$$\quad | \quad\ | \quad\ | \quad\ |$$
$$\quad CH_3 \ CH_3 \ CH_3 \ CH_3$$

_____

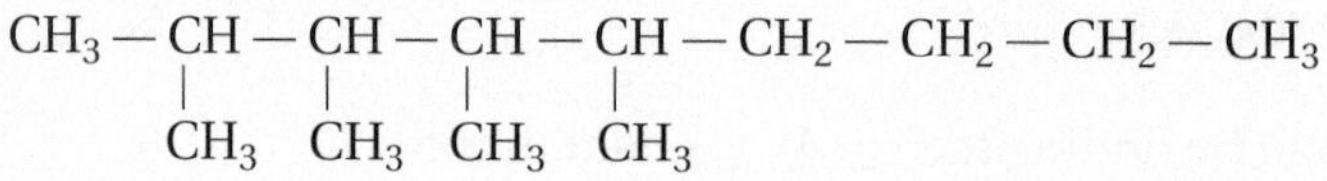

20. Name the following compound, using the IUPAC system.

$$\qquad\qquad H$$
$$\qquad\qquad |$$
$$\qquad\ H-C-H$$
$$\qquad\qquad |$$
$$\quad H\ H-C-H\ H\quad H\ \ H$$
$$\quad |\ \ \ |\quad\ \ |\ \ \ |\ \ \ |$$
$$H-C\ —\ C\ —\ C-C=C-H$$
$$\quad |\quad\ \ |\quad\ \ |$$
$$\quad H\quad\ H\quad\ H$$

_____

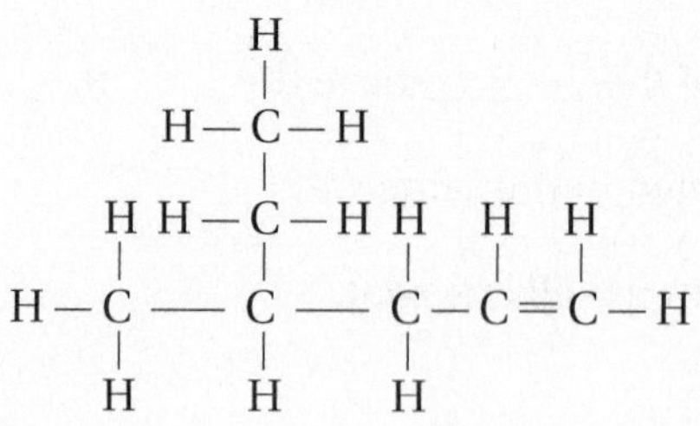

21. Draw the structural formula for the following compound.
    7-ethyl-2,4,9-trimethyl-5-decyne.

22.3   ISOMERS

Section Review

Objectives

- Explain why structural isomers have different properties
- Describe the conditions under which geometric isomers are possible
- Identify optical isomers

Vocabulary

- isomers
- structural isomers
- stereoisomers

- geometric isomers
- *trans* configuration
- *cis* configuration

- asymmetric carbon
- optical isomers

Part A Completion

Use this completion exercise to check your understanding of the concepts and terms that are introduced in this section. Each blank can be completed with a term, short phrase, or number.

Isomers have the same __1__ formula but different

molecular __2__. For example, 2–methylpropane is an

isomer of __3__. Isomers are different compounds with different

__4__.

__5__ isomers differ in the orientation of groups around

a double bond. The two possible double-bond configurations are

the __6__ configuration and the __7__ configuration.

Geometric isomers are one type of __8__. The other type

contains a carbon atom with four different groups attached,

which is called an __9__ carbon. Isomers with an asymmetric

carbon are __10__ isomers.

Models of optical isomers are like __11__ images, which

cannot be __12__.

1. _____

2. _____

3. _____

4. _____

5. _____

6. _____

7. _____

8. _____

9. _____

10. _____

11. _____

12. _____

Part B True-False

Classify each of these statements as always true, AT; sometimes true, ST; or never true, NT.

_____ **13.** Structural isomers are compounds with identical molecular structures.

_____ **14.** Compounds containing double bonds have *cis, trans* isomers.

_____ **15.** Isomers with the atoms joined in the same order are structural isomers.

_____ **16.** A carbon with four different groups attached is an asymmetric carbon.

Part C Matching

Match each description in Column B to the correct term in Column A.

Column A	**Column B**
_____ **17.** isomers	**a.** a carbon with four different groups attached
_____ **18.** structural isomers	**b.** configuration with substituted groups on the same side of the double bond
_____ **19.** stereoisomers	**c.** isomers that differ in the concentration of groups around a double bond
_____ **20.** geometric isomers	**d.** molecules in which the atoms are joined in the same order, but the arrangements of the atoms in space are different
_____ **21.** *trans* configuration	**e.** compounds that have the same molecular formula, but the atoms are joined in a different order
_____ **22.** *cis* configuration	**f.** configuration with substituted groups on opposite sides of the double bond
_____ **23.** asymmetric carbon	**g.** pairs of molecules that differ only in the way four different groups are arranged around a central carbon atom
_____ **24.** optical isomers	**h.** compounds that have the same molecular formula but different molecular structures

Name _____ Date _____ Class _____

Part D Problems

Answer the following in the space provided.

25. Draw three structural isomers of pentane.

26. Identify the asymmetric carbon in this compound.

$$\overset{5}{CH_3} - \overset{4}{CH_2} - \overset{3}{CH_2} - \overset{2}{\underset{\underset{F}{|}}{\overset{\overset{H}{|}}{C}}} - \overset{1}{CH_3}$$

_____

27. Draw the *cis* and *trans* isomers for 3-hexene.

22.4 HYDROCARBON RINGS

Section Review

Objectives

- Identify cyclic ring structures
- Describe bonding in benzene

Vocabulary

- cyclic hydrocarbons
- aromatic compound

Part A Completion

Use this completion exercise to check your understanding of the concepts and terms that are introduced in this section. Each blank can be completed with a term, short phrase, or number.

Compounds with hydrocarbon rings are called ___1___

hydrocarbons. Benzene is the simplest form of an ___2___

compound. The benzene molecule consists of ___3___ carbons

joined in a ring with a ___4___ atom attached to each carbon.

Two different structures can be written for benzene in which

___5___ and single bonds alternate. The actual bonding in

benzene does not alternate between the ___6___ structures.

Many substituted benzenes have common names. ___7___

is also called toluene, while the dimethylbenzenes are known as

___8___. 1,2–disubstitution on a benzene ring is also know as

___9___ disubstitution, while 1,3 is known as ___10___, and 1,4 is

known as ___11___ disubstitution.

1. _____

2. _____

3. _____

4. _____

5. _____

6. _____

7. _____

8. _____

9. _____

10. _____

11. _____

Part B True-False

Classify each of these statements as always true, AT; sometimes true, ST; or never true, NT.

_____ **12.** Aromatic compounds contain 6 carbon atoms.

_____ **13.** Benzene is the simplest arene.

_____ **14.** Compounds that contain rings are aromatic hydrocarbons.

_____ **15.** Another name for 1,3-dimethylbenzene is *m*-xylene.

_____ **16.** Aromatic compounds have pleasant odors.

Part C Matching

Match each description in Column B to the correct term in Column A.

Column A   **Column B**

_____ **17.** cyclic hydrocarbons   **a.** when two or more equally valid structures can be
                                             drawn for a molecule

_____ **18.** resonance   **b.** group of hydrocarbons that contain a benzene ring
                                             or a ring with bonding like that of benzene

_____ **19.** phenyl group   **c.** name given to a benzene ring when it is a substituent

_____ **20.** aromatic compounds   **d.** organic compounds that contain hydrocarbon rings

Part D Problems

Answer the following in the space provided.

21. Draw the structural formula for propylbenzene.

22. Draw the structural formula for 3-phenyl-1-butene.

23. Name the following compounds, using the IUPAC system.

a.
$$CH_2 - CH_2$$
$$CH_2 \qquad\qquad CH_2$$
$$| \qquad\qquad\qquad |$$
$$CH_2 \qquad\qquad CH_2$$
$$CH_2 - CH_2$$

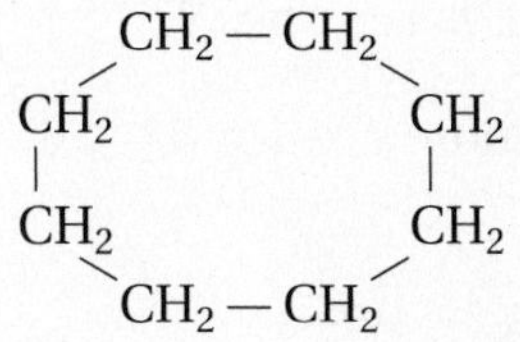

b.
$$CH_2CH_3$$
$$CH_2CH_3$$

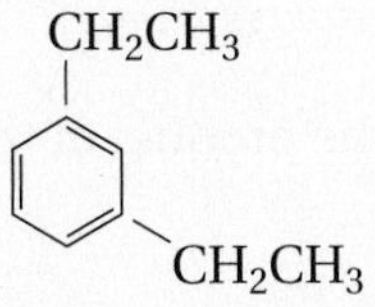

22.5 HYDROCARBONS FROM EARTH'S CRUST

Section Review

Objectives

- Identify three important fossil fuels and describe their origins
- Describe the composition of natural gas, petroleum, and coal
- Describe what happens when petroleum is refined

Vocabulary

- cracking

Part A Completion

Use this completion exercise to check your understanding of the concepts and terms that are introduced in this section. Each blank can be completed with a term, short phrase, or number.

The three fossil fuels are ___1___, petroleum, and ___2___ .

The majority of natural gas, about 80 percent, is ___3___ .

Most of the hydrocarbons in petroleum and natural gas are

___4___ hydrocarbons. Petroleum is refined by ___5___ it into

fractions according to ___6___ .

Coal is produced when peat, which is derived from plant

material, changes to ___7___ , or brown coal. This in turn

becomes ___8___ , or soft coal, then ___9___ , or hard coal.

Coal is made up largely of condensed ___10___ compounds.

1. _____

2. _____

3. _____

4. _____

5. _____

6. _____

7. _____

8. _____

9. _____

10. _____

Part B True-False

Classify each of these statements as always true, AT; sometimes true, ST; or never true, NT.

_____ 11. Carbon monoxide is the product of the complete combustion
of a hydrocarbon.

_____ 12. Natural gas is composed mostly of aromatic hydrocarbons.

_____ **13.** Among the various types of coal, anthracite has the highest carbon content.

_____ **14.** Hydrocarbons produce carbon monoxide when burned.

Part C Matching

Match each description in Column B to the correct term in Column A.

Column A	**Column B**
_____ **15.** cracking	**a.** hard coal, which is high in carbon content
_____ **16.** petroleum	**b.** process by which hydrocarbons are broken down into smaller molecules
_____ **17.** distillation	**c.** brown coal, consisting of about 50 percent carbon
_____ **18.** lignite	**d.** fossil fuel containing straight- and branched-chain alkanes
_____ **19.** anthracite	**e.** process by which petroleum is separated into fractions

Part D Problems

Answer the following in the space provided.

20. Balance the equation for the incomplete combustion of pentane to form CO and H_2O.

21. Balance the following equation.

$$C_6H_6 + O_2 \rightarrow CO_2 + H_2O$$

22 HYDROCARBON COMPOUNDS

Practice Problems

In your notebook, solve the following problems.

SECTION 22.1 HYDROCARBONS

1. Name this hydrocarbon, according to the IUPAC system.

$$
\begin{array}{ccc}
& CH_3 & \quad CH_3 \\
& | & \quad | \\
CH_3-CH_2-CH_2- & C-CH_2- & C-CH_3 \\
& | & \quad | \\
& CH_2 & \quad CH_2 \\
& | & \quad | \\
& CH_3 & \quad CH_3
\end{array}
$$

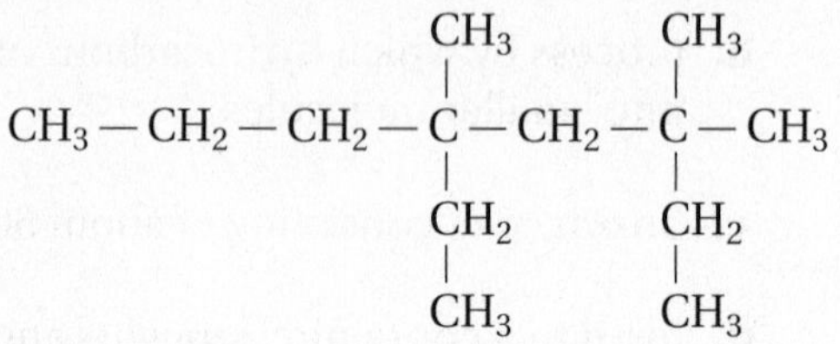

2. Name this hydrocarbon, according to the IUPAC system.

$$
\begin{array}{cccc}
& CH_3 & \quad CH_3 \\
& | & \quad | \\
CH_3-CH- & C-CH_2- & C-CH_2-CH_3 \\
| & | & \quad | \\
CH_3 & CH_2 & \quad CH_2 \\
& | \\
& CH_3
\end{array}
$$

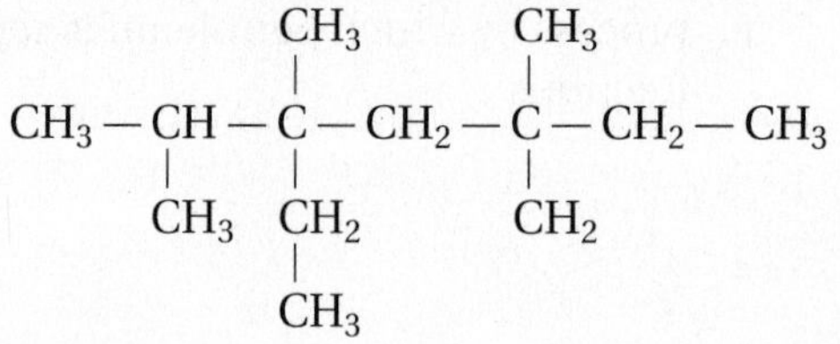

3. Write the structural formula for each of the following compounds.

    a. 3-ethyl-2,3-dimethylpentane

    b. 3,4-diethylhexane

    c. 2,3,4,5-tetramethylnonane

4. Draw condensed structural formulas for the straight-chain alkanes with seven and eight carbons.

5. How many single bonds are in a hexane molecule?

SECTION 22.2 UNSATURATED HYDROCARBONS

1. Name this compound, according to the IUPAC system.

$$
\begin{array}{c}
CH_3 \\
| \\
CH_3-C=CH-CH-CH_3 \\
| \\
CH_2 \\
| \\
CH_3
\end{array}
$$

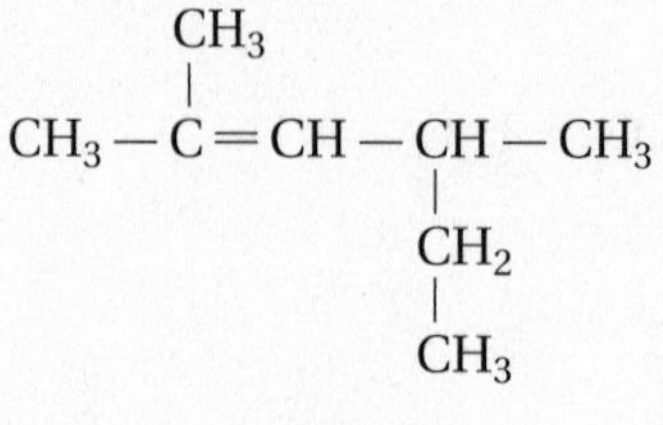

2. Name this compound, according to the IUPAC system.

$$
\begin{array}{c}
CH_3 \\
| \\
CH\equiv C-CH-CH-CH_3 \\
| \\
CH_3
\end{array}
$$

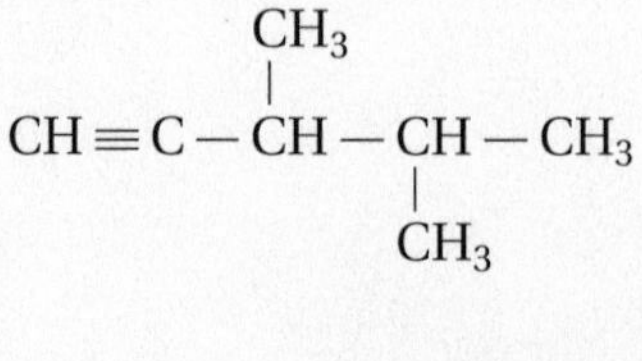

3. Name and draw all of the alkynes with the molecular formula C_5H_8.

4. Write structural formulas for the following hydrocarbons.

   a. 3,5-dimethyl-1-hexene

   b. 4-methyl-1-pentene

   c. 3,3-dimethyl-1-butyne

SECTION 22.3 ISOMERS

1. Name this compound, according to the IUPAC system.

$$\underset{CH_3}{\overset{H}{\diagdown}}C=C\underset{CH_2CH_3}{\overset{H}{\diagup}}$$

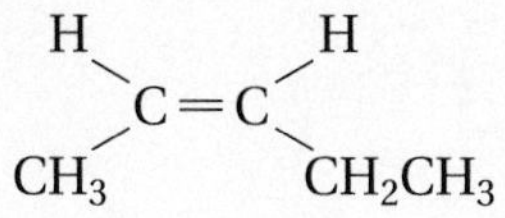

2. Name this compound, according to the IUPAC system.

$$\underset{H}{\overset{CH_3-CH_2}{\diagdown}}C=C\underset{CH_2-CH-CH_3}{\overset{H}{\diagup}}$$
$$\underset{CH_3}{\mid}$$

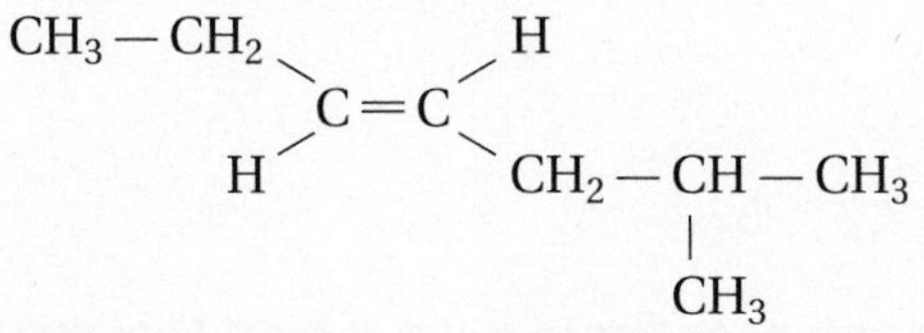

3. Write the structural formula for *trans*–2–heptene.

4. Which of the following can exist as *cis, trans* isomers?

   a. 2-butene

   b. 1-butene

   c. 2-methyl-2-butene

   d. 3-hexene

5. Identify the asymmetric carbon in the following compound.

$$\overset{5}{C}H_3-\overset{4}{C}H_2-\overset{3}{C}H-\overset{2}{C}H-\overset{1}{C}H_3$$
$$\underset{CH_3}{\mid}\quad\underset{CH_3}{\mid}$$

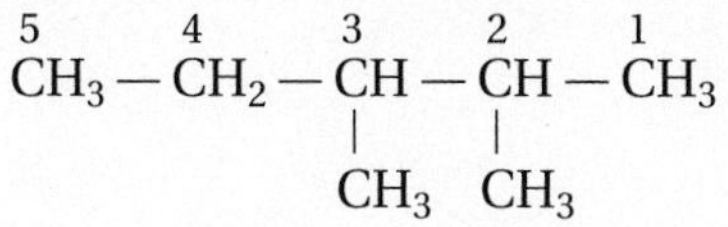

6. Which of the following compounds have an asymmetric carbon?

   a. 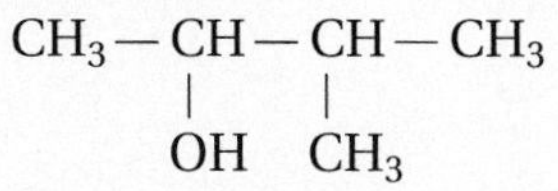 $CH_3-CH-CH-CH_3$
   $$\underset{OH}{\mid}\quad\underset{CH_3}{\mid}$$

   b. 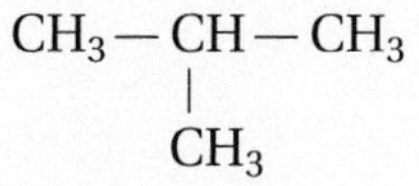 $CH_3-CH-CH_3$
   $$\underset{CH_3}{\mid}$$

   c. 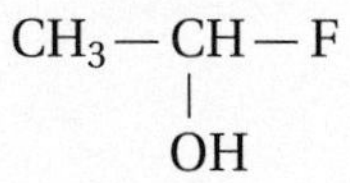 CH_3-CH-F
   $$\underset{OH}{\mid}$$

SECTION 22.4 HYDROCARBON RINGS

1. Name this compound, according to the IUPAC system.

$$CH_2\,CH_3$$

$$CH_3$$

2. Name this compound, according to the IUPAC system.

$$CH_3 - CH = CH - CH_2 - CH - CH_3$$

3. Write structural formulas for the following compounds.
   a. 1,3-dimethylcyclohexane
   b. *cis*-1,2-diphenylethene
   c. 1,4-diethylbenzene

SECTION 22.5 HYDROCARBONS FROM EARTH'S CRUST

1. Write a balanced equation for the complete combustion of 2-methylheptane.
2. Describe three types of fuels obtained by refining petroleum.

Name _____ Date _____ Class _____

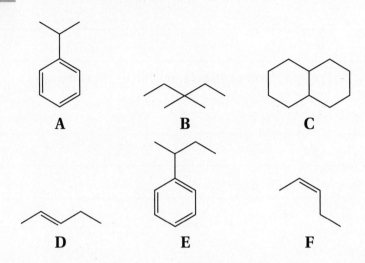

In Section 22.1, you were introduced to different methods for drawing hydrocarbon structures. Use the above line-angle formulas to answer the following questions.

1. Which structure corresponds to 2-phenylpropane?

_____

2. Which structure corresponds to a nonaromatic cyclic alkane?

_____

3. Name compound B, using the IUPAC system.

_____

4. Which structures represent a pair of *cis, trans* isomers? Name the compounds.

_____

5. Which compound contains an asymmetric carbon? Name the compound and identify the asymmetric carbon atom.

_____

_____

6. What is the total number of single bonds in compound B?

_____

7. What is the total number of carbon atoms in compound E?

_____

8. Which of the structures represent aromatic compounds? Write IUPAC names for each.

_____

_____

_____

9. Would you expect the boiling points of compounds D and F to be the same or different? Explain.

_____

_____

_____

Name _____ Date _____ Class _____

22 HYDROCARBON COMPOUNDS

Vocabulary Review

Each clue describes a vocabulary term. Read the clues and write the letters of each term on the lines provided.

1. Clue: hydrocarbons containing carbon-carbon triple bonds.

   __ __ __ Ⓞ __ __ __

2. Clue: group of atoms that takes the place of a hydrogen in a parent hydrocarbon.

   __ __ Ⓞ __ __ __ __ __ __ __ __ __

3. Clue: geometric isomer with substituted groups on the same side of the double bond.

   __ __ __ Ⓞ __ __ __ __ __ __ __ __ __ __ __ __

4. Clue: series of compounds related by a constant increment of change.

   Ⓞ __ __ __ __ __ __ __ __ __ Ⓞ __ __ __

5. Clue: controlled process of breaking down hydrocarbons.

   __ __ Ⓞ __ __ __ __ __

6. Clue: another name for an aromatic hydrocarbon.

   __ Ⓞ __ __ __

7. Clue: molecules that differ in the arrangement of atoms in space.

   __ __ __ __ Ⓞ __ __ __ __ __ Ⓞ

8. Clue: organic compounds that contain the maximum number of hydrogen atoms per carbon atom.

   __ __ __ __ __ __ __ __ Ⓞ

   __ Ⓞ __ __ __ Ⓞ __ __

Write the letter found inside the circles on the lines below. Then unscramble them to find the name for the class of organic compounds that contain only carbon and hydrogen.

Scrambled letters: __ __ __ __ __ __ __ __ __ __ __ __

Solution: __ __ __ __ __ __ __ __ __ __ __ __

22 HYDROCARBON COMPOUNDS

Chapter Quiz

Classify each of these statements as always true, AT; sometimes true, ST; or never true, NT.

_____ **1.** Hydrocarbons are unsaturated. 22.2

_____ **2.** The IUPAC name for $CH_3(CH_2)_3CH_3$ is butane. 22.1

_____ **3.** When naming branched-chain alkanes, the rule is to list the names of 22.1
the alkyl substituents in order of their placement in the molecule.

_____ **4.** Compounds that have the same molecular formula but the atoms are 22.3
joined in a different order are called structural isomers.

_____ **5.** Hydrocarbons are organic compounds that contain hydrogen, carbon, 22.1
and oxygen.

_____ **6.** A benzene ring is represented as a pentagon. 22.4

_____ **7.** A benzene ring contains 6 carbon atoms and 12 hydrogen atoms. 22.4

_____ **8.** Cracking is a controlled process by which hydrocarbons are broken 22.5
down or rearranged into smaller, more useful molecules.

_____ **9.** Coal is more than 80 percent carbon. 22.5

_____ **10.** Methylbenzene is the IUPAC name for toluene. 22.4

11. Name this compound: 22.2

_____

12. Draw the structural formula for 1,2,4-triphenylpentane. 22.4

HYType... HYDROCARBON COMPOUNDS

22

Chapter Test A

A. Matching

Match each term in Column B with the correct description in Column A. Write the letter of the correct term on the line.

Column A   **Column B**

_____ 1. a group of compounds in which there is a   **a.** alkane
constant increment of change in molecular
structure from one compound to the next

_____ 2. any organic compound that contains only carbon   **b.** alkene
and hydrogen

_____ 3. hydrocarbon that contains only single covalent   **c.** cracking
bonds

_____ 4. a method of naming organic compounds   **d.** arene

_____ 5. a hydrocarbon with an unsaturated ring   **e.** alkyne

_____ 6. a process by which hydrocarbons are broken   **f.** isomers
down or rearranged into smaller molecules

_____ 7. compounds that have the same molecular   **g.** homologous series
formula but different molecular structures

_____ 8. organic compound containing a carbon-carbon   **h.** IUPAC system
triple bond

_____ 9. organic compound that contains double or triple   **i.** hydrocarbon
carbon-carbon bonds

_____ 10. organic compound containing a carbon-carbon   **j.** unsaturated compound
double bond

B. Multiple Choice

Choose the best answer and write its letter on the line.

_____ 11. Which of the following has the highest carbon content?
  a. bituminous coal   **c.** anthracite
  b. lignite   **d.** peat

_____ 12. A saturated straight-chain hydrocarbon with seven carbons is
     a. hexane.   c. heptane.
     b. octane.   d. hexene.

_____ 13. Structural isomers have
     a. the same molecular formula.
     b. the same physical and chemical properties.
     c. the same order of atoms.
     d. all of the above

_____ 14. The condensed structural formula for 2,2,3–trimethylbutane is
     a. $CH_3CH_2CH(CH_3)C(CH_3)_3$.   c. $CH_3C(CH_3)_2C(CH_3)_3$.
     b. $CH_3C(CH_3)_2CH(CH_3)_2$.   d. $CH_3CH(CH_3)CH(CH_3)_2$.

_____ 15. What is the IUPAC name for the following?

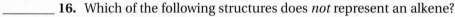

     a. 2-ethyl-2,4,5-trimethylpentane
     b. 2-ethyl-2,4-dimethylhexane
     c. 3,5,5-trimethylheptane
     d. 3,3,5-trimethylheptane

_____ 16. Which of the following structures does *not* represent an alkene?
     a. $CH_3CH{=}CH_2$ c.

     b.   d.

_____ 17. Hydrocarbons with low molar masses are generally
     a. soluble in water.   c. gases or low-boiling liquids.
     b. extremely reactive chemically.   d. all of the above

_____ 18. The name of an alkyl group that contains three carbon atoms is
     a. diphenyl.   c. trimethyl.
     b. ethyl.   d. propyl.

_____ 19. Name this compound.

                           $CH_3CH_2C(CH_3)_3$
     a. 2,2–dimethylbutane   c. 1,1,1,2–tetramethylpropane
     b. tetramethylpropane   d. isoheptane

_____ 20. A structural isomer of pentane is
     a. 2,2,–dimethylpropane.   c. benzene.
     b. cyclopentane.   d. 2-methylpentane.

_____ **21.** The carbon-carbon bonds in alkanes are
      a. double bonds.   **c.** free to rotate.
      b. quite polar.   **d.** none of the above

_____ **22.** An organic compound that contains only carbon and hydrogen and a single triple bond is classified as an
      a. alkane.   **c.** alkyne.
      b. alkene.   **d.** arene.

_____ **23.** All of the following are unsaturated hydrocarbons *except*
      a. 3–octene.   **c.** cyclohexyne.
      b. butane.   **d.** ethene.

C. Problems

Solve the following problems in the space provided.

24. Give the correct IUPAC name for the following compound:

25. Draw the two structural isomers of butane.

26. Draw the correct structural formula for: 4–ethyl–2,6–dimethyl–2–heptene.

27. Write a balanced equation for the complete combustion of liquid hexane.

D. Essay

Write a short essay for the following.

28. Given the name of an alkane, tell how you can reconstruct its structural formula, according to IUPAC rules.

_____

_____

_____

_____

_____

_____

_____

E. Additional Problems

Solve the following problems in the space provided. Show your work.

29. Identify the asymmetric carbon in this compound by number.

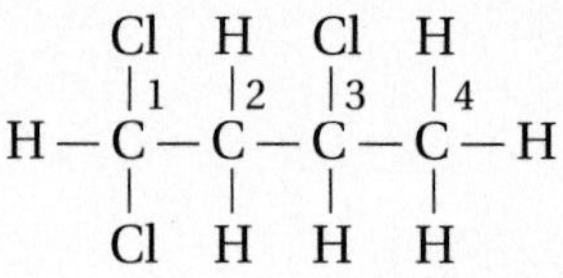

$$
\begin{array}{cccc}
Cl & H & Cl & H \\
|1 & |2 & |3 & |4 \\
H-C- & C- & C- & C-H \\
| & | & | & | \\
Cl & H & H & H \\
\end{array}
$$

30. Draw the geometric isomers of 4–methyl–2–hexene.

F. True-False

Classify each of the statements as always true, AT; sometimes true, ST; or never true, NT.

_____ **31.** Stereoisomers are molecules with the same molecular structure that differ only in the arrangement of the atoms in space.

_____ **32.** In the *cis* configuration, the substituted groups are on the same side of the double bond.

_____ **33.** Geometric isomers differ only in the orientation of groups around a double bond.

_____ **34.** An asymmetric carbon is a carbon atom to which three different groups are attached.

Name _____ Date _____ Class _____

22 HYDROCARBON COMPOUNDS

Chapter Test B

A. Matching

Match each term in Column B with the correct description in Column A. Write the letter of the correct term on the line.

Column A	Column B
_____ 1. organic compounds containing carbon-carbon double bonds	**a.** hydrocarbons
_____ 2. pairs of molecules that differ only in the way four different groups are arranged around a central carbon atom	**b.** alkenes
_____ 3. hydrocarbons that contain only single covalent bonds	**c.** homologous series
_____ 4. isomers that differ only in the orientation of groups around a double bond	**d.** cyclic hydrocarbons
_____ 5. compounds that have the same molecular formula but the atoms are joined in a different order	**e.** unsaturated compounds
_____ 6. organic compounds that contain only carbon and hydrogen	**f.** alkanes
_____ 7. compounds that contain a carbon ring	**g.** geometric isomers
_____ 8. a group of compounds in which a constant increment of change in molecular structure occurs from one compound in the series to the next	**h.** structural isomers
_____ 9. organic compounds containing carbon-carbon triple bonds	**i.** optical isomers
_____ 10. organic compounds that contain double or triple carbon-carbon bonds	**j.** alkynes

B. Multiple Choice

Choose the best answer and write its letter on the line.

_____ 11. Which of the following is true concerning methane?
   a. It is a gas at standard temperature and pressure.
   b. It consists of one carbon atom and four hydrogen atoms.
   c. It is the major component of natural gas.
   d. all of the above

_____ **12.** The increment of change in the homologous series of straight-chain alkanes is

    a. C.   **c.** CH_2.

    b. CH.   **d.** CH_3.

_____ **13.** The chemical formula for hexane is

    a. C_5H_{12}.   **c.** C_7H_{16}.

    b. C_6H_{14}.   **d.** C_8H_{18}.

_____ **14.** What is the hydrocarbon represented by the following structural formula?

$$CH_3 - CH_2 - CH_2 - CH_2 - CH_3$$

    a. butane   **c.** hexane

    b. pentane   **d.** heptane

_____ **15.** What is the IUPAC name for the following hydrocarbon?

$$
\begin{array}{ccccccc}
 & & & CH_3 & & CH_3 & \\
 & & & | & & | & \\
CH_3 - CH_2 - CH - & CH - & CH - & CH_2 - & CH_2 \\
 & & | & & & | & \\
 & & CH_2 & & & CH_3 & \\
 & & | & & & & \\
 & & CH_3 & & & &
\end{array}
$$

    a. 4–ethyl–1,3,5–trimethylheptane

    b. 3,5–dimethyl–4–ethyloctane

    c. 5–ethyl–3,5–dimethyloctane

    d. 3,5,7–trimethyl–4–ethylheptane

_____ **16.** Which of the following is true about the alkanes?

    a. They are polar molecules.

    b. They tend to exist as solids at room temperature.

    c. They dissolve in water.

    d. They contain only single covalent bonds.

_____ **17.** Which of the following is a structural isomer of hexane?

    a. 2,3–dimethylpentane

    b. 2,2–dimethylbutane

    c. 3–methylhexane

    d. 3–ethyl–3–methylpentane

_____ **18.** Which of the following is true about the alkenes?

    a. They contain carbon–carbon double bonds.

    b. They are unsaturated compounds.

    c. They can form *cis, trans* isomers.

    d. all of the above

_____ **19.** The name of the alkyl group that contains four carbon atoms is:

    a. methyl.   **c.** propyl.

    b. ethyl.   **d.** butyl.

_____ **20.** What is the IUPAC name for the following compound?

$$CH_3$$
$$|$$
$$CH_2$$
$$|$$
$$CH_3 - CH_2 - CH = CH - C - CH - CH_3$$
$$|\quad\ |$$
$$CH_3\ CH_3$$

    a. 2,3–dimethyl–3–ethyl–4–heptene
    b. 5,6–dimethyl–5–ethyl–3–heptene
    c. 3–ethyl–2,3–dimethyl–4–heptene
    d. 5–ethyl–5,6–dimethyl–3–heptene

_____ **21.** Which of the following is true about the alkynes?
    a. They contain both carbon–carbon double and triple bonds.
    b. They are unsaturated compounds.
    c. They are plentiful in nature.
    d. all of the above

_____ **22.** Which of the following is the formula for butyne?
    a. C_4H_{10} **c.** C_4H_6
    b. C_4H_8 **d.** C_4H_4

_____ **23.** In the *trans* configuration of geometric isomers, the substituted groups
    a. have the same number of carbon atoms.
    b. have different numbers of carbon atoms.
    c. are on opposite sides of the double bond.
    d. are on the same side of the double bond.

_____ **24.** An asymmetric carbon atom is one
    a. that forms a double bond.
    b. that forms a triple bond.
    c. that has four like groups attached.
    d. that has four different groups attached.

_____ **25.** The saturated hydrocarbon among the following is
    a. 2–methylhexane.   **c.** 2–butyne.
    b. 2–pentene.   **d.** acetylene.

_____ **26.** Among the following, which is the compound with the asymmetric carbon atom?
    a. $CH_3CH_2CH_3$ **c.**

$$CH_3$$
$$|$$
$$CH_3 - C - CH_3$$
$$|$$
$$OH$$

    b. $CH_3CH_2CH_2CH_3$ **d.** $CH_3 - CH - CH_2 - CH_3$
$$|$$
$$OH$$

_____ **27.** Which of the following is true about benzene?
    a. It is an aliphatic compound.
    b. Its formula is C_6H_6.
    c. Its carbon atoms form single bonds.
    d. all of the above

_____ **28.** Hard coal is known as:
    a. peat.   **c.** bituminous.
    b. lignite.   **d.** anthracite.

C. True-False

Classify each of these statements as always true, AT; sometimes true, ST; or never true, NT.

_____ **29.** Organic compounds that contain only carbon and hydrogen are called hydrocarbons.

_____ **30.** Carbon atoms always form four covalent bonds.

_____ **31.** As the number of carbon atoms in straight-chain alkanes increases, the boiling and melting points of these alkanes decrease.

_____ **32.** An alkyl group is an alkane with a hydrogen removed.

_____ **33.** The expression "like dissolves like" is a good rule of thumb in predicting whether one substance will dissolve in another.

_____ **34.** The common name of ethyne is acetylene.

_____ **35.** Geometric isomers can form when each carbon atom of a double bond has at least one substituent.

_____ **36.** Optical isomers can be considered mirror images, which can be superimposed.

_____ **37.** Aliphatic compounds contain rings.

_____ **38.** Gasoline is obtained through the cracking of long-chain hydrocarbons.

D. Problems

Solve the following problems in the space provided.

39. Draw condensed structural formulas for each of the following compounds with the C—H bonds understood.
    a. 2,3–dimethylpentane

    b. 4–ethyl–2,3–dimethyl–2–hexene

c. 5,5–diethyl–4,6,7–trimethyl–2–octyne

40. Name each of the following according to the IUPAC system.

a.

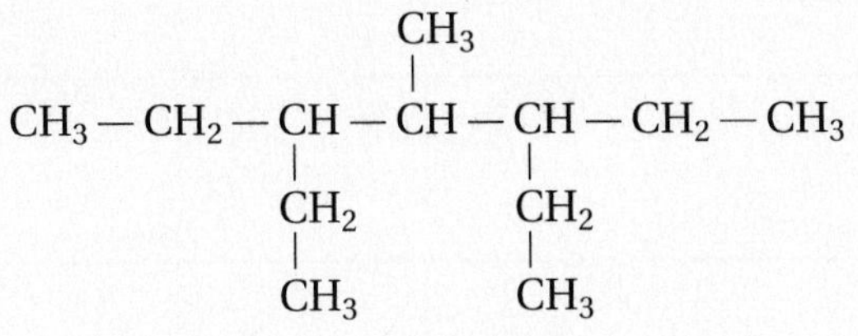

$$CH_3$$
$$|$$
$$CH_3-CH_2-CH-CH-CH-CH_2-CH_3$$
$$|\qquad\qquad|$$
$$CH_2\qquad CH_2$$
$$|\qquad\qquad|$$
$$CH_3\qquad CH_3$$

_____

b.

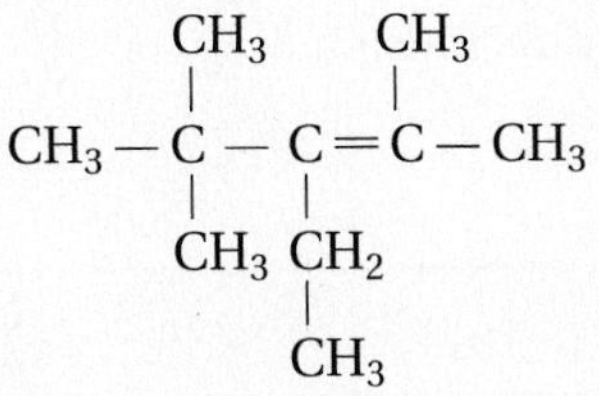

$$CH_3\qquad CH_3$$
$$|\qquad\qquad|$$
$$CH_3-C\ -\ C=C-CH_3$$
$$|\qquad|$$
$$CH_3\ CH_2$$
$$|$$
$$CH_3$$

_____

c.

$$CH_3$$
$$|$$
$$CH_2\qquad CH_3$$
$$|\qquad\qquad|$$
$$CH_3\qquad CH_2\qquad CH_2$$
$$|\qquad\quad|\qquad\quad|$$
$$CH_3-CH-C\equiv C-CH-CH-CH-CH-CH_2-CH_3$$
$$|\qquad\qquad|$$
$$CH_2\qquad CH_3$$
$$|$$
$$CH_3$$

_____

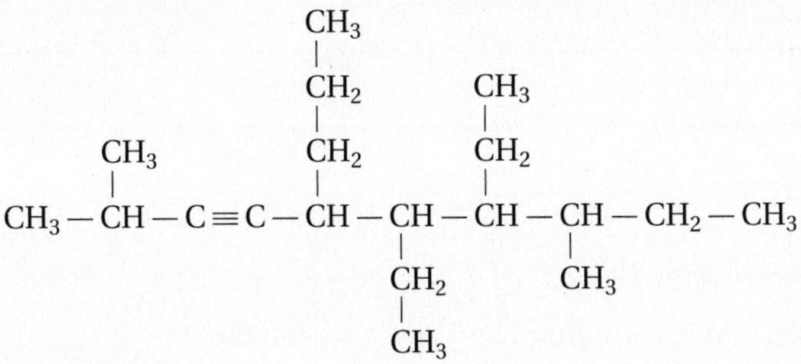

41. Draw and name all the structural isomers of pentane.

42. Draw and name all the geometric isomers of 2–butene.

Name _____ Date _____ Class _____

E. Essay

Write a short essay for the following.

43. Provide a chemical formula, draw the structural formula, and name one straight-chain isomer of a six-carbon hydrocarbon that is

    a. an alkane.

    _____

    b. an alkene.

    _____

    c. an alkyne.

    _____

    Explain the reason for the variation in the number of hydrogen atoms in each of these compounds.

    _____

    _____

    _____

    _____

    _____

F. Additional Problems

Solve the following problems in the space provided.

44. Select the asymmetric carbon atom in this compound and give a reason for your choice.

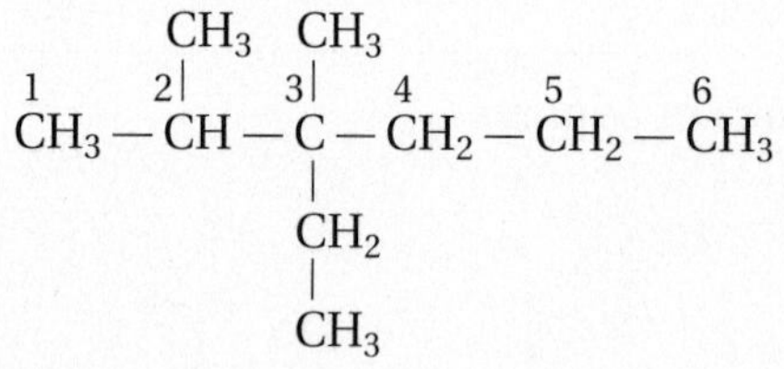

$$
\begin{array}{cccccc}
 & \overset{2}{\underset{|}{CH_3}} & \overset{3}{\underset{|}{CH_3}} & & & \\
\overset{1}{CH_3} - \overset{2}{CH} - \overset{3}{C} - \overset{4}{CH_2} - \overset{5}{CH_2} - \overset{6}{CH_3} \\
 & & \underset{|}{CH_2} & & & \\
 & & \underset{|}{CH_3} & & &
\end{array}
$$

_____

_____

_____

45. Give the IUPAC name for each of the following compounds.

a. 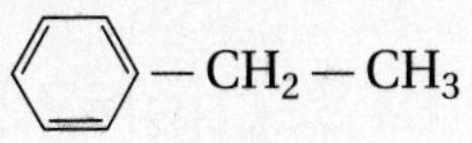

____

b. 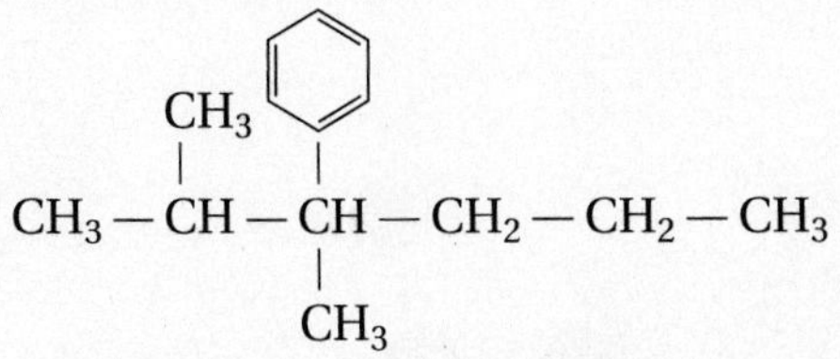

____

QUICK LAB: Structural Isomers of Heptane

Laboratory Recordsheet   Use with Section 22.3

PURPOSE

To build ball-and-stick models and
name the nine structural isomers of heptane (C_7H_{16}).

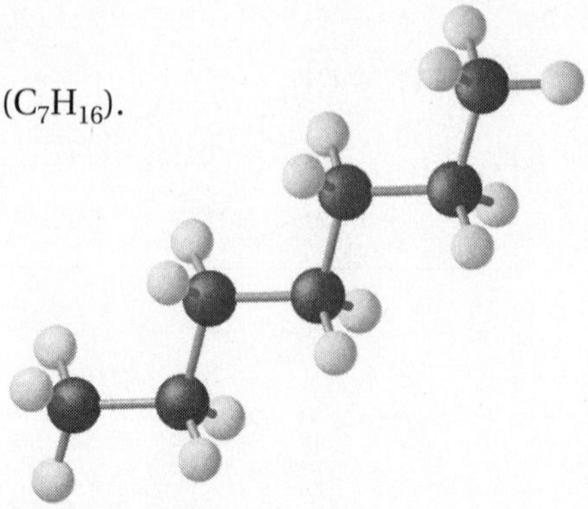

MATERIALS

- ball-and-stick molecular model kit

PROCEDURE

1. Build a model for the straight-chain molecule of C_7H_{16}. Draw the structural formula and write the IUPAC name for this isomer.

2. Move one carbon atom from the end of the chain and add a methyl substituent to the chain. Draw the structural formula and name this isomer.

3. Move the methyl group to a new position on the chain. Then draw and name this third isomer. Is there a third position that this methyl group can be moved to on the chain of six carbons to form yet another different isomer?

4. Make other structural isomers by shortening the longest straight chain and using the removed carbons as substituents. Draw the structural formulas and name each isomer.

ANALYSES AND CONCLUSIONS

1. What are the names of the nine structural isomers C_7H_{16}?

_____

_____

_____

2. What is the shortest possible straight carbon chain in the isomers?

_____

_____

_____

_____

3. Why does each structural isomer have its own unique name?

_____

_____

SMALL-SCALE LAB: Hydrocarbon Isomers

Laboratory Recordsheet   Use with Section 22.3

SAFETY

Use safe and proper laboratory procedures.

PURPOSE

To draw line-angle formulas and name some of the isomers in gasoline.

MATERIALS

- toothpicks
- modeling clay

PROCEDURE

Gasoline is a complex mixture of hydrocarbon molecules. Each molecule contains between five and ten carbon atoms. Many of the components of gasoline are isomers with the same molecular formula. These components include the isomers of pentane. Study the formulas and names of the isomers of C_5H_{12} in the chart below. Make a model of each isomer, using toothpicks and modeling clay. Compare the models and make accurate drawings of the models.

Formulas Representing Isomers of C_5H_{12}

Condensed	Line-angle	Space-filling
$CH_3CH_2CH_2CH_2CH_3$ pentane	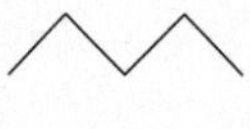	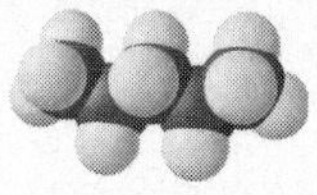
$CH_3CHCH_2CH_3$ | CH_3 2-methylbutane	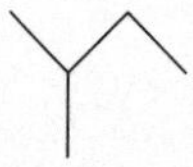	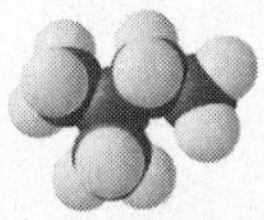
CH_3 | CH_3CCH_3 | CH_3 2,2-dimethylpropane		

Name _____ Date _____ Class _____

ANALYZE

Using your experimental data, record the answers to the following questions.

1. Complete structural formulas include all the atoms and the chemical bonds in a molecule. Draw the complete structural formulas for each isomer of C_5H_{12} in the chart.

2. In a line-angle formula, each line represents a carbon-carbon bond. Each end of a line, as well as the intersection of lines, represents a carbon atom. All hydrogen atoms are understood. Knowing that carbon always forms four bonds in organic compounds, explain how to determine the number of hydrogen atoms bonded to each carbon in a line-angle formula.

_____

_____

_____

_____

3. Because butane can vaporize readily, it is used in the formulations of gasolines in cold climates during winter. Draw the condensed structural formulas, the line-angle formulas, and the space-filling formulas for the two isomers of butane (C_4H_{10}). Make models of each isomer.

YOU'RE THE CHEMIST

Use the space below to write your observations to the small-scale activities in the *You're the Chemist* section.

Name _____ Date _____ Class _____

23.1 INTRODUCTION TO FUNCTIONAL GROUPS

Section Review

Objectives

- Explain how organic compounds are classified
- Identify the IUPAC rules for naming halocarbons
- Describe how halocarbons can be prepared

Vocabulary

- functional group
- halocarbons
- alkyl halides
- aryl halides
- substitution reaction

Part A Completion

Use this completion exercise to check your understanding of the concepts and terms that are introduced in this section. Each blank can be completed with a term, short phrase, or number.

The chemical reactions of most organic compounds involve
___1___ groups. Functional groups are the chemically ___2___
parts of an organic molecule. Common functional groups include
the double and triple carbon-carbon bonds of ___3___ and
___4___, respectively. ___5___ are a class of organic compounds
containing one or more covalently bonded halogen atoms.

A common type of organic reaction is a ___6___ reaction in
which an atom or a group of atoms replaces another atom or group
of atoms. For example, treating methane with bromine in the
presence of a catalyst causes the substitution of a ___7___ atom
with a ___8___ atom. Similarly, halogens on carbon chains are
readily replaced by hydroxide ions to produce an ___9___ and a
___10___.

1. _____

2. _____

3. _____

4. _____

5. _____

6. _____

7. _____

8. _____

9. _____

10. _____

Part B True-False

Classify each of these statements as always true, AT; sometimes true, ST; or never true, NT.

_____ 11. A functional group is a specific arrangement of atoms in an organic compound that is capable of characteristic reactions.

_____ 12. Many halocarbons are found in nature.

_____ 13. A product of a substitution reaction is a hydrogen halide.

_____ 14. The common name of $CH_3CH_2CH_2Br$ is propyl bromide.

Part C Matching

Match each description in Column B to the correct term in Column A.

	Column A	**Column B**
_____	15. functional group	a. the reaction of chlorine with ethane to produce ethyl chloride and hydrogen chloride
_____	16. alkyl halide	b. $CH_3CH_2CH_2CH_2I$
_____	17. substitution reaction	c. a class of organic compounds in which one or more halogen atoms are joined to a carbon of an arene ring
_____	18. aryl halides	d. a specific arrangement of atoms in an organic compound that is capable of characteristic chemical reactions

Part D Problems

Answer the following in the space provided.

19. Identify the functional group in each of the following compounds.

a.
$$CH_3 - \underset{\underset{H}{|}}{\overset{\overset{OH}{|}}{C}} - CH_3$$

_____

c.
an aryl ring — $\overset{\overset{O}{\|}}{C} - H$

_____

b.
$$CH_3 - CH_2 - \overset{\overset{O}{\|}}{C} - CH_3$$

_____

d.
$$CH_3 - CH_2 - CH_2 - \overset{\overset{O}{\|}}{C} - OH$$

_____

20. Give the structural formula for each compound.

a. *o*-chlorotoluene

b. 2,2-dichloropentane

Name _____ Date _____ Class _____

23.2 ALCOHOLS AND ETHERS

Section Review

Objectives

- Identify how alcohols are classified and named
- Predict how the solubility of an alcohol varies with the length of its carbon chain
- Name the reactions of alkenes that may be used to introduce functional groups
- Construct the general structure of an ether and describe how ethers are named

Vocabulary

- alcohol
- hydroxyl group
- fermentation
- denatured alcohol
- addition reaction
- hydration reaction
- hydrogenation reaction
- ether

Part A Completion

Use this completion exercise to check your understanding of the concepts and terms that are introduced in this section. Each blank can be completed with a term, short phrase, or number.

___1___ are organic compounds with a hydroxyl group.

Aliphatic alcohols can be classified as ___2___, ___3___, or

___4___ alcohols depending on the number of R groups attached

to the carbon with the hydroxyl group. For example, 2-propanol

represents a ___5___ alcohol. In general, alcohols are more soluble

in water than alkanes containing comparable numbers of atoms

because they are capable of intermolecular ___6___.

Alcohols can be prepared from alkenes by a ___7___ reaction.

In this type of reaction, ___8___ is added at the carbon-carbon

double bond of the alkene. Another form of addition reaction is

___9___. In this reaction, which is catalyzed by platinum or

palladium, hydrogen is added to the carbon-carbon double bonds

in a molecule to produce an ___10___.

Organic compounds whose general formula can be written as

R-O-R are called ___11___. Ethers usually have ___12___ boiling

points than alcohols of comparable formula mass.

1. _____
2. _____
3. _____
4. _____
5. _____
6. _____
7. _____
8. _____
9. _____
10. _____
11. _____
12. _____

Part B True-False

Classify each of these statements as always true, AT; sometimes true, ST; or never true, NT.

_____ **13.** The addition of water to an alkene is called a hydration reaction.

_____ **14.** Hydrogenation of a double bond is an oxidation reaction.

_____ **15.** ⬡–O–⬡ is an ether.

_____ **16.** The benzene ring usually undergoes addition rather than substitution.

Part C Matching

Match each description in Column B to the correct term in Column A.

Column A

_____ **17.** hydration reaction

_____ **18.** fermentation

_____ **19.** alcohols

_____ **20.** addition

_____ **21.** hydrogenation

Column B

a. the production of ethanol from sugars by the action of yeast or bacteria

b. the reaction of HBr with propene to form 1-bromopropane

c. the reaction of hydrogen with butene to form butane

d. a class of organic compounds whose structures contain an –OH group

e. the addition of water to an alkene

Part D Problems

Answer the following in the space provided.

22. Identify the following compounds as primary, secondary, or tertiary alcohols.

a.

$$CH_3 - CH_2 - \underset{\underset{CH_3}{|}}{\overset{\overset{OH}{|}}{C}} - CH_3$$

b. $CH_3 - CH_2 - OH$

_____   _____

23. Give the structure for the expected organic product from each reaction.

a.

$$\underset{H}{\overset{CH_3}{\diagdown}} C = C \underset{CH_3}{\overset{H}{\diagup}} \quad + H_2 \xrightarrow{\text{Pt}}$$

b.

$$\underset{H}{\overset{CH_3}{\diagdown}} C = C \underset{H}{\overset{H}{\diagup}} \quad + H_2O \xrightarrow{H^+}$$

23.3 CARBONYL COMPOUNDS

Section Review

Objectives

- Identify the structure of a carbonyl group as found in aldehydes and ketones
- Construct the general formula for carboxylic acids and explain how they are named
- Describe an ester
- Explain how dehydration is an oxidation reaction

Vocabulary

- carbonyl group
- aldehydes
- ketones
- carboxylic acid
- carboxyl group
- fatty acids
- esters
- dehydrogenation reaction

Part A Completion

Use this completion exercise to check your understanding of the concepts and terms that are introduced in this section. Each blank can be completed with a term, short phrase, or number.

A carbonyl group consists of a carbon atom and an ___1___

atom joined by a ___2___ bond. Aldehydes, ___3___, ___4___, and

esters are all classes of organic compounds that contain carbonyl

groups. The general formula for an ___5___ can be written as RCHO.

The general formula of a ___6___ can be written as RCOOH.

The simplest aldehyde is methanal, also called ___7___.

Methanal is used industrially to manufacture synthetic resins.

Ethanoic, propanoic, and butanoic acids are examples of ___8___.

Organic compounds formed from the reaction of a carboxylic acid

with an alcohol are called ___9___. For example, propyl ethanoate

could be synthesized by reacting ___10___ with ethanoic acid.

Carbonyl-containing compounds and alcohols can be

interconverted using ___11___ reactions. For example, the

primary alcohols methanol and ethanol can be converted to

aldehydes by treating them with acidified ___12___.

1. _____

2. _____

3. _____

4. _____

5. _____

6. _____

7. _____

8. _____

9. _____

10. _____

11. _____

12. _____

Name ____________________ Date ______________ Class ______________

Part B True-False

Classify each of these statements as always true, AT; sometimes true, ST; or never true, NT.

_______ **13.** Many continuous-chain carboxylic acids are called fatty acids.

_______ **14.** Benedict's test is used to detect ketones.

_______ **15.** The hydrolysis of ethyl butanoate in an acid solution would yield ethanoic acid and butanol.

_______ **16.** 2-methyl-2-propanol cannot be oxidized to propanone using acidified potassium dichromate.

Part C Matching

Match each description in Column B to the correct term in Column A.

Column A	Column B
_______ **17.** dehydrogenation reaction	**a.** a group of atoms that consists of a carbonyl group attached to a hydroxyl group
_______ **18.** esters	**b.** long continuous-chain carboxylic acids isolated from fats
_______ **19.** ketones	**c.** the loss of hydrogen
_______ **20.** fatty acids	**d.** a derivative of carboxylic acids in which the –OH of the carbonyl group has be replaced by an –OR from an alcohol
_______ **21.** carboxyl group	**e.** organic compounds in which the carbon of the carbonyl group is joined to two other carbons

Part D Problems

Answer the following in the space provided.

22. Show how alcohols, aldehydes, ketones, and carboxylic acids are related by oxidation and reduction reactions.

23. Give the IUPAC name for the following compound.

$$\begin{array}{c} O \\ \| \\ CH_3\,CH_2\,C\,CH_2\,CH_2\,CH_3 \end{array}$$

23.4 POLYMERIZATION

Section Review

Objectives

- Describe how additional polymers are formed
- Describe how condensation polymers are formed

Vocabulary

- polymer
- monomers

Part A Completion

Use this completion exercise to check your understanding of the concepts and terms that are introduced in this section. Each blank can be completed with a term, short phrase, or number.

A __**1**__ is a large molecule formed by the covalent bonding

of repeating smaller molecules. __**2**__ polymerization occurs when

unsaturated monomers react to form a polymer. __**3**__ polymers

are formed by the head-to-tail joining of monomer units.

__**4**__, formed by the joining of ethene molecules, is an

example of an addition polymer. __**5**__, formed by the joining of

dicarboxylic acids and dihydroxy alcohols, are examples of

condensation polymers. The physical properties of polymers, such

as hardness and rigidity, depend in part on the __**6**__ of the

carbon chains in the polymer molecules.

1. _____

2. _____

3. _____

4. _____

5. _____

6. _____

Part B True-False

Classify each of these statements as always true, AT; sometimes true, ST; or never true, NT.

_____ 7. Polymerization reactions require a catalyst.

_____ 8. Addition polymers form when unsaturated monomers react to form a polymer.

_____ **9.** The condensation polymerization of a carboxylic acid with an amine produces a polyester and water.

_____ **10.** Various types of nylon are polyamides.

_____ **11.** The basic repeating unit of polyvinyl chloride could be written as

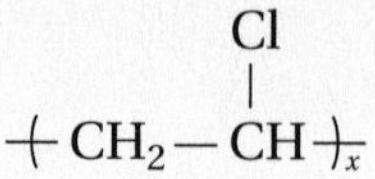

$$\begin{array}{c} \text{Cl} \\ | \\ \text{+CH}_2\text{—CH+}_x \end{array}$$

Part C Matching

Match each description in Column B to the correct term in Column A.

Column A

_____ **12.** polymer

_____ **13.** addition polymer

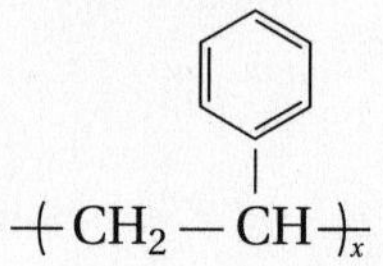

_____ **14.** condensation polymerization

_____ **15.** Kevlar™

_____ **16.** polystyrene

Column B

a.

$$\begin{array}{c} \bigcirc \\ | \\ \text{+CH}_2\text{—CH+}_x \end{array}$$

b. a large molecule formed by the covalent bonding of repeating smaller molecules

c. polypropylene

d. requires that there be two functional groups on each monomer molecule

e. a tough, flexible, and flame-resistant condensation polymer used to construct bullet-proof vests

Part D Questions and Problems

Answer the following in the space provided.

17. Show the addition polymerization of ethene to form polyethylene.

18. Describe the characteristics of a polyester. Give an example of a polyester.

23 FUNCTIONAL GROUPS AND ORGANIC REACTIONS

Practice Problems

In your notebook, solve the following problems.

SECTION 23.1 INTRODUCTION TO FUNCTIONAL GROUPS

1. Identify the functional group in each of the following compounds.

   a. 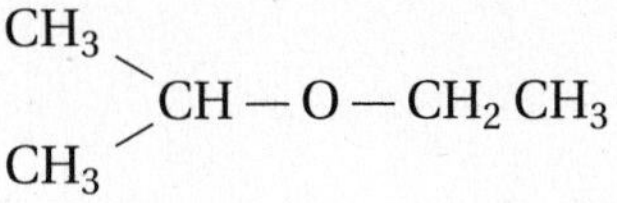
   $$CH_3 \diagdown CH - O - CH_2\,CH_3$$
   $$CH_3 \diagup$$

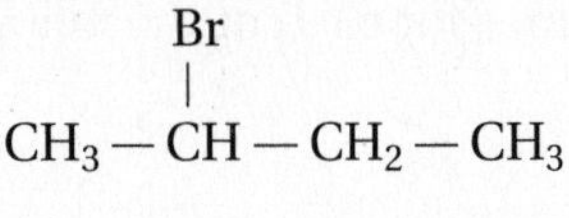

   b. 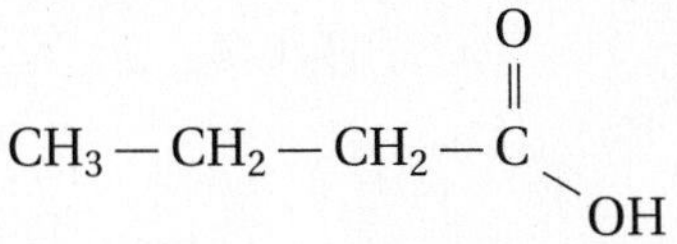
   $$\overset{\displaystyle O}{\underset{\displaystyle \parallel}{}}$$
   $$CH_3 - CH_2 - CH_2 - C \diagdown OH$$

   c.
   $$\overset{\displaystyle Br}{\underset{\displaystyle |}{}}$$
   $$CH_3 - CH - CH_2 - CH_3$$

   d. 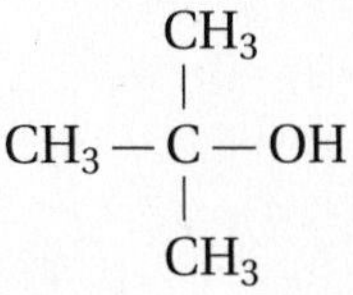
   $$\overset{\displaystyle CH_3}{\underset{\displaystyle |}{}}$$
   $$CH_3 - C - OH$$
   $$\underset{\displaystyle |}{}$$
   $$CH_3$$

2. What class of organic compounds do each of the following substances belong to? Write IUPAC names for each structure.

   a.

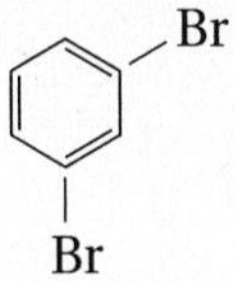

   b. $CH_3\, CH\, Cl\, Br$

   c. 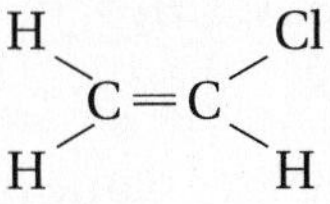
   $$H \diagdown C = C \diagdown Cl$$
   $$H \diagup \diagup H$$

3. Write the formulas of the expected products for the following reactions.

   a. 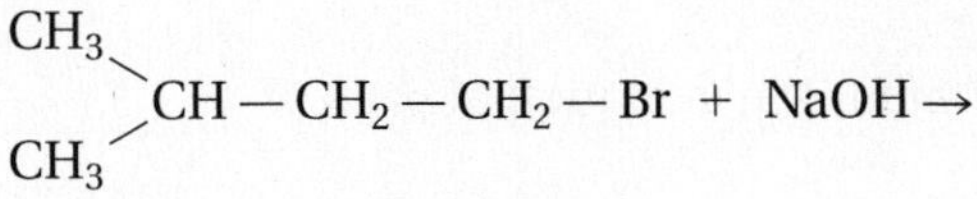
   $$CH_3 \diagdown CH - CH_2 - CH_2 - Br \; + \; NaOH \rightarrow$$
   $$CH_3 \diagup$$

   b. $CH_4 + 4Cl_2 \xrightarrow{\text{catalyst}}$

4. Give the structural formula for each of the following compounds.

   a. 1-bromo-3-ethylbenzene

   b. 1-bromo-3,4-dimethylheptane

SECTION 23.2 ALCOHOLS AND ETHERS

1. Write the IUPAC names for each of the following compounds. Classify each alcohol as primary, secondary, or tertiary.

   a. 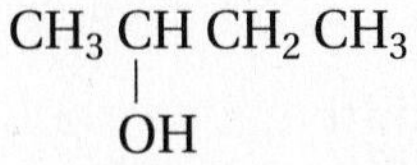 $CH_3\, CH\, CH_2\, CH_3$
   $$\underset{\displaystyle OH}{|}$$

   b. 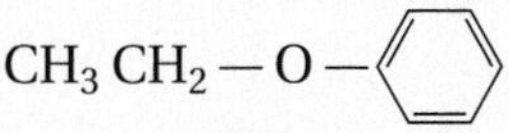 $CH_3\, CH_2 - O -$ ⬡

   c. 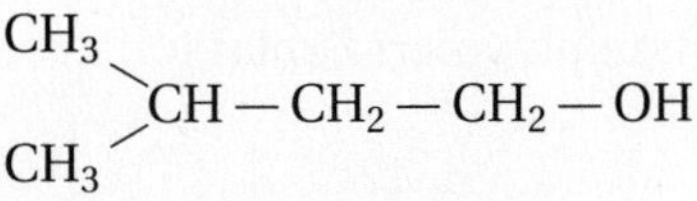
   $$CH_3 \diagdown CH - CH_2 - CH_2 - OH$$
   $$CH_3 \diagup$$

   d. $CH_3CH_2CH_2CH_2CH_2OH$

2. Write the structural formulas for dipropyl ether, 2-methyl-1-butanol, and 2,3-butanediol. Which of these compounds is expected to be most soluble in water?

3. Write an equation for the synthesis of

   a. 2-chlorobutane from 1-butene and hydrogen chloride

   b. bromobenzene from benzene and bromine

4. Classify each of the reactions in problem 3 as an addition or substitution reaction.

SECTION 23.3 CARBONYL COMPOUNDS

1. Write IUPAC names for each of the following compounds.

   a.

   b.

   $$CH_3\,CH_2 - \overset{\overset{\textstyle O}{\|}}{C} - CH_3$$

   c.

   $$CH_3\,CH_2\,\overset{\overset{\textstyle CH_3}{|}}{C}\,CH_2\,\overset{\overset{\textstyle O}{\|}}{C}\diagdown_{OH}$$

   d.

   $$CH_3\,CH_2\,CH_2\,\overset{\overset{\textstyle O}{\|}}{C}\diagdown_{O\,CH_2\,CH_3}$$

   e.

2. Write the IUPAC name of the expected product for the reduction of each of the following compounds.

   a. ethanoic acid

   b. propene

   c. butanal

3. Write the IUPAC name of the expected product(s) for the oxidation of each of the following compounds.

   a. 2-pentanol

   b. octanal

   c. butane

4. Write an equation for the synthesis of

   a. isopropyl butanoate from isopropanol and butanoic acid

   b. butanoic acid from 1-butanol

5. Classify each of the reactions in problem 4 as an oxidation-reduction, substitution, addition, or esterfication reaction.

SECTION 23.4 POLYMERIZATON

1. Draw the structures of propene (propylene) and tetrafluoroethene. Draw the basic repeating units when each of these compounds polymerizes. Describe some practical uses of each polymer.

2. Draw the basic repeating unit of polyethylene terephthalate (PET). Classify PET as a polyamide or polyester. Is PET a condensation or addition polymer? Explain.

INTERPRETING GRAPHICS

23

Use with Section 23.3

The oxidation of alcohols by acidified potassium dichromate is a convenient way for chemists to quantify the amount of primary and/or secondary alcohols in a solution. An acidic solution of dichromate ion ($Cr_2O_7^{2-}$) is bright orange before reaction, but turns green upon reduction by a primary or secondary alcohol. The rate and intensity of the color change is proportional to the concentration of the alcohol in the sample being tested. Chemists use an instrument known as a spectrophotometer to measure this color change as a function of time. Data for the oxidation of ethanol and 2-methyl-2-propanol with acidified potassium dichromate are shown in Tables 1 and 2. Use the data to answer the following questions.

Table 1 Oxidation of an Alcohol with $K_2Cr_2O_4/H_2SO_4$

Time (min)	Absorbance Data from Spectrophotometer	log (Absorbance)
0.0	1.000	
1.0	1.380	
2.0	2.013	
3.0	2.917	
4.0	4.240	
5.0	5.835	

Table 2 Oxidation of an Alcohol with $K_2Cr_2O_4/H_2SO_4$

Time (min)	Absorbance Data from Spectrophotometer
0.0	1.000
1.0	1.003
2.0	1.001
3.0	1.000
4.0	1.000
5.0	1.002

1. Which of the tables lists data for the oxidation of ethanol? Explain.

_____

_____

2. Why is 2-methyl-2-propanol included in this chemical test?

_____

_____

_____

3. You learned in Chapter 18 that the rate of a chemical reaction can be expressed in mathematical terms as a rate law—an expression relating the rate of a reaction to the concentration of reactants.

    a. Write the chemical equation for the reaction of acidified potassium dichromate with ethanol.

    b. Assume that potassium dichromate is present in large excess and does not affect the rate of the reaction. Write the rate law for this reaction, which is first order with respect to [ethanol].

4. Chemists can use spectrophotometric data, such as those listed in Table 1, to determine the specific rate constant of a reaction because the amount of product formed per unit time is directly related to the change in color of the solution per unit time.

    a. Complete Table 1 by calculating the log of each of the absorbance values listed.

    b. Plot the (x,y) data points [Time, log(Absorbance)] on the graph below. Connect the points with a straight line.

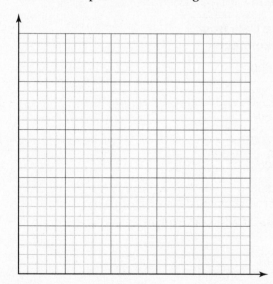

    c. Find the slope of the line in your graph. Use the formula slope $= \dfrac{k}{2.303}$ to find the specific rate constant, k, for the oxidation of ethanol by dichromate ion.

23 FUNCTIONAL GROUPS AND ORGANIC REACTIONS

Vocabulary Review

Each clue describes a vocabulary term. Read the clues and write the letters of each term on the lines provided.

1. Clue: a specific arrangement of atoms in an organic compound that is capable of characteristic chemical reactions.

   __ __ __ __ __ __ __ __ __ __   __ __ __ __ ⃝

2. Clue: halocarbons in which the halogen functional group(s) is(are) attached to an arene ring.

   __ ⃝ __ __   __ __ __ __ __ __ __

3. Clue: a common type of organic reaction in which an atom or group of atoms replaces another atom or group of atoms.

   __ __ __ __ __ __ __ __ __ __ __ __

   __ __ ⃝ __ __ __ ' __ __

4. Clue: a class of organic compounds whose structures contain a hydroxyl group.

   __ __ __ __ __ __ ⃝

5. Clue: the name given to reaction in which water is added at the double bond of an alkene.

   __ __ __ __ __ __ ⃝ __ __

   __ __ __ __ __ __ __ __

6. Clue: the addition of hydrogen to a carbon-carbon double bond.

   __ __ __ __ __ __ __ __ __ __ ⃝ __ __

7. Clue: organic compounds in which the carbon of the carbonyl group is joined to two other carbons.

   __ __ __ __ ⃝ __ __

Write the letters found inside the circles on the lines below. Then unscramble them to find the common name of 2-acetyloxybenzoic acid.

Scrambled letters:

__ __ __ __ __ __ __

Solution:

__ __ __ __ __ __ __

23 FUNCTIONAL GROUPS AND ORGANIC REACTIONS

Chapter Quiz

1. Write an equation using structural formulas for the reaction of benzene and iodine.   *23.1*

$$\overset{\displaystyle H}{\underset{\displaystyle \bigcirc}{|}} + I_2 \rightarrow$$

Classify each of these statements as always true, AT; sometimes true, ST; or never true, NT.

_____ **2.** The symbol R is used to represent functional groups.   *23.1*

_____ **3.** Methyl chloride and chloromethane are the same compound.   *23.1*

_____ **4.** Alcohols are soluble in water.   *23.2*

_____ **5.** $R-\overset{\displaystyle H}{\underset{\displaystyle H}{\overset{|}{\underset{|}{C}}}}-OH$ is the formula for a primary alcohol.   *23.2*

_____ **6.** The reaction of methane and chlorine produces a mixture of mono-, di-, tri-, and tetrachloromethanes.   *23.1*

_____ **7.** Aldehydes and ketones form intermolecular hydrogen bonds.   *23.3*

_____ **8.** The hydrogenation of a double bond is an oxidation reaction.   *23.3*

_____ **9.** R–O–R is the general formula of an ether.   *23.2*

_____ **10.** The addition of water to an alkene is a hydrogenation reaction.   *23.2*

_____ **11.** Compounds containing a carbonyl group are carboxylic acids.   *23.3*

_____ **12.** The more reduced a carbon compound is, the more energy it can release upon its complete oxidation to carbon dioxide.   *23.3*

_____ **13.** Monomers are molecules that combine to form the repeating unit of a polymer.   *23.4*

_____ **14.** The abbreviated formula for a carboxylate ester is RCOOR.   *23.3*

_____ **15.** The formation of polyester is an example of condensation polymerization.   *23.4*

_____ **16.** The oxidation of an alcohol produces a ketone.   *23.3*

Name _____ Date _____ Class _____

23 FUNCTIONAL GROUPS AND ORGANIC REACTIONS

Chapter Test A

A. Matching

Match each term in Column B with the correct description in Column A. Write the letter of the correct term on the line.

Column A   **Column B**

_____ 1. a specific arrangement of atoms in an organic compound   **a.** addition reaction
that is capable of characteristic chemical reactions

_____ 2. halocarbons in which a halogen attaches to a carbon of   **b.** hydroxyl group
an aliphatic chain

_____ 3. R—NH$_2$ **c.** carbonyl group

_____ 4. organic compounds that partially dissociate in aqueous   **d.** ether
solution to give a carboxylate ion and a hydrogen ion

_____ 5. a compound in which oxygen is bonded to two carbon   **e.** functional group
atoms

_____ 6. oxidation products of secondary alcohols   **f.** amine

_____ 7. a carbon atom and an oxygen atom joined by a double   **g.** carboxylic acids
bond

_____ 8. large molecules formed by the covalent bonding of   **h.** ketones
repeating smaller molecules

_____ 9. the addition of a substance to a double or triple bond   **i.** alkyl halide

_____ 10. the OH functional group in alcohols   **j.** polymers

B. Multiple Choice

Choose the best answer and write its letter on the line.

_____ 11. Hydrogenation
    a. is the same as dehydrogenation.
    b. can be classified as a reduction reaction.
    c. can be classified as an oxidation reaction.
    d. is the addition of a water molecule to the double bond of a
       carbon compound.

_____ 12. An example of a secondary alcohol is shown by the structure

    a. CH_3CH_2Cl

    b. CH_3CCH_3
$$\underset{O}{\overset{\|}{}}$$

    c. $CH_3CH_2CHCH_3$
$$\underset{OH}{\overset{|}{}}$$

    d. $CH_3CH_2C(CH_3)_2$
$$\underset{OH}{\overset{|}{}}$$

_____ 13. Which of these compounds would you expect to be most soluble in water?

    a. $CH_3CH_2CH_2OH$

    b. $CH_3CH_2CH_2CH_3$

    c. $CH_3CH_2CH_2F$

    d. CH_3CH_2Cl

_____ 14. Aldehydes have the general structure

    a.
$$\overset{O}{\overset{\|}{R-C-R}}$$

    b.
$$\overset{O}{\overset{\|}{R-C-H}}$$

    c.
$$\overset{O}{\overset{\|}{R-C-OH}}$$

    d.
$$\overset{O}{\overset{\|}{R-C-OR}}$$

_____ 15. Based on your knowledge of intramolecular forces, which of these would you expect to have the highest boiling point?

    a. propanal

    b. propane

    c. propanone

    d. 1-propanol

_____ 16. Name the structure $CH_3CH_2OCH_2CH_3$.

    a. diethyl ether

    b. dipropyl ether

    c. butyl ether

    d. butyl oxide

_____ 17. Phenols are characterized by

    a. their behavior as gases.

    b. ether linkages.

    c. an —OH group on a benzene ring.

    d. their use as flavoring agents.

_____ 18. Ketones have the general structure

    a.
$$\underset{O}{\overset{}{R-C-OR}}\ \overset{\|}{}$$

    b.
$$\underset{O}{\overset{}{R-C-H}}\ \overset{\|}{}$$

    c. $R-O-R$

    d.
$$\underset{O}{\overset{}{R-C-R}}\ \overset{\|}{}$$

_____ 19. Hydrogen bonding *cannot* occur between which of the following pairs of molecules?

    a. water–alcohol

    b. water–carboxylic acid

    c. water–amine

    d. water–alkane

_____ **20.** Name this compound.

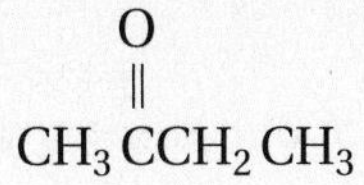

$$CH_3 \overset{\overset{\text{O}}{\|}}{C} CH_2 CH_3$$

    a. butanal   **c.** butanone

    b. butane   **d.** butanol

_____ **21.** Which of the following reactions could be used to synthesize 1,2-dibromopropane?

    a. $CH_3CH_2CH_3 + HCl \rightarrow$ **c.** $CH_2{=}CHCH_3 + Br_2 \rightarrow$

    b. propene $+ Cl_2 \rightarrow$ **d.** $CH_2{=}CHCH_3 + HBr \rightarrow$

_____ **22.** Which pair of formulas represent the same compound?

    a. $CH_3COH(CH_3)_2$; $(CH_3)_3COH$

    b. $(CH_3)_2CO$; CH_3COH

    c. CH_3CH_2CHO; CH_3CH_2COOH

    d. C_2H_5OH; CH_3OCH_3

_____ **23.** A carboxylic acid with six carbons in a straight chain would be named

    a. phenolic acid.   **c.** dimethylbutanoic acid.

    b. hexanalic acid.   **d.** hexanoic acid.

_____ **24.** What product is formed from the reaction $CH_3CH_2CH_2OH \xrightarrow[H_2SO_4]{K_2Cr_2O_7}$

    a. butyraldehyde   **c.** propanal

    b. ethanoic acid   **d.** propane

_____ **25.** Identify the functional groups present in aspirin (acetylsalicylic acid).

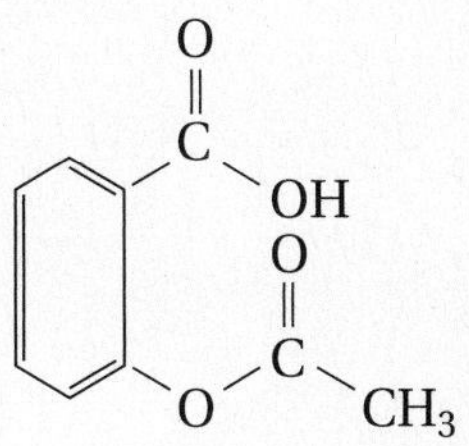

    a. amino, halogen   **c.** ester, carboxyl

    b. ester, hydroxyl   **d.** aldehyde, ketone

_____ **26.** What is the expected organic product for the following reaction?

$CH_3CH_2CH_2OH + CH_3COOH \xrightarrow{H^+}$

    a. formyl propanoate   **c.** propyl ethanoate

    b. ethyl acetate   **d.** ethyl propanoate

_____ **27.** Which of the compounds below represents the product formed by the reduction of butanone?

    a. $CH_3CH_2CH_2CH_2OH$ **c.**

$$CH_3 \overset{\overset{\text{OH}}{|}}{C}H CH_2 CH_3$$

    b.

$$CH_3 - \overset{\overset{\displaystyle CH_3}{|}}{\underset{\underset{\displaystyle CH_3}{|}}{C}} - OH$$

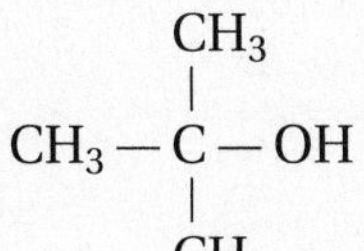

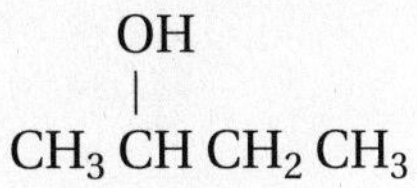

    d. $CH_3CH_2CH_2CH_3$

Name ______________________ Date ________________ Class ________________

C. Problems

Solve the following problems in the space provided. Show your work.

28. Write balanced equations for the following reactions. Use structural formulas.

a. 2-butene + water →

b. benzene + chlorine →

29. Name each organic product formed in question 28.

a. ____

b. ____

30. Write the general structure for each of the following types of compounds.

a. halocarbon

b. ether

c. ester

d. carboxylic acid

Name ______________________ Date ________________ Class ________________

D. Essay

Write a short essay for the following.

31. What are polymers and why are they important? Distinguish between addition polymers and condensation polymers.

23 FUNCTIONAL GROUPS AND ORGANIC REACTIONS

Chapter Test B

A. Matching

Match each term in Column B with the correct description in Column A. Write the letter of the correct term on the line.

Column A	**Column B**
_____ 1. the –OH functional group in alcohols	**a.** hydrogenation reaction
_____ 2. a type of organic reaction in which hydrogen is added to a carbon–carbon double bond to give an alkane	**b.** carboxylic acids
_____ 3. a specific arrangement of atoms in an organic compound that is capable of characteristic chemical reactions	**c.** ketones
_____ 4. halocarbons in which a halogen attaches to a carbon of an aliphatic chain	**d.** polymer
_____ 5. a type of organic reaction in which a substance is added at the double or triple bond of an alkene or alkyne	**e.** substitution reaction
_____ 6. organic compounds that partially dissociate in aqueous solution to give a carboxylate ion and a hydrogen ion	**f.** fermentation
_____ 7. the production of ethanol from sugars by the action of yeast or bacteria	**g.** functional group
_____ 8. a large molecule formed by the covalent bonding of repeating smaller molecules	**h.** alkyl halide
_____ 9. a type of organic reaction in which an atom or group of atoms is replaced by another atom or group of atoms	**i.** hydroxyl group
_____ 10. oxidation products of secondary alcohols	**j.** addition reaction

B. Multiple Choice

Choose the best answer and write its letter on the line.

_____ 11. The chemical reactions of organic compounds are largely determined by
  a. the physical state of the compound.
  b. the type of bonding within the compound.
  c. the identity of the functional group(s) within the compound.
  d. whether the compound is saturated or unsaturated.

_____ 12. What is the type of reaction illustrated by the following?

$$CH_3-CH_2-CH_2-OH + HBr \rightarrow CH_3-CH_2-CH_2-Br + H_2O$$

    a. substitution   **c.** hydrogenation
    b. addition   **d.** oxidation

_____ 13. The name of the organic reactant in question 12 is

    a. propanoic acid.   **c.** propyl ether.
    b. 1-propanol.   **d.** propanone.

_____ 14. The compound $CH_3-CH_2-CH_2-CH_2-\overset{\displaystyle OH}{\underset{\displaystyle CH_3}{\overset{|}{\underset{|}{C}}}}-CH_3$ is an example of

    a. a primary alcohol.   **c.** a tertiary alcohol.
    b. a secondary alcohol.   **d.** a carboxylic acid.

_____ 15. Which of the following is true about alcohols?

    a. All alcohols are soluble in water in all proportions.
    b. Alcohols boil at lower temperatures than alkanes containing
        comparable numbers of atoms.
    c. Alcohols are capable of intermolecular hydrogen bonding.
    d. all of the above

_____ 16. To which of the following should water be added in order to produce
4-methyl-2-pentanol?

    a. 4-methyl-1-pentene   **c.** either a or b
    b. 4-methyl-2-pentene   **d.** neither a nor b

_____ 17. The compound 1,2-dichloropropane could be produced from a
reaction between

    a. propane and hydrogen chloride.   **c.** propane and chlorine.
    b. propene and hydrogen chloride.   **d.** propene and chlorine.

_____ 18. Isopropyl alcohol is also known as

    a. 1-propanol.   **c.** rubbing alcohol.
    b. 2-propanol.   **d.** both b and c

_____ 19. The compound $CH_3-O-CH_2-CH_2-CH_2-CH_3$ is

    a. 1-pentanol.   **c.** butylmethyl ether.
    b. pentanone.   **d.** 1-pentanoic acid.

_____ 20. Which group among the following includes flavoring agents such as
almond, cinnamon, and vanilla?

    a. alcohols   **c.** halocarbons
    b. aldehydes   **d.** carboxylic acids

_____ 21. The compound $CH_3-CH_2-CH_2-CH_2-CH_2-COOH$ is

    a. hexanal.   **c.** hexanoic acid.
    b. 1-hexanol.   **d.** hexanone.

_____ 22. The IUPAC name for acetic acid is

    a. methanoic acid.   **c.** propanoic acid.
    b. ethanoic acid.   **d.** butanoic acid.

_____ **23.** Which of the following could result from the oxidation of propane?
      a. propene.   **c.** propanol.
      b. propyne.   **d.** all of the above

_____ **24.** The hydrogenation of butene results in the production of
      a. butane.   **c.** butanol.
      b. butyne.   **d.** butanoic acid.

_____ **25.** Which of the following is true about esters?
      a. They are derivatives of carboxylic acids.
      b. They can be detected by Fehling's reagent.
      c. They form intermolecular hydrogen bonds.
      d. all of the above

_____ **26.** Which of the following reactions could be used to synthesize
1,2-dibromopropane?
      a. $CH_3CH_2CH_3 + HCl \rightarrow$ **c.** $CH_2{=}CHCH_3 + Br_2 \rightarrow$
      b. propene $+ Cl_2 \rightarrow$ **d.** $CH_2{=}CHCH_3 + HBr \rightarrow$

_____ **27.** What product is formed from the following reaction?

$$CH_3CH_2CH_2OH \xrightarrow[\text{H}_2\text{SO}_4]{\text{K}_2\text{Cr}_2\text{O}_7}$$

      a. butyraldehyde   **c.** propanal
      b. ethanoic acid   **d.** propane

_____ **28.** Hydrogenation
      a. is the same as dehydrogenation.
      b. can be classified as a reduction reaction.
      c. can be classified as an oxidation reaction.
      d. is the addition of a water molecule to the double bond of a carbon
          compound.

C. Problems

Solve the following problems in the space provided. Show your work.

29. Name each of the following organic compounds.

   a.

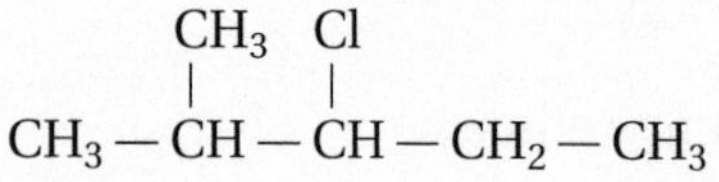

$$CH_3 - \overset{\overset{\displaystyle CH_3}{|}}{CH} - \overset{\overset{\displaystyle Cl}{|}}{CH} - CH_2 - CH_3$$

_____

   b.

$$CH_3 - \overset{\overset{\displaystyle CH_3}{|}}{CH} - \underset{\underset{\displaystyle OH}{|}}{\overset{\overset{\displaystyle CH_3}{|}}{C}} - CH_3$$

_____

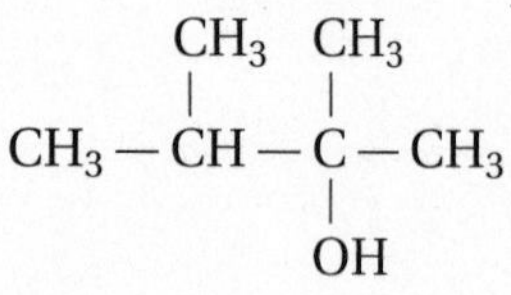

Name ______________________ Date ______________ Class ______________

c. $CH_3-CH_2-CH_2-\overset{\overset{\displaystyle O}{\|}}{C}-H$

____

d. $CH_3-\overset{\overset{\displaystyle O}{\|}}{C}-CH_2-CH_2-CH_2-CH_3$

____

e. $CH_3-\overset{\overset{\displaystyle O}{\|}}{C}-O-CH_2-CH_2-CH_3$

____

30. Identify the type of compound indicated by each of the following general structures.

a. $R-\overset{\overset{\displaystyle O}{\|}}{C}-H$

____

b. $R-\overset{\overset{\displaystyle O}{\|}}{C}-O-R$

____

c. $R-OH$

____

d. $R-\overset{\overset{\displaystyle O}{\|}}{C}-OH$

____

e. $R-O-R$

____

f. $R-\overset{\overset{\displaystyle O}{\|}}{C}-R$

____

31. Use condensed structural formulas to write balanced equations for the following reactions.

a. ethyl iodide + potassium hydroxide →

b. 3-heptene + hydrogen bromide →

c. benzene + iodine →

Name ______________________ Date __________________ Class __________________

D. Essay

Write a short essay for the following.

32. Ethylene glycol (1,2-ethandiol) is the principal ingredient of antifreeze. What properties of this substance account for its use for this purpose? How does its presence in the radiator of a car provide both winter and summer protection?

____

____

____

____

QUICK LAB: Testing for an Aldehyde

Laboratory Recordsheet   Use with Section 23.3

PURPOSE

To distinguish an aldehyde from an alcohol or a ketone, using Tollens's reagent.

MATERIALS

- 1*M* sodium hydroxide
- 6*M* aqueous ammonia
- 5% silver nitrate
- 4 small test tubes
- test-tube rack
- plastic eyedroppers
- methanal
- propanone
- ethanol

PROCEDURE

1. Add 1 drop of 1*M* sodium hydroxide to 2 mL of 5% silver nitrate in a test tube. Add 6*M* aqueous ammonia drop by drop, shaking after each addition until the brownish precipitate dissolves. This will be your Tollens's reagent.

2. Place 10 drops of Tollens's reagent in each of three clean, labeled test tubes.

3. To test tube 1, add 2 drops of methanal solution. To test tube 2, add 2 drops of propanone. To test tube 3, add 2 drops of ethanol. Shake the test tubes to mix the contents.

4. Observe the test tubes, leaving them undisturbed for at least 5 minutes.

ANALYSES AND CONCLUSIONS

1. What evidence of a chemical reaction did you observe in test tube 1? In test tube 2? In test tube 3?

_____

_____

_____

_____

Name ______________________ Date ________________ Class ________________

2. Write the equation for any chemical reaction you observed.

____

____

____

____

3. If you observed a chemical reaction in one or more of the test tubes, what practical uses might the reaction have?

____

____

____

SMALL-SCALE LAB: Polymers

Laboratory Recordsheet   Use with Section 23.4

SAFETY 🦺👤

Wear safety glasses and follow the standard safety procedures outlined on page 7 of this manual.

PURPOSE

To cross-link some polymers and examine their properties.

MATERIALS

- $3\frac{1}{2}$-oz plastic cup
- plastic spoon
- soda straw
- powdered guar gum
- pipet
- 4% borax solution

PROCEDURE

1. Half fill a $3\frac{1}{2}$-oz cup with water.

2. Use a soda straw as a measuring scoop to obtain approximately 2 cm of powdered guar gum. Gently sprinkle the guar gum powder into the water while stirring with a plastic spoon. Add the guar gum powder slowly to prevent it from clumping. Stir the mixture well.

3. While stirring, add one full pipet (about 4 mL) of borax solution. Continue to stir until a change occurs.

ANALYZE

Using your experimental data, record the answers to the following questions.

1. Describe the polymer you just made. Is it a liquid or a solid? What special characteristics does it have?

   _____

   _____

   _____

   _____

   _____

2. Guar gum is a carbohydrate, or a polymer with many repeating alcohol functional groups (—OH). Draw a zig-zag line to represent a crude polymer chain.

3. Add —OH groups along the chain to represent the alcohol functional groups.

4. Borate ions combine with alcohol to form water and borate complexes of the alcohol.

$$\begin{array}{ccc}
\text{HO}\diagdown\quad\diagup\text{OH} & & \text{HO}\diagdown\quad\diagup\text{OH} \\
\quad\text{B}^- & +\ \text{R}-\text{OH}\ \longrightarrow & \quad\text{B}^- \qquad +\ \text{HOH} \\
{}^-\text{O}\diagup\quad\diagdown\text{OH} & & {}^-\text{O}\diagup\quad\diagdown\text{OR}
\end{array}$$

Write a similar equation that replaces all of the —OH groups on the borate with —OR groups.

5. If two polymer chains each contain two nearby —OH groups, borate will cross-link the polymer chains by forming a complex with two alcohols on each chain. Draw a structure similar to the one you drew for question 4, but replace your four R groups with two polymer chains.

YOU'RE THE CHEMIST

Use the space below to write your observations to the small-scale activities in the *You're the Chemist* section.

_____

_____

_____

_____

_____

_____

_____

_____

_____

_____

_____

_____

_____

_____

_____

_____

_____

_____

_____

_____

_____

_____

_____

_____

_____

_____

_____

_____

_____

Name _____ Date _____ Class _____

A STRATEGY FOR LIFE

Section Review

Objectives
- Identify the fundamental units of life
- Describe how organisms get energy for their needs

Vocabulary
- photosynthesis

Key Equations
- Photosynthesis:

$$6CO_2 + 6H_2O + Energy \rightarrow C_6H_{12}O_6 + 6O_2$$

Carbon   Water   from   Glucose   Oxygen
dioxide   sunlight

- Energy used by cells:

$$C_6H_{12}O_6 + 6O_2 \rightarrow 6CO_2 + 6H_2O + Energy$$

Glucose   Oxygen   Carbon   Water
                    dioxide

Part A Completion

Use this completion exercise to check your understanding of the concepts and terms that are introduced in this section. Each blank can be completed with a term, short phrase, or number.

Two major cell designs occur in nature: __1__ cells and

__2__ cells. The cells of __3__ are prokaryotic, and the cells of

other organisms including __4__ and animals are eukaryotic.

Eukaryotic cells are easily distinguished from prokaryotic cells by

the presence of small membrane-enclosed structures called

__5__, which are located in the interior of the cell. These

structures are the sites of many specialized functions in eukaryotic

cells. __6__ are the source of cellular energy, __7__ are sites

for the digestion of substances taken into the cell, and the __8__

contains genetic materials necessary for reproducing the cell.

1. _____

2. _____

3. _____

4. _____

5. _____

6. _____

7. _____

8. _____

Organisms must have energy to survive. ___9___ is directly or   9. _____

indirectly the source of all energy obtained by organisms. ___10___   10. _____

is the process by which cells directly capture and use solar energy   11. _____

to reduce carbon dioxide to sugar compounds. Photosynthetic

organisms produce the ___11___ found in Earth's atmosphere.

Part B True-False

Classify each of these statements as always true, AT; sometimes true, ST; or never true, NT.

_____ 12. Examination of fossilized remains indicates that eukaryotic cells
appeared on Earth before prokaryotic cells.

_____ 13. Photosynthesis is the process by which cells capture and use solar energy
to make chemical energy.

_____ 14. Ribosomes are the sites in the cell where proteins are made.

_____ 15. To carry out photosynthesis, cells require carbon dioxide and water.

_____ 16. Oxygen is produced when animals oxidize the nutrients produced by
plants.

Part C Matching

Match each description in Column B to the correct term in Column A.

Column A

_____ 17. chloroplast

_____ 18. prokaryotic cells

_____ 19. carbon cycle

_____ 20. eukaryotic cell

Column B

a. the movement of carbon through the environment
between photosynthetic organisms and animals

b. specialized organelle that contains a light-harvesting
system to convert solar energy into chemical energy

c. cells of bacteria

d. a cell that has a nucleus and membrane-bound
organelles

Part D Question

Answer the following in the space provided.

21. Plant cells contain chloroplasts and mitochondria. Why would plant cells
require both types of organelles?

_____

Name _____ Date _____ Class _____

24.2 CARBOHYDRATES

Section Review

Objectives

- Describe the structural characteristics of carbohydrates
- Explain how glucose polymers form

Vocabulary

- carbohydrates
- monosaccharides
- disaccharides
- polysaccharides

Part A Completion

Use this completion exercise to check your understanding of the concepts and terms that are introduced in this section. Each blank can be completed with a term, short phrase, or number.

____1____ are monomers and polymers of aldehydes and ketones that have numerous hydroxy groups attached. In animals and plants, carbohydrates function as ____2____ reserves. Plants also utilize some forms of carbohydrate, such as ____3____, to provide structural rigidity and form. The simplest carbohydrates are called ____4____, or simple sugars. Carbohydrates formed from the joining of two simple sugars are called ____5____. When many sugar monomers polymerize, the resulting carbohydrate is referred to as a ____6____.

Two types of carbohydrates produced by plants are ____7____ and cellulose. Starch and cellulose are polymers of ____8____.

____9____ is the major storage form of carbohydrates in animals. Animals store carbohydrate reserves in the muscles and ____10____.

1. _____

2. _____

3. _____

4. _____

5. _____

6. _____

7. _____

8. _____

9. _____

10. _____

Part B True-False

Classify each of these statements as always true, AT; sometimes true, ST; or never true, NT.

_____ **11.** Two well-known polysaccharides are glucose and fructose.

_____ **12.** Fructose is a polyhydroxy ketone.

_____ **13.** In aqueous solution, the straight-chain and cyclic forms of glucose exist in dynamic equilibrium.

_____ **14.** Glucose and fructose can react by means of a condensation reaction to form sucrose.

_____ **15.** Carbohydrates are soluble in water.

Part C Matching

Match each description in Column B to the correct term in Column A.

Column A

_____ **16.** carbohydrates

_____ **17.** disaccharide

_____ **18.** glucose

_____ **19.** fructose

_____ **20.** starch

Column B

a. a simple sugar that occurs in a large number of fruits and honey

b. sucrose

c. a monosaccharide that can polymerize to form starch

d. a carbohydrate produced and stored by plants

e. monomers and polymers of polyhydroxy aldehydes and polyhydroxy ketones

Part D Questions

Answer the following in the space provided.

21. What are the major functions of carbohydrates in plants?

_____

_____

_____

22. What monosaccharides are obtained by the hydrolysis of sucrose?

_____

23. What functional group is present in all carbohydrates?

_____

24.3 AMINO ACIDS AND THEIR POLYMERS

Section Review

Objectives

- Describe the structure of an amino acid
- Distinguish between peptides and proteins
- Explain how enzymes affect biochemical reactions

Vocabulary

- amino acid
- peptide
- peptide bond
- protein
- enzymes
- substrates
- active site

Part A Completion

Use this completion exercise to check your understanding of the concepts and terms that are introduced in this section. Each blank can be completed with a term, short phrase, or number.

An ____1____ is any compound that contains amino and
carboxylic acid groups in the same molecule. The amino acids
commonly found in nature consist of a carboxyl group, an
amino group, a hydrogen atom, and a ____2____ covalently bonded
to a central carbon atom. The chemical nature of the ____3____
accounts for the differences in properties of the standard set of 20
naturally occurring amino acids.

Two amino acids can react to form a ____4____. In this reaction,
the carboxyl group of one amino acid combines with the amino
group from the other amino acid to form a ____5____ bond and a
molecule of ____6____. When the number of amino acids joined
together in one continuous chain exceeds 100, the resulting
polypeptide is called a ____7____.

In cells, proteins often function as ____8____. Proteins that
catalyze biological reactions are generally referred to as ____9____.

1. _____

2. _____

3. _____

4. _____

5. _____

6. _____

7. _____

8. _____

9. _____

Part B True-False

Classify each of these statements as always true, AT; sometimes true, ST; or never true, NT.

_____ **10.** The side chains of amino acids are nonpolar.

_____ **11.** The majority of naturally occurring amino acids are right-handed stereo isomers.

_____ **12.** The order in which the amino acids of a peptide molecule are linked is called the amino acid sequence.

_____ **13.** Proteins have a characteristic three-dimensional shape that is determined by the interactions between the amino acids in the protein.

Part C Matching

Match each description in Column B to the correct term in Column A.

Column A

_____ **14.** enzyme–substrate complex

_____ **15.** coenzyme

_____ **16.** substrate

Column B

a. a metal ion or small molecule that must be present for a catalyzed reaction to occur

b. the structure that forms when a molecule attaches to an active site of an enzyme

c. a molecule on which an enzyme acts

Part D Problem

Answer the following in the space provided.

17. The formula of aspartame (Nutra-Sweet®) is shown below. Aspartame is a dipeptide of phenylalanine and aspartic acid. Identify (1) the central carbons, (2) the side-chain groups, (3) the peptide bond, (4) the free amino end of the dipeptide, and (5) the free carboxyl end of the dipeptide. (Note that the free carboxyl group of phenylalanine is modified to a methyl ester in aspartame.)

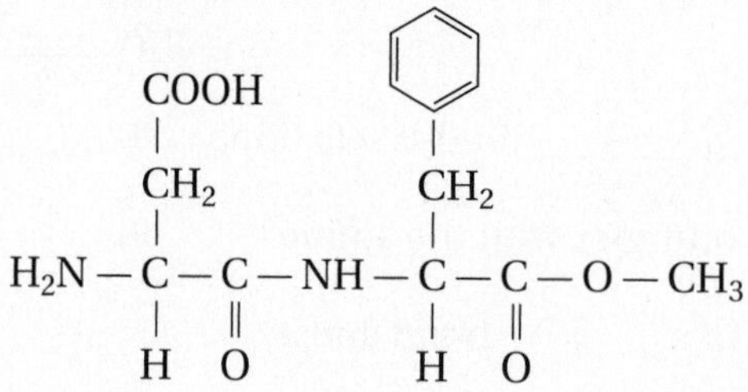

$$\begin{array}{ccccccc}
COOH & & & & & & \\
| & & & & & & \\
CH_2 & & & & CH_2 & & \\
| & & & & | & & \\
H_2N-C-C-NH-C-C-O-CH_3 \\
| \quad \| & & \quad | \quad \| \\
H \quad O & & \quad H \quad O
\end{array}$$

24.4 LIPIDS

Section Review

Objectives

- Distinguish lipids from other classes of biological molecules
- Describe the structure of a lipid bilayer

Vocabulary

- lipids
- triglycerides
- saponification
- phospholipids
- waxes

Part A Completion

Use this completion exercise to check your understanding of the concepts and terms that are introduced in this section. Each blank can be completed with a term, short phrase, or number.

Fats, oils, and waxes are members of the ___1___ family of

biological molecules. Compared to most carbohydrates and

proteins, lipids are generally ___2___ in aqueous solvents. Fats and

oils occur naturally as mixtures of ___3___, which are triesters of

glycerol with long-chain carboxylic acids. ___4___ are important

as the long-term storage form of energy in the body.

___5___, a process used to make soap, involves the hydrolysis

of triglycerides with an alkali metal hydroxide. The products of the

reaction are alkali metal salts of fatty acids, or soaps, and ___6___.

___7___ are lipids that contain phosphate groups. This class of

lipids is unique in that the "head" of the molecule is ___8___ and

the "tails" are ___9___. These dipolar features promote the

spontaneous clustering of phospholipid molecules to form a

___10___ in aqueous solution. ___11___ consist primarily of lipid bilayers.

1. _____
2. _____
3. _____
4. _____
5. _____
6. _____
7. _____
8. _____
9. _____
10. _____
11. _____

Part B True-False

Classify each of these statements as always true, AT; sometimes true, ST; or never true, NT.

_____ **12.** Sodium stearate can be classified as a soap.

_____ **13.** In a typical lipid bilayer of a cell membrane, the vast majority of the phospholipids are oriented so that their phosphate groups do not have contact with water.

_____ **14.** Waxes are esters of long-chain fatty acids and long-chain alcohols.

_____ **15.** Fats and oils tend to dissolve readily in nonpolar solvents.

_____ **16.** Enzymes are bound to the interior surface of cell membranes.

Part C Matching

Match each description in Column B to the correct term in Column A.

Column A	Column B
_____ **17.** saponification	**a.** components of the cell membrane that help ferry nutrients across the lipid bilayer
_____ **18.** triglycerides	**b.** triesters of glycerol and long-chain carboxylic acids
_____ **19.** phospholipids	**c.** lipids that contain phosphate groups
_____ **20.** membrane proteins	**d.** the hydrolysis of triglycerides with an alkali metal hydroxide

Part D Questions

Answer the following in the space provided.

21. What are some of the functions of waxes in plants and animals?

_____

_____

_____

22. What physical features do soaps and phospholipids have in common?

_____

_____

_____

24.5 NUCLEIC ACIDS

Section Review

Objectives

- Identify the structural components of nucleic acids
- Explain how information is coded in genetic material and how it can be affected by mutations
- Describe recombinant DNA technology

Vocabulary

- nucleic acids
- nucleotides
- gene

Part A Completion

Use this completion exercise to check your understanding of the concepts and terms that are introduced in this section. Each blank can be completed with a term, short phrase, or number.

Nucleic acids are nitrogen-containing polymers in which the repeating unit is a ___1___. Two kinds of nucleic acids are found in cells—___2___ (DNA) and ___3___ (RNA). DNA carries the information needed to make ___4___ and governs the reproduction and growth of cells. The nucleotide monomers that make up DNA and RNA consist of a phosphate group, a five-carbon sugar, and a ___5___. There are four types of nitrogen bases found in DNA— ___6___, ___7___, ___8___, and ___9___. In RNA, the base thymine is replaced by ___10___.

DNA has a double-stranded structure referred to as a ___11___. This structure is stabilized by the formation of ___12___ between opposing nitrogen bases. Typically, in the double helix, adenine pairs with ___13___, and guanine pairs with ___14___.

1. _____

2. _____

3. _____

4. _____

5. _____

6. _____

7. _____

8. _____

9. _____

10. _____

11. _____

12. _____

13. _____

14. _____

Part B True-False

Classify each of these statements as always true, AT; sometimes true, ST; or never true, NT.

_____ **15.** A gene is a segment of DNA that codes for one kind of protein.

_____ **16.** The genetic code is a set of 61 triplet code words used to specify amino acids in protein synthesis plus three triplet code words that signal "stop" when a protein has been synthesized.

_____ **17.** Gene mutations are beneficial to the survival of an organism.

_____ **18.** Except for identical twins, the base sequences of DNA are different for different individuals.

Part C Matching

Match each description in Column B to the correct term in Column A.

Column A	Column B
_____ **19.** nucleic acids	**a.** a DNA chain produced in the laboratory by breaking apart and recombining DNA chains from different organisms
_____ **20.** DNA fingerprint	**b.** a polymer of ribonucleotides or deoxyribonucleotides found primarily in cell nuclei
_____ **21.** clone	**c.** an exact duplication of an organism's DNA and, therefore, of an organism's characteristics
_____ **22.** recombinant DNA	**d.** one of the monomers that make up DNA and RNA
_____ **23.** nucleotide	**e.** the band patterns that form when DNA fragments—obtained when enzymes catalyze the cutting of DNA chains—are separated and visualized in the laboratory

Part D Question

Answer the following question in the space provided.

24. What are DNA mutations and how do they affect proteins? Give an example of one type of DNA mutation.

_____

_____

_____

_____

24.6 METABOLISM

Section Review

Objectives

- Explain the function of ATP in living cells
- Distinguish between catabolism and anabolism
- Explain the nitrogen cycle

Vocabulary

- adenosine triphosphate
- metabolism
- catabolism
- anabolism

Part A Completion

Use this completion exercise to check your understanding of the concepts and terms that are introduced in this section. Each blank can be completed with a term, short phrase, or number.

____1____ is the primary energy-storing molecule found in cells of all organisms. ATP is formed when a molecule of ____2____ condenses with a molecule of phosphoric acid. The energy needed to phosphorylate ADP comes from the energy released by the ____3____ of higher-energy compounds.

Every mole of ATP hydrolyzed back to ADP releases about ____4____ of energy. Cells use this energy to drive processes that would ordinarily be ____5____. ATP is used to transmit energy between ____6____ reactions and ____7____ reactions in the cell. Because cellular ____8____ never stops, the cycle of producing and breaking down ATP occurs continuously.

The set of reactions in living cells in which substances are broken down and energy is produced is called ____9____. The set of reactions in which the simple compounds produced by catabolism are used to synthesize more complex molecules is called ____10____.

1. _____

2. _____

3. _____

4. _____

5. _____

6. _____

7. _____

8. _____

9. _____

10. _____

Part B True-False

Classify each of these statements as always true, AT; sometimes true, ST; or never true, NT.

_____ **11.** The complete oxidation of glucose to carbon dioxide and water is one of the most important catabolic reactions in the cell.

_____ **12.** Metabolism is the sum of the enzyme-catalyzed chemical and energy changes that occur in cells.

_____ **13.** Anabolic reactions produce energy.

_____ **14.** Adenosine triphosphate (ATP) is a ribonucleotide.

_____ **15.** ATP has less potential chemical energy than ADP.

Part C Matching

Match each description in Column B to the correct term in Column A.

Column A

_____ **16.** catabolism

_____ **17.** metabolism

_____ **18.** anabolism

_____ **19.** ATP

Column B

a. an energy-storing molecule used to drive anabolic processes in the cell

b. the set of all chemical reactions that occur within a living organism

c. reactions in which simple molecules are used to synthesize more complex molecules

d. energy-yielding reactions in which larger molecules are degraded to smaller molecules

Part D Question

Answer the following question in the space provided.

20. Many reactions associated with the growth and replication of cells in living organisms are nonspontaneous. How are these reactions driven forward?

_____

_____

_____

_____

24 INTERPRETING GRAPHICS

Use with Section 24.6

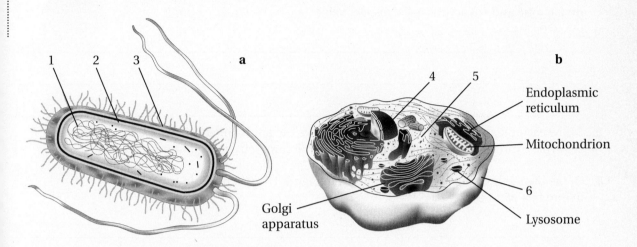

Figure 1. Comparison of prokaryotic and eukaryotic cell structure.

In Section 24.1, you learned that cells are the fundamental units of life. All organisms are made of one or more cells; even the largest organisms on Earth begin life as a single cell. Every living cell carries the information needed to make an exact copy of itself. Cells vary in shape and size. The shape, size, and internal structure of a cell is related to its function.

Part A

Match each of the numbered components in Figures 1a and 1b with the correct term on the right. Some terms may be used more than once.

1. _____   cell wall

2. _____   cytoplasm

3. _____   nucleus

4. _____   cell membrane

5. _____

6. _____

Name _____ Date _____ Class _____

Part B

Answer the following in the space provided.

1. Which of the diagrams in Figure 1 represents a prokaryotic cell? Which represents a eukayotic cell? Explain. What types of organisms are composed of prokaryotic and eukaryotic cells, respectively?

_____

_____

_____

2. Below each diagram, in the space provided, write the approximate size of each cell type. Express your answers in millimeters, micrometers, and nanometers.

3. Of the organelles labeled in the cell shown in Figure 1b, which would you expect to find in a plant cell?

_____

4. What organelle(s) would you expect to find in plant cells that are not depicted in Figure 1b?

_____

_____

5. In which of the organelles in the eukaryotic cell would you most likely find enzymes associated with the production of ATP?

_____

_____

6. How do you think the number of mitochondria in a skin cell would compare to the number of mitochondria in a heart muscle cell?

_____

_____

7. In this chapter, you have studied four classes of biological molecules essential to all living organisms. Match each class of molecules with the cell structure(s) shown in Figures 1a and 1b. Briefly discuss the function of each class of biochemical molecules.

_____

_____

_____

_____

_____

24 THE CHEMISTRY OF LIFE

Vocabulary Review

Match the correct vocabulary term to each numbered statement. Write the letter of the correct term on the line.

Column A   **Column B**

_____ 1. class of relatively water-insoluble organic compounds of   **a.** saponification
which waxes, fats, and oils are members

_____ 2. protein that catalyzes a chemical reaction in a living   **b.** peptide
organism

_____ 3. any combination of amino acids in which the amino   **c.** lipids
group of one acid is united with the carboxylic acid
group of another

_____ 4. process by which green plants and algae convert radiant   **d.** polysaccharide
energy from the sun into chemical energy

_____ 5. a random change in the sequence of nucleotides in DNA   **e.** active site

_____ 6. a small organic molecule or metal ion necessary for an   **f.** enzyme
enzyme's biological activity

_____ 7. the location in an enzyme molecule into which the   **g.** photosynthesis
substrate of a chemical reaction fits

_____ 8. a polymer of deoxyribonucleotides found primarily in   **h.** coenzyme
the nucleus of a cell

_____ 9. segment of DNA that codes for one kind of protein   **i.** gene

_____ 10. complex carbohydrate formed by the linkage of many   **j.** deoxyribonucleic
monosaccharide monomers   acid

_____ 11. hydrolysis of fats or oils using hot aqueous sodium   **k.** mutation
hydroxide

THE CHEMISTRY OF LIFE

Chapter Quiz

Classify each of these statements as always true, AT; sometimes true, ST; or never true, NT.

_____ **1.** Eukayotic cells are smaller than prokaryotic cells and lack a nucleus and membrane-bound organelles.   *24.1*

_____ **2.** Cell membranes consist of a bilayer of phospholipids with embedded proteins.   *24.4*

_____ **3.** Photosynthesis is the process by which glucose is broken down to yield oxygen and energy.   *24.1*

_____ **4.** Sucrose is a disaccharide composed of glucose and fructose.   *24.2*

_____ **5.** ATP is produced by metabolic reactions in the cell.   *24.6*

Choose the best answer and write its letter on the line.

_____ **6.** The essential structural difference between starch and cellulose is due to   *24.2*

    a. the presence of one extra carbon in each of the monomers that make up starch.
    b. the absence of hydroxy groups in cellulose.
    c. the fact that cellulose is more highly branched.
    d. the orientation of the bond between the glucose units.

_____ **7.** A lipid is a biological molecule that   *24.4*

    a. reacts with acids and bases to produce an aldehyde.
    b. is soluble in nonpolar solvents but relatively insoluble in aqueous solvents.
    c. is soluble in most polar solvents.
    d. contains only carbon and hydrogen.

_____ **8.** How many peptide bonds are formed when the amino acids glutamine, tryptophan, and glycine are joined to form a tripeptide?   *24.3*

    a. one
    b. two
    c. three
    d. four

_____ **9.** Which of the following statements about the 20 common amino acids is *false*?   *24.3*

    a. Some amino acids exist as stereoisomers.
    b. The side-chain groups of some amino acids are nonpolar.
    c. Nearly all the amino acids found in nature are of the left-handed, or L form.
    d. none of the above

24 THE CHEMISTRY OF LIFE

Chapter Test A

A. Matching

*Match each description in Column A to the correct term in Column B. Write the letter
of the correct term on the line.*

	Column A	**Column B**

_____ **1.** a peptide with more than roughly 100 amino acids

    a. enzyme–substrate complex

_____ **2.** any combination of amino acids in which the amino group of one acid is united with the carboxyl group of another

    b. peptide

_____ **3.** a simple carbohydrate molecule

    c. lipids

_____ **4.** proteins that act as biological catalysts

    d. phospholipid

_____ **5.** a class of relatively water-insoluble compounds that includes fats, oils, and waxes

    e. protein

_____ **6.** a carbohydrate produced and stored by plants

    f. starch

_____ **7.** a weak association of an enzyme and its substrate necessary for an enzyme to exert its catalytic activity

    g. monosaccharide

_____ **8.** a complex lipid that is a major component of most cell membranes

    h. prokaryotic

_____ **9.** cell type that does not contain a nucleus or membrane-bound organelles

    i. enzymes

_____ **10.** process by which green plants and algae convert radiant energy from the sun into chemical energy

    j. photosynthesis

B. Multiple Choice

Choose the best answer and write its letter on the line.

_____ **11.** Proteins that act as catalysts are called:
    a. substrates.
    b. nucleic acids.
    c. peptides.
    d. enzymes.

_____ **12.** Proteins are
    a. polyesters.
    b. polypeptides.
    c. polyacetals.
    d. polyamines.

_____ 13. Base-pairing in DNA involves
  a. an acid–base reaction.   c. covalent bonds.
  b. hydrogen bonds.   d. ionic bonds.

_____ 14. A typical nucleotide is composed of
  a. base + sugar + triglyceride.   c. base + phosphate + ester.
  b. sugar + phosphate + enzyme.   d. phosphate + sugar + base.

_____ 15. Starch, table sugar, cotton, and wood are all examples of
  a. aldehydes.   c. lipids.
  b. carbohydrates.   d. proteins.

_____ 16. Which of the following is true about nucleic acids?
  a. They are polymers found primarily in the nuclei of cells.
  b. They are essential in all living things.
  c. The types of nucleic acids that are found in cells are DNA and RNA.
  d. all of the above

_____ 17. The genetic plan for an organism is determined by the order of the
  nitrogen bases in
  a. the DNA of the organism.   c. both a and b
  b. the RNA of the organism.   d. neither a nor b

_____ 18. Which of the following statements about metabolism is correct?
  a. Catabolism includes all reactions in living cells in which small
     molecules are combined to form larger molecules.
  b. Catabolic reactions consume energy.
  c. Anabolism includes all enzyme-catalyzed reactions that acquire
     and use energy.
  d. Anabolic reactions produce energy.

_____ 19. The missing structural unit in the following block diagram for the
  nucleotide deoxyguanosine monophosphate is

  a. phosphate.   c. guanine.
  b. ribose sugar.   d. none of the above

_____ 20. Which of the following compounds are the expected products from
  saponification of the triglyceride tristearin using sodium hydroxide?
  a. potassium stearate and glycerol
  b. sodium stearate and glycerol
  c. mixture of low molar mass esters
  d. carbon dioxide gas and water

_____ 21. Gene mutations
  a. are always harmful and never beneficial.
  b. may result in the synthesis of a faulty protein or no protein at all.
  c. may occur when one or more nucleotides are added to the DNA
     molecule.
  d. both b and c

_____ 22. Which of the following statements about enzymes is not correct?
      a. Enzymes are proteins that act as biological catalysts.
      b. Enzymes do not change the normal equilibrium of a reaction.
      c. Some enzymes require nonprotein coenzymes to catalyze the transformation of biological substrates.
      d. In an enzyme-catalyzed reaction, the substrate never makes contact with the enzyme.

_____ 23. The 20 common amino acids are distinguished from one another by
      a. the location of the amino group.
      b. the presence or absence of a carboxylic acid group.
      c. the chemical nature of the side-chain group.
      d. the number of side-chain groups attached to the central carbon atom.

_____ 24. Which of the following statements about proteins is not correct?
      a. The three-dimensional shape of a protein is unaffected by interactions between the amino acids in its peptide chain.
      b. Protein shape is partly maintained by hydrogen bonds between adjacent parts of the folded chains.
      c. Separate polypeptide chains may be joined into a single protein through covalent bonding between sulfur atoms.
      d. Differences in the biological properties of proteins result from differences in the amino acid sequences of the proteins.

_____ 25. In a DNA sample, 36% of the bases are determined to be thymine. This means that
      a. 64% of the bases are guanine.
      b. 36% of the bases are guanine.
      c. 36% of the bases are adenine.
      d. 64% of the bases are adenine.

C. True-False

Classify each of these statements as always true, AT; sometimes true, ST; or never true, NT.

_____ 26. Recombinant DNA technology makes it possible to produce some human proteins in microorganisms.

_____ 27. Photosynthetic organisms use the energy of the sun to reduce carbon dioxide to glucose.

_____ 28. The amino acid sequence Ala-Trp-Cys-Gly-Phe could be classified as a hexapeptide.

_____ 29. A comparison of DNA fingerprints can be used to identify people.

_____ 30. Enzymes require metal ion cofactors to catalyze the transformation of substrate to product.

_____ 31. Fats and oils are both triesters of glycerol.

_____ **32.** The hydrolysis of sucrose catalyzed by the enzyme *sucrase* is expected to yield glucose only.

_____ **33.** Four nucleotide monomers in a gene arranged in a specific sequence are required to specify one amino acid in a peptide or protein chain.

_____ **34.** Diseases that result from gene mutations are called inborn errors or molecular diseases.

_____ **35.** The flow of genetic information in the cell could be described as follows: DNA → RNA → Protein.

D. Questions and Problems

Answer the following questions and solve the following problems in the space provided.

36. Use Table 24.2 to translate the following DNA sequence into an amino acid sequence.

ACCGCTCGAGAATTGATT

_____

37. a. Write a condensed chemical equation describing the hydrolysis of ATP.

b. Write the expression for the equilibrium constant (K_{eq}) of the hydrolysis of ATP. Given that $\Delta G^0 = -30.5$ kJ/mol for the hydrolysis of ATP to ADP, use $<$ or $>$ to write an inequality to show whether K_{eq} is greater than or less than 1 under standard conditions.

c. Is the hydrolysis of ATP under standard conditions spontaneous or nonspontaneous?

_____

38. Phosphorus and nitrogen are important elements in living organisms. Explain why.

_____

_____

_____

Name ______________________ Date ______________ Class ______________

39. Propose an experiment to test whether an unknown substance isolated from a cell is a lipid or a carbohydrate.

____

____

40. What structural features distinguish a eukaryotic cell from a prokaryotic cell?

____

____

41. Using electron microscopy, scientists have determined that the phospholipid bilayer comprising the cell membrane is 5 to 10 nm thick.

a. What does this result imply about the dimensions of membrane proteins that act as ion-specific channels?

____

____

b. What does this result imply about the approximate length of a phospholipid molecule?

____

____

E. Essay

Write a short essay for the following.

42. What are nucleic acids, and why are they important?

____

____

____

____

____

____

24 THE CHEMISTRY OF LIFE

Chapter Test B

A. Matching

Match each term in Column B to the correct description in Column A. Write the letter of the correct term on the line.

Column A   **Column B**

_____ 1. a class of relatively water-insoluble compounds that includes fats, oils, and waxes   **a.** metabolism

_____ 2. a peptide with more than roughly 100 amino acids   **b.** peptide

_____ 3. a complex carbohydrate formed by the linkage of many monosaccharide monomers   **c.** lipids

_____ 4. proteins that act as biological catalysts   **d.** protein

_____ 5. any combination of amino acids in which the amino group of one acid is united with the carboxylic group of another   **e.** phospholipid

_____ 6. the set of all chemical reactions that occur within a living organism   **f.** enzyme–substrate complex

_____ 7. the weak association of an enzyme and its substrate necessary for an enzyme to exert its catalytic activity   **g.** polysaccharide

_____ 8. a complex lipid that contains a phosphate group and is a major component of most cell membranes   **h.** deoxyribonucleic acid (DNA)

_____ 9. a polymer of deoxyribonucleotides found primarily in the nucleus of a cell   **i.** enzymes

_____ 10. process by which green plants and algae convert radiant energy from the sun into useful chemical energy to synthesize glucose from carbon dioxide and water   **j.** photosynthesis

B. Multiple Choice

Choose the best answer and write its letter on the line.

_____ 11. The two types of nucleic acids found in every living cell are
    a. guanine and thymine.   **c.** DNA and RNA.
    b. starch and cellulose.   **d.** fats and oils.

_____ 12. The source of stored energy for animals is
    a. glucose.   **c.** cellulose.
    b. starch.   **d.** glycogen.

_____ 13. The DNA double-helical structure is stabilized by
        a. a redox reaction.   **c.** covalent bonds.
        b. hydrogen bonds.   **d.** ionic bonds.

_____ 14. The genetic plan for an organism is determined by the order of the nitrogen bases in
        a. the DNA of the organism.   **c.** proteins
        b. the RNA of the organism.   **d.** none of the above

_____ 15. Interferon, urease, HIV protease, and hemoglobin are all examples of
        a. aldehydes.   **c.** lipids.
        b. carbohydrates.   **d.** proteins.

_____ 16. Which of the following is true about nucleic acids?
        a. They are polymers found primarily in the nuclei of cells.
        b. They contain nitrogen and phosphorus.
        c. The types of nucleic acids that are found in cells are DNA and RNA.
        d. all of the above

_____ 17. A typical nucleotide is composed of
        a. base + sugar + triglyceride.   **c.** base + phosphate + ester.
        b. sugar + phosphate + enzyme.   **d.** phosphate + sugar + base.

_____ 18. Which of the following statements about anabolism is correct?
        a. Anabolism includes all reactions in living cells in which substances are broken down.
        b. The energy produced during anabolism is captured in the formation of ATP.
        c. Anabolism includes all reactions in which simple molecules are combined to form larger and more complex molecules.
        d. all of the above

_____ 19. The missing structural unit in the following block diagram for the nucleotide deoxyadenosine monophosphate is

        a. phosphate.   **c.** adenine.
        b. ribose sugar.   **d.** none of the above

_____ 20. Myoglobin could be characterized as
        a. an enzyme that catalyzes the synthesis of urea.
        b. an oxygen-storage protein in muscle tissue.
        c. a lipid found in cell membranes.
        d. an oxygen-carrying protein of blood.

_____ 21. Gene mutations
        a. are always harmful.
        b. may occur when nucleotides are added to a DNA molecule.
        c. may occur when nucleotides are substituted in a DNA molecule.
        d. both b and c

_____ **22.** Which of the following statements about enzymes is not correct?
   a. Enzymes increase the rate of biological reactions.
   b. Enzymes change the normal equilibrium of a reaction.
   c. Each enzyme catalyzes only one reaction.
   d. In an enzymatic reaction, the substrate must make contact with the enzyme.

_____ **23.** The 20 common amino acids are distinguished from one another by
   a. the presence or absence of a peptide bond.
   b. the presence or absence of a hydroxyl group.
   c. the chemical nature of the side-chain group.
   d. the asymmetric nature of the central carbon atom.

_____ **24.** In a DNA sample, 36% of the bases are determined to be thymine. What percentage of the bases are cytosine?
   a. 64%   **c.** 14%
   b. 36%   **d.** 28%

_____ **25.** Which of the following statements about proteins is correct?
   a. The three-dimensional shape of a protein is unaffected by the interactions between the amino acids in its peptide chain.
   b. Proteins are peptides with fewer than 100 amino acids.
   c. Separate polypeptide chains may be joined into a single protein through the hydrogen bonding between sulfur atoms in the side-chain groups of cysteine monomers.
   d. Differences in the biological properties of proteins in a cell result from differences in the amino acid sequences of the proteins.

C. True-False

Classify each of these statements as always true, AT; sometimes true, ST; or never true, NT.

_____ **26.** Cell membranes consist mainly of a carbohydrate bilayer and proteins.

_____ **27.** Waxes are esters of long-chain fatty acids and long-chain alcohols.

_____ **28.** Unlike eukaryotic cells, prokaryotic cells do not have a nucleus.

_____ **29.** Comparing DNA fingerprints can be used to identify people.

_____ **30.** Enzymes require metal ion cofactors to catalyze the transformation of substrate to product.

_____ **31.** Starch, cellulose, and cotton are all examples of carbohydrates.

_____ **32.** The hydrolysis of sucrose catalyzed by the enzyme *sucrase* is expected to yield glucose and fructose.

_____ **33.** Three nucleotide monomers in a gene arranged in a specific sequence are required to specify one amino acid in a peptide or protein chain.

Name _____ Date _____ Class _____

_____ **34.** Atmospheric carbon dioxide is reduced to carbohydrates in photosynthesis.

_____ **35.** The flow of genetic information in the cell could be described as follows: Protein → RNA → DNA.

D. Questions and Problems

Answer the following questions and solve the following problems in the space provided.

36. Use Table 24.2 in your textbook to write the nucleotide base sequence that would code for the tripeptide:

Cys-Gln-Pro-end.

_____

37. The graph below shows the total amount of product formed from a chemical reaction that was carried out at three different enzyme concentrations. The same enzyme was used for each trial. Explain why these results were obtained.

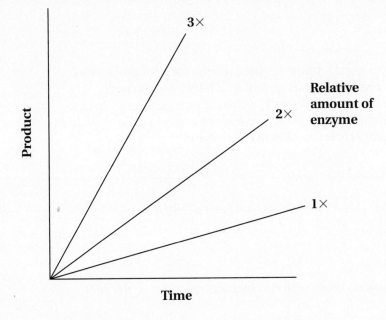

_____

_____

38. Propose an experiment to test whether an unknown substance isolated from a cell is a lipid or a protein.

_____

_____

39. The turnover of ATP in living cells is extremely high. ATP is formed and hydrolyzed continuously. If a person expends 2000 kJ of energy each day, and every mole of ATP hydrolyzed to ADP releases 30.5 kJ, how many kilograms of ATP are consumed during this time period? (molar mass of ATP = 507.2 g)

40. Write the equation for the condensation reaction between alanine and glycine to form a dipeptide.

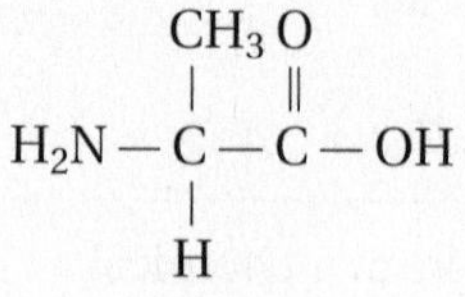

$$
\begin{array}{cc}
\underset{\text{Alanine}}{
\begin{array}{c}
\text{CH}_3\ \ \text{O} \\
|\quad\ \ \| \\
\text{H}_2\text{N}-\text{C}-\text{C}-\text{OH} \\
| \\
\text{H}
\end{array}}
&
\underset{\text{Glycine}}{
\begin{array}{c}
\text{H}\ \ \ \text{O} \\
|\quad\ \ \| \\
\text{H}_2\text{N}-\text{C}-\text{C}-\text{OH} \\
| \\
\text{H}
\end{array}}
\end{array}
$$

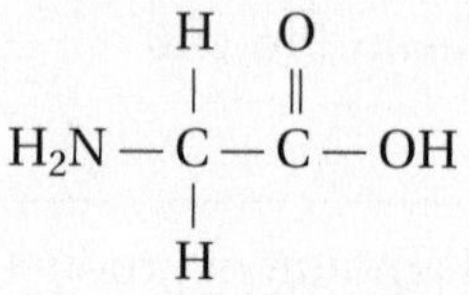

41. According to one theory, general anesthetics used during surgical procedures exert their effects on the central nervous system by altering the physical properties of nerve cell membranes. Typically, substances used as anesthetics are nonpolar, or hydrophobic, compounds. Suggest one reason why nonpolarity might be an important property for an effective anesthetic.

_____

_____

E. Essay

Write a short essay for the following.

42. What are enzymes and how do they facilitate chemical reactions in the cell?

_____

_____

_____

_____

_____

_____

_____

SMALL-SCALE LAB: The Egg: A Biochemical Storehouse

Laboratory Recordsheet   Use with Section 24.3

SAFETY

Use safe and proper laboratory procedures.

PURPOSE

To explore some physical and chemical properties of a chicken egg.

MATERIALS

- chicken egg
- pencil
- paper
- ruler
- balance

PROCEDURE

Obtain a chicken egg. Examine the egg's shape and measure its length and width in centimeters. Measure the mass of the egg. Make an accurate, life-size sketch of your egg and record all your data on the sketch.

ANALYZE

Using your experimental data, record the answers to the following questions below your drawing.

1. A common way to compare the shapes of eggs is by using the shape index. The shape index is the width of an egg expressed as a percentage of its length.

$$\text{Shape index} = \frac{\text{width}}{\text{length}} \times 100$$

Calculate the shape index of your egg.

2. The volume, original mass (when freshly laid), and surface area of an egg can easily be estimated by using the following equations.

$$V = (0.5236)(lw^2) \quad M = (0.5632)(lw^2) \quad A = (3.138)(lw^2)^{2/3}$$

V = volume $\qquad M$ = original mass $\quad A$ = surface area
l = length $\qquad\quad w$ = width

Use your data to calculate the volume, original mass, and surface area of your egg. Show your work and record your results.

3. Compare your measured mass of the egg with your calculated mass. Which is greater? Suggest why the mass of an egg might change over time.

_____

_____

4. Using your measured mass and calculated volume, calculate the density of your egg. Compare this value with the density of a freshly laid egg ($d = 1.075$ g/cm^3).

YOU'RE THE CHEMIST

Use the space below to write your observations to the small-scale activities in the *You're the Chemist* section.

_____

_____

_____

_____

_____

_____

_____

QUICK LAB: A Model of DNA

Laboratory Recordsheet   Use with Section 24.5

PURPOSE

To construct a model of double-stranded DNA.

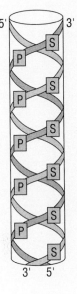

MATERIALS

- cardboard tube from paper-towel roll
- 10 toothpicks
- felt-tip markers (two colors)
- thumbtack
- metric ruler

PROCEDURE

1. The typical tube has a seam that when viewed from one end describes a spiral that moves away from the observer. This spiral is a helix. Outline the spiral seam with a colored marker.

2. Using a different-colored marker, draw a second spiral midway between the lines of the first. These two spirals represent the two strands of double-stranded DNA.

3. Measure along the tube and mark a dot on each spiral every 5 cm. Label each dot with the letter S to indicate a sugar unit. Make a hole in the spirals at each S mark with the thumbtack. Move down each spiral and mark a letter P to indicate a phosphate group halfway between each two S dots.

4. Color each toothpick along half its length with a marker. A toothpick represents a base pair in the DNA molecule.

5. Starting at the top of the tube, insert a toothpick in one hole at an S label and guide it so it emerges through the hole in the S on the opposite side of the tube. Repeat the process for the other holes.

ANALYSES AND CONCLUSIONS

1. Are the bases on the interior or the exterior of the double helix? Are they randomly arranged or neatly stacked?

   _____

   _____

   _____

Name ______________________ Date ________________ Class ________________

2. Are the phosphate groups on the exterior or the interior of the DNA structure?

____

____

3. Are the sugar groups on the interior or the exterior of the DNA molecule?

____

____

25.1 NUCLEAR RADIATION

Section Review

Objectives

- Explain how an unstable nucleus releases energy
- Describe the three main types of nuclear radiation

Vocabulary

- radioisotopes
- radioactivity
- radiation
- alpha particle
- beta particle
- gamma ray

Part A Completion

Use this completion exercise to check your understanding of the concepts and terms that are introduced in this section. Each blank can be completed with a term, short phrase, or number.

Isotopes with unstable nuclei are ___1___ and are called

___2___ . The ___3___ of radioisotopes decay to ___4___ nuclei

plus emission of large amounts of ___5___ . The radiation may

be alpha, ___6___ , or gamma. ___7___ radiation consists of

alpha particles (positively charged ___8___ nuclei) that are easily

stopped by a sheet of paper. Beta radiation is composed of

fast-moving particles, which are ___9___ . Beta radiation is more

penetrating than alpha radiation; it is stopped by ___10___ .

___11___ radiation is electromagnetic radiation. Gamma radiation

has no ___12___ or electrical charge. It is extremely penetrating.

___13___ bricks and ___14___ reduce the intensity of gamma

radiation but do not completely ___15___ it.

1. _____

2. _____

3. _____

4. _____

5. _____

6. _____

7. _____

8. _____

9. _____

10. _____

11. _____

12. _____

13. _____

14. _____

15. _____

Part B True-False

Classify each of these statements as always true, AT; sometimes true, ST; or never true, NT.

_____ **16.** Beta radiation is emitted when a radioisotope decays.

_____ **17.** Gamma radiation has a negative charge

_____ **18.** Gamma radiation is high-energy electromagnetic radiation.

_____ **19.** $^{238}_{92}U + ^{0}_{-1}e \rightarrow ^{239}_{92}U$

_____ **20.** When a beta particle is emitted, the atomic number increases by 1, and the mass number stays the same.

Part C Matching

Match each description in Column B to the correct term in Column A.

Column A	Column B
_____ **21.** radioisotopes	**a.** the process in which an unstable nucleus releases energy by emitting radiation
_____ **22.** radioactive decay	**b.** isotopes that have unstable nuclei and undergo radioactive decay
_____ **23.** gamma ray	**c.** high-energy photon with no mass or electrical charge
_____ **24.** alpha particles	**d.** electrons resulting from the breaking apart of a neutron in an atom
_____ **25.** beta particles	**e.** helium nuclei emitted from a radioactive source

Part D Problems

Answer the following in the space provided.

26. Write nuclear equations for these processes.

    a. The alpha decay of $^{218}_{84}Po$

_____

    b. The beta decay of $^{210}_{82}Pb$

_____

25.2 NUCLEAR TRANSFORMATIONS

Section Review

Objectives

- Describe the type of decay a radioisotope undergoes
- Make calculations that involve half-life
- Explain the two ways transmutations can occur

Vocabulary

- band of stability
- positron
- half-life
- transmutation
- transuranium elements

Part A Completion

Use this completion exercise to check your understanding of the concepts and terms that are introduced in this section. Each blank can be completed with a term, short phrase, or number.

Nuclei that lie outside the ___1___ undergo spontaneous

radioactive decay. Nuclei with too many neutrons undergo

___2___ emission as neutrons are converted to protons. A ___3___

is a particle with a positive charge and the mass of an electron.

Every radioisotope decays at a characteristic ___4___. A

___5___ is the time required for one half of the nuclei in a radio-

isotope to decay. The product nuclei may or may not be ___6___.

Half-lives vary from fractions of a second to ___7___ of years.

The conversion of atoms of one element to atoms of another

is called ___8___. This process can occur by ___9___ or when

particles bombard the nucleus of an atom. All of the elements

with ___10___ above 92 have been ___11___ in nuclear reactors

or accelerators.

1. _____

2. _____

3. _____

4. _____

5. _____

6. _____

7. _____

8. _____

9. _____

10. _____

11. _____

Part B True-False

Classify each of these statements as always true, AT; sometimes true, ST; or never true, NT.

_____ 12. If you start with one mole of a radioisotope, after 10 half-lives, there will
be none of the isotope left.

_____ 13. A radioisotope has a half-life of 12 minutes. After 36 minutes only one
third of the radioactive atoms initially present will remain.

_____ 14. Transuranium elements have atomic numbers greater than 92.

_____ 15. Transmutation reactions occur spontaneously.

_____ 16. Positively charged particles have the mass of an electron.

Part C Matching

Match each description in Column B to the correct term in Column A.

Column A

_____ 17. band of stability

_____ 18. positron

_____ 19. half-life

_____ 20. transmutation

_____ 21. transuranium
elements

Column B

a. conversion of an atom of one element to an atom of
another element

b. time required for one half of the nuclei of a
radioisotope to decay to products

c. region containing stable nuclei in a neutron vs.
proton plot

d. elements with atomic numbers higher than 92

e. particle with the same mass as an electron but with a
positive charge

Part D Questions

Answer the following in the space provided.

22. Sodium-24 has a half-life of 15 hours. How much sodium-24 will remain in an
18.0-g sample after 60 hours?

23. After 42 days, a 2.0-g sample of phosphorus-32 contains only 0.25 g of isotope.
What is the half-life of phosphorus-32?

Name _____ Date _____ Class _____

 25.3 # FISSION AND FUSION OF ATOMIC NUCLEI

Section Review

Objectives

- Describe what happens in a nuclear chain reaction
- Explain the role of water in the storage of spent fuel rods
- Compare and contrast fission and fusion reactions

Vocabulary

- fission
- neutron absorption
- neutron moderation
- fusion

Part A Completion

Use this completion exercise to check your understanding of the concepts and terms that are introduced in this section. Each blank can be completed with a term, short phrase, or number.

Nuclear ___1___ occurs when fissionable isotopes are

bombarded with ___2___. The ___3___ breaks into two fragments

of about the same size, and in the process they release more

neutrons and ___4___.

Neutron ___5___ is the process that reduces the speed of

neutrons. Neutron ___6___ is the process that decreases the

number of slow-moving neutrons. In nuclear ___7___, nuclei

combine to make nuclei of greater ___8___. The sun's ___9___

is produced when ___10___ nuclei fuse to make ___11___ nuclei.

Fusion releases even more energy than fission.

1. _____

2. _____

3. _____

4. _____

5. _____

6. _____

7. _____

8. _____

9. _____

10. _____

11. _____

Part B True-False

Classify each of these statements as always true, AT; sometimes true, ST; or never true, NT.

_____ **12.** Water is used as a moderator in nuclear reactors.

_____ **13.** In nuclear fusion, the nuclei of two large atoms fuse together.

_____ **14.** Moderation of neutrons is used to slow nuclear fission.

_____ **15.** Nuclear fusion can be easily produced under laboratory conditions.

Part C Matching

Match each description in Column B to the correct term in Column A.

Column A	**Column B**

_____ **16.** fission

a. the splitting of an atomic nucleus into smaller fragments

_____ **17.** neutron moderation

b. combination of two nuclei to produce a nucleus of greater mass

_____ **18.** neutron absorption

c. process used to reduce the speed of neutrons

_____ **19.** fusion

d. isotope capable of fission

_____ **20.** uranium-235

e. process used to decrease the number of slow-moving neutrons

Part D Questions and Problems

Answer the following in the space provided.

21. How many neutrons are produced in each of the following fission reactions?

    a. $^{239}_{94}\text{Pu} + ^{1}_{0}n \rightarrow ^{90}_{38}\text{Sr} + ^{147}_{56}\text{Ba} + ?^{1}_{0}n$

    b. $^{235}_{92}\text{U} + ^{1}_{0}n \rightarrow ^{72}_{30}\text{Zn} + ^{160}_{62}\text{Sm} + ?^{1}_{0}n$

22. What is the role in a nuclear reactor of

    a. neutron moderation?

    b. neutron absorption?

25.4 RADIATION IN YOUR LIFE

Section Review

Objectives

- Describe three devices that are used to detect radiation
- List examples of how radioisotopes are used in medicine

Vocabulary

- ionizing radiation
- Geiger counter
- scintillation counter
- film badge
- neutron activation analysis

Part A Completion

Use this completion exercise to check your understanding of the concepts and terms that are introduced in this section. Each blank can be completed with a term, short phrase, or number.

The radiation emitted by radioisotopes is known as ___1___

radiation because of its ability to strip ___2___ from atoms of a

bombarded substance. It is not possible to detect ionizing radiation

with your ___3___.

A ___4___ counter uses a ___5___-filled tube to detect ionizing

radiation. A ___6___ counter uses a phosphor-coated surface to

detect ___7___ types of ionizing radiation.

Radioisotopes have many practical uses. For example, ___8___

is used to detect thyroid problems, while ___9___ is used to detect

skin cancers. ___10___ analysis is a procedure used to detect trace

amounts of elements in samples.

1. _____
2. _____
3. _____
4. _____
5. _____
6. _____
7. _____
8. _____
9. _____
10. _____

Part B True-False

Classify each of these statements as always true, AT; sometimes true, ST; or never true, NT.

_____ 11. The film badge is a personal radiation monitor.

_____ 12. A Geiger counter is the best alpha particle detector.

_____ 13. A scintillation counter is used to detect gamma radiation.

_____ 14. Iodine-131 can detect thyroid problems.

Part C Matching

Match each description in Column B to the correct term in Column A.

Column A	Column B
_____ 15. ionizing radiation	**a.** radiation detector consisting of several layers of photographic film
_____ 16. Geiger counter	**b.** radiation with enough energy to knock electrons off some of the atoms it strikes
_____ 17. scintillation counter	**c.** device that uses a coated surface called a phosphor to detect ionizing radiation
_____ 18. film badge	**d.** procedure used to detect trace amounts of elements in samples
_____ 19. neutron activation analysis	**e.** gas-filled tube used to detect radiation

Part D Questions

Answer the following in the space provided.

20. Which of the following is the best means of monitoring radiation for individuals who work with radioactive material? *Circle the letter of the correct answer.*
    a Geiger counter
    b. film badge
    c. scintillation counter

21. List applications of radioisotopes in research and medicine.

    _____

    _____

    _____

NUCLEAR CHEMISTRY

25

Practice Problems

In your notebook, solve the following problems.

SECTION 25.1 NUCLEAR RADIATION

1. What happens to the mass number and atomic number of an atom that undergoes beta decay?

2. A radioisotope of an element undergoes alpha particle decay. How do the atomic number and mass number of the particle change?

3. Give the composition of the nucleus of the following isotopes.

   a. $^{64}_{28}Ni$ **b.** $^{136}_{53}I$ **c.** $^{195}_{79}Au$

4. Complete each of the following equations.

   a. $^{14}_{6}C \rightarrow \,^{0}_{-1}e \, + \, ?$

   b. $^{241}_{95}Am \rightarrow \,^{4}_{2}He + ?$

   c. $^{16}_{7}N \rightarrow \,^{16}_{8}O + ?$

SECTION 25.2 NUCLEAR TRANSFORMATIONS

1. Write a nuclear equation for the following radioactive processes.

   a. alpha decay of francium-208

   b. electron capture by beryllium-7

   c. beta emission by argon-37

   d. positron emission by fluorine-17

2. Complete the equations for these transmutation reactions.

   a. $^{6}_{3}Li + \,^{1}_{0}n \rightarrow \,^{4}_{2}He + ?$

   b. $^{235}_{92}U + \,^{1}_{0}n \rightarrow ? + \,^{141}_{56}Ba + 3^{1}_{0}n$

   c. $^{27}_{13}Al + \,^{4}_{2}He \rightarrow ? + \,^{1}_{0}n$

   d. $^{235}_{92}U \rightarrow \,^{90}_{38}Sr + ? + \,^{1}_{0}n + 4^{0}_{-1}e$

   e. $^{1}_{0}n + ? \rightarrow \,^{144}_{58}Ce + \,^{90}_{38}Sr + 6^{1}_{0}n + 2^{0}_{-1}e$

3. Polonium-214 has a relatively short half-life of 164 s. How many seconds would it take for 8.0 g of this isotope to decay to 0.25 g?

4. How many days does it take for 16 g of palladium-103 to decay to 1.0 g? The half-life of palladium-103 is 17 days.

5. By approximately what factor would the mass of a sample of copper-66 decrease in 51 minutes? The half-life of copper-66 is 5.10 min.

6. In 5.49 seconds, 1.20 g of argon-35 decay to leave only 0.15 g. What is the half-life of argon-35?

SECTION 25.3 FISSION AND FUSION OF ATOMIC NUCLEI

1. How many free neutrons are produced in each of the following uranium-235 fission reactions?

   a. $^1_0n + ^{235}_{92}U \rightarrow ^{90}_{37}Rb + ^{144}_{55}Cs + ?\,^1_0n$

   b. $^1_0n + ^{235}_{92}U \rightarrow ^{87}_{35}Br + ^{146}_{57}La + ?\,^1_0n$

   c. $^1_0n + ^{235}_{92}U \rightarrow ^{72}_{30}Zn + ^{160}_{62}Sm + ?\,^1_0n$

2. The fission energy of uranium-235 is 2.0×10^7 kcal/g. The heat of combustion of coal is about 8.0 kcal/g. Approximately what mass of coal must be burned to produce the energy released by the fission of 1.0 gram of uranium-235?

3. What is the product of the following fusion reaction?
$$4\,^1_1H + 2\,^0_{-1}e \rightarrow ?$$

SECTION 25.4 RADIATION IN YOUR LIFE

1. How are radioisotopes used to study chemical reactions?

2. What is teletherapy?

25 INTERPRETING GRAPHICS

Use with Section 25.2

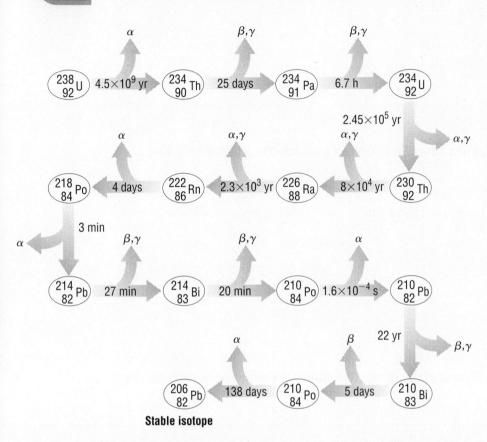

The figure above maps the radioactive decay of uranium-238 to lead-206. Use the figure to answer the following questions.

1. How many alpha particles are produced as one atom of uranium-238 decays to an atom of lead-206?

_____

_____

2. How many beta particles are produced in the sequence in problem 1?

_____

_____

3. How much of a 20-g sample of radon-222 will remain after eight days?

4. How many atoms of a 1.0-mole sample of bismuth-214 will remain after 20 minutes?

5. What product will most of the decayed bismuth-214 atoms form in 20 minutes?

_____

_____

6. How long will it take a 16-g sample of bismuth-210 to decay such that 2.0 g of the element remains?

7. Explain why lead-206 is a stable isotope.

_____

_____

25 NUCLEAR CHEMISTRY

Vocabulary Review

Match the correct vocabulary term to each numbered statement. Write the letter of the correct term on the line.

Column A	Column B

Column A

_____ 1. time required for one half of the nuclei of a radioisotope sample to decay to products

_____ 2. elements in the periodic table with atomic numbers above 92

_____ 3. conversion of an atom of one element to an atom of another element

_____ 4. isotopes that have unstable nuclei and undergo radioactive decay

_____ 5. high-energy photon with no mass or electrical charge

_____ 6. fast-moving electrons released by a radioactive nucleus

_____ 7. the splitting of an atomic nucleus into smaller fragments

_____ 8. gas-filled metal tube used to detect the presence of radiation

_____ 9. positively charged particle consisting of two protons and two neutrons

_____ 10. penetrating rays and particles emitted by a radioactive source

_____ 11. device that uses a coated phosphor surface to detect ionizing radiation

_____ 12. reaction in which two light nuclei combine to form a nucleus of greater mass

Column B

a. radioisotopes

b. half-life

c. Geiger counter

d. beta particles

e. fission

f. radiation

g. transmutation

h. scintillation counter

i. gamma ray

j. fusion

k. alpha particles

l. transuranium elements

25 NUCLEAR CHEMISTRY

Chapter Quiz

Choose the best answer and write its letter on the line.

_____ **1.** Which of these could stop the penetration of an alpha particle? 25.1
   a. the top layer of your skin   **c.** a piece of paper
   b. aluminum foil   **d.** all of the above

_____ **2.** Ionizing radiation that consists of helium nuclei is 25.1
   a. X-rays.   **c.** beta radiation.
   b. alpha radiation.   **d.** gamma radiation.

_____ **3.** The most penetrating form of radiation is 25.1
   a. alpha radiation.   **c.** gamma radiation.
   b. beta radiation   **d.** ultraviolet light.

_____ **4.** When a neutron decomposes, which of the following is formed? 25.1
   a. an alpha particle   **c.** a proton only
   b. a proton and an electron   **d.** a beta particle only

_____ **5.** An unstable nucleus 25.2
   a. may have too many neutrons.
   b. may have too few electrons.
   c. gains energy by emitting radiation.
   d. all of the above

_____ **6.** A reaction in which two light nuclei combine to form a heavier 25.3
   nucleus is termed
   a. fission.   **c.** alpha decay.
   b. a chemical reaction.   **d.** fusion.

_____ **7.** Which of these processes results in a *splitting* of a nucleus? 25.3
   a. a chemical reaction   **c.** a fission reaction
   b. a fusion reaction   **d.** an ionizing reaction

_____ **8.** What particle is needed to complete this nuclear reaction? 25.1
   $^{222}_{86}Rn \rightarrow \,^{218}_{84}Po + \underline{\quad ? \quad}$
   a. $^{0}_{-1}e$ **c.** $^{0}_{+1}e$
   b. $^{4}_{2}He$ **d.** $^{1}_{0}n$

_____ **9.** A transmutation reaction must always involve 25.2
   a. a change in the number of protons in a nucleus of the atom.
   b. a decrease in the number of neutrons in the nucleus of the atom.
   c. an increase in the number of neutrons in the nucleus of the atom.
   d. a decrease in the number of electrons in the atom.

_____ **10.** Controlled nuclear chain reactions 25.3
   a. take place in nuclear reactors.
   b. are always fusion reactions.
   c. never produce radioactive by-products.
   d. are characteristic of atomic bombs.

25 NUCLEAR CHEMISTRY

Chapter Test A

A. Matching

Match each term in Column B to the correct description in Column A. Write the letter of the correct term on the line.

Column A	Column B
_____ 1. a fast-moving electron formed by the decomposition of a neutron	**a.** beta particle
_____ 2. uses a phosphor to detect radiation	**b.** half-life
_____ 3. an element that has an atomic number above 92	**c.** gamma radiation
_____ 4. the most penetrating radiation	**d.** Geiger counter
_____ 5. a particle that has two protons and two neutrons	**e.** film badge
_____ 6. several layers of photographic film covered with black light-proof paper encased in a plastic or metal holder	**f.** ionizing radiation
_____ 7. uses a gas-filled metal tube to detect radiation	**g.** transuranium element
_____ 8. knocks electrons off some atoms of the bombarded substance to produce ions	**h.** radiation
_____ 9. the penetrating rays emitted by a radioactive source	**i.** scintillation counter
_____ 10. the time required for one-half of the atoms of a radioisotope to emit radiation and to decay to products	**j.** alpha particle

B. Multiple Choice

Choose the best answer and write its letter on the line.

_____ 11. Electromagnetic radiation includes
    a. alpha particles and X-rays.
    b. gamma rays and X-rays.
    c. beta particles and gamma rays.
    d. gamma rays and alpha particles

_____ 12. A radioisotope commonly used to detect thyroid problems is
    a. U-235.   **c.** I-131.
    b. Co-60.   **d.** C-14.

_____ **13.** Which of the following is *not* true concerning an alpha particle?
- **a.** It has a mass of 4 amu.
- **b.** It has a 1+ charge.
- **c.** It is a helium nucleus.
- **d.** It contains two neutrons.

_____ **14.** Ionizing radiation that is negatively charged is
- **a.** alpha radiation.
- **b.** beta radiation.
- **c.** gamma radiation.
- **d.** X-rays.

_____ **15.** Which type of ionizing radiation can be blocked by clothing?
- **a.** alpha particle
- **b.** gamma radiation
- **c.** X-radiation
- **d.** beta particle

_____ **16.** The production of carbon-14
- **a.** occurs to a large extent in nuclear reactors.
- **b.** is mostly due to fallout from nuclear explosions.
- **c.** takes place in the upper atmosphere.
- **d.** occurs during photosynthesis in plants.

_____ **17.** Which of these naturally occurring radioisotopes would be most useful in dating objects thought to be millions of year old?
- **a.** carbon-14, $t_{1/2} = 5.73 \times 10^3$ years
- **b.** potassium-40, $t_{1/2} = 1.28 \times 10^9$ years
- **c.** thorium-234, $t_{1/2} = 25$ days
- **d.** radon-222, $t_{1/2} = 3.8$ days

_____ **18.** A piece of wood found in an ancient burial mound contains one-fourth as much carbon-14 as a piece of wood cut from a living tree growing nearby. If the half-life ($t_{1/2}$) for carbon-14 is 5730 years, what is the approximate age of the ancient wood?
- **a.** 1432.5 years
- **b.** 2865 years
- **c.** 5730 years
- **d.** 11,460 years

_____ **19.** If an isotope undergoes beta emission
- **a.** the mass number changes.
- **b.** the atomic number changes.
- **c.** the atomic number remains the same.
- **d.** the number of neutrons remains the same.

_____ **20.** Which of the following particles is needed to complete this nuclear equation?

$$^{55}_{25}\text{Mn} + {}^{2}_{1}\text{H} \rightarrow \underline{\quad ? \quad} + 2\,{}^{1}_{0}n$$

- **a.** $^{56}_{27}\text{Co}$
- **b.** $^{57}_{26}\text{Fe}$
- **c.** $^{55}_{26}\text{Fe}$
- **d.** $^{58}_{24}\text{Cr}$

_____ **21.** Which of the following statements is correct?
- **a.** Water is used to moderate (slow down) neutrons in a nuclear reactor.
- **b.** Carbon control rods are used to absorb neutrons in a nuclear fission reaction.
- **c.** A very high temperature is required to initiate a nuclear fission reaction.
- **d.** The energy released from the sun is the result of nuclear fission reactions.

_____ **22.** In nuclear fission
      a. certain atoms break into fragments when struck by neutrons.
      b. a chain reaction cannot occur.
      c. energy is absorbed.
      d. all of the above

_____ **23.** Nuclear fusion
      a. occurs when large nuclei fuse together.
      b. takes place in the sun.
      c. generally produces hydrogen nuclei.
      d. all of the above

_____ **24.** What particle is needed to complete this equation?

$$^{14}_{7}N + \underline{\quad ? \quad} \rightarrow {}^{14}_{6}C + {}^{1}_{1}H$$

      a. $^{1}_{0}n$ **c.** $^{4}_{2}He$
      b. $^{0}_{-1}e$ **d.** $^{0}_{+1}e$

_____ **25.** Radioisotopes taken internally for medical reasons
      a. must be eliminated from the body slowly.
      b. should be fissionable isotopes.
      c. should have stable nuclei.
      d. should have a short half-life.

_____ **26.** A device that is used primarily for the detection of beta radiation is
      a. the film badge.   **c.** the scintillation counter.
      b. the Geiger counter.   **d.** all of the above

C. Problems

Solve the following problems in the space provided. Show your work.

27. Complete the following nuclear reactions by filling in the blanks with the correct numbers.

a. $^{42}_{?}K \rightarrow {}^{0}_{-1}e + {}^{?}_{20}Ca$

b. $^{?}_{92}U \rightarrow {}^{4}_{2}He + {}^{231}_{?}Th$

28. After 252 days, a 24-g sample of scandium-42 contains only 3.0 g of the isotope. What is the half-life of scandium?

29. Iodine-131, a radioisotope, has a half-life of 8 days. If the amount of iodine-131 in a sample is 4.0 g, how much iodine-131 will remain after 40 days?

D. Essay

Write a short essay for the following.

30. Explain how the sun produces its energy.

_____

_____

_____

_____

_____

_____

25 NUCLEAR CHEMISTRY

Chapter Test B

A. Matching

Match each term in Column B to the correct description in Column A. Write the letter of the correct term on the line.

Column A	Column B
_____ 1. the splitting of a nucleus into smaller fragments	**a.** gamma radiation
_____ 2. $_{-1}^{0}e$	**b.** half-life
_____ 3. the process whereby a stable nucleus loses energy by emitting radiation	**c.** radioactive decay
_____ 4. a particle with the mass of an electron, but with a positive charge	**d.** positron
_____ 5. a particle that contains two protons, two neutrons, and has a 2+ charge	**e.** alpha particle
_____ 6. isotopes that emit radiation because they have unstable nuclei	**f.** fusion
_____ 7. the most penetrating type of radiation	**g.** radioisotopes
_____ 8. a device that uses a gas-filled metal tube to detect radiation	**h.** Geiger counter
_____ 9. the time required for one-half of the atoms of a radioisotope to decay to products	**i.** beta particle
_____ 10. the combination of two nuclei to produce a nucleus of heavier mass	**j.** fission

B. Multiple Choice

Choose the best answer and write its letter on the line.

_____ 11. Which of the following is *always* true about radioisotopes?
  a. They have unstable nuclei.
  b. Their neutron-to-proton ratio is 1:1.
  c. Their decay products are stable isotopes.
  d. all of the above

_____ 12. Radioactive decay
   a. is a spontaneous process.
   b. occurs when an unstable nucleus loses energy.
   c. does not require any input of energy.
   d. all of the above

_____ 13. Which of the following types of radiation has no mass and no charge?
   a. alpha   **c.** gamma
   b. beta   **d.** positron

_____ 14. When U-238 undergoes radioactive decay by losing an alpha particle, the other product is
   a. U-234.   **c.** Pu-234.
   b. Th-234.   **d.** U-242.

_____ 15. When Rn-222 undergoes decay to become Po-218, it emits
   a. an alpha particle.   **c.** gamma radiation.
   b. a beta particle.   **d.** X-rays.

_____ 16. Which of the following is true concerning a plot of number of neutrons vs. number of protons?
   a. A band of stability is created that is indicative of stable nuclei.
   b. The nuclei that fall outside the band undergo spontaneous radioactive decay.
   c. The position of a nucleus with respect to the band determines the type of decay that it will undergo.
   d. all of the above

_____ 17. Alpha emission
   a. occurs among nuclei in region A, to the left of the band of stability.
   b. results in an increase in the neutron-to-proton ratio.
   c. is a favorable change in that it increases nuclear energy.
   d. all of the above

_____ 18. Which of the following is true about the concept of half-life?
   a. Half-life measures the rate of decay of a radioisotope.
   b. The shorter the half-life, the more dangerous the radioisotope.
   c. Half-life predicts which atoms in a radioactive sample will decay.
   d. all of the above

_____ 19. The transuranium elements
   a. are the elements with atomic numbers above 92.
   b. occur in nature.
   c. are sometimes radioactive.
   d. all of the above

_____ 20. When an atom of N-14 is bombarded by an alpha particle, the single product is
   a. $^{18}_{9}N$.   **c.** $^{18}_{9}F$.
   b. $^{5}_{10}B$.   **d.** $^{19}_{7}N$.

_____ **21.** Which of the following is true concerning gamma radiation?
     a. The mass number of the radioisotope decreases by four.
     b. The atomic number of the radioisotope decreases by two.
     c. The atomic number of the radioisotope increases by one.
     d. Neither the mass number nor the atomic number changes.

_____ **22.** When nuclear fission occurs
     a. two nuclei combine to produce a heavier nucleus.
     b. the chain reaction that results cannot be controlled.
     c. it is a spontaneous reaction.
     d. it must be initiated by bombardment with neutrons.

_____ **23.** Nuclear reactors
     a. use controlled fission to produce energy.
     b. use neutron moderation and absorption to control the chain reaction.
     c. cannot produce a nuclear explosion.
     d. all of the above

_____ **24.** Which of the following is true concerning nuclear fusion?
     a. It generally releases more heat than nuclear fission.
     b. It involves the splitting of a nucleus into smaller fragments.
     c. It can occur at room temperature.
     d. all of the above

_____ **25.** Which of the following is true concerning radioisotopes?
     a. They can be used as tracers to study chemical reactions and molecular structures.
     b. They can be used to diagnose certain diseases.
     c. They can be used to treat certain forms of cancer.
     d. all of the above

C. Problems

Solve the following problems in the space provided. Show your work.

26. Complete the following nuclear reactions.

  a. $^{226}_{88}\text{Ra} \rightarrow\ ^{?}_{?}\text{Rn} + ^{4}_{2}?$

  b. $^{234}_{91}\text{Pa} \rightarrow\ ^{234}_{92}\text{U} + ^{?}_{?}?$

  c. $^{234}_{?}\text{Th} \rightarrow\ ^{?}_{?}? + ^{0}_{-1}e$

27. The half-life of Pa-234 is 6.75 hours. If a sample of Pa-234 contains 12.0 g, how much will remain after 27.0 hours?

28. After 71.5 years, a 4.00-g sample of P-32 has decayed such that only 0.125 g remain. What is the half-life of P-32?

D. Essay

Write a short essay for the following.

29. Distinguish between chemical reactions and nuclear reactions in terms of each of the following.

   a. the driving force behind the occurrence of each

_____

_____

_____

_____

   b. the relative amounts of energy involved in each

_____

_____

   c. the effect of changes in temperature, pressure, and the presence of a catalyst on each

_____

_____

_____

SMALL-SCALE LAB: Radioactivity and Half-Lives

Laboratory Recordsheet   Use with Section 25.2

SAFETY

Use safe and proper laboratory procedures.

PURPOSE

To simulate the transformation of a radioactive isotope over time and to graph the data and relate it to radioactive decay and half-lives.

MATERIALS

- pencil
- penny
- graph paper
- ruler
- paper

PROCEDURE

For trial number 1, flip a penny 100 times and in Figure A, record the total number of heads that result. Now flip the penny the same number of times as the number of heads that you obtained in the first 100 flips. Record the total number of flips and the number of heads that result. Continue this procedure until you obtain no more heads. Record all your data in Figure A.

Trial #	Number of flips	Number of heads
1	100	
2		
3		
4		
5		
6		
7		

Figure A

ANALYZE

Using your experimental data, record the answers to the following questions.

1. Use your graph paper to plot the number of flips (*y*-axis) versus the trial number (*x*-axis). Draw a smooth line through the points.

2. Examine your graph. Is the rate of the number of heads produced over time linear or nonlinear? Is the rate constant over time or does it change?

   _____

   _____

3. Why does each trial reduce the number of heads by approximately one-half?

   _____

   _____

   _____

4. A half-life is the time required for one-half of the atoms of a radioisotope to emit radiation and to decay to products. What value represents one half-life for the process of flipping coins?

   _____

   _____

YOU'RE THE CHEMIST

Use the space below to write your observations to the small-scale activities in the *You're the Chemist* section.

_____

_____

_____

_____

_____

_____

_____

_____

_____

_____

_____

QUICK LAB: Studying Inverse-Square Relationships

Laboratory Recordsheet   Use with Section 25.4

PURPOSE

To demonstrate the relationship between radiation intensity and the distance from the radiation source.

MATERIALS

- flashlight
- strips of duct tape
- scissors
- poster board, white (50 cm × 50 cm)
- meter ruler or tape measure
- flat surface, long enough to hold the meter ruler
- graph paper
- pen or pencil
- light sensor (optional)

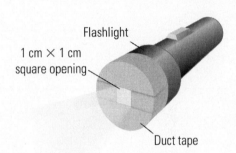

Flashlight

1 cm × 1 cm square opening

Duct tape

PROCEDURE

1. Measure and record the distance (A) from the bulb filament to the front surface of the flashlight.

2. Cover the end of a flashlight with tape. Leave a 1 cm × 1 cm square hole in the center.

3. Place the flashlight on its side on a flat, horizontal surface. Turn on the flashlight. Darken the room.

4. Mount a large piece of white poster board in front of the flashlight, perpendicular to the horizontal surface.

5. Move the flashlight away from the board in short increments. At each position, record the distance (B) from the flashlight to the board and the length (L) of one side of the square image on the board.

6. On a sheet of graph paper, plot L on the y-axis versus $A + B$ on the x-axis. On another sheet, plot L^2 on the y-axis versus $A + B$ on the x-axis.

ANALYSES AND CONCLUSIONS

1. As the flashlight is moved away from the board, what do you notice about the intensity of the light in the illuminated square? Use your graphs to demonstrate the relationship between intensity and distance.

_____

_____

_____

_____

2. When the distance of the flashlight from the board is doubled and tripled, what happens to the areas and intensities of the illuminated squares?

_____

_____

_____

INTRODUCTION TO CHEMISTRY

Reviewing Content

34. Although air is "invisible," it has mass and occupies space.

35. the changes that matter undergoes

36. Organic chemistry is the study of carbon-containing chemicals; inorganic chemistry is the study of chemicals that do not contain carbon.

37. pure chemistry; His experiments tested the proposal of another chemist. His results led to applied chemistry—the large-scale production of nylon.

38. The group of chemicals in the body that produce pain are also involved in the formation of blood clots. Aspirin blocks the production of these chemicals.

39. A firefighter needs to know which chemicals to use to fight different types of fires; knowledge of chemistry will help a reporter gather information during an interview of a chemist.

40. In a macroscopic view you can see an object like a burr with the unaided eye; to observe the tiny hooks on a burr's surface requires magnification *(a microscopic view)*.

41. Insulation acts as a barrier to heat flow. If heat flow is reduced, energy is conserved.

42. to understand the structure of matter found in cells and chemical changes that occur in cells

43. gene therapy and production of chemicals such as insulin

44. Testing reveals if soil contains the right chemicals to grow a crop and suggests way to improve soil.

45. A pollutant is a material found in air, soil, or water that is harmful to living organisms.

46. Lead poisoning can cause nervous system damage in growing children.

47. by analyzing the light they transmit to Earth

48. They based their conclusions on experimental evidence.

49. the scientific method

50. to test a hypothesis

51. c

52. The manipulated variable is changed during an experiment; the responding variable is observed during an experiment.

53. Repeat the experiment. If you get the same result, you must propose a new hypothesis.

54. A scientific law summarizes the results of many experiments; a theory explains them.

55. to share knowledge across disciplines and resources between industry and academia

56. b, c, and d

57. developing a plan and implementing that plan

58. step 1, analyze

59. 54 games

60. 4,320 times an hour, 103,680 times a day

61. 12 days

Understanding Concepts

62. Answers will vary, but possible answers are 1c, 2d, 3e, 4b, and 5a.

63. Answers will vary but should demonstrate an understanding that chemistry is the study of matter and the changes it undergoes.

64. One possible answer is development of the materials to produce an artificial limb.

65. Students are likely to choose biochemist because biochemistry is the study of processes that take place in organisms. However, a student might choose physical chemist because physical chemistry includes the study of energy transfer as matter undergoes a change.

66. The doctor's hypothesis is that the sore throat is the result of bacteria that cause strep throat. She tests the hypothesis by testing a sample to for the presence of the bacteria.

67. Your experiment may be correct, but your hypothesis may be wrong. You should reexamine your hypothesis and repeat the experiment.

68. a. The manipulated variable is the temperature of the basketball. The responding variable is the height of the basketball's bounce.
  b. The method for dropping the basketball before it bounces; the method for measuring the height of the bounce

69. Answers will vary but should reflect knowledge of the steps in a scientific method including making observations and testing hypotheses.

70. a. amount of salt added
  b. freezing point
  c. Changing the volume of the water would change the concentration of the salt solution and affect the results.
  d. Yes, to a point. The freezing point appears to be leveling off at about 15°C.

71. 300 miles

Critical Thinking

72. One possible answer is that with both areas of study, students slowly build up a vocabulary and a set of concepts that relate the new terms. Both areas rely on a systematic approach—grammar versus a scientific method. Chemistry deals with matter and words don't qualify as matter. Science is independent of a specific culture; language varies from culture to culture.

73. A possible answer is that scientists accept hypotheses that are supported by the results of experiments and reject hypotheses that are not supported by experimental results.

74. a. the brand of paper towel
  b. Answers might include strongest, most absorbent, strongest when wet, largest area per sheet, easiest to tear from roll.
  c. Sample answer: The best towel will absorb the most liquid.
  d. Answers might include size of paper towel sample, type of liquid, amount of liquid, method for measuring absorbency, method for measuring strength.

75. A person who is educated in the theories and practice of chemistry is more likely to recognize the significance of an accidental discovery and have the means and motivation to develop that accidental discovery into an important scientific contribution.

76. Divide the weight of 4 beakers by 2 or multiply the weight of 1 beaker by 2 (2.0 lb/2 or 0.5 lb $\times$ 2 = 1 lb).

77. A theory can never be proven. It is a well-tested explanation of a broad set of observations. A theory may need to be changed in the future to explain new observations.

78. b

Concept Challenge

79. Students' diagrams should show one string that is threaded through both holes A and C. The string at hole B is a separate thread from the string passing through holes A and C.

80. 150 in.

81. 144,000 eggs

82. the number of gallons in a barrel

83. a. $1.00 per package
  b. number of envelopes in a package

Reviewing Content

35. An extensive property depends on the amount of matter; an intensive property depends on the type of matter. Mass and volume are extensive properties. Color and hardness are intensive properties.

36. Answers could include reddish-yellow color, conductor of heat and electricity, malleable, melting point of 1084°C, and boiling point of 2562°C.

37. melting point and boiling point

38. State; both are gases.

39. a. solid   **b.** liquid
    c. gas   **d.** liquid
    e. gas   **f.** liquid

40. A vapor; the term *vapor* is used to refer to the gaseous state of a substance which normally exists as a liquid or solid at room temperature.

41. The particles in a solid are packed tightly together in an orderly arrangement. Particles in a liquid are in close contact, but not in a orderly arrangement. The particles in a gas are relatively far apart.

42. Chlorine condenses. Mercury, bromine and water freeze.

43. Sharpening a pencil is an irreversible change. Making ice cubes is a reversible change.

44. Heterogeneous mixtures have a non-uniform composition consisting of two or more phases. Homogeneous mixtures have a uniform composition throughout the sample.

45. one; Solutions are homogeneous mixtures with uniform composition throughout.

46. a. heterogeneous
    b. homogeneous
    c. depends on how well the batter is mixed
    d. homogeneous

47. The goal is to separate the components of a solution. The solution is boiled to produce a vapor, which is condensed to a liquid. Dissolved solids are left behind.

48. Compounds can be separated by chemical means into simpler substances. Elements cannot.

49. a. Hydrogen and oxygen are the elements that make up the compound water.
    b. Nitrogen and oxygen are elements present in the mixture air.
    c. Sodium and chlorine are elements in the compound sodium chloride (table salt).
    d. Carbon is an element and water is a compound. They are the final products of heating table sugar (sucrose).

50. a. nitrogen, hydrogen
    b. potassium, oxygen
    c. carbon, hydrogen, oxygen
    d. calcium, sulfur

51. In W, the single letter is capitalized. In Hg, the first letter is a capital and the second letter is lowercase.

52. The compound water contains two parts hydrogen to one part oxygen.

53. The composition of the reactants in a chemical change is different from the composition of the products. In a physical change, the chemical composition of a sample doesn't change. When heated, sulfur and iron react and form iron sulfide.

54. a. physical
    b. chemical (color change)
    c. chemical (production of a gas)
    d. physical

55. chemical property

56. 18 g of water

Understanding Concepts

57. Mass is an extensive property, which depends only on the amount of matter in the sample, not on the composition of the sample.

58. Malleability is an intensive property, which depends on the type of matter in a sample.

59. Substances are classified as solids, liquids, or gases according to their state at room temperature, which in this book is 20°C.

60. ethanol

61. neon

62. sulfur

63. sulfur

64. The particles in solids are packed tightly together. The particles in a gas are spaced relatively far apart.

65. kitchen, mixtures; park, mixtures

66. **a.** heterogeneous mixture
    b. compound
    c. homogeneous mixture
    d. heterogeneous mixture

67. **a.** physical   **b.** physical
    c. physical   **d.** physical
    e. chemical

68. **a.** Both are elements and solids at room temperature; they are a different color and have different melting points and boiling points.
    b. Both are clear liquids at room temperature; distilled water is an element and saltwater is a mixture.
    c. Both are white, solid compounds. Sugar is composed of carbon, hydrogen, and oxygen. Salt is composed of sodium and chlorine.

69. In photograph A, bubbles indicate the production of a gas. In photograph B, there is a color change and a precipitate.

70. **a.** Gas is produced.
    b. formation of a precipitate
    c. color and texture change
    d. energy change, odor change

71. A gas may be released during a physical change. For example, bubbles form when water boils.

72. The wax appears to disappear because the products of the reaction—carbon dioxide and water vapor—are colorless gases.

Critical Thinking

73. A gas expands to fill any space; a gas has no shape or volume without a container. A solid has a definite shape and volume; a solid doesn't need a container to maintain its shape and volume.

74. The appearance of a substance will change during a change of state, which is a physical change.

75. Gallium (c) will freeze first; mercury (b) will freeze last.

76. Add sufficient water to dissolve all of the sugar. Separate the charcoal and sand from the sugar water by filtration. Large pieces of charcoal could be separated on the basis of color. Small pieces of charcoal could be burned.

77. Iron rusts when it reacts with oxygen in the air to form an oxide (Fe_2O_3). The mass of the rust is the sum of the mass of the iron and the mass of the oxygen that combined with the iron.

78. Smelling something burning is one possible answer.

79. **a.** Yes; because the graph is a straight line, the proportion of iron to oxygen is a constant, which is true for a compound.
    b. No; a point for the values given wouldn't fall on the line. The mass ratio of iron to oxygen is different.

Concept Challenge

80. **a.** oxygen and calcium
    b. silicon, aluminum, and iron
    c. Different; the second most abundant element in Earth's crust, silicon, is not present in the human body, and the second most abundant element in the human body, carbon, is not among the most abundant elements in Earth's crust. If the elements are different, then the compounds must also be different.

81. **a.** mercury and sulfur
    b. Sulfur melts at 113°C and boils at 445°C. Between 113°C and 445°C, it exists as a liquid. Mercury melts at –39°C and boils at 357°C. Between these temperatures, it exists as a liquid.
    c. Possibilities include: by color, by boiling point, or in alphabetical order.

82. Many answers are possible. Sample answer: helpful chemical change: cooking food (color change, odor change); harmful chemical change: formation of soap scum (precipitate forms)

SCIENTIFIC MEASUREMENT

Reviewing Content

57. Lissa: inaccurate and imprecise
Lamont: accurate and precise
Leigh Anne: inaccurate and precise

58. a. infinite   **b.** 4
    c. infinite   **d.** infinite

59. a. 98.5 L   **b.** 0.000 763 cg
    c. 57.0 m   **d.** 12.2°C

60. a. 43 g   **b.** 225.8 L
    c. 92.0 kg   **d.** 32.4 m^3

61. (59) **a.** 9.85×10^1 L   **b.** 7.63×10^{-4} cg
    c. 5.70×10^1 m   **d.** 1.22×10^{1}°C
    (60) **a.** 4.3×10^1 g   **b.** 2.258×10^2 L
    c. 9.20×10^1 kg   **d.** 3.24×10^1 m^3

62. The error is the difference between the experimental value and the accepted. The percent error is the error divided by the accepted value multiplied by 100.

63. a. second   **b.** meter
    c. kelvin   **d.** kilogram

64. pm, nm, μm, mm, cm, dm, m, km;
1 km = 10^3 m, 1 dm = 10^{-1} m,
1 cm = 10^{-2} m. 1 mm = 10^{-3} m,
1 μm = 10^{-6} m, 1 nm = 10^{-9} m,
1 pm = 10^{-12} m

65. a. 2.4 mm
    b. 13.95 cm
    c. 27.50 cm

66. 1235 K

67. conversion factor

68. They must equal one another.

69. The unit of the conversion factor in the denominator must be identical to the unit in the given measurement or the previous conversion factor.

70. a. 1.57 s   **b.** 4.27×10^4 mL
    c. 2.61×10^{-4} mm   **d.** 6.5×10^2 dm
    e. 6.42×10^{-3} kg   **f.** 8.25×10^9 ng

71. a. 7.3 μL/s   **b.** 78.6 mg/mm^2
    c. 1.54 g/cm^3

72. 10^6 mL

73. 2.83×10^2 mg, 0.283 g, 2.83×10^{-4} kg;
6.6 g, 6.6×10^2 cg, 6.6×10^{-3} kg;

2.8×10^{-1} mg, 2.8×10^{-2} cg, 2.8×10^{-7} kg

74. density = mass/volume

75. Yes, neither mass nor volume of a solid or liquid changes appreciably with location.

76. No, the density of the metal bar is 12 g/cm^3, but density of gold is 19 g/cm^3.

77. The carbon dioxide–filled balloon would sink. The neon and hydrogen-filled balloons would rise, the hydrogen at a much faster rate.

Understanding Concepts

78. Improper calibration or improper use of the measuring device.

79. e, d, c, f, a, b

80. a. accurate and precise
    b. inaccurate and precise
    c. inaccurate and imprecise

81. °F = 1.8°C + 32

82. germanium

83. 1 g/10^2 cg, 10^2 cg/1 g, 1 g/10^3 mg, 10^3 mg/1 g, 10^2 cg/10^3 mg,

    10^3 mg/10^2 cg

84. 81.3 kg

85. 0.69 – 0.789 g/cm^3

86. 4.20 x 10^4 cm^3

87. 0.804 g/cm^3

88. 3.6 min lost

89. 0.92 kg/L

90. a. $C_2 = -90$°C, $C_4 = 0$°C, $C_6 = 70$°C, $C_8 = 125$°C
    b. C_1 through C_4
    c. three
    d. From C_1 through C_9, the increase is approximately 39°C/additional carbon. Over the range C_3 through C_9, the increase is approximately 32°C/additional carbon.

91. 8.3 min

92. 73 g

93. 5.52 kg/dm^3

94. 24.0 kg of water

Critical Thinking

95. Yes, the mass of an object is constant. The weight of an object varies with location.

96. 16.3 g

97. 31.1 m/s

98. You do not change your estimate. Counting the extra 15 ducks would suggest greater precision than was used in the estimate.

99. Answers will vary. Lakes would freeze solid from the bottom up; aquatic life would be destroyed; possible climate changes.

100. Gasoline is a mixtures and has a variable composition.

101. density of sulfur = 2.1 g/cm^3;

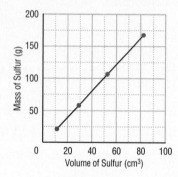

102. a. The oxygen-filled balloon will sink; the nitrogen-filled balloon will rise.
b. nitrogen; The "weighted" average density of air is closer to the density of nitrogen.

Concept Challenge

103. Volume of iron = 45.1 cm^3
Mass of lead = 514 g Pb

104. 8.0 g Sr

105. 1.8×10^3 kg

106. a. 85 g
b. 1.3 g/mL

107. 1.79 mL

108. a. corn oil on top of water on top of mercury
b. The density of sugar is greater than the density of water and less than the density of mercury; it floats between the layers of mercury and water.
c. The sugar cube will dissolve in the water over time.

ATOMIC STRUCTURE

Reviewing Content

34. The smallest particle of an element that still has the properties of that element.

35. Democritus's ideas were not helpful in explaining chemical behavior because they lacked experimental support.

36. Dalton would agree with all four statements because they all fit his atomic theory.

37. The atoms are separated, joined, and rearranged.

38. a. A beam of electrons (cathode rays) is deflected by an electric field toward the positively charged plate.
   b. The cathode rays were always composed of electrons regardless of the metal used in the electrodes or the gas used in the cathode-ray tube.

39. repel

40. The mass of the proton and neutron are equal; protons are positively charged and neutrons are neutral.

41. Atoms are neutral: number of protons = number of electrons. Loss of an electron means that the number of p^+ is greater than the number of e^-, so the remaining particle is positively charged.

42. The electrons were stuck in a lump of positive charge.

43. He did not expect alpha particles to be deflected at a large angle.

44. positive

45. protons and neutrons (Rutherford suspected there was something in the nucleus in addition to protons—but didn't know them as neutrons.)

46. It has equal numbers of protons and electrons.

47. the number of protons in the nucleus

48. a. 15   **b.** 42
   c. 13   **d.** 48
   e. 24   **f.** 82

49. The atomic number is the number of protons. The mass number is the sum of the protons and neutrons.

50.

9	19	9	10	9	F
14	29	14	15	14	Si
22	47	22	25	22	Ti
25	55	25	30	25	Mn

51. mass numbers, atomic masses, number of neutrons, relative abundance

52. because of the existence of isotopes

53. which isotopes exist, their masses, and their natural percent abundance

54. Average atomic mass is the arithmetic mean of the isotopes. Weighted average atomic mass considers both the mass and the relative abundance of the isotopes.

55. The atomic mass is the weighted average of the masses of all the isotopes.

56. according to their atomic numbers

57. Properties in the table recur at regular intervals.

Understanding Concepts

58. very, very, very tiny—but larger than protons and electrons

59. The nucleus is very small and very dense compared with the atom.

60. 5 protons and 6 neutrons in the nucleus: 5 electrons outside the nucleus

61. All atoms of the same element are not identical (isotopes). The atom is not the smallest particle of matter.

62. He used the quantity of charge value and the charge-to-mass ratio measured by Thomson.

63. They are the same value.

64. The masses of isotopes in a sample of the element are averaged, based on relative abundance. The result is the element's atomic mass.

65. 207 amu

66. No; in general he proposed a valid theory in line with the experimental evidence available to him.

67. Atoms are the smallest particle of an element that retains the properties of that element.

68. **a.** 92.90%   **b.** 99.89%
    c. 0.00993%

69. $^{14}_{7}N$: 14.003 amu; 99.63% $^{15}_{7}N$: 15.000 amu; 0.37%
    average atomic mass = 14.01 amu

70. They were attracted to a positively charged plate.

71. Atomic number is the same as the number of protons and electrons; mass number minus atomic number equals number of neutrons.

72. Because they have identical numbers of protons, they also have identical numbers of electrons; electrons are the subatomic particles that are responsible for chemical behavior.

73. The pattern repeats.

Critical Thinking

74. **a.** the nucleus of an atom;
    b. very small volume; almost all the mass of the atom; high density; positive charge;
    c. electron

75. Change the metal used as a target and account for differences in deflection patterns.

76. The following are reasonable hypotheses: The space in an individual atom is large relative to the volume of the atom, but very small relative to an object the size of a hand. There are many layers of atoms in a wall or a desk. The space that exists is distributed evenly throughout the solid, similar to the distribution of air pockets in foam insulation.

77. The theory must be modified and then retested.

78. Yes—but answers will vary.

79. In a chemical change, atoms are not created or destroyed; they are rearranged.

Concept Challenge

80. Because diamond is more dense than graphite, pressure could be used to "squeeze" the carbon atoms closer together.

81. 92.5%

82. 4×10^{-25} g

Cumulative Review

83. Pure chemistry involves the accumulation of scientific knowledge for its own sake. Applied chemistry is accumulating knowledge to attain a specific goal.

84. Scientific theory attempts to explain why experiments give certain results. Scientific law describes a natural phenomenon but does not explain it.

85. **a.** element   **b.** mixture
    c. mixture   **d.** mixture

86. 48 g

87. 6.38×10^5 cm^3

88. 99.5 g

5 ELECTRONS AND ATOMS

Reviewing Content

22. could not explain why metals and metal compounds give off characteristic colors when heated, nor could it explain the chemical properties of the elements; electrons

23. that electrons traveled in circular paths around the nucleus

24. In Rutherford's model, negatively charged electrons surround a dense, positively charged nucleus. In Bohr's model, the electrons are assigned to concentric circular orbits of fixed energy.

25. An electron is found 90% of the time inside this boundary.

26. a region in space around the nucleus in which there is a high probability of finding an electron

27. 3

28. The $1s$ orbital is spherical. The $2s$ orbital is spherical with a diameter larger than that of the $1s$ orbital. The three $2p$ orbitals are dumbbell shaped and oriented at right angles to each other.

29. a. 1   **b.** 2
     c. 3   **d.** 4

30. a. 2   **b.** 1
     c. 3   **d.** 6

31. Electrons occupy the lowest possible energy levels. An atomic orbital can hold at most two electrons. One electron occupies each of a set of orbitals with equal energies before any pairing of electrons occurs.

32. a. $1s^2 2s^2 2p^6 3s^2 3p^3$ **b.** $1s^2 2s^2 2p^6 3s^2$
     c. $1s^2 2s^2 2p^5$ **d.** $1s^2 2s^2 2p^6 3s^2 3p^6$

33. The p orbitals in the third quantum level have three electrons.

34. a. $1s^2 2s^2 2p^6 3s^1$ **b.** $1s^2 2s^2 2p^6 3s^2 3p^4$
     c. $1s^2 2s^2 2p^6 3s^2$ **d.** $1s^2 2s^2 2p^6$
     e. $1s^2 2s^2 2p^6 3s^2 3p^6 4s^1$

35. **b** and **c**

36. a. 2   **b.** 6
     c. 2   **d.** 10
     e. 6   **f.** 2
     g. 14   **h.** 6

37. $2s, 3p, 4s, 3d$

38. a. 8   **b.** 8   **c.** 8

39. a. $1s^2 2s^2 2p^6 3s^2 3p^6 3d^{10} 4s^2 4p^4$
     b. $1s^2 2s^2 2p^6 3s^2 3p^6 3d^3 4s^2$
     c. $1s^2 2s^2 2p^6 3s^2 3p^6 3d^8 4s^2$
     d. $1s^2 2s^2 2p^6 3s^2 3p^6 4s^2$

40. Violet, indigo, blue, green, yellow, orange, red

41. Frequency is the number of wave cycles that pass a given point per unit time. Frequency units are cycles/sec or reciprocal seconds or Hertz. Wavelength and frequency are inversely related.

42. Diagrams should look similar to those in Figure 5.9.

43. Classical physics views energy changes as continuous. In the quantum concept energy changes occur in tiny discrete units called quanta.

44. Both travel at the same speed. Ultraviolet is short wavelength and high frequency; microwave is long wavelength and low frequency.

45. a. v, vi, iv, iii, i, ii   **b.** It is the reverse.

46. Students may say that ultraviolet is used for tanning the skin and growing plants, X-rays for taking pictures of the interior of the body, visible for seeing, infrared for warmth, radio waves for communication, and microwaves for cooking.

47. The electron of the hydrogen atom is raised (excited) to a higher energy level.

48. The outermost electron of sodium absorbs photons of wavelength 589 nm as it jumps to a higher energy level.

49. visible spectrum, Balmer series

Understanding Concepts

50. a. Ar   **b.** Ru
     c. Gd

51. $1s^2 2s^2 2p^6 3s^2 3p^6 3d^{10} 4s^2 4p^3$; level 1, 2; level 2, 8; level 3, 18; level 4, 5; The fourth energy level is not filled.

52. a. 2   **b.** 4
     c. 10   **d.** 3

53. $1s^2 2s^2 2p^3$ nitrogen; 3

54. 2.61×10^4 cm

55. a. 4.36×10^{-5} cm   **b.** visible
     c. $6.88 \times 10^{14} \text{s}^{-1}$

56. a. 5.890×10^{-5} cm and 5.896×10^{-5} cm
     b. $5.090 \times 10^{14} \text{ s}^{-1}$ (Hz) and $5.085 \times 10^{14} \text{ s}^{-1}$ (Hz)
     c. yellow

57. a. Na, sodium
     b. N, nitrogen
     c. Si, silicon
     d. O, oxygen
     e. K, potassium
     f. Ti, titanium

58. The frequency is inversely proportional to the wavelength, so if the frequency increases by a factor of 1.5, the wavelength will decrease by a factor of 1.5.

59. It is not possible to know both the position and the velocity of a particle at the same time.

60. 2

61. c

62. c

63. a

64. a

Critical Thinking

65. An orbit confines the electron to a fixed circular path around the nucleus; an orbital is a region around the nucleus in which electrons are likely to be found.

66. Answers will vary. Some students may note that radio waves have the lowest energy in the electromagnetic spectrum, and thus would not be energetic enough to cook food. Others may reason that if microwaves cook food faster than infrared radiation, then radio waves would cook food even faster.

67. Answers will vary. The model of the atom is based on the abstract idea of probability.

Light is considered a particle and a wave at the same time. Atoms and light cannot be compared to familiar objects or observations because humans cannot experience atoms or photons directly and because matter and energy behave differently at the atomic level than at the level humans can observe directly.

68. a. Electrons in $2p$ boxes should not be paired—there should be one electron in each.
     b. Magnesium has 12 electrons. Two more electrons need to be added to $3s$.

69. a. $n = 1$ level
     b. $n = 4$ level
     c. $n = 4$ level
     d. $n = 1$ level

70. a. fluorine   **b.** germanium
     c. vanadium

71. a. potassium, excited state, valence electron has been promoted from $4s$ to $5p$
     b. potassium, ground state, correct electron configuration
     c. impossible configuration, $3p$ can hold a maximum of 6 electrons, not 7

72. The electrons obey Hund's rule.

Concept Challenge

73. a. Frequency(s^{-1}): 5.20×10^{12}; 4.40×10^{13}; 9.50×10^{13}; 1.70×10^{14}; 2.20×10^{14}; 4.70×10^{14}
     b.

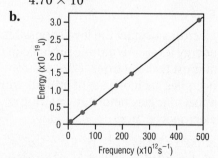

     c. 6.62×10^{-34} joule·second.
     d. The slope is Planck's constant.

74. 6.93×10^2 s

75. H: ($n = 1$), 1312kJ/mol); ($n = 2$), 328 kJ
     Li$^+$: ($n = 1$), 1.18×10^4 kJ

76. 2.12×10^{-22} J

Cumulative Review

77. a and b are heterogeneous; c is homogeneous

78. Answers will vary but could include, water is lost as steam and burned meat gives off carbon dioxide.

79. A compound has constant composition; the composition of a mixture can vary.

80. a heterogeneous mixture

81. 7.7×10^{-5} μm

82. 18.9 cm^{-3}

83. the piece of lead

84. **a.** 3.9×10^{-5} kg
    b. 7.84×10^{-2} L
    c. 8.30×10^{-2} g
    d. 9.7×10^{6} ng

85. a and b are exact

86. Mass remains the same; weight decreases because gravity on moon is less than gravity on earth.

87. 8.92 g/cm^{-3}

88. 154 g, 1.54×10^{-1} kg

89. Helium gas is less dense than the nitrogen gas and oxygen gas in the air.

90. **a.** 55 protons, 55 electrons
    b. 47 protons, 46 electrons
    c. 48 protons, 46 electrons
    d. 34 protons, 36 electrons

91. Accuracy is a measure of how close the value is to the true value; precision is a measure of how close a series of measurements are to one another.

92. a

93. Neon-20 has 10 neutrons; neon-21 has 11 neutrons.

94. The value 35.453 amu is a weighted average. Its calculation is based on the percentage natural abundance of two isotopes, chlorine-35 and chlorine-37.

THE PERIODIC TABLE

Reviewing Content

24. so that known elements with similar properties could be put in the same group

25. The close match between the predicted and actual properties of gallium helped gain wider acceptance for Mendeleev's periodic table.

26. a periodic repetition of their physical and chemical properties

27. Yes, both carbon and silicon are in Group 4A, and each has four (valence) electrons.

28. a. nonmetal   **b.** nonmetal
    c. metal   **d.** nonmetal
    e. metal

29. Metalloids have properties that are similar to those of metals and nonmetals. How a metalloid behaves depends on the conditions.

30. Group 1A, Group 2A, Group 7A, and Group 8A, respectively

31. Na, Mg, Cl

32. helium

33. a. aluminum

34. a. $1s^2 2s^2 2p^1$
    b. $1s^2 2s^2 2p^6 3s^2 3p^6 3d^{10} 4s^2 4p^2$
    c. $1s^2 2s^2 2p^5$
    d. $1s^2 2s^2 2p^6 3s^2 3p^6 3d^{10} 4s^2$
    e. $1s^2 2s^2 2p^6 3s^2 2p^1$

35. a. Ar, $1s^2 2s^2 2p^6 3s^2 3p^6$
    b. Si, $1s^2 2s^2 2p^6 3s^2 3p^2$
    c. Mg, $1s^2 2s^2 2p^6 3s^2$

36. a. sodium   **b.** strontium
    c. germanium   **d.** selenium

37. The first ionization energy is the energy needed to remove a first electron from an atom. The second ionization energy is the energy needed to remove a second electron.

38. a. boron   **b.** magnesium
    c. aluminum

39. a. Sr, Mg, Be   **b.** Cs, Ba, Bi
    c. Na, Al, S

40. It is relatively easy to remove the first electron from an alkali metal atom; it is much more difficult to remove the second.

41. The ionic radius of a cation is smaller than the atomic radius of the metal atom.

42. a. Na   **b.** S^{2-}
    c. I^- **d.** Al

43. a. F   **b.** N
    c. Mg   **d.** As

44. Noble gases, with rare exception, do not form compounds.

45. a. O   **b.** F
    c. O   **d.** S

46. a and c

Understanding Concepts

47. a. 1801–1850
    b. Mendeleev's periodic table helped scientists predict the existence of undiscovered elements.
    c. 75%

48. a. C   **b.** La
    c. Ne, P, Br   **d.** Sb, Bi

49. b; Nitrogen and phosphorus are in the same group (Group 5A).

50. Fluorine has a smaller atomic radius than oxygen because fluorine has a larger nuclear charge. Fluorine has a smaller radius than chlorine because it has eight fewer electrons.

51. nonmetals; The trend is for ionization energy to increase from left to right across a period.

52. a. Ca^{2+} **b.** P^{3-}
    c. Cu^+

53. a. H, Li, Na, K, Rb, Cs, Fr
    b. O, S, Se, Te, Po   **c.** Zn, Cd, Hg, Uub

54. An element's electron configuration determines its location (group) in the periodic table.

55. c

56. 170 pm

57. First ionization energy increases across a period.

58. It is relatively easy to remove two electrons from magnesium; it is much more difficult to remove a third electron. It is relatively easy to remove three electrons from aluminum; it is much more difficult to remove a fourth.

59. a. The atomic radius increases from top to bottom within the group.
   b. Cations are smaller than their corresponding atoms. The attraction between the nucleus and any remaining electron is greater. There is one fewer occupied energy level.

Critical Thinking

60. Yes, 113; 1 through 112 are known.

61. a. Electronegativity increases as first ionization energy increases.
   b. Both properties depend on the attraction between the nucleus and electrons in the highest occupied energy level. The nuclear charge increases, but the shielding effect is constant.

62. Zinc has a greater nuclear charge (more protons) than calcium.

63. a. The electrons in calcium are removed from the same energy level. In potassium, the second electron is removed from a lower energy level.
   b. Because cesium has a larger atomic radius than lithium, the nuclear charge in a cesium atom has a smaller effect on the electrons in the highest occupied energy level.
   c. The third electron removed from a magnesium atom is in a lower energy level.

Concept Challenge

64. Mg^{2+} has more protons in its nucleus; its attraction for electrons is greater.

65. The ionic radii would decrease from S^{2-} to Sc^{3+}. The number of electrons and the shielding effect do not change, but the number of protons increases from left to right in this series. So the ionic size decreases. The same is true for the series O^{2-} to Mg^{2+}.

66. There is not a 1:1 correspondence. Explanations will vary.

67. a.

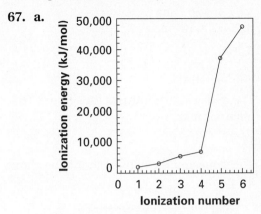

   b. The largest increase is between ionization numbers 4 and 5 because carbon easily loses the first four electrons from the second energy level. The fifth electron is removed from the first energy level.

68. a. Possible cations are Rb^+ and Sr^{2+}; possible anions are Br^-, Se^{2-}, and As^{3-}.
   b. No; a cation is isoelectronic with the noble gas in the preceding period, and an anion is isoelectronic with the noble gas in the same period.

69. Electron affinity should increase (become more negative) from left to right across a period because the nuclear charge increases and the shielding effect is constant.

Cumulative Review

70. Answers will vary but should mention scientific method, observations, experimentation, and hypotheses.

71. a. physical change
   b. chemical change
   c. physical change
   d. chemical change

72. Use a magnet; iron beads are attracted to magnet, copper beads are not. Use tweezers and a magnifying glass; iron beads are silvery black, copper beads are dull red.

73. 4

74. a. 3
   b. 8, the tenths place

75. The density of the cube is 0.984 g/cm^3. The cube will float.

76. **a.** 2.24×10^{-9} m
    b. 8.13×10^{-2} m
    c. 7.4×10^{-12} m
    d. 9.37×10^{-3} m

77. 5.2%

78. 5.2×10^3 g

79. The density of the olive is 1.05 g/cm^3. The olive will sink.

80. 173

81. The slope and the density should be about 2.1 g/cm^3.

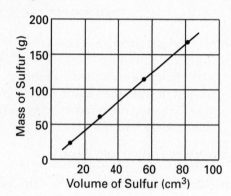

82. 2.57×10^2 mL

83. 4.54 g/cm^3

84. **a.** 48
    b. 44
    c. 114
    d. 110

85. **a.** silver, 62 neutrons
    b. tin, 50 protons
    c. molybdenum, 42 electrons
    d. scandium, 21 electrons

86. **a.** none
    b. one, $2p$
    c. none
    d. none

Reviewing Content

30. by gaining or losing electrons

31. a. gain of 1 electron
b. loss of one electron
c. gain of 3 electrons
d. loss of 2 electrons
e. loss of 1 electron
f. gain of 1 electron

32. a. bromide, anion **b.** sodium, cation
c. arsenide, anion **d.** calcium, cation
e. copper, cation **f.** hydride, anion

33. electrons in the highest occupied energy level

34. a. 7, 5A **b.** 3, 1A
c. 15, 5A **d.** 56, 2A
e. 35, 7A **f.** 6, 4A

35. a. $:\ddot{Cl}\cdot$ **b.** $\cdot\ddot{S}\cdot$
c. $\cdot Al\cdot$ **d.** $Li\cdot$

36. a. 2 **b.** 3
c. 1 **d.** 2

37. a. Al^{3+} **b.** Li^+
c. Ba^{2+} **d.** K^+
e. Ca^{2+} **f.** Sr^{2+}

38. Most nonmetals gain 1, 2, or 3 electrons to achieve a noble-gas electron configuration.

39. a. S^{2-} **b.** Na^-
c. F^- **d.** P^{3-}

40. a. 3 **b.** 2
c. 1 **d.** 3

41. a, c, e

42. a. Ca^{2+}, F^- **b.** Al^{3+}, Br^-
c. Li^+, O^{2-} **d.** Al^{3+}, S^{2-}
e. K^+, N^{3-}

43. The positive charges balance the negative charges.

44. a, b, d

45. a. K^+, Cl^- **b.** Ba^{2+}, SO_4^{2-}
c. Mg^{2+}, Br^- **d.** Li^+, CO_3^{2-}

46. Their network of electrostatic attractions and repulsions forms a rigid structure.

47. Ions are free to move in molten $MgCl_2$.

48. They have many mobile valence electrons. Electrons in the current replace the electrons leaving the metal.

49. body-centered cubic: Na, K, Fe, Cr, or W; face-centered cubic: Cu, Ag, Au, Al, or Pb; hexagonal close-packed: Mg, Zn, or Cd

50. Answers will vary and could include tableware, steel in cars and buses, high-speed dental drill bits, solder in stereos and televisions, and structural steel in buildings.

51. The properties of the steel will vary according to its composition. In addition to iron, steel can contain varying amounts of carbon and such metals as chromium, nickel, and molybdenum.

Understanding Concepts

52.

Group number	Valence electrons lost or gained of ion	Formula
1A	1	Na^+
2A	2	Ca^{2+}
3A	3	Al^{3+}
5A	3	N^{3-}
6A	2	S^{2-}
7A	1	Br^-

53. a. $\cdot\dot{C}\cdot$ **b.** $\cdot Be\cdot$
c. $\cdot\ddot{O}\cdot$ **d.** $:\ddot{F}\cdot$
e. $Na\cdot$ **f.** $\cdot\ddot{P}\cdot$

54. For the representative elements the number of electrons in the electron dot structure is the group number.

55. It has lost valence electrons.

56. It has gained valence electrons.

57. a. oxygen atom, sulfur atom, oxide ion, sulfide ion
b. sodium ion, potassium ion, sodium atom, potassium atom

58. a. $1s^2 2s^2 2p^6 3s^2 3p^6 3d^6$
b. $1s^2 2s^2 2p^6 3s^2 3p^6 3d^7$
c. $1s^2 2s^2 2p^6 3s^2 3p^6 3d^8$

59. **a.** $1s^22s^22p^63s^23p^63d^3$
    b. $1s^22s^22p^63s^23p^63d^4$
    c. $1s^22s^22p^63s^23p^63d^5$

60. They have little chemical reactivity; their outermost occupied energy levels are filled.

61. **a.** Br^- **b.** H^-
    c. As^{3-} **d.** Se^{2-}

62. All have the noble-gas configuration of $1s^22s^22p^63s^23p^6$.

63. All are $1s^22s^22p^6$. All have the same configuration as neon.

64. fluorine, chlorine, bromine, and iodine; Group 7A, 7 valence electrons

65. **a.** $1s^22s^22p^63s^23p^6$
    b. $1s^22s^22p^6$; Each has a noble-gas electron configuration

66. The positively charged cations exactly balance the negatively charged anions.

67. a, c, e, f

68. No, the packing of ions in a crystalline structure depends on a number of factors including the relative sizes of the ions. The coordination number of an element can vary from compound to compound.

69. 12

70. Hexagonal close-packed units cells have twelve neighbors for every atom or ion. Face-centered cubic unit cells also have twelve neighbors for every atom or ion, with an atom or ion in the center of each face. Body-centered cubic units cells have eight neighbors for every atom or ion, with an atom or ion at the center of each cube.

71. Brass is a mixture of copper and zinc. The properties of a particular sample of brass will vary with the relative proportions of the two metals.

Critical Thinking

72. Each dot in the electron dot structure represents a valence electron in the electron configuration diagram.

73. By gaining or losing electrons the atoms of elements achieve a noble-gas electron configuration.

74. An atom of silver has the electron configuration $1s^22s^22p^63s^23p^63d^14s^24p^6$ $4d^{10}5s^1$. To achieve the configuration of the preceding noble gas, krypton, a silver atom would have to lose eleven electrons and form Ag^{11+}. To achieve the configuration of the following noble gas xenon, a silver atom must gain seven electrons and form Ag^{7-}. Because ions with such high charges are unlikely, silver does not achieve a noble-gas configuration. However, if a silver atom loses its $5s^1$ electron, the result is an outer electron configuration of eighteen electrons, written as $4s^24p^64d^{10}$. This configuration is favored and stable. It is known as a pseudo-noble-gas configuration.

75. No, sodium chloride is composed of equal numbers of sodium ions and chloride ions; the ions are in a 1:1 ratio. Each sodium ion is surrounded by chloride ions, and each chloride is surrounded by sodium ions.

76. In sodium chloride crystals the sodium and chloride ions vibrate about fixed points; in the molten state, the ions are free to move.

77. The spheres are more closely packed in (a); there is less empty space in (a), and a rough count shows 25 spheres in (a) compared with 22 spheres in (b).

78. Metals are ductile (can be drawn into wires) and malleable (can be hammered into shapes). These changes are possible because a metal consists of metal cations in a sea of valence electrons. When subjected to pressure, the cations easily slide past one another.

79. Both metals and ionic compounds are composed of ions. Both are held together by electrostatic bonds. Metals always conduct electricity, and ionic compounds conduct only when melted or in water solution. Ionic compounds are composed of cations and anions, but metals are composed of cations and free-floating valence electrons. Metals are ductile, but ionic compounds are brittle.

Concept Challenge

80. **a.** cation: lose $1e^-$ **b.** cation: lose $1e^-$
    c. unreactive **d.** anion: gain $1e^-$
    e. cation: lose 2e

81. Na^+ and Cs^+ differ greatly in size. Na^+ and Cl^- are similar in size to Mn^{2+} and S^{2-}.

82. 0.1445 nm

83. **a.** copper and zinc
  b. silver and copper
  c. copper and tin
  d. iron, chromium, nickel, and carbon
  e. iron, chromium, nickel, and molybdenum
  f. iron, chromium, and carbon

Cumulative Review

84. Organic chemistry is the study of chemicals containing carbon; inorganic chemistry is the study of chemicals that do not contain carbon.

85. an analytical chemist

86. use insulation

87. a, b, and d are chemical changes. c is a physical change.

88. b and e; c is not a mixture, it is a pure substance

89. **a.** liquid, vapor
  b. vapor,
  c. vapor liquid,
  d. liquid vapor

90. **a.** 56.6 g
  b. 0.0048 m
  c. 1.81 L
  d. 4.0×10^3 mg

91. a

92. −269°C

93. 27.0 cm^3

94. **a.** $^{64}_{30}$ Zn   **b.** $^{37}_{17}$ Cl
  c. $^{3}_{1}$ H   **d.** $^{40}_{20}$ Ca

95. 14 amu

96. Each of the isotopes has 8 protons and 8 electrons; oxygen-16 also has 8 neutrons, oxygen-17 has 9 neutrons, and oxygen-18 has 10 neutrons.

97. **a.** 1
  b. 3
  c. 1
  d. 5

98. **a.** N, $1s^22s^22p^3$
  b. Be, $1s^22s^2$
  c. P, $1s^22s^22p^63s^23p^2$
  d. K, $1s^22s^22p^63s^23p^64s^1$

99. chlorine, Cl, $1s^22s^22p^63s^23p^5$

100. **a.** 5×10^{-7} m
  b. the visible region, green

101. **a.** K, $1s^22s^22p^63s^23p^64s^1$
  b. Al, $1s^22s^22p^63s^23p^1$
  c. S, $1s^22s^22p^63s^23p^4$
  d. Ba, $1s^22s^22p^63s^23p^63d^{10}4s^24p^64d^{10}5s^25p^66s^2$

102. the electron

103. sodium (Na), cesium (Cs), rubidium (Rb), lithium (Li)

Reviewing Content

39. ionic

40. a. 6 C, 8 H, 6 O   **b.** 12 C, 22 H, 11 O
   c. 7 C, 5 H, 3 N, 6 O

41. Nitrogen and oxygen achieve stability as diatomic molecules. Argon exists as individual atoms because it has a stable noble-gas electron configuration.

42. Neon has an octet of electrons. A chlorine atom achieves an octet by sharing an electron with another chlorine atom.

43. a. ionic   **b.** ionic
   c. covalent   **d.** covalent

44. Ionic bonds depend on electrostatic attraction between ions. Covalent bonds depend on electrostatic attraction between shared electrons and nuclei of combining atoms.

45. A double covalent bond has four shared electrons (two bonding pairs); a triple covalent bond has six shared electrons (three bonding pairs).

46. a. :Ï:Ï: **b.** :F̈:Ö:F̈:

   c. H:S̈:H   **d.** :Ï:N̈:Ï:
                    :Ï:

47. One atom contributes both electrons to a coordinate covalent bond as in CO.

48. An unshared pair of electrons is needed for a coordinate covalent bond. There are no unshared pairs in C-H or C-C bonds.

49. [:Ö:N::Ö:]⁻ ↔ [:Ö::N:Ö:]⁻

50. b and c; assuming only single bonds, the P and S atoms each have 10 valence electrons.

51. Bond dissociation energy is defined as the energy needed to break one covalent bond.

52. Increasing bond dissociation energy is linked to lower chemical reactivity.

53. A pi bond is formed by the side-by side overlap of two half-filled p atomic orbitals to produce a pi molecular orbital. In a pi bond, the bonding electrons are most likely to be found in sausage-shaped regions above and below the bond. See Figure 8.15.

54. a. linear   **b.** tetrahedral
   c. trigonal planar   **d.** bent
   e. linear   **f.** bent

55. The $2s$ and the $2p$ orbitals form two sp^2 hybrid orbitals on the carbon atom. One sp^2 hybrid orbital forms a sigma bond with the carbon atom. Pi bonds between each oxygen atom and the carbon are formed by the unhybridized $2p$ orbitals.

56. a. sp^3 **b.** sp^2
   c. sp **d.** sp

57. The electronegativities of the two atoms will differ by about 0.4 to 2.0.

58. c, d, a, f, b, e.

59. A hydrogen bond is formed by an electrostatic interaction between a hydrogen atom that is covalently bonded to an electronegative atom, and an unshared electron pair of a nearby atom.

60.

61. More energy is required to separate the molecules.

Understanding Concepts

62. The $3s$ and three $3p$ orbitals of phosphorus hybridize to form four sp^3 atomic orbitals. The resulting shape is pyramidal with a bond angle of 107° between the sigma bonds.

63. :C̈l:S̈:C̈l:
     :Ö:

64. a. C does not have an octet. [:C::N:]⁻

   b. One F has more than an octet. :F̈:P̈:F̈:
                              :F̈:

65. a. tetrahedral, 109.5°
  b. trigonal planar, 120°
  c. etrahedral, 109.5°
  d. bent, 105°

66. a. The percent ionic character increases as the difference in electronegativities increases.
  b. 1.6
  c. (1) 85% (2) 10% (3) 62% (4) 23%

67. a. 109.5°
  b. 120°
  c. 180°

68. a. trigonal planar
  b. pyramidal
  c. linear
  d. tetrahedral

69. a. Phosphorus in PBr_5 has 10 valence electrons

70. a.

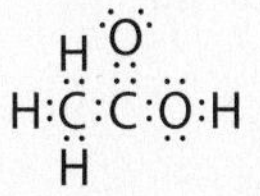

H:C:C:O:H with H and O groups

  b. No, the molecule contains one carbon-oxygen double bond and one carbon-oxygen single bond.
  c. polar bond
  d. Yes, it has polar oxygen atoms at one end of the molecule and a nonpolar CH_3^- group at the opposite end.

Critical Thinking

71. C, O, H, S, N, F, Cl, I, Br: These elements are all nonmetals.

72. Answers will vary. Table 8.3 suggests there is no clear difference. The student's argument could be based on chemical properties, such as conductivity of the compound in the liquid state.

73. a. two covalent bonds to both hydrogens

H:C::C:H

  b. Fluorine and oxygen have only four electrons

:F:O:F:

  c. Halogens form one covalent bond, not three.

H:S:H

  d. Nitrogen forms three covalent bonds, not four.

:I:N:I:
:I:

74. Ethyl alcohol can form intermolecular hydrogen bonds between its polar –OH groups, but dimethyl ether can not form hydrogen bonds.

75. a. bent
  b. etrahedral
  c. pyramidal

76. False. The bond dissociation energies exhibit no particular trend and, in fact, are fairly constant.

Concept Challenge

77.

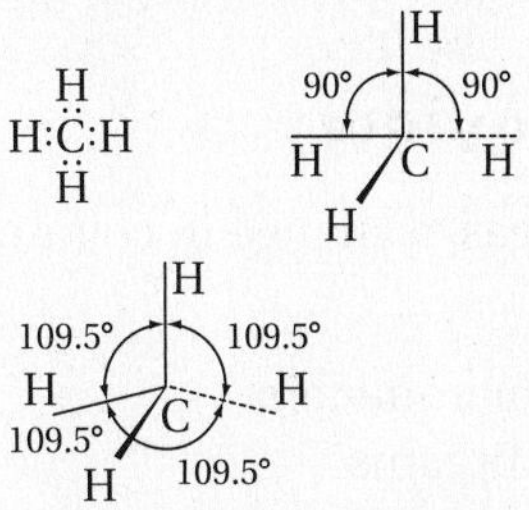

The first sketch shows carbon's three bonds oriented at 90° angles. The fourth bond angle is not specified. The second sketch is a tetrahedron. The bond angles in the second sketch are all 109.5° The second sketch is correct. (Note: The wedge-shaped lines come out of the page; the dotted lines recede into the page.)

78.

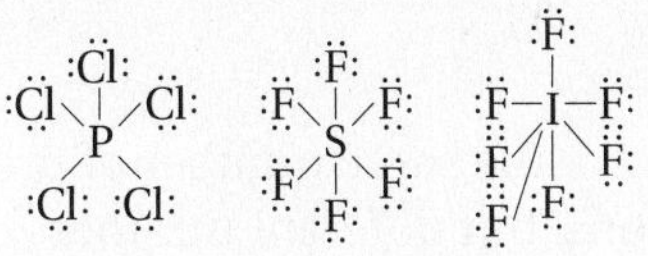

P forms 5 hybrid orbitals (dsp^3), S forms 6 hybrid orbitals (d^3sp^3), and I forms 7 hybrid orbitals (d^3sp^3).

79.

:O:
H:C:O:H

80.

:O:O:
H:O:C:C:O:H

81. H:N::N:N: ⟷ H:N:N::N:

82. a. Be has only 4 valence electrons.

b. S has 12 valence electrons.

c. Cl has only 7 valence electrons.

d. B has only 6 valence electrons.

e. Xe has 10 valence electrons. :F̈–Ẍe–F̈:

Cumulative Review

83. formation of a gas, a change in color or odor

84. a. 6.65×10^4 micrometers
b. 4×10^{-4} centigrams
c. 5.62×10^{-1} decigram per liter
d. 2.4×10^1 meters per second

85. a. 2
b. 2
c. 3
d. 3

86. a. 16
b. 12
c. 8
d. 26

87. Isotopes have the same number of protons and electrons, but different numbers of neutrons.

88. Protons and electrons must be equal.

89. a. 6
b. 2
c. 5
d. 0

90. The wavelength decreases as the frequency increases.

91. The d sublevel of the third principal energy level contains 5 electrons.

92. a. $1s^2 2s^2 2p^6 3s^1$
b. $1s^2 2s^2 2p^6 3s^2 3p^4$
c. $1 s^2 2s^2 2p^6 3s^2 3p^3$
d. $1s^2 2s^2 2p^3$

93. The anion is larger than the corresponding neutral atom.

94. Mendeleev arranged the elements by increasing atomic mass in vertical rows and by similarities in chemical and physical properties. Mosely arranged the elements by increasing atomic number in vertical rows and by similarities in chemical and physical properties.

95. a. K, $1s^2 2s^2 2p^6 3s^2 3p^6 4s^1$
b. Al, $1s^2 2s^2 2p^6 3s^2 3p^1$
c. S, $1s^2 2s^2 2p^6 3s^2 3p^4$
d. Ba, $1s^2 2s^2 2p^6 3s^2 3p^6 3d^{10} 4s^2$ $4p^6 4d^{10} 5s^2 5p^6 6s^2$

96. a. barium
b. silicon
c. sodium

97. e. II and III only

98. All have the same number of electrons as a noble gas.

99. b. cesium

100. a. 8
b. 3
c. 6
d. 2

101. a. $1s^2 2s^2 2p^6$
b. $1s^2 2s^2 2p^6$
c. $1s^2 2s^2 2p^6$
d. $1s^2 2s^2 2p^6 3s^2 3p^6$

102. No, an alloy is a homogeneous mixture.

CHEMICAL NAME AND FORMULAS

Reviewing Content

42. a. 2– **b.** 1+
  c. 1– **d.** 3+

43. a. 2+ **b.** 2+
  c. 3+ **d.** 1+

44. a. barium ion **b.** iodide ion
  c. silver ion **d.** mercury(II) ion

45. cyanide, CN^- and hydroxide, OH^-

46. a. hydroxide ion **b.** lead(IV) ion
  c. sulfate ion **d.** oxide ion

47. zero; A compound is electrically neutral.

48. The symbols for the cation and anion are written and the charges are balanced with subscripts. The name of the cation is followed by the name of the anion.

49. Determine the charge of the anion then work the formula backwards to find the charge of the transition metal cation needed to give a net charge of zero for the formula unit.

50. The symbols for the cation and anion are written and the charges are balanced with subscripts. Parentheses are used around the polyatomic ion if a subscript is needed. The name of the cation is followed by the name of the anion.

51. a and **b**

52. When more than a single polyatomic ion is needed to balance the formula

53. NH_4NO_3, ammonium nitrate;

$(NH_4)_2CO_3$, ammonium carbonate;

NH_4CN, ammonium cyanide;

$(NH_4)_3PO_4$, ammonium phosphate;

$Sn(NO_3)_4$, tin(IV) nitrate; $Sn(CO_3)_2$, tin(IV) carbonate; $Sn(CN)_4$, tin(IV) cyanide;

$Sn_3(PO_4)_4$, tin(IV) phosphate; $Fe(NO_3)_3$, iron(III) nitrate; $Fe_2(CO_3)_3$, iron(III) carbonate; $Fe(CN)_3$, iron(III) cyanide; $FePO_4$, iron(III) phosphate; $Mg(NO_3)_2$, magnesium nitrate; $MgCO_3$, magnesium carbonate; $Mg(CN)_2$, magnesium cyanide; $Mg_3(PO_4)_2$, magnesium phosphate

54. two nonmetals

55. a. tri- **b.** mono-
  c. di- **d.** hexa-
  e. penta- **f.** tetra–

56. For formulas, write the correct symbols for each element with a subscript corresponding to the prefix before each element in the name. For naming, name each element in the order given. Use the subscript to determine the prefixes before each element in the name. The name ends in -*ide*.

57. a. BCl_3 **b.** dinitrogen pentoxide
  c. N_2H_4 **d.** carbon tetrachloride

58. a. hydrochloric acid **b.** H_2SO_4
  c. nitric acid **d.** $HC_2H_3O_2$

59. No, to be an acid the compound must produce H^+ ions in water solution.

60. a. HNO_2 **b.** $Al(OH)_3$
  c. H_2Se **d.** $Sr(OH)_2$
  e. H_3PO_4

61. a. $Fe(OH)_2$ **b.** lead(II) hydroxide
  c. $Cu(OH)_2$ **d.** cobalt(II) hydroxide

62. In all samples of the same chemical compound, the masses of the elements are always in the same proportions.

63. Whenever two elements form more than one compound, the different masses of one element that combine with the same mass of the other element are in the ratio of small whole numbers.

64. no; The ratio of nitrogen to oxygen is 42:26, which is not a 7:4 ratio.

Understanding Concepts

65. a. $KMnO_4$ **b.** $Ca(HCO_3)_2$
  c. Cl_2O_7 **d.** Si_3N_4
  e. NaH_2PO_4 **f.** PBr_5
  g. CCl_4

66. a. MgS **b.** Na_3PO_3
  c. $Ba(OH)_2$ **d.** $Cu(NO_2)_2$
  e. K_2SO_3 **f.** $CaCO_3$
  g. $NaBr$ **h.** $Fe_2(SO_4)_3$

67. a. sodium chlorate
   b. mercury(I) bromide
   c. potassium chromate
   d. perchloric acid
   e. tin(IV) oxide
   f. iron(III) acetate
   g. potassium hydrogen sulfate
   h. calcium hydroxide
   i. barium sulfide

68. a. lithium perchlorate
   b. dichlorine monoxide
   c. mercury(II) fluoride
   d. calcium oxide
   e. barium phosphate
   f. iodine
   g. strontium sulfate
   h. copper(I) acetate
   i. silicon tetrachloride

69. a. magnesium permanganate
   b. beryllium nitrate
   c. potassium carbonate
   d. dinitrogen tetrahydride
   e. lithium hydroxide
   f. barium fluoride
   g. phosphorus triiodide
   h. zinc oxide
   i. phosphorous acid

70. a. $CaBr_2$ **b.** $AgCl$
   c. Al_4C_3 **d.** NO_2
   e. $Sn(CN)_4$ **f.** LiH
   g. $Sr(C_2H_3O_2)_2$ **h.** Na_2SiO_3

71. binary molecular compound

72. lithium carbonate, Li_2CO_3

73. $SnCl_4$

74. a. 2:1
   b. PbI_2, lead(II) iodide and PbI_4, lead(IV) iodide

75. a. 9.85%
   b. nitrogen, oxygen, and chlorine; 54.9 billions of kg
   c. 34.7%
   d. H_2SO_4, N_2, O_2, NH_3, CaO, H_3PO_4, $NaOH$, Cl_2, Na_2CO_3, HNO_3

Critical Thinking

76. A molecular formula shows the number of each kind of atom in a molecule of the compound. The formula unit shows the lowest whole-number ratio of ions in a compound.

77. on the right side

78. Common names vary in different languages and are difficult to remember and convert to formulas.

79. The statement is true for the representative metals but not for the transition metals, which often have multiple charges.

80. Possible answers include: cations always come before anions; when a cation has more than one ionic charge, the charge is indicated by a Roman numeral; monatomic anions use an *–ide* ending. Each rule has a specific purpose; for example, an ionic charge is necessary information because it determines how many ions are in the formula unit of the compound.

81. a. N_2O, dinitrogen monoxide
   b. NO_2, nitrogen dioxide
   c. NO, nitrogen monoxide
   d. N_2O_4, dinitrogen tetroxide

82. a. Cu_2S, copper(I) sulfide and CuS, copper(II) sulfide
   b. $FeSO_4$, iron(II) sulfate and $Fe_2(SO_4)_3$, iron(III) sulfate
   c. PbO, lead(II) oxide and PbO_2 lead(IV) oxide

83. a. The charges do not balance, $CsCl$.
   b. The charges do not balance, ZnO.
   c. Neon does not form compounds.
   d. The subscripts are not the lowest whole-number ratio, BaS.

84. binary ionic compounds: d and g; binary molecular compounds: a and f; compounds with polyatomic ions: *b, c, e, h,* and *i;* acids: *b* and *e;* base: *c*

Concept Challenge

85. Spot check student answers.

86. a. Potassium carbonate has greater water solubility than $CaCO_3$.
   b. The copper compound is blue; the iron compound is white.
   c. Add water to dissolve the NH_4Cl; then filter out the insoluble $BaSO_4$.
   d. chlorine (nonmetal), sulfur (nonmetal), bromine (nonmetal), barium (metal), iodine (nonmetal), mercury (metal)
   e. barium sulfate, calcium carbonate, potassium carbonate, copper(II) sulfate pentahydrate, iron(II) sulfate pentahydrate, ammonium chloride

f. 639 g

g. 7.54 cm^3

h. color, density, melting point, or boiling point

Cumulative Review

87. Answers may include: color (physical), solid (physical), magnetic (physical), conducts electricity (physical), burns (chemical).

88. a. 4   **b.** 2
c. 2   **d.** 4
e. 2   **f.** 1

89. 5.2 cm

90. a. $7.75 \times 105 \text{ µL}$ **b.** 208 K
c. 0.832 cg

91. 0.538 g/cm^3

92. a. b   **b.** protons
c. electrons   **d.** neutrons

93. Both are in the nucleus and have a mass of about 1 amu. A proton is positively charged; a neutron has no charge.

94. a. neon   **b.** carbon
c. boron helium

95. a. 1   **b.** 6
c. 5   **d.** 2
e. 7   **f.** 8

96. The metalloids border a line separating the metals from the nonmetals. Their properties are intermediate between those of metals and nonmetals.

97. a. cesium, potassium, sodium, lithium
b. lithium, boron, carbon, fluorine, neon

98. a. Li   **b.** I
c. S   **d.** O
e. N   **f.** F

99. When metallic elements of Group 1A and 2A form ions, they lose all their outer shell electrons. This increases the attraction by the nucleus for the fewer remaining electrons and results in ions that are smaller than the neutral atoms. The electron that a Group 7A element gains in forming an ion enters the outer shell, resulting in a decrease in the effective nuclear attraction of the increased number of electrons. The anion is larger than the neutral atom.

100. $1s^2 2s^2 2p^6$; Possible answers are N^{3-}, O^{2-}, F^-, Na^+, Mg^{2+}, and Al^{3+}.

101. a. 12 p^+ and 10 e^- **b.** 35 p^+ and 36 e^-
c. 38 p^+ and 36 e^- **d.** 16 p^+ and 18 e^-

102. b and c; Molecular compounds formed by two nonmetals have covalent bonds.

103. b., d., and f.

104. a. :C̈l·C̈l: **b.** :C:::O:

c. :O::C::O: **d.** H:N̈:H (H above and below)

e. :C̈l·C̈:·C̈l: with :C: above and below

f. H:Ö:H

g. H:C̈:H with H above and below

105. A hydrogen bond is an intermolecular force between a hydrogen atom covalently bonded to a very electro–negative atom and an unshared pair of electrons from another electronegative atom.

106. ionic bond: electrons are transferred

$Na· + ·F̈: \rightarrow Na^+ :F̈:^-$

covalent bond: electrons are shared

$H· + ·H \rightarrow H:H$

Reviewing Content

47. Number, mass, or volume; examples will vary.

48. **a.** molecule
b. formula unit
c. molecule
d. atom

49. **a.** 3
b. 2
c. 9
d. 10

50. All contain 6.02×10^{23} molecules

51. mol C_2H_6

52. **a.** 1.81×10^{24} atoms Sn
b. 2.41×10^{23} formula units KCl
c. 4.52×10^{24} molecules SO_2
d. 2.89×10^{21} formula units NaI

53. **a.** 98.0 g/mol
b. 76.0 g/mol
c. 100.1 g/mol
d. 132.1 g/mol
e. 89.0 g/mol
f. 159.8 g/mol

54. **a.** 60.1 g/mol
b. 28.0 g/mol
c. 106.8 g/mol
d. 63.5 g/mol

55. Answers will vary but should include
1. Determine the moles of each atom from the formula.
2. Look up the atomic mass of each element.
3. Multiply the number of moles of each atom times its molar mass.
4. Sum these products.

56. 71.0 g/mol Cl_2

57. Answers will vary.

58. **a.** 0.258 mol SiO_2
b. 4.80×10^{-4} mol AgCl
c. 1.12 mol Cl_2
d. 0.106 mol KOH
e. 5.93 mol $Ca(C_2H_3O_2)_2$
f. 2.00×10^{-2} mol Ca

59. **a.** 108 g C_5H_{12}
b. 547 g F_2

c. 71.8 g $Ca(CN)_2$
d. 0238 g H_2O_2
e. 224 g NaOH
f. 1.88 g Ni

60. **a.** 1.7×10^2 L Ar
b. 9.9 L C_2H_6

61. **a.** 1.96 g/L
b. 0.902 g/L
c. 2.05 g/L

62. **a.** 234 L SO_3
b. 2.99×10^{-22} g $C_9H_8O_4$
c. 3.13×10^{25} atoms

63. **a.** 5.9% H, 94.1% S
b. 22.6% N, 6.5% H, 19.4% C, 51.6% O
c. 41.7% Mg, 54.9% O, 3.4% H
d. 42.1% Na, 18.9% P, 39.0% O

64. **a.** 3.33 g S
b. 5.65 g N
c. 40.6 g Mg
d. 152 g P

65. **d.** 77.7% Fe in FeO

66. H_2O_2

67. **a.** molecular
b. molecular
c. empirical

68. **a.** $C_3H_6O_3$
b. Hg_2Cl_2

69. **a.** H_2O_2
b. $C_6H_6O_4$

Understanding Concepts

70. You can measure the mass of 22.4 L of the compound at STP; this is the molar volume of the gas. The mass of the molar volume is the molar mass.

71. **a.** A, $C_2H_4O_2$; D, $C_5H_{10}O_5$; E, $C_6H_{12}O_6$
b. slope = 2.5/1, which is the ratio of the molar mass of the empirical formula to the mass of carbon in the empirical formula: 30/12 = 2.5/1.
c. mass of carbon = 36(x); molar mass = 90(y) mass of carbon = 48(x); molar mass = 120(y)

72. a. A molecule is composed of two or more atoms.
  b. There are 6.02×10^{23} molecules in 1 mol of a molecular substance.
  c. A mole of CO_2 has 3 times Avogadro's number of atoms.

73. b. 0.842 mol C_2H_4

74. 24.5 g

75. a. CO
  b. $C_2O_2NH_5$
  c. Cl_2OC

76. a. 27 amu
  b. aluminum

77. 3.01×10^{13} km

78. a. $CuBr_2$
  b. CH_3

79. $C_3H_6O_3$

80. 3.34×10^{25} molecules H_2O

81. 2.73×10^{20} F atoms

82. 0.982 g He

Critical Thinking

83. C_2H_6O

84. A molecular formula is a whole number multiple of its empirical formula.

85. Sulfur atoms have a greater atomic mass. The most abundant sulfur atom has 16 protons, 16 electrons, and 16 neutrons; carbon is composed of 6 protons, 6 electrons, and 6 neutrons. Therefore, 6.02×10^{23} sulfur atoms will have a greater mass than the same number of carbon atoms.

86. Gas molecules are separated by so much empty space their own volumes are insignificant in determining how much space a certain quantity of gas molecules takes up.

87. a. $C_9H_{11}O_2N$ **b.** $C_9H_{11}O_2N$

Concept Challenge

88. $C_3H_5O_9N_3$

89. 21.9 cm^3

90. 3.54×10^{23} O_2 molecules

91. a.

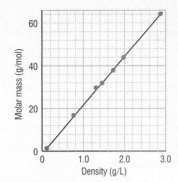

  b. 22.4 L/mol
  c. 24.6 g/mol
  d. 2.5 g/L

92. 2.4×10^9 kg Au; 2×10^{11} L H_2O; not feasible

93. 6.025×10^{23} formula units/mol

Cumulative Review

94. chemical change: wax burning
physical change: wax melting
physical change: wax vaporizing

95. a. physical change   **b.** chemical change
  c. chemical change   **d.** physical change
  e. chemical change   **f.** physical change

96. a. false   **b.** true
  c. true   **d.** false

97. A molecule is composed of two or more atoms.

98. No; the student has ignored the units. The density of sugar is 1.59 g/mL; the density of carbon dioxide is much less, 1.83 g/L.

99. It will float. Its density, 0.848 g/mL, is less than the density of water.

100. a. 4.72×10^3 mg
  b. 97 km/h
  c. 4.4×10^{-2} dm

101. a. 40, 40, 50   **b.** 46, 46, 62
  c. 35, 35, 46   **d.** 51, 51, 72

102. a. $1s^2 2s^2 2p^5$ **b.** $1s^2 2s^1$
  c. [Kr] $5s^1$

103. Magnesium and barium are both in group 2A and have 2 valence electrons.

104. Cr, Cd, Cu, and Co

105. For group A elements, the group number equals the number of valence electrons.

106. **a.** pyramidal $H:\overset{..}{P}:H$
     $\overset{|}{H}$
     b. linear $:O:::C:$

c. linear $\overset{..}{S}::C::\overset{..}{S}:$ **d.** tetrahedral $:F:$
$:F:C:F:$
$:F:$

107. For single bond a single line connects the atoms (X—X). Atoms are connected by two lines in a double bond (X=X), and three lines in a triple bond (X≡X).

108. Answers will vary.
     a. carbon monoxide (CO)
     b. ozone (O_3)
     c. nitrogen dioxide (NO_2)

109. Calculate the electronegativity difference between two atoms. If the difference is small (0.0 —0.4) the bond is nonpolar covalent. If the difference ≥ 2.0, the bond is most likely ionic. For values between 0.4 and 2.0, the bond is polar covalent.

110. **d.**CaS_2 **f.** $Ba(OH)$

111. **a.** iron(III) hydroxide
     b. ammonium iodide
     c. sodium carbonate
     d. carbon tetrachloride

112. **a.** KNO_3 **b.** CuO
     c. Mg_3N_2 **d.** AgF

Reviewing Content

36. a. reactants: sodium and water; products: hydrogen and sodium hydroxide

b. reactants: carbon dioxide and water; products: oxygen and glucose

37. Dalton said that the atoms of reactants are rearranged to form new substances as products.

38. The arrow separates the reactants from the products and indicates a reaction that progresses in the forward direction. A plus sign separates individual reactants and individual products from one another.

39. a. Gaseous ammonia and oxygen react in the presence of a platinum catalyst to produce nitrogen monoxide gas and water vapor.

b. Aqueous solutions of sulfuric acid and barium chloride are mixed to produce a precipitate of barium sulfate and aqueous hydrochloric acid.

c. The gas dinitrogen trioxide reacts with water to produce an aqueous solution of nitrous acid.

40. A catalyst speeds up a chemical reaction.

41. a. $C + 2F + 2G \rightarrow CF_2G_2$

b. $F + 3W + S + 2P \rightarrow FW_3SP_2$

42. A formula is a unique identifier of a substance. A different formula would indicate a different substance, not the one that is taking part in the reaction you are trying to balance.

43. a. $2PbO_2 \rightarrow 2PbO + O_2$

b. $2Fe(OH)_3 \rightarrow Fe_2O_3 + 3H_2O$

c. $(NH_4)_2CO_3 \rightarrow 2NH_3 + H_2O + CO_2$

d. $2NaCl + H_2SO_4 \rightarrow Na_2SO_4 + 2HCl$

44. a single product

45. a. $2Mg + O_2 \rightarrow 2MgO$

b. $4P + 5O_2 \rightarrow 2P_2O_5$

c. $Ca + S \rightarrow CaS$

46. a single reactant

47. a. $2Ag_2O \xrightarrow{\Delta} 4Ag + O_2$

b. $NH_4NO_3 \xrightarrow{\Delta} N_2O + 2H_2O$

48. a. no reaction

b. $Zn(s) + 2AgNO_3(aq) \rightarrow$
$$(Zn(NO_3)_2(aq) + 2Ag(s)$$

c. $2Al(s) + 3H_2SO_4(aq) \rightarrow$
$$Al_2(SO_4)_3(aq) + 3H_2(g)$$

49. a. $H_2C_2O_4(aq) + 2KOH(aq) \rightarrow$
$$K_2C_2O_4(aq) + 2H_2O(l)$$

b. $CdBr_2(aq) + Na_2S(aq) \rightarrow$
$$CdS(s) + 2NaBr(aq)$$

50. oxygen

51. a. $C_4H_8 + 6O_2 \rightarrow 4CO_2 + 4H_2O$

b. $C_3H_6O + 4O_2 \rightarrow 3CO_2 + 3H_2O$

52. a. $3Hf + 2N_2 \rightarrow Hf_3N_4$; combination

b. $Mg + H_2SO_4 \rightarrow MgSO_4 + H_2$; single replacement

c. $2C_2H_6 + 7O_4 \rightarrow 4CO_2 + 6H_2O$; combustion

d. $Pb(NO_3)_2 + 2NaI \rightarrow PbI_2 + 2NaNO_3$; double replacement

e. $3Fe + 2O_2 \rightarrow Fe_3O_4$; combination

53. an ion that does not participate in the reaction

54. a. $H^+(aq) + OH^-(aq) \rightarrow H_2O(l)$

b. $Ag^+(aq) + Cl^-(aq) \rightarrow AgCl(s)$

55. a. $2Al(s) + 6H^+(aq) \rightarrow 2Al^{3+}(aq) + 3H_2(g)$

b. $H^+(aq) + OH^-(aq) \rightarrow H_2O(l)$

c. no reaction

Understanding Concepts

56. a. $Cl_2 + 2NaI \rightarrow 2NaCl + I_2$

b. $2NH_3 \rightarrow N_2 + 3H_2$

c. $4Na + O_2 \rightarrow 2Na_2O$

57. a. $Cl_2(g) + 2KI(aq) \rightarrow I_2(aq) + 2KCl(aq)$

b. $2Fe(s) + 6HCl(aq) \rightarrow$
$$2FeCl_3(aq) + 3H_2(g)$$

c. $P_4O_{10}(s) + 6H_2O(l) \rightarrow 4H_3PO_4(aq)$

58. a. $ZnS(aq) + H_2SO_4(aq) \rightarrow$
$$H_2S(g) + ZnSO_4(aq)$$

b. $NaOH(aq) + HNO_3(aq) \rightarrow$
$$H_2O(l) + NaNO_3(aq)$$

c. $2KF(aq) + Ca(NO_3)_2(aq) \rightarrow$
$$CaF_2(s) + 2KNO_3(aq)$$

59. a. $Na_2O(s) + H_2O(l) \rightarrow 2NaOH(aq)$

b. $H_2(g) + Br_2(g) \rightarrow 2HBr(g)$

c. $Cl_2O_7(l) + H_2O(l) \rightarrow 2HClO_4(aq)$

60. a. $Fe(s) + H_2SO_4(aq) \rightarrow FeSO_4(aq) + H_2(g)$
  b. no reaction
  c. $Br_2(l) + BaI_2(aq) \rightarrow BaBr_2(aq) + I_2(aq)$

61. a. tube A
  b. $2Na(s) + 2H_2O(l) \rightarrow 2NaOH(aq) + H_2(g)$; single-replacement

62. a. $2C_8H_{18} + 25O_2 \rightarrow 16CO_2 + 18H_2O$
  b. $C_6H_{12}O_6 + 6O_2 \rightarrow 6CO_2 + 6H_2O$
  c. $HC_2H_3O_2 + 2O_2 \rightarrow 2CO_2 + 2H_2O$

63. a. $2Al_2O_3 \xrightarrow{\text{energy}} 4Al + 3O_2$

  b. $Sn(OH)_4 \xrightarrow{\Delta} SnO_2 + 2H_2O$

  c. $Ag_2CO_3 \xrightarrow{\Delta} Ag_2O + CO_2$

64. a. $H^+(aq) + OH^-(aq) \rightarrow H_2O(l)$
  b. $S^{2-}(aq) + H^+(aq) \rightarrow H_2S(g)$
  c. $3OH^-(aq) + Fe^{3+}(aq) \rightarrow Fe(OH)_3(s)$

65. a. $CdS(s)$
  b. $Na^+(aq)$ and $NO_3^-(aq)$
  c. $Cd^{2+}(aq) + S^{2-}(aq) \rightarrow CdS(s)$

66. a. $K_2O(s) + H_2O(l) \rightarrow 2KOH(aq)$; combination
  b. $C_{19}H_{40}(s) + 29O_2(g) \rightarrow 19CO_2(g) + 20H_2O(l)$; combustion
  c. $2Rb(s) + 2H_2O(l) \rightarrow H_2(g) + 2RbOH(aq)$; single-replacement

Critical Thinking

67. a. $2K(s) + 2H_2O(l) \rightarrow 2KOH(aq) + H_2(g)$
  b. $C_2H_5OH(l) + 3O_2(g) \rightarrow 2CO_2(g) + 3H_2O(g)$
  c. $2Bi(NO_2)_3(aq) + 3H_2S(g) \rightarrow Bi_2S_3(s) + 6HNO_3(aq)$
  d. $2Al(s) + 3Br_2(l) \rightarrow 2AlBr_3(s)$
  e. $2HNO_3(aq) + Ba(OH)_2(aq) \rightarrow Ba(NO_3)_2(aq) + 2H_2O(l)$

68. Smoking is not permitted near an oxygen source because a fire will burn faster in an area of high oxygen concentration. However, if a match were struck in a room full of oxygen and isolated from combustible material, it would only burn more vigorously.

69. a. $C_5H_{12} + 8O_2 \rightarrow 5CO_2 + 6H_2O$
  $C_9H_{20} + 14O_2 \rightarrow 9CO_2 + 10H_2O$
  b. $2C_{12}H_{26} + 37O_2 \rightarrow 24CO_2 + 26H_2O$
  $C_{17}H_{36} + 26O_2 \rightarrow 17CO_2 + 18H_2O$
  c. $n = CO_2$; $(n + 1) = H_2O$

Concept Challenge

70. a. $3NaI + H_3PO_4 \rightarrow 3HI + Na_3PO_4$; double-replacement
  b. $K_2O + H_2O \rightarrow 2KOH$; combination

  c. $2H_2SO_4 \xrightarrow{\Delta} 2H_2O + O_2 + 2SO_2$; decomposition

  d. $2Al + 3H_2SO_4 \rightarrow 3H_2 + Al_2(SO_4)_3$; single-replacement
  e. $C_5H_{12} + 8O_2 \rightarrow 5CO_2 + 6H_2O$; combustion

71. a. (1) combination
    (2) single-replacement
    (3) combustion
    (4) double-replacement
  b. (1) $2Al(s) + 3Br_2(l) \rightarrow 2AlBr_3(s)$
    (2) $Cu(s) + 2AgNO_3(aq) \rightarrow Cu(NO_3)_2(aq) + 2Ag(s)$
    (3) $C_3H_8(g) + 5O_2(g) \rightarrow 3CO_2(g) + 4H_2O(g)$
    (4) $Pb(NO_3)_2(aq) + 2KI(aq) \rightarrow PbI_2(s) + 2KNO_3(aq)$

72. a. single-replacement
  b. $Cl_2(g) + 2I^-(aq) \rightarrow I_2(aq) + 2Cl^-(aq)$

Cumulative Review

73. a. water
  b. water vapor in the air
  c. physical change

74. Element: gold; compounds: sodium chloride, ice with water; homogeneous mixtures, salt water, air; heterogeneous mixture: salt and sand; substance: sodium chloride, gold, water with ice

75. 36.6 kg

76. 22 protons, 28 neutrons, and 22 electrons

77. a. $s^2 2s^2 2p^6 3s^2 3p^6 4s^2 3d^{10} 4p^6$
  b. $1s^2 2s^2 2p^6 3s^2 3p^6$
  c. $1s^2 2s^2 2p^6 3s^2 3p^6 3d^{10}$
  d. $1s^2 2s^2 2p^6 3s^2 3p^6 3d^{10}$

78. Electronegativity is the tendency for an atom to attract bonded electrons to itself. Electronegativity values increase from left to right in a period.

79. a. incorrect; KBr
  b. correct
  c. incorrect; Ca_3N_2
  d. correct

80. a. K_2CrO_4
  b. $NaHSO_3$
  c. permanganic acid
  d. potassium oxalate

81. a. 2.41 mol
  b. 6.91×10^{-2} mol
  c. 0.934 mol
  d. 7.09 mol

82. a. $FeSO_4$
  b. $FeSO_4$, iron(II) sulfate; $Fe_3(SO_4)_3$, iron(III) sulfate

83. $C_8H_{10}O_2N_4$

84. a.

mol $CaCl_2$	mol H_2O
0.156	0.312
0.439	0.878
1.12	2.24
3.03	6.06

b.

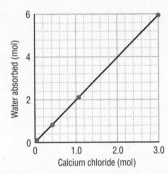

c. Two molecules of water.

Reviewing Content

36. a. Two formula units $KClO_3$ decompose to form two formula units KCl and three molecules O_2.

b. Four molecules NH_3 react with six molecules NO to form five molecules N_2 and six molecules H_2O.

c. Four atoms K react with one molecule O_2 to form two formula units K_2O.

37. a. Two mol $KClO_3$ decompose to form two mol KCl and three mol O_2.

b. Four mol NH_3 react with six mol NO to form five mol N_2 and six mol H_2O.

c. Four mol K react with one mol O_2 to form two mol K_2O.

38. a. 245.2 g   **b.** 248.0 g
c. 188.4 g
All obey the law of conservation of mass.

39. Acceptable answers include the idea of writing a ratio using the coefficients of two substances from a balanced equation as the number of moles of each substance reacting or being formed.

40. a. 0.54 mol   **b.** 13.6 mol
c. 0.984 mol   **d.** 236 mol

41. a. 11.3 mol CO, 22.5 mol H_2
b. 112 g CO, 16.0 g H_2
c. 11.4 g H_2

42. a. 372 g F_2
b. 1.32 g NH_3
c. 123 g N_2F_4

43. The coefficients indicate the relative number of moles (or particles) of reactants and products.

44. a. 51.2 g H_2O
b. 5.71×10^{23} molecules NH_3
c. 23.2 g Li_3N

45. The amount of the limiting reagent determines the maximum amount of product that can be formed. The excess reagent is only partially consumed in the reaction.

46. To identify the limiting reagent, express quantities of reactants as moles; compare to the mole ratios from the balanced equation.

47. a. Al
b. 3.0 mol $AlCl_3$
c. 0.8 mol Cl_2

48. 91.5%

Understanding Concepts

49. a. 2.36 g H_3PO_4
b. 1.89 g CO_2

50. a. 5.70×10^{21} atoms Zn
b. 95.2 g Zn

51. a. 7.0×10^2 L N_2
b. no reagent in excess

52. a. 96.4%
b. 45.0 g

53. 10.7 kg $CaSO_4$

54. 224 L gas

55. a. Initially, the amount of NaCl formed increases as the amount of Na used increases. For this part of the curve, sodium is the limiting reagent. Beyond a mass of about 2.5 g of Na, the amount of product formed remains constant because chlorine is now the limiting reagent.

b. Chlorine becomes the limiting reagent when the mass of sodium exceeds 2.5 g. This corresponds to a mass of about 3.9 g chlorine.

56. 50.0% yield; 0.500 mol; 0.0500 mol; 20.0% yield

Critical Thinking

57. The percent yield is 115%; such a yield could be attributed to experimenter error, or to unreacted starting material, or to outside materials contaminating the product.

58. Yes, a net ionic equation is balanced and thus obeys the law of conservation of mass.

59. **a.** 29 frames
    b. 58 wheels
    c. 174 pedals
    d. 87 seats

60. 1.1×10^6 L air

61. 13 days

Concept Challenge

62. 1.86 g/L

63. 87.4% $CaCO_3$

64. KOH is the limiting reagent.

65. **a.** 347 g Fe
    b. 239 g CO

66. 6.51 g SO_3

Cumulative Review

67. **a.** 22, 22, 25
    b. 50, 50,70
    c. 8, 8,10
    d. 12,12,14

68. **a.** ultraviolet
    b. ultraviolet
    c. ultraviolet

69. **a.** sodium
    b. arsenic
    c. cesium

70. **a.** Cs·
    b. :B̈r·
    c. ·Ca·
    d. ·P̈·

71. c and d

72. single bond, one pair shared electrons;
    double bond, two pairs of shared electrons;
    triple bond, three pairs of shared electrons

73. Yes, an ionic compound with at least one polyatomic ion has covalent bonds.

74. A cation has a positive charge, and an anion has a negative charge.

75. **a.** phosphate ion
    b. aluminum ion
    c. selenide ion
    d. ammonium ion

76. **a.** silicon dioxide
    b. potassium sulfate
    c. carbonic acid
    d. magnesium sulfide

77. **a.** $Al_2(CO_3)_3$
    b. NO_2
    c. K_2S
    d. $MnCrO_4$
    e. NaBr

78. 1.30×10^{-22} g

79. 7.38 g Be

80. $C_2H_2O_4$

81. **a.** 0.473 mol KNO_3
    b. 9.91×10^{-2} mol SO_2
    c. 3.74×10^{-2} mol PCl_3

82. **a.** $2Pb(NO_3)_2 \rightarrow 2PbO + 4NO_2 + O_2$
    b. $2C_3H_7OH + 9O_2 \rightarrow 6CO_2 + 8H_2O$
    c. $2Al + 3FeO \rightarrow 3Fe + Al_2O_3$

83. **a.** 1, 1, 1, 2
    b. 1, 3, 3, 1
    c. 1, 1, 1, 2

84. **a.** $Ba^{2+}(aq) + SO_4^{2-}(aq) \rightarrow BaSO_4(s)$
    b. $Ag^+(aq) + Cl^-(aq) \rightarrow AgCl(s)$
    c. $H^+(aq) + OH^-(aq) \rightarrow H_2O(l)$

85. **a.** sodium ion and nitrate ion
    b. aluminum ion and nitrate ion
    c. magnesium ion and sulfate ion

86. $C_5H_{10}O_5 + 5O_2 \rightarrow 5CO_2 + 5H_2O$

Reviewing Content

26. In an elastic collision energy is transferred between particles.

27. a, b, c, e, and f

28. pascal (Pa), SI; millimeter of mercury (mm Hg); atmosphere (atm)

29. 16.35 atm

30. **a.** 25 kPa
    b. 0.25 atm

31. The Kelvin temperature is directly proportional to the average kinetic energy.

32. If the temperature does not change, the average kinetic energy is not affected.

33. STP stands for standard temperature (0°C) and pressure (101.3 kPa or 1 atm).

34. At absolute zero, the motion of particles would cease.

35. The average kinetic energy triples.

36. The particles in a gas are relatively far apart compared to the particles in a liquid. Because of the extra space between particles, a gas is less dense and easier to compress.

37. In both cases, particles with sufficient kinetic energy move from the liquid to the vapor phase. In a closed container, a dynamic equilibrium is set up between the contained liquid and its vapor.

38. Two opposing processes are occurring at identical rates.

39. More molecules have enough energy to escape attractions within the liquid.

40. No. In an open container, most of the particles that escape from the surface of the liquid as vapor do not condense back to liquid.

41. It increases the average kinetic energy, which increases the vapor pressure.

42. The boiling point is the temperature at which the vapor pressure equals the external pressure. At the normal boiling point, the external pressure is 101.3 kPa.

43. **a.** about 50 mm Hg
    b. about 94°C
    c. 760 mm Hg is standard pressure

44. Escaping molecules have more kinetic energy than the average. Thus, the average kinetic energy and temperature of the remaining molecules are lower.

45. Ionic compounds generally have higher melting points than molecular solids do.

46. The particles have sufficient kinetic energy to overcome the attractive forces holding them in place.

47. The intermolecular attractions between the molecules are weaker than the attractions between ions.

48. Water from the food sublimed and condensed on the lid.

49. The temperature is constant while the liquid boils because the added energy is used to vaporize the molecules.

50. The average kinetic energy of the molecules is greater because, by definition, a fever is a state of increased body temperature.

Understanding Concepts

51. **a.** 121°C
    b. chloroform
    c. chloroform
    d. The external pressure on ethanol would have to increase; the external pressure on ethanoic acid would have to decrease.

52. Evaporation is the conversion of a liquid to a gas or vapor when the liquid is below the boiling point. The vapor pressure is the force per unit area exerted by the vaporized particles on the walls of a sealed container. The boiling point is the temperature at which the vapor pressure of the liquid becomes equal to the external pressure.

53. Although the net amounts of vapor and liquid remain constant, some molecules are evaporating while an equal number of particles are condensing.

54. Graphs should show a steeply rising smooth curve when temperature is plotted on the *x*-axis and vapor pressure on the *y*-axis.
    a. 80°C
    b. 100°C

55. decrease; As the attractions become stronger, it becomes more difficult for molecules to overcome the attractions and vaporize.

56. a. liquid
    b. vapor
    c. liquid
    d. vapor
    e. solid
    f. solid

57. about 77°C

58. Atmospheric pressure results from the collisions of particles in air with objects. There are fewer particles in a given volume of air at the top of a mountain than at sea level.

59. As the temperature drops to −196°C, the average kinetic energy of particles in the air decreases drastically as does the pressure. So the volume of the balloon, which is a flexible container, decreases. As the balloon warms back to room temperature, the average kinetic energy of the particles increases and the balloon expands to its previous volume.

Critical Thinking

60. When you draw on a straw, the pressure inside the straw is less than the pressure (atmospheric) on the liquid in the container; so liquid is pushed into your mouth.

61. Possible answers: Since the beaker is an open container the water should boil at 100°C, at or close to sea level. Your partner probably misread the thermometer and should recheck the value.

62. Possible answers: Odors will travel through a room; ink will move throughout a beaker of water.

63. It is the same, because the temperature is the same.

64. No. Collisions between large objects involve some loss of kinetic energy to heat.

65. Because the evaporation of perspiration is an endothermic process the skin is cooled.

66. The intermolecular attractions in some compounds are stronger than in others.

67. Vapor pressure depends only on the kinetic energy of the escaping molecules.

68. No. At 15 kPa water would boil at a temperature of about 50°C, which is much higher than room temperature.

69. The kinetic energy of the escaping molecules is the same, and so the vapor pressure is the same.

70. At high altitude, the boiling point of water is less than 100°C because the atmospheric pressure is lower. The increased pressure in the pressure cooker increases the temperature at which water boils.

71. condensation of the water vapor on a cold surface

Concept Challenge

72. $Na^+Cl^-Na^+Cl^-$
    $Cl^-Na^+Cl^-Na^+$
    $Na^+Cl^-Na^+Cl^-$
    $Cl^-Na^+Cl^-Na^+$

73. a. orthorhombic
    b. rhombohedral
    c. tetragonal
    d. triclinic
    e. cubic

74. a. body-centered cubic
    b. 8
    c. CsCl (one Cl^- ion and $8 \times 1/8$ equals one Cs^+ ion)

75. No; if (a) = (b) then water vapor will condense to the liquid state at the same rate that liquid forms vapor.

76. increases

Cumulative Review

77. inversely related

78. a. S
    b. K

79. a. $1s^2 2s^2 2p^6 3s^2 3p^6$
    b. $1s^2 2s^2 2p^6 3s^2 3p^6$
    c. $1s^2$

80. **a.** 2
    b. 2

81. dispersion forces, dipole interactions, hydrogen bonds

82. **a.** Cu_2SO^3
    b. HNO_2

83. **a.** CO
    b. PBr_3

84. **a.** Fe^{3+}
    b. Cd^{2+}

85. **a.** 53.7% Fe
    b. 34.6% Al

86. **a.** 13.9 mol SO_2
    b. 0.0472 mol NH_3

87. **a.** 51.2 g Cl_2O_7
    b. 30.6 mL H_2O

88. **a.** 0.38 mol CO_2
    b. 3.73 mol NH_3

89. $H_2S(aq) + Cd(NO_3)_2(aq) \rightarrow$
    $$2HNO_3(aq) + CdS(s)$$

90. **a.** $V_2O_5 + 2H_2 \rightarrow V_2O_3 + 2H_2O$
    b. $(NH_4)_2Cr_2O_7 \rightarrow Cr_2O_3 + N_2 + 4H_2O$

91. **a.** Mg
    b. Li

92. **a.** combination
    b. combustion

93. **a.** 198 g H_2O
    b. 23 mol products
    c. 144 g C

94. C_2H_4

95. 39.4 g FeS (0.448 mol)

96. 41.9%

Reviewing Content

39. The space between particles is reduced.

40. The increased kinetic energy of the particles causes collisions to occur more frequently and with more force.

41. The volume decreases. The molecules have less kinetic energy and cause less pressure on the inside of the balloon.

42. The pressure doubles.

43. The pressure quadruples.

44. As particles are removed from the container, there is a decrease in the number of collisions and a decrease in pressure.

45. $V_1 / T_1 = V_2 / T_2$

V_1 and V_2 are the initial and final volumes; T_1 and T_2 are the initial and final temperatures.

46. 1.00×10^2 kPa

47. 1.80 L

48. 18 L

49. 846 K (573°C)

50. $(P_1 V_1) / T_1 = (P_2 V_2) / T_2$

51. 1.10×10^3 kPa

52. When the volume is constant, $V_1 = V_2$, so the volume terms cancel, leaving an equation for Gay-Lussac's law.

53. Its particles have no volume, there are no attractions between them, and collisions are elastic. An ideal gas follows the gas laws at all temperatures and pressures.

54. Particles in a real gas have a finite volume and are attracted to one another at low temperatures and high pressures.

55. 33.0 L

56. 17.6 L

57. 3.60×10^2 kPa

58. 42 g He

59. The total pressure of a gaseous mixture is equal to the sum of the individual pressures of each gas.

60. At any temperature hydrogen gas diffuses faster than chlorine gas by an approximate factor of six.

61. molecular oxygen

62. 2.25:1

63. 3.08:1

Understanding Concepts

64. Gases are easily compressed because there is a lot of space between the particles.

65. Boiling the water fills the can with steam. When the can is plunged upside down into ice water the steam is trapped and rapidly condenses, reducing gas pressure inside the can. The walls of the can are not strong enough to withstand the comparatively high atmospheric pressure and the can collapses.

66. The results would be much less dramatic. The change in volume (and in internal pressure) from heated air to cold air is much less dramatic than when steam (a vapor) condenses to water (a liquid).

67. High temperatures increase the pressure of the contents of the container and may cause it to explode.

68. The pressure will double.

69. Temperatures measured on the Kelvin scale are directly proportional to the average kinetic energy of the particles. Celsius temperatures are not.

70. The water boils at a higher temperature, which speeds the cooking process.

71. The variables are directly proportional.

72. 165°C

73. The particles in a real gas have a finite volume and are attracted to one another.

74. The number of particles would be equal.

75. Helium atoms have a smaller molar mass than oxygen and nitrogen molecules and effuse faster through pores in the balloon.

76. 2.0 g

77. 2.0×10^2 g

78. Ammonia diffuses faster than hydrogen chloride. The ammonia molecules travel about twice the distance of the hydrogen chloride molecules, in the same time, based on the location of the reaction product.

Critical Thinking

79. A vacuum contains no matter to allow the transfer of kinetic energy between molecules.

80. The gases that make up the atmosphere, just like any other form of matter, are held near Earth by the force of gravity.

81. Helium gas, which is composed of small atoms with little attraction for each other.

82. The partial pressure of oxygen would be greater than at sea level, because the atmospheric pressure would be greater than at sea level.

83. **a.** 1.63×10^2 kPa
    b. 4.48×10^2 kPa

84. There could be different amounts of each gas or they could be at different pressures.

Concept Challenge

85. 2 mol KNO_2 for each 1 mol O_2

86. 46% CH_4

87. **a.** 2.0×10^{-3}%
    b. 2.0%

88. Because attractions between molecules in gases such as nitrogen and oxygen are insignificant, these gases have the molar volume of an ideal gas, 22.4 L at STP. Based on their molar volumes at STP, there are attractions between molecules of CH_4, CO_2, and NH_3. These attractions increase in strength from methane to carbon dioxide to ammonia.

Cumulative Review

89. K = °C + 273

90. 10.6 g/cm^3

91. 82 protons, 82 electrons, 124 neutrons

92. zinc, Zn

93. a. tungsten

94. c. selenium

95. b. SO_2

96. **a.** tin(II) bromide
    b. barium sulfate
    c. magnesium hydroxide
    d. iodine pentafluoride

97. 206 g

98. **a.** 158 g
    b. 98 g
    c. 342 g
    d. 331 g

99. It is the volume occupied by 1 mol of a gas at STP.

100. **a.** $C_4H_8O_2$
     b. C_8H_8
     c. $C_3H_6O_3$

101. **a.** single-replacement
     b. decomposition

102. **a.** $P_4O_{10} + 6H_2O \rightarrow 4H_3PO_4$
     b. $Al_2S_3 + 6H_2O \rightarrow 2Al(OH)_3 + 3H_2S$

103. 60.0% C, 13.3% H, 26.7% O

104. **a.** $4Al + 3O_2 \rightarrow 2Al_2O_3$
     b. 3.09×10^2 g Al; 2.75×10^2 g O_2

105. The motion of particles in a gas is constant, random, and rapid.

106. Gas pressure is the result of the collisions of gas particles with the container wall.

Reviewing Content

22. Strong hydrogen bonding causes an inward pull that tends to minimize the surface area.

23. Surface molecules are attracted to the liquid molecules below but not to the air above.

24. Drops are spherical; objects denser than a liquid can float on its surface.

25. A wetting agent such as a soap or detergent; A surfactant interferes with hydrogen bonding between water molecules and reduces surface tension.

26. Hydrogen bonds hold water molecules to each other, so the tendency for them to escape the solution is low.

27. The water has a low vapor pressure.

28. Ice is a regular open framework of hydrogen-bonded water molecules arrange like a honeycomb. This structure collapses in liquid water.

29. Bodies of water would freeze from the bottom up. This would kill many forms of aquatic life.

30. Hydrogen bonds between water molecules hold the molecules in a regular, open structure.

31. An aqueous solutions is a solution that has water as the solvent.

32. Water: solvent; sugar: solute.

33. Polar water molecules electrostatically attract ions and polar covalent molecules, but nonpolar compounds are unaffected, because they have no charges.

34. No; the molecules and ions are smaller than the pores of the filter.

35. Cations and anions become surrounded by solvent molecules.

36. **a.** HCl (polar) dissolves.
  b. NaI (ionic) dissolves.
  c. NH_3 (polar) dissolves.
  d. $MgSO_4$ (ionic) dissolves.
  e. CH_4 (nonpolar) will not dissolve.
  f. $CaCO_3$ (strong ionic forces) will not dissolve.

37. Water is polar, and gasoline is nonpolar

38. ions

39. Its ions are free to move toward an electrode.

40. A strong electrolyte is almost totally ionized.

41. water in the crystal structure of a substance

42. **a.** $Na_2SO4 \cdot 10H_2O$
  b. $CaCl_2 \cdot 2H_2O$
  c. $Ba(OH)_2 \cdot 8H_2O$

43. **a.** tin(IV) chloride pentahydrate
  b. iron(II) sulfate heptahydrate barium
  c. bromide tetrahydrate
  d. iron(III) phosphate tetrahydrate

44. $MgSO_4 \cdot 7H_2O \rightarrow MgSO4 \cdot H_2O + 6H_2O$

45. They absorb water vapor from the air.

46. They absorb water vapor from air.

47. Efflorescence is the loss of water of hydration that occurs when the hydrate has a higher vapor pressure than that of the water vapor in air.

48. A suspension has large particles that settle to the bottom. The particles in a solution stay suspended.

49. solutions, colloids, suspensions

50. scattering of visible light by colloids and suspensions

51. The molecules or ions are too small to have reflective surfaces.

52. collisions of the molecules of the dispersing medium with the small, dispersed colloidal particles

53. Brownian motion and repulsion between like-charged ions adsorbed on the surfaces of colloidal particles.

54. Add ions with a charge opposite that of the colloidal particles.

55. repulsions between like-charged particles and Brownian motion

Understanding Concepts

56. hexane, ethanol, water

57. Water molecules have maximum density at 4°C. Below 4°C the molecules arrange in a regular network because of the attractions between them. As a result, ice has a lower density than water.

58. **a.** 1.00 g/mL
    b. 4°C
    c. No; the density of ice is 0.917 g/mL at 0°C. There would be a break in the curve at 0°C as liquid water at 0°C changes to ice at 0°C.

59. **a.** Water expands when it freezes.
    b. Water is polar and wax is nonpolar, and water has a higher surface tension.
    c. Water has a lower vapor pressure than alcohol.

60. The container would break because water expands as it freezes.

61. **a.** gasoline
    b. water
    c. gasoline
    d. water

62. Anions are attracted to the hydrogen atoms of the water molecule because they have a partial positive charge. Cations are attracted to the oxygen atom in the water molecule because it has a partial negative charge.

63. **a.** No, they both dissolve in water.
    b. drying to examine the crystals, testing for electrical conductivity, doing a flame test

64. Ethanol has both a polar hydroxyl end (–OH) that dissolves in water and a nonpolar hydrocarbon end (C_2H_5–) that dissolves in gasoline.

65. No; nonpolar molecules do not dissolve in polar solvents.

66. **a.** $NH_4Cl(s) \rightarrow NH_4{+}(aq) + Cl^-(aq)$
    b. $Cu(NO_3)_2(s) \rightarrow Cu^{2+}(aq) + 2NO_3{}^-(aq)$
    c. $HC_2H_3O_2(s) \rightarrow H^+(aq) + C2H_3O_2{}^-(aq)$
    d. $HgCl_2(s) \rightarrow Hg^{2+}(aq) + 2Cl^-(aq)$

67. **a.** sodium carbonate monohydrate, 14.5 % H_2O
    b. magnesium sulfate heptahydrate, 51.2% H_2O

68. 15.6 g $CuSO_4$

69. $CaCl_2 \cdot 2H_2O$

70. **a.** (1), (3), (6), (8)
    b. (1), (2), (5), (6), (7), (9)
    c. (2), (4), (5)

Critical Thinking

71. The hydrogen-bonded structures in water are disrupted when ethyl alcohol is added because the alcohol competes for hydrogen bonds with water molecules and the water structure collapses. Thus, mixtures of water and ethyl alcohol have less volume than the sum of the volumes of the components. Mixing of two liquids could result in a greater volume than the sum of the volumes of the components if there is greater structural ordering in the mixture than in the separated components.

72. Ice would form on top and sink to the bottom. The pond would freeze more quickly because no surface ice would insulate the water below from the freezing air.

73. Most of the important chemical reactions of life take place in aqueous solutions inside cells.

74. The liquid would form a layer on top of the water if its density was less than that of water and on the bottom if its density was greater. The mixture would form a temporary emulsion

75. Sunlight is scattered by particles in the atmosphere. The shorter wavelengths of visible light (blue and violet) are more visible at midday when the sun is closest to Earth. The longer wavelengths of visible light (yellow and red) are more visible at sunrise and sunset, when the sun is at its greatest distance from Earth.

Concept Challenge

76.

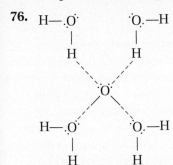

77. A surfactant helps to wet the burning material, so less water rolls off carrying pollutants into the environment.

78. In spring, when the ice melts and the temperature of the surface water increases to 4°C, it becomes heavier than the water below it and sinks. The downward movement of surface water forces water in the deeper parts of the lake upward, where it is warmed.

79. Water enters cracks in pavement and expands when it freezes, creating larger cracks. Continuous freeze-thaw cycles cause pavement to break up.

80. **a.** The volume of 1 g of ice at 0°C is greater.
b. The volume of 1 g of liquid water at 100°C is less

81. **a.** pink
b. pink
c. blue
d. 45.4%
e. water or water vapor

Cumulative Review

82. **a.** 195 g
b. 1.95×10^5 mg
c. 0.195 kg

83. **a.** 5
b. 2
c. 2
d. 4

84. $1s^2 2s^2 2p^6$, neon

85. $H^+ + H \colon \overset{..}{\underset{..}{O}} \colon H \longrightarrow H \colon \overset{..}{\underset{H}{O}} \colon H^+$

86. **a.** 22.4 L.
b. mass He: 4.00 g; mass CH_4: 16.0 g; mass O_2: 32.0 g
c. density He: 0.179 g/L; density CH_4: 0.716 g/L; density O_2: 1.43 g/L
d. Balloons containing He and CH_4 will rise; O_2 balloon will sink.

87. **a.** $6CO_2 + 6H_2O \rightarrow C_6H_{12}O_6 + 6O_2$
b. $2Na + 2H_2O \rightarrow 2Na^+ + 2OH^- + H_2$

88. 9.07 g H_2; 72.0 g O_2

89. 3.60×10^{-2} g H_2O, 2.24×10^{-2} L O_2

90. 25.7 g H_2O

91. 636 g C_2H_4O

92. **a.** 0.300 mol O_2
b. 6.72 L O_2

93. **a.** hydrogen
b. 0.048 g H_2O
c. oxygen
d. 0.010 L

94. **a.** raises the boiling point
b. lowers the boiling point

95. 1.27 atm

Reviewing Content

42. The solvent is the substance in which the solute is dissolved.

43. Random collisions of the solvent molecules with the solute particles provide enough force to overcome gravity.

44. solubility: the amount of a substance that dissolves in a given quantity of solvent at specified conditions of temperature and pressure to produce a saturated solution.

saturated solution: a solution containing the maximum amount of solute for a given amount of solvent at a constant temperature and pressure. **unsaturated solution:** a solution that contains less solute than a saturated solution at a given temperature and pressure. **miscible:** describes liquids that dissolve in each other. **immiscible:** describes liquids that are insoluble in each other.

45. Particles of solute crystallize.

46. No; if there were undissolved solute, the excess solute would come out of a supersaturated solution.

47. 5.56×10^2 g $AgNO_3$

48. Solubility increases with pressure.

49. a. 1.6×10^{-2} g/L
b. 4.7×10^{-2} g/L

50. *Dilute* and *concentrated* are relative terms and are not quantitative. Molarity provides the exact number of moles of solute per liter of solution.

51. Molarity is the number of moles of solute dissolved in one liter of solution.
a. 1.3M KCl
b. 3.3×10^{-1}M $MgCl_2$

52. 2.00×10^1 mL

53. a. 5.0×10^{-1} mol NaCl, 29 g NaCl
b. 1.0 mol KNO_3, 1.0×10^{-2} g KNO_3
c. 2.5×10^{-2} mol $CaCl_2$, 2.8 g $CaCl_2$

54. a. 2.3×10^1 g NaCl
b. 2.0 g $MgCl_2$

55. a. 16% (v/v) ethanol
b. 63.6% (v/v) isopropyl alcohol

56. Colligative properties are properties of a solution that depend only on the number of solute particles; boiling-point elevation, freezing-point depression, and vapor-pressure lowering. Boiling points are elevated because shells of solvent form around solute particles, reducing the amount of solvent molecules that have sufficient energy to escape the solution; relative to the pure solvent, the amount of energy required to cause vaporization or boiling increases. Solutes disrupt the ordering of the solvent structure, so more kinetic energy must be withdrawn from a solution for it to solidify. This lowers the freezing point of the solution.

57. a. sea water
b. $1.5M$ KNO_3
c. $0.100M$ $MgCl_2$

58. The effective molality of the $Ca(NO_3)_2$ solution is $3m$. The effective molality of the $NaNO_3$ solution is $2m$.

59. When vapor pressure is lowered relative to pure solvent, more energy must be supplied to reach the boiling point; thus the boiling point is increased relative to pure solvent.

60. The salt lowers the freezing point of the ice-water cooling mixture.

61. $1M$ solution: 1 mol of solute in 1 L of solution; $1m$ solution: 1 mol of solute in 1000 g of solvent

62. Add 27.0 g H_2O to 32.0 g CH_3OH.

63. a. 100.26°C
b. 101.54°C

64. a. −4.46°C
b. −2.2°C

65. a. −1.1°C
b. −0.74°C
c. −1.5°C

Understanding Concepts

66. a. The freezing-point depression is twice as great for solute B; solute B must provide twice as many particles in solution.

   b. Solute A probably forms a saturated solution.

67. $\Delta T_f = -9.60°C$; $\Delta T_b = +4.74°C$

68. Each gram of acetone requires 0.93 g of water.

69. The mole fraction of $NaHCO_3$ is 0.020; of water is 0.98. The solution is 1.1m.

70. The mole fraction of NaCl is 2.69×10^{-3}; the mole fraction of H_2O is 9.97×10^{-1}.

71. Add one crystal of KNO_3. If the solution is supersaturated, crystallization occurs. If it is saturated, the crystal does not dissolve; if unsaturated, the crystal dissolves.

72.

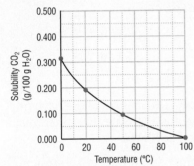

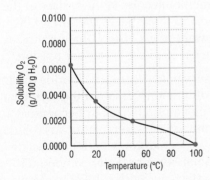

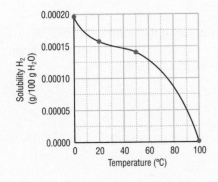

73. a. about 1.14 g/cm³
   b. about $-7.2°C$
   c. about $-9.5°C$

74. fp = $-1.86°C$; bp = 100.512°C

75. $X_{C_2H_5OH} = 0.20$; $X_{H_2O} = 0.80$

76. $-0.413°C$

77. a. 44.2 g KCl
   b. 5.8 g KCl

78. a. 0.30 mol
   b. 0.40 mol
   c. 0.50 mol
   d. 0.20 mol

Critical Thinking

79. unsaturated

80. 100.680°C

81. a. 7.5 g H_2O_2
   b. $8.8 \times 10^{-1}M$

82. 5.2×10^1 g $NaNO_3$

83. 8.55×10^1 g/mol

84. $X_{H_2O} = 0.972$; $X_{C_{12}H_{22}O_{11}} = 0.028$

85. $CaCl_2$ produces three particles upon dissolving; NaCl produces only two particles. Freezing-point depression depends on the number of solute particles in the solvent.

86. chloride: 96.9 g
   sodium: 54.1 g
   magnesium: 6.44 g
   calcium: 2.07 g
   potassium: 1.99 g

87. The solution with the higher concentration of ions will have the greater boiling point elevation; 6.00 g $Ca(NO_3)_2$ in 30 g of water.

Concept Challenge

88. $1.2 \times 10^{-1} M$ HCl

89. 1.10×10^2 mL HNO_3

90. a. 76°C: 15 mol/kg; 33°C: 5 mol/kg
   b. 82°C
   c. 30° C

91. $9.0 \times 10^{-2} M$ Na_2SO_4

92. Determine the freezing point of a suitable solvent. Dissolve a known mass of the unknown molecular compound in a known mass of the solvent. Determine the freezing point of the solution. This gives the freezing point depression. Use $\Delta T_f = K_f \times m$ to find the molality of the solution. Use the molality to find the moles of solute. Use the moles of solute and the measured mass of solute to calculate the molar mass.

$$\frac{\text{g solute}}{\text{g solvent}} \times \frac{1000 \text{ g solvent}}{1 \text{ kg solvent}} \times \frac{1 \text{ kg solvent}}{1 \text{ mol solute}} = \frac{\text{g solute}}{1 \text{ mol solute}}$$

The molar mass obtained is valid only for an undissociating molecular solute.

Cumulative Review

93. a. 1.98×10^2 g H_2O
   b. 1.98×10^5 mg H_2O
   c. 1.98×10^{-1} kg H_2O

94. a. 3.47×10^{-1} kg
   b. 7.3×10^{-5} kg
   c. 9.43×10^{-6} kg
   d. 8.77×10^{-4} kg

95. Rutherford's model contains a nucleus.

96. a. manganese, Mn
   b. indium, In
   c. francium, Fr
   d. polonium, Po

97. Calcium permanganate is $Ca(MnO_4)_2$. Four formula units contain 4 Ca atoms, 8 Mn atoms, and 32 O atoms.

98. $C_8H_6O_4$

99. a. 5.58×10^1 g Fe, 6.35×10^1 g Cu, 2.01×10^2 g Hg, 3.21×10^1 g S
   b. Each sample contains 6.02×10^{23} atoms.
   c. 4.48×10^{-1} mol Fe, 3.93×10^{-1} mol Cu, 1.25×10^{-1} mol Hg, 7.80×10^{-1} mol S

100. 1.7×10^4 L

101. a. combination
   b. decomposition
   c. single-replacement
   d. combustion
   e. single replacement
   f. double-replacement

102. $2H^+(aq) + S^{2-}(aq) \rightarrow H_2S(g)$

103. a. $NH_4Cl(s) \rightarrow NH_4+(aq) + Cl^-(aq)$
   b. $Cu(NO_3)_2(s) \rightarrow Cu^{2+}(aq) + 2NO_3^-(aq)$
   c. $HNO_3(aq) \rightarrow H^+(aq) + NO_3^-(aq)$
   d. $HC_2H_3O_2(l) \rightarrow H^+(aq) + C_2H_3O_2^-(aq)$
   e. $Na_2SO_4(s) \rightarrow 2Na^+(aq) + SO_4^{2-}(aq)$
   f. $HgCl_2(s) \rightarrow Hg^{2+}(aq) + 2Cl^-(aq)$

104. 4.9×10^1 L

105. a. $\ddot{\ddot{I}}\cdot$ **b.** $\cdot\ddot{Te}\cdot$
   c. $\cdot\ddot{Sb}\colon$ **d.** $\cdot Sr \cdot$

106. 1.08×10^2 kPa

107. The particles in an ideal gas have no volume and there are no attractions between particles.

108. Unbalanced intermolecular attractions between molecules at the surface of the liquid and those below the surface create an inward pull, or force, that minimizes the surface area to create surface tension.

109. The very polar hydrogen chloride produces hydronium ions (H_3O^+) and chloride ions (Cl^-) that are stabilized by becoming surrounded by water in aqueous solution. Hydrogen chloride does not dissociate in nonpolar benzene. Polar compounds generally have low solubility in nonpolar solvents.

110. a solution, if the soap mixture is very dilute; More concentrated mixtures of soap in water form colloids.

17 THERMOCHEMISTRY

Reviewing Content

38. Answers will vary, but should include the idea that energy is conserved in every physical and chemical process.

39. Heat flows from the object at the higher temperature to the object at the lower temperature. For example, holding a cold soft-drink can makes your hand cold.

40. Potential energy is energy stored in a substance because of its chemical composition.

41. the chemical composition of the substance and its mass

42. 1 Cal = 1000 cal = 1 kcal

43.
  a. 8.50×10^{-1} Calorie
  b. 1.86×10^3 J
  c. 1.8×10^3 J
  d. 1.1×10^2 cal

44. Answers will vary, but should mention that thermochemistry measures heat flow across the boundary between the system and the surroundings.

45. A negative sign is given to heat flow from the system to the surroundings. A positive sign is given to heat flow to the system from the surroundings.

46.
  a. exothermic
  b. The immediate surroundings are the glass beaker and the air. If one or more of the substances is in water, the water is also considered part of the surroundings.

47.
  a. exothermic
  b. endothermic
  c. exothermic
  d. endothermic

48. enthalpy

49. A calorimeter is an instrument used to measure heat changes in physical or chemical processes.

50. The foam cup will absorb heat. Some heat will be lost to the air. If the reactants are not completely mixed, temperature measurements will not be accurate.

51. bomb calorimeter

52. one atmosphere pressure (101.3 kPa); all reactants and products in their normal physical state at 25°C.

53. Amount of heat released or absorbed in a chemical change at constant pressure

54. Heat is being used to melt the ice.

55.
  a. -2.10×10^1 kJ
  b. -1.8×10^1 kJ
  c. -5.56×10^2 kJ
  d. 6.5 kJ

56. increase

57. Hess's law allows the calculation of the enthalpy of a reaction from the known enthalpies of two or more other reactions.

58.
  a. -1.676×10^3 kJ
  b. exothermic

59. 3.02 101 kJ

60. zero

61. The statement is true, since stability implies lower energy. The greater the release of heat, the more stable is the compound relative to its elements (all of which have $\Delta H_f = 0$).

Understanding Concepts

62. Substance B; For equal masses, the substance with the greater heat capacity undergoes the smaller temperature change.

63. 4.00×10^1 g water; 9.60×10^2 g ice

64.
  a. Graphs should show the mass on the x-axis and heat (in calories) on the y-axis.
  b. about 54 cal/g
  c. The two values are essentially the same.

65. 2.44×10^2 cal; 1.02×10^2 J

66. -7.50×10^2 kJ

67.
  a. -8.902×10^2 kJ
  b. -5.660×10^2 kJ

68. The standard heat of formation (ΔH^0) of a compound is the change in enthalpy that accompanies the formation of one mole of a compound from its elements with all substances in their standard states at 25°C.

69. a. -2.21×10^2 kJ
    b. -1.96×10^2 kJ
    c. -9.046×10^2 kJ

70. a. 3.19×10^3 cal, 3.19 kcal, 1.34×10^4 J
    b. 1.28×10^2 g H_2O

71. 2.36×10^1 kJ

72. 1.42×10^3 g

73. 2.38×10^2 kJ

74. 1.8×10^2 kJ

75. 6.71×10^1 kJ

Critical Thinking

76. Your fingers feel cold because heat always passes from a warmer object (fingers) to a cooler object (ice).

77. a. 1.5×10^2 kJ
    b. The refrigerator absorbs 1.5×10^2 kJ of heat.
    c. assumes the mineral water has the same specific heat as chemically pure water, that no heat is lost by the refrigerator, and the volume of the water is exactly 2 L

78. a. -184.8 kJ
    b. -138.6 kJ
    c. -46.19 kJ

79. When a solid reaches its melting point, additional heat must be absorbed to convert it to a liquid. Therefore, fusion of a solid is endothermic. This heat of fusion is released when a liquid freezes, so freezing is exothermic.

80. When the vapor condenses to a liquid, the heat of vaporization is released. Therefore, the energy content of the vapor must have been higher than that of the liquid. The statement is incorrect.

81. -1207 kJ

82. -2816 kJ

Concept Challenge

83. a. 3.24×101 kcal, 1.36×102 kJ
    b. 8.13 kg

84. -1.37×102 kJ

85. 9.6 g

86. ΔH_{vap} for water at 70°C is approximately 42 kJ/mol. 1 L of water (1000 mL) has a mass of 1000 g and contains 55.6 mol water. Therefore, the amount of heat required is 42 kJ/mol × 55.6 mol = 2.34×10^3 kJ

Cumulative Review

87. The manipulated variable is the variable you change during an experiment. The responding variable is the variable you observe during an experiment.

88. a. Cr
    b. Cu
    c. C
    d. Ca
    e. Cs
    f. Cl

89. a. 6.99
    b. 10.68
    c. 3.6×10^2
    d. 4.44

90. See table below

Particle	Charge	Relative Mass	Location
proton	1+	1	nucleus
Neutron	0	1	nucleus
Electron	1–	1/1840	outside nucleus

91. 32.2 m

92. phosphorus, arsenic, germanium

93. a. 2
    b. 2
    c. 3
    d. 1

94. A covalent bond is nonpolar when the electrons of the bonding atoms are shared equally. A covalent bond is polar when the electrons of the bonding atoms are shared unequally. The bond between oxygen atoms in the oxygen molecule (O_2) is nonpolar. The bond between a carbon atom and an oxygen atom in the carbon monoxide molecule is polar

95. a. K_3N
    b. Al_2S_3
    c. $Ca(NO_3)_2$
    d. $CaSO_4$

96. 1.20×10^{24} H_2 molecules

97. $Ag^+(aq) + Cl^-(aq) \rightarrow AgCl(s)$

98. $N_2(g) + O_2(g) \rightarrow 2NO(g)$
$2NO(g) + O_2(g) \rightarrow 2NO_2(g)$

99. $1.18 \times 10^1 \text{ g O}_2$

100. 0.40

101. 11.1 L

102. Water is a very good solvent and dissolves at least a small part of most of what it comes in contact with in nature.

103. solutions; suspensions

Reviewing Content

43. Chemical reactions require collisions with sufficient energy to break and form bonds.

44. Reactant particles must have a certain minimum amount of energy to react to form product, just as it takes a certain amount of energy to climb over a wall or barrier.

45. A catalyst increases the rate of reactions by providing an alternative reaction mechanism with a lower activation energy.

46. c

47. Gas molecules and oxygen molecules do not have enough energy to react at room temperature. The flame raises the temperature and the energy of collisions, so the reaction begins. The heat released by the reaction maintains the high temperature, and the reaction continues spontaneously.

48. In a reversible reaction, reactants are continuously forming products and products are continuously forming reactants.

49. They are equal.

50. A system in dynamic equilibrium changes to relieve a stress applied to it. Carbonated drinks in closed containers are in a state of dynamic equilibrium between the CO_2 in the liquid and above it. When containers are opened, CO_2 gas above the liquid escapes. The gas bubbles out of the liquid in an attempt to reestablish equilibrium.

51. a. $K_{eq} = \dfrac{[H_2S]^2 \times [CH_4]}{[H_2]^4 \times [CS_2]}$

b. $K_{eq} = \dfrac{[PCl_3] \times [Cl_2]}{[PCl_5]}$

52. a. highly favorable
   b. favorable
   c. highly unfavorable

53. a. $[Ni^{2+}][S^{2-}]$ **b.** $[Ba^{2+}][CO_3^{2-}]$

54. the product of the ion concentrations raised to the power of their coefficients

55. c, b, d, a

56. lowers the solubility

57. A spontaneous reaction has a negative free energy.

58. a measure of the disorder of a system

59. unfavorable

60. a. ice
   b. sodium chloride crystals

61. a. entropy increases
   b. entropy decreases

62. No; some endothermic processes are spontaneous because of their favorable change in entropy.

63. The favorable exothermic change of the condensation process offsets the unfavorable entropy change.

64. the enthalpy change and the entropy change

65. a. proportionality constant that relates concentrations of reactants to rate of reaction **b.** reaction rate directly proportional to concentration of one reactant **c.** expression of rate of reaction in terms of concentrations of reactants

66. 100 minutes

67. $2NO + O_2 \rightleftharpoons 2NO_2$

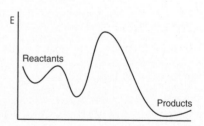

Understanding Concepts

68. a. 1.22×10^{-4} mol/(L·s)
   b. 1.94×10^{-4} mol/(L·s)

69. c

70. 25 kJ

71. The change from **a** to **b** is spontaneous, favored by an increase in entropy. The change from **b** to **c** will not occur, because it would result in a decrease in entropy, causing the process to be nonspontaneous.

72. a. yes; a solid becomes a gas
   b. yes; A single solid becomes two products, one of them a gas.
   c. no; Two particles become one.
   d. yes; One particle becomes two.

73. increase in products

74. $K_{eq} = \dfrac{[SO_3]^3}{[SO_2]^2 \times [O_2]}$

75. $K_{eq} = 6.59 \times 10^{-1}$

76. Increasing pressure tends to reduce volume and increase density, so the system responds by favoring production of liquid, which is more dense.

77. The product of the concentrations of the ions must be greater than the ion-product constant (K_{sp}).

78. $3.0 \times 10^{-5}M$

79.

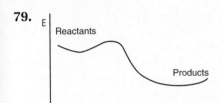

80. A catalyst will establish equilibrium more quickly, but it does not change the equilibrium position.

81. a. IO^-
   b. No; the I^- is changed in the reaction. A catalyst would not appear in the reaction as a reactant, an intermediate, or a product.
   c. two
   d. the slow reaction
   e. $2H_2O_2 \rightarrow 2H_2O + O_2$

82. $2.0 \times 10^{-8}M$

Critical Thinking

83. a. favors products
   b. favors reactants
   c. favors reactants
   d. no effect

84. A catalyst increases the efficiency of the collisions; more collisions result in the formation of the product.

85. Possible answers: using a blow dryer, flushing a toilet, mowing the lawn, cooking breakfast, driving a car, and breathing

86. a. Fanning brings more oxygen into contact with the campfire.
   b. Dust particles have a large surface area to react with oxygen with explosive rapidity.
   c. MnO_2 is a catalyst; the reaction occurs with explosive rapidity.

87. first order in NO_2, first order in $NH_4{}^+$, second order overall

Concept Challenge

88. a.

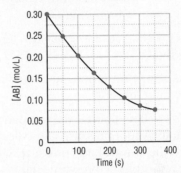

   b. The rate when $t = 100$ s is 8×10^{-4} mol/L•s. The rate when $t = 250$ s is 4×10^{-4} mol/L•s.

89. a. 3 g
   b. 1.3 g
   c. It decreases.

Cumulative Review

90. a. $1s^2 2s^2 2p^6 3s^2 3p^6 3d^{10} 4s^2 4p^2$ $\cdot\dot{Ge}\cdot$
   b. $1s^2 2s^2 2p^6 3s^2 3p^6 4s^2$ $\dot{Ca}\cdot$
   c. $1s^2 2s^2 2p^4$ $:\dot{O}\cdot$
   d. $1s^2 2s^2 2p^6 3s^2 3p^6$ $:\dot{\ddot{Ar}}:$
   e. $1s^2 2s^2 2p^6 3s^2 3p^5$ $:\dot{\ddot{Cl}}\cdot$
   f. $1s^2 2s^2 2p^6 3s^2 3p^3$ $\dot{P}\cdot$

91. Potassium chloride is an ionic compound, not a molecular compound.

92. a. fluoride anion
   b. copper(II) cation
   c. phosphide anion
   d. hydrogen cation
   e. sodium cation
   f. iodide anion
   g. oxide anion
   h. magnesium cation

93. a. sodium perchlorate, $ClO_4{}^-$
   b. potassium permanganate, $MnO_4{}^-$
   c. calcium phosphate, $PO_4{}^{3-}$

    d. magnesium carbonate, $CO_3{}^{2-}$
    e. sodium sulfate, $SO_4{}^{2-}$
    f. potassium dichromate, $Cr_2O_7{}^{2-}$

94. negative: **a, c**; positive: **b, d–h**

95. a. 2.51×10^2 g
    b. 4.59×10^1 g
    c. 2.99×10^{-22} g
    d. 9.57 g

96. a. $Ag^+(aq) + NO_3{}^-(aq) + K^+(aq) + I^-(aq) \rightarrow$
      $AgI(s) + K^+(aq) + NO_3{}^-(aq)$
    b. potassium ions and nitrate ions
    c. $Ag^+(aq) + I^-(aq) \rightarrow AgI(s)$

97. a. $2KClO_3(s) + \text{heat} \rightarrow 2KCl(s) + 3O_2(g)$
    b. 1.91 g O_2

98. Pascal (Pa), atmosphere (atm), millimeters of mercury (mm Hg)

99. No; the boiling point is the temperature at which the vapor pressure of the liquid equals the atmospheric pressure; it changes if the atmospheric pressure changes.

100. a. increases
    b. decreases
    c. increases

101. 1.71×10^1 L

102. a, c, d

103. 19.5%

104. b

105. 1.58 mol

106. 1.25 L

107. a. The solute is ethanol; the solvent is water.
    b. below

108. -2.80×10^1 kJ/mol

109. exothermic

110. -1.65×10^3 kJ

Reviewing Content

44. Acids ionize to give hydrogen ions in aqueous solution. Bases ionize to give hydroxide ions in aqueous solution.

45. a. base
 b. acid
 c. base
 d. acid
 e. acid
 f. acid

46. a. $KOH \rightarrow K^+ + OH^-$
 b. $Mg(OH)_2 \rightarrow Mg^{2+} + 2O^-$

47. a. $2Li + 2H_2O \rightarrow 2LiOH + H_2$
 b. $Ba + 2H_2O \rightarrow Ba(OH)_2 + H_2$

48. a. HNO_3, acid; H_2O, base
 b. CH_3COOH, acid; H_2O, base
 c. H_2O, acid; NH_3, base
 d. H_2O, acid; CH_3COO^-, base

49. a. HNO_3 with NO_3^-, H_2O with H_3O^+
 b. CH_3COOH with CH_3COO^-, H_2O with H_3O^+
 c. H_2O with OH^-, NH_3 with NH_4^+
 d. H_2O with OH^-, CH_3COO^- with CH_3COOH

50. A Lewis acid accepts a pair of electrons to form a covalent bond. A Lewis base donates a pair of electrons to form a covalent bond. The Lewis theory explains the behavior of compounds that act like bases without accepting hydrogen ions or that act like acids without donating hydrogen ions.

51. $H_2O \rightleftharpoons H^+ + OH^-$

52. $1.0 \times 10^{-7} M$ for both H^+ and OH^- at 25°C

53. the negative logarithm of the $[H^+]$

54. The hydrogen ion concentration of pure water at 25°C is $10 \times 10^{-7} M$. The negative logarithm or pH of this concentration is 7.0.

55. a. pH = 2.00, acidic
 b. pH = 12.00, basic
 c. pH = 6.00, acidic

56. a. $1.0 \times 10^{-10} M$
 b. $1.0 \times 10^{-6} M$
 c. $1.0 \times 10^{-2} M$

57. a. 5.62
 b. $6.3 \times 10^{-14} M$

58. a. strong base
 b. strong acid
 c. weak base
 d. strong acid

59. A strong acid is completely dissociated; K_a must be large.

60. They have high K_b ratios. Their concentration in saturated solution is low because of their low solubility.

61. a. $K_a = \dfrac{[H^+][F]}{[HF]}$ **b.** $K_a = \dfrac{[H^+][HCO_3^-]}{[H_2CO_3]}$

62. Acid + base → salt + water

63. a. $HNO_3 + KOH \rightarrow KNO_3 + H_2O$
 b. $2HCl + Ca(OH)_2 \rightarrow CaCl_2 + 2H_2O$
 c. $H_2SO_4 + 2NaOH \rightarrow Na_2SO_4 + 2H_2O$

64. The indicator changes color.

65. a. $1.40 M$
 b. $2.61 M$

66. salts with a cation from a weak base and an anion from a strong acid, or with a cation from a strong base and an anion from a weak acid

67. $HCO_3^-(aq) + H_2O(l) \rightarrow$
$$H_2CO_3(aq) + OH^-(aq)$$

68. Weak-acid anions accept protons from water, increasing the pH of the solution. Weak-base cations donate protons to water, decreasing the pH.

69. a. basic
 b. acidic
 c. neutral
 d. basic
 e. neutral
 f. acidic

70. Eventually the buffer capacity of the buffer is exceeded and the pH will change significantly with the addition of a strong acid or base.

Understanding Concepts

71. Yes, acids like acetic acid dissolve well but ionize poorly.

72. $HPO_4^{2-} \rightarrow H^+ + PO_4^{3-}$ (acting as an acid); $HPO_4^{2-} + H^+ \rightarrow H_2PO_4^-$ (acting as a base)

73. 4.6×10^{-4}

74. a. CO_3^{2-}, carbonate ion
    b. I^-, iodide ion
    c. NH_3, ammonia
    d. HSO_3^-, hydrogen sulfite ion

75. a. $HClO_2$, chlorous acid
    b. H_3PO_4, phosphoric acid
    c. H_3O^+, hydronium ion
    d. NH_4^+, ammonium ion

76. a. $[OH^-] = 4.0 \times 10^{-10} M$
    b. $pH = 12.26$
    c. $[OH^-] = 2.0 \times 10^{-5} M$
    d. $pH = 5.86$

77. $H_3PO_4 \rightleftharpoons H^+ + H_2PO_4^-$; $H_2PO_4^- \rightleftharpoons H^+ + H_2PO_4^{2-}$; $HPO_4^{2-} \rightleftharpoons H^+ + PO_4^{3-}$

78. a. KOH is the base; HBr is the acid.
    b. HCl is the acid; H_2O is the base.

79. a. HSO_4^-
    b. CN^-
    c. OH^-
    d. NH_3

80. $H_2PO_4^- + OH^- \rightleftharpoons H_2O + HPO_4^{2-}$
    $HPO_4^{2-} + H^+ \rightleftharpoons H_2PO_4^-$
    Added OH^- is neutralized by $H_2PO_4^-$, and added acid is neutralized by HPO_4^{2-}.

81. a. $2HCl + Mg(OH)_2 \rightarrow MgCl_2 + 2H_2O$
    b. $2HCl + CaCO_3 \rightarrow H_2O + CO_2 + CaCl_2$
    c. $Al(OH)_3 + 3HCl \rightarrow AlCl_3 + 3H_2O$

82. a. Shift to the left
    b. Shift to the right

83. a. 8.73
    b. phenolphthalein or phenol red

84. $NaC_2H_3O_2 + H_2O \rightarrow Na^+ + HC_2H_3O_2 + OH^-$

85. b, c, d, a

86. a. $NaOH + HCl \rightarrow NaCl + H_2O$
    b. $0.72 M$ NaOH

Critical Thinking

87. a. Answers will vary; students are likely to consider the Arrhenius theory the easiest to understand, and the Lewis theory the best because it is the most general. All three theories are accepted behavior of a certain group of compounds. The Brønsted-Lowry theory includes a greater number of compounds than the Arrhenius theory because it is more general, and the Lewis theory includes the greatest number of compounds because it is the most general.
    b. Each theory has advantages in certain circumstances.

88. Because $\log (a \times b) = \log a + \log b$, and $K_w = [H^+] \times [OH^-] = 1.0 \times 10^{-14}$, taking the log of each concentration term gives: $\log[H^+] + \log[OH^-] = -14$; $-\log[H^+] - \log[OH^-] = 14$; $pH + pOH = 14$.

89. The y-axis might correspond to $[H^+]$ because HCl is a strong acid.

90. CO_2 concentration is higher in pure water. Less CO_2 becomes carbonate because pure water does not have the OH^- ions needed to reduce H^+ concentration.

91. a. False; an indicator determines a range of pH values.
    b. False; an Arrhenius base dissociates to give hydroxide ions in aqueous solution. Ammonia does not do this.
    c. False; strength is a measure of dissociation or ionization, not concentration.

92. Hyperventilation releases CO_2. The equilibrium shift causes H_2CO_3 and H^+ to decrease. The loss of H^+ increases the basicity of the blood and alkalosis results. Hypoventilation does not release enough CO_2. The CO_2 build up increases the H_2CO_3 and H^+ concentrations. The H^+ concentration increases the acidity of the blood and acidosis results.

Concept Challenge

93. pH = 10.66

94. $K_w = K_a K_b = \dfrac{[H^+][A^-]}{[HA]} \times \dfrac{[HA][OH^-]}{[A^-]} = [H^+][OH^-]$

95. a. 7.4721, 7.2675, 7.0835, 6.9165, 6.7675, 6.6310

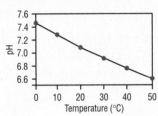

b. 7.37   **c.** 35°C

96. $HOCN + OH^- \rightleftharpoons H_2O + OCN^-$
$OCN^- + H^+ \rightleftharpoons HOCN$

97. 50.0 mL; The pH = 7 when $[H^+] = [OH^-]$. Because HCl is a strong acid that supplies one hydrogen ion per formula unit and NaOH is a strong base that supplies one hydroxide ion per formula unit, $[H^+] = [OH^-]$ when equal volumes of solutions of the same molarity are combined.

98. $5.00 \times 10^{-2}M$

99. 5.0 % NaClO solution, density 1.0 g/mL, K_a of HClO = 3.5 → 10^{-8}

$M = \dfrac{50.\ g\ NaClO}{L} - \dfrac{1\ mol\ NaClO}{74.44\ g\ NaClO} = 0.67\ mol\,/\,L$

$ClO^- + H_2O \rightarrow HClO + OH^- - K_h = K_w \div K_a = (1.0 \times 10^{-14}) \div (3.5 \times 10^{-8}) = 2.9 \times 10^{-7}$

$2.9 \times 10^{-7} = [OH^-]^2 \div 0.67;$
$[OH^-] = 4.4 \times 10^{-4}$

$pOH = -\log (4.4 \times 10^{-4}M) = 3.36$

$pH = 14.00 - pOH = 10.64$

The answers are $[OH^-] = 4.4 \times 10^{-4}$ and pH = 10.64

Cumulative Review

100. a. $K_2S(s)$
  b. $CaS(s)$
  c. $AlF_3(s)$

101. 131 g O_2

102. liquid

103. The total pressure in a mixture of gases is equal to the sum of the partial pressures of each gas in the mixture.

104. b. Boyle's law

105. suspension

106. c. $SiO_2(s)$

107. hydrogen bond

108. 2.25 g KCl

109. Dissolve 0.272 mol KOH(s) in water and add sufficient water to give 400.0 mL of solution.

110. 0.49 L

111. b, c, and d

112. $1.8 \times 10^4\,J$

113. a. 144 J
  b. $1.0 \times 10^3\,kJ$
  c. 82.9 cal

114. $2.8 \times 10^3\,kJ$

115. The product of the concentrations of the two ions must be greater than the solubility product.

116. a. $K_a = \dfrac{[CO]^2 \times [O_2]}{[CO_2]^2}$

  b. $\dfrac{[NH_3]^2}{[N_2] \times [N_2]^3}$

117. $2.0 \times 10^{-8}M$

118. a. NaCl(s)
  b. $CO_2(g)$
  c. hot water

119. a. shift right
  b. no change
  c. shift right
  d. shift right
  e. shift right

120. The reaction is first order in A, second order in B, and zero order in C. The overall reaction order, therefore, is 1 + 2 + 0 = 3.

Reviewing Content

26. oxidation

27. The oxidizing agent is reduced.

28. a. $Ba(s) + O_2(g) \rightarrow 2BaO(s)$; barium is oxidized
    b. $CuO(s) + H_2(g) \rightarrow Cu(s) + H_2O(l)$; copper is reduced
    c. $C_2H_4(g) + 3O_2(g) \rightarrow 2CO_2(g) + 2H_2O(l)$; carbon is oxidized
    d. $3CaO(s) + 2Al(s) \rightarrow Al_2O_3(s) + 3Ca(s)$; calcium is reduced

29. a. oxidation
    b. oxidation
    c. oxidation
    d. oxidation

30. a. oxidizing agent
    b. reducing agent
    c. oxidizing agent
    d. oxidizing agent

31. a. H_2 is oxidized; S is reduced.
    b. N_2 is reduced; H_2 is oxidized.
    c. S is oxidized; O_2 is reduced.
    d. H_2 is oxidized; O_2 is reduced.

32. a. H_2 is the reducing agent; S is the oxidizing agent.
    b. N_2 is the oxidizing agent; H_2 is the reducing agent.
    c. S is the reducing agent; O_2 is the oxidizing agent.
    d. H_2 is the reducing agent; O_2 is the oxidizing agent.

33. An oxidation number is the charge an atom would have if the electrons in each bond were assigned to the atoms of the more electronegative element.

34. c is false.

35. a. +2
    b. +3
    c. Na, +1; Cr, +6
    d. +5
    e. +7

36. a. O, –2; H, +1
    b. P, +5; O, –2
    c. I, +5; O, –2
    d. H, +1; P, +5; O, –2
    e. H, +1; S, +6; O, –2

37. a. Al is oxidized; Mn is reduced.
    b. K is oxidized; H is reduced.
    c. Hg is reduced; O is oxidized.
    d. P is oxidized; O is reduced.

38. a. $2Al(s) + 3Cl_2(g) \rightarrow 2AlCl_3(s)$
    b. $2Al(s) + Fe_2O_3(s) \rightarrow Al_2O_3(s) + Fe(s)$
    c. $3Cl_2(g) + 6KOH\ (aq) \rightarrow$
        $KClO_3(aq) + 5KCl(aq) + 3H_2O(l)$
    d. $2HNO_3(aq) + 3H_2S(aq) \rightarrow$
        $3S(s) + 2NO(g) + 4H_2O(l)$
    e. $KIO_4(aq) + 7KI(aq) + 8HCl(aq) \rightarrow$
        $8KCl(aq) + 4I_2(s) + 4H_2O(l)$

39. redox: a, b, c, d, e

40. a. $4MnO_4^-(aq) + 3ClO_2^-(aq) + 2H_2O(l) \rightarrow$
        $4MnO_2(s) + 3ClO_4^-(aq) + 4OH^-(aq)$
    b. $2Cr^{3+}(aq) + 3ClO^-(aq) + 10OH^-(aq) \rightarrow$
        $2CrO_4^{2-}(aq) + 3Cl^-(aq) + 5H_2O(l)$
    c. $6Mn^{3+}(aq) + I^-(aq) + 6OH^-(aq) \rightarrow$
        $6Mn^{2+}(aq) + IO_3^-(aq) + 3H_2O(l)$

Understanding Concepts

41. a. $4Al(s) + 3MnO_2(s) \rightarrow 2Al_2O_3(s) + 3Mn(s)$
    b. $2K(s) + 2H_2O(l) \rightarrow 2KOH(aq) + H_2(g)$
    c. $2HgO(s) \rightarrow 2Hg(l) + O_2(g)$
    d. $P_4(s) + 5O_2(g) \rightarrow P_4O_{10}(s)$

42. a. $2Li(s) + 2H_2O(l) \rightarrow 2LiOH(aq) + H_2(g)$
    b. $K_2Cr_2O_7(aq) + 14HCl(aq) \rightarrow 2KCl(aq) +$
        $2CrCl_3(aq) + 7H_2O(l) + 3Cl_2(g)$
    c. $2Al(s) + 6HCl(aq) \rightarrow 2AlCl_3(aq) + 3H_2(g)$
    d. $Cl_2(g) + H_2O(l) \rightarrow HCl(aq) + HClO(aq)$
    e. $I_2O_5(s) + 5CO(g) \rightarrow I_2(s) + 5CO_2(g)$
    f. $H_2O(l) + SO_3(g) \rightarrow H_2SO_4(aq)$

43. a. +4
    b. +5
    c. +5
    d. +3
    e. +5
    f. +3

44. K_2CrO_4, Cr +6; $K_2Cr_2O_7$, Cr +6

45. a. Cl oxidized, Mn reduced, Mn oxidizing agent, reducing agent
    b. Cu oxidized, N reduced, N oxidizing agent, Cu reducing agent
    c. P oxidized, N reduced, N oxidizing agent, P reducing agent
    d. Sn oxidized, Bi reduced, Bi oxidizing agent, Sn reducing agent

46.
a. $MnO_2(s) + 4HCl(aq) \rightarrow$
$\qquad MnCl_2(aq) + Cl_2(g) + 2H_2O(l)$
b. $Cu(s) + 4HNO_3(aq) \rightarrow$
$\qquad Cu(NO_3)_2(aq) + 2NO_2(g) + 2H_2O(l)$
c. $3P(s) + 5HNO_3(aq) + 2H_2O(l)$
$\qquad \rightarrow 5NO(g) + 3H_3PO_4(aq)$
d. $2Bi(OH)_3(s) + 3Na_2SnO_2(aq) \rightarrow$
$\qquad 2Bi(s) + 3Na_2SnO_3(aq) + 3H_2O(l)$

47.
a. $16H^+(aq) + 2Cr_2O_7^{2-}(aq) + C_2H_5OH(aq) \rightarrow$
$\qquad 4Cr^{3+}(aq) + 2CO_2(g) + 11H_2O(l)$
b. oxidizing agent

48.
a. $WO_3(s) + 3H_2(g) \rightarrow W(s) + 3H_2O(g)$
b. H_2
c. H

49.
a. oxidized
b. H is the oxidizing agent; Ag is the reducing agent.
c. $2Ag(s) + H_2S(s) \rightarrow Ag_2S(s) + H_2(g)$

50. Lead atoms are oxidized by losing 2 electrons to form Pb^{2+} ions. Oxygen atoms are reduced by gaining 2 electrons to form O^{2-} ions.

51.
a. Yes, the oxidation number of bismuth changes from +3 to zero; the oxidation number of carbon changes from zero to +2.
b. No, there is no change in oxidation number of any of the atoms in this reaction.
c. No, there is no change in oxidation number of any of the atoms in this reaction.

52. $N_2O_4(l) + 2N_2H_4(l) \rightarrow 3N_2(g) + 4H_2O(g)$

Based on oxidation number changes, nitrogen atoms from N_2O_4 gain electrons in forming N_2 and nitrogen atoms from H_2H_4 lose electrons in forming N_2.

53.
a. reactant, 0; product, +3
b. reactant, –2; product, –2
c. X
d. H

Critical Thinking

54. When one reactant loses electrons another reactant must gain them.

55. $1s^2\, 2s^2\, 2p^6\, 3s^2\, 3p^5$

A chlorine atom can "lose" its seven valence electrons or it can gain one electron to complete the third energy level.

56. A sodium atom achieves a stable electron configuration by losing its one valence electron making it a reducing agent. A sodium ion has a stable electron configuration.

57. Double-replacement reactions never involve the transfer of electrons; instead they involve the transfer of positive ions in aqueous solution.

58. In every redox reaction one species loses one or more electrons and is a reducing agent. Another substance gains one or more electrons and is an oxidizing agent.

59.
a. SO_4^{2-}
b. H_2O_2
c. NO_3-
d. $Cr_2O_7^{2-}$
e. H_2O

60. Group 1A metals; a reducing agent must give up electrons. Group 1A metals achieve stability by giving up electrons and forming positively charged ions.

61.
a. $Rb(s) + I_2(s) \rightarrow RbI_2(s)$; oxidizing agent is I
b. $Ba(s) + 2H_2O(l) \rightarrow Ba(OH)_2(aq) + H_2(g)$; oxidizing agent is H
c. $2Al(s) + 3FeSO_4(aq) \rightarrow Al_2(SO_4)_3(aq) + 3Fe(s)$; oxidizing agent is Fe
d. $C_4H_8(g) + 6O_2(g) \rightarrow 4CO_2(g) + 4H_2O(l)$; oxidizing agent is O
e. $Zn(s) + 2HBr(aq) \rightarrow ZnBr_2(aq) + H_2(g)$; oxidizing agent is H
f. $Mg(s) + Br_2(l) \rightarrow MgBr_2(s)$, oxidizing agent is Br

62. Rhenium is oxidized and selenium is reduced, because the bonded electrons would shift toward the more electronegative element, selenium.

63. MnO_4^-, because the manganese is at its highest oxidation state.

Concept Challenge

64. 0.406 g Cu

65. 104 mL $K_2Cr_2O_7$

66.
a. $5CO + I_2O_5 \rightarrow I_2 + 5CO_2$
b. C is oxidized. I is reduced.
c. 0.22 g CO

67.
a. +5
b. –3
c. +3

d. +3
e. +1
f. –3
g. +2
h. +4

68. $2F_2 + O_2 \rightarrow 2F_2O$; fluorine is oxidized; oxygen is reduced

69. Nitride ion has the minimum oxidation number of -3, therefore it cannot gain additional electrons and be an oxidizing agent. It can lose electrons however and be a reducing agent. Nitrate ion has the maximum oxidation number of +5, therefore it cannot lose additional electrons and be a reducing agent. It can gain electrons however and be an oxidizing agent.

70. a. $3Hg^{2+} + 2Al \rightarrow 3\,Hg + 2Al^{3+}$
   b. $MnO_2 + 4H^+ + Fe \rightarrow Mn^{2+} + 2H_2O + Fe^{2+}$
   c. $2Fe^{3+} + Cd \rightarrow 2Fe^{2+} + Cd^{2+}$

Cumulative Review

71. a.

Alkane burned	O_2 used (mol)	CO_2 produced (mol)	H_2O produced (mol)
CH_4	2	1	2
C_2H_6	3.5	2	3
C_3H_8	5	3	4
C_4H_{10}	6.5	4	5
C_5H_{12}	8	5	6
C_6H_{14}	9.5	6	7

   b. $C_xH_y + [x + (y/4)]O_2 \rightarrow xCO_2 + (y/2)H_2O$

72. sublimation

73. 1.8×10^2 kPa

74. suspension; particles settle out of a suspension; not a solution

75. a, c, and d

76. Dilute 110 mL of $6.0M$ HCl to 440 mL total volume.

77. $Ca(NO_3)_2$; boiling point elevation is a colligative property that depends on the number of particles in solution. $Ca(NO_3)_2$ gives three particles per formula unit; LiF gives two particles per formula unit.

78. $0.379M\ H_3PO_4$

79. Solubility $PbBr_2 = 8.1 \times 10^{-3}M$

80. Test tube B has the NaCl added to it. Due to the common ion effect, the addition of either sulfate ion or barium ion to a saturated solution of $BaSO_4$ will cause the solubility product of $BaSO_4$ to be exceeded and barium sulfate will precipitate as shown in test tubes A and C.

81. a. $1.0 \times 10^{-2}M$
   b. $1.0 \times 10^{-11}M$
   c. $1.6 \times 10^{-9}M$

82. 56.3 mL KOH

83. a. NH_4^+ and NH_3; H_2O and H_3O^+
   b. H_2SO_3 and HSO_3^-; NH_2^- and NH_3
   c. HNO_3 and NO_3^-; I^- and HI

84. a. acidic
   b. basic
   c. basic
   d. acidic

85. a. 5.00
   b. 10.00
   c. 13.00
   d. 6.52

86. large

Reviewing Content

26. An equation that represents the oxidation or the reduction in a redox reaction.

27. Oxidation: $Al(s) \rightarrow Al^{3+}(aq) + 3e^-$
Reduction: $Cu^{2+}(aq) + 2e^- \rightarrow Cu(s)$

28. Nothing

29. **a.** Cu
b. Ca
c. Mg
d. Sn
e. Zn
f. Al

30. cathode

31. The salt bridge allows ions to pass from one half-cell to the other but prevents the solutions from mixing.

32. anode: zinc, cathode: carbon (graphite)

33. Water is produced by the redox reaction and sulfuric acid is used up; water has a lower density than sulfuric acid.

34. $Pb(s)|PbSO_4(aq)||PbO_2(s)|PbSO_4(s)$

35. Fuel cells cannot generate electricity as economically as more conventional forms of electrical generation.

36. A fuel cell needs no recharging; it does not produce toxic wastes; and if the fuel is hydrogen gas, it is lighter.

37. It was arbitrarily set at zero.

38. the ability of a voltaic cell to produce a current

39. The relative order is the same because both tables rank the elements according to their tendency to undergo oxidation/reduction.

40. Connect the aluminum half-cell to a standard hydrogen half-cell and use a voltmeter. The indicated voltage is the standard reduction potential for the aluminum half-cell.

41. **a.** nonspontaneous, –0.34 V
b. nonspontaneous, –1.24 V

42. **a.** 1.61 V
b. 0.94 V

43. A direct current flows in one direction only.

44. The teaspoon is the cathode in an electrolytic cell with silver cyanide as the electrolyte. When the DC current flows, the silver ions deposit as silver on the teaspoon.

45. $2H_2O(l) \rightarrow O_2(g) + 2H_2(g)$

46. electrode A

47. The small spheres representing molecules of H_2 and Cl_2 would be in 1:1 ratio.

48. Voltaic cells convert chemical energy into electrical energy. Electrolytic cells use electrical energy to cause a chemical reaction.

49. Two half-cells are needed because oxidation or reduction cannot occur in isolation. One half-cell gains electrons and one loses them, producing an electric current.

Understanding Concepts

50. The anode and cathode grids are both packed with $PbSO_4$. The electrolyte is very dilute sulfuric acid.

51. Some of the iron dissolves and the nail becomes coated with copper.

Oxidation: $Fe \rightarrow Fe^{2+} + 2e^-$

Reduction: $Cu^{2+} + 2e^- \rightarrow Cu$

$Fe(s) + CuSO_4(aq) \rightarrow FeSO_4(aq) + Cu(s)$

52. **a.** $Sn(s) + Pb^{2+}(aq) \rightarrow Sn^{2+}(aq) + Pb(s)$ $E^0_{cell} = +0.01$ V
b. $H_2(g) + Br_2(l) \rightarrow 2H^+(aq) + 2Br^-(aq)$ $E^0_{cell} = +1.07$ V

53. Lead(II) sulfate and lead dioxide are very insoluble in sulfuric acid.

54. **a.** 2.0, 1.0
b. 18.0, 2.0
c. 90, 80
d. 4.9, 39.5
e. 7.07, 4.40
f. 7.3, 41.1

55. **a.** oxidation: $6Cl^-(l) \rightarrow 3Cl_2(g) + 6e^-$ (anode) reduction: $2Al(l) + 6e^- \rightarrow 2Al(l)$ (cathode)
   b. overall reaction: $2AlCl_3(l) \rightarrow 2Al(l) + 3Cl_2(g)$
   c. anode, chlorine gas; cathode, liquid aluminum

56. If the cell potential for a redox reaction is positive, the reaction is spontaneous as written.

57. In each type of cell, oxidation occurs at the anode and reduction occurs at the cathode.

58. a, e, and f are spontaneous; b, c, and d are nonspontaneous.

59. **a.** $Zn \rightarrow Zn^{2+} + 2e^-$
   e. $Fe \rightarrow Fe^{2+} + 2e^-$
   f. $Na \rightarrow Na^+ + e^-$

60. **a.** $Zn + Pb^{2+} \rightarrow Zn^{2+} + Pb$
   e. $Fe + Pb^{2+} \rightarrow Fe^{2+} + Pb$
   f. $2Na + Cl_2 \rightarrow 2Na^+ + 2Cl^-$

61. **a.** + 0.63 V
   e. + 0.21 V
   f. + 4.07 V

62. It will be the reaction that has the larger cell potential, or more readily oxidized or reduced.

63. **a.** possible oxidation reactions at anode:
   (i) $2Cl^-(aq) \rightarrow Cl_2(g) + 2e^-$
   (ii) $2H_2O(l) \rightarrow O_2(g) + 4H^+(aq) + 4e^-$
   b. possible reduction reactions at cathode:
   (i) $Na^+(aq) + e^- \rightarrow Na(s)$
   (ii) $2H_2O(l) + 2e^- \rightarrow H_2(g) + 2OH^-(aq)$
   c. (i) Chloride ions are more readily oxidized to chlorine gas than water molecules are oxidized to oxygen.
   d. (ii) Water molecules are more easily reduced than sodium ions.

64. **a.** Li^+
   b. Fe^{3+}
   c. Cu^{2+}
   d. I_2

65. Gold belongs near the bottom, below silver, because it is one of the least active metals.

66. The paste in a dry cell allows for the movement of electrons but not ions.

Critical Thinking

67. The chemists' definition focuses on the electrons that are produced by oxidation at the anode of a voltaic cell; the dictionary definition is probably based on an electrolytic cell, whose electrodes are defined by the battery terminals to which they are attached.

68. The spoon is being plated with silver.

69. d; the voltage falls steadily.

70. It will not work as a battery.

71. As electrons flow from the anode to the cathode in the external circuit, anions must flow from the cathode compartment to the anode compartment to maintain neutrality in the electrolytes. Anions cannot flow through wire made of copper or any other metal. The cell will not function if the salt bridge is replaced with a metal wire.

Concept Challenge

72. **a.** $2AgCl + Ni \rightarrow 2Ag + NiCl_2$; $E^0_{cell} = +0.47$ V
   b. $3Cl_2 + 2Al \rightarrow 2AlCl_3$; $E^0_{cell} = +3.02$ V

73. Oxidation: $2Cu(impure) + 2H_2SO_4 \rightarrow 2Cu^{2+} + 2H_2 + SO_4^{2+}$
   Reduction: $2Cu^{2+} + 2SO_4^{2+} + 2H_2O \rightarrow 2Cu(pure) + 2H_2SO_4 + O_2$
   Overall reaction: $2Cu(impure) + 2H_2O \rightarrow 2Cu(pure) + 2H_2 + O_2$

74. **a.** The iron electrode is the anode; the nickel electrode is the cathode.
   b. The anode is negative; the cathode is positive.
   c. Anode: $Fe(s) \rightarrow Fe^{2+}(aq) + 2e^-$
   Cathode: $Ni^{2+}(aq) + 2e^- \rightarrow Ni(s)$
   d. $E^0_{cell} = +0.19$ V

75. The battery output would not be 12V.

Cumulative Review

76. **a.** 3, 2, 3, 2, 4
   b. 2, 1, 1, 2
   c. 3, 6, 5, 1, 3

77. 467 mL

78. **a.** $SnCl_4 \cdot 5H_2O$
   b. $MgSO_4 \cdot 7H_2O$
   c. $FePO_4 \cdot 4H_2O$
   d. $CaCl_2 \cdot 2H_2O$

79. **a.** 0.0125g NaCl
   b. 101g KNO_3

80. Dilute 31 mL 16M HNO_3 to 500 mL with water.

81. **a.** 4.32×10^2 kJ
 b. 2.55×10^5 cal
 c. 2.70×10^3 J

82. **a.** -2.78×10^2 kJ
 b. -7.03 kJ
 c. 13 kJ
 d. -27 kJ

83. 267 kJ

84. a and c; $K_{eq} < 1$

85. $\dfrac{[N_2] \times [H_2]^3}{[NH_3]^2}$

86. **a.** pH = 8.00
 b. pH = 5.00
 c. pH = 10.00
 d. pH = 5.00

87. **a.** $[OH^-] = 1 \times 10^{-7} M$
 b. $[OH^-] = 1 \times 10^{-10} M$
 c. $[OH^-] = 1 \times 10^{-6} M$

88. **a.** $2Na(s) + 2H_2O(l) \rightarrow 2NaOH(aq) + H_2(g)$
 b. $Ca(s) + 2H_2O(l) \rightarrow Ca(OH)_2(aq) + H_2(g)$

89. **a.** +6
 b. -2
 c. +4
 d. +2
 e. 0
 f. +4

90. **a.** Ca, +2; Cr, +6; O, -2
 b. K, +1; Mn, +7; O, -2
 c. Ca, +2; N, +5; O, -2
 d. Al, +3; O, -2; H +1

91. b; Ca is oxidized, Cl_2 is reduced.
 d; Ca is oxidized, H is reduced.

92. **a.** 3, 6, 1, 5, 3
 b. 1, 3, 2, 3

93. **a.** Cr, +6
 b. I, +5
 c. Mn, +7
 d. Fe, +3

22 HYDROCARBON COMPOUNDS

Reviewing Content

37. pentane: $CH_3CH_2CH_2CH_2CH_3$
hexane: $CH_3CH_2CH_2CH_2CH_2CH_3$

38. a. propane
b. octane
c. pentane

39.

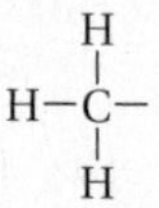
methyl

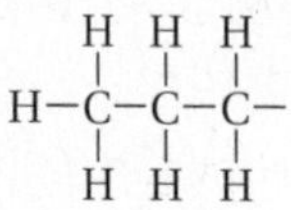
propyl

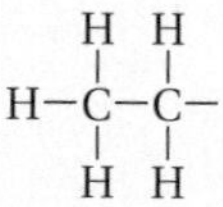
ethyl

40. a. 2-methylbutane
b. 2,3-dimethylbutane
c. 3-methylhexane

41. The carbon-carbon bonds are nonpolar and the carbon-hydrogen bonds are very weakly polar.

42. a. propene
b. *trans*-2-pentene
c. 4-methyl-1-pentene
d. 3-ethyl-2-methyl-2-pentene

43. $CH_2{=}CHCH_2CH_2CH_3$
1-pentene
$CH_3CH{=}CHCH_2CH_3$
2-pentene

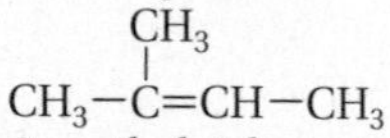
2-methyl-2-butene

44. Five structural isomers with the molecular formula C_6H_{14} exist.

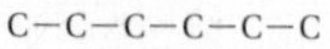
hexane

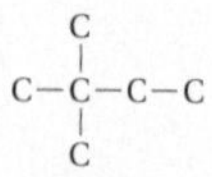
2, 2-dimethylbutane

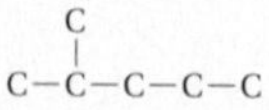
2-methylpentane

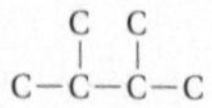
2, 3-dimethylbutane

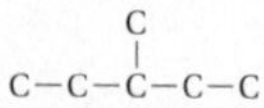
3-methylpentane

45. a. Accept any isomer with 5 carbons and 12 hydrogens.
b. Accept any isomer with 7 carbons and 16 hydrogens.

46. a.

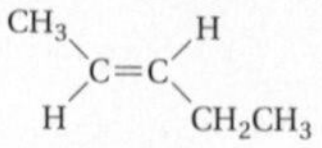
trans-2-pentene

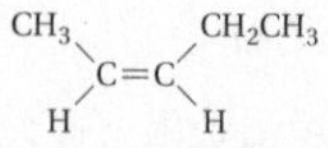
cis-2-pentene

b.

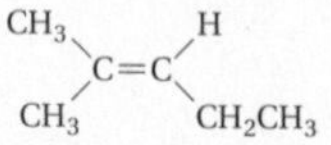
2-methyl-2-pentene

c.

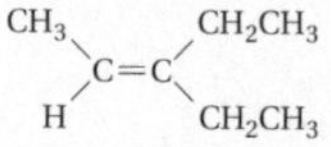
3-ethyl-2-pentene

47. No, molecules with at least one asymmetric carbon have optical isomers.

48. No; Hexane contains no substituted groups.

49. a.

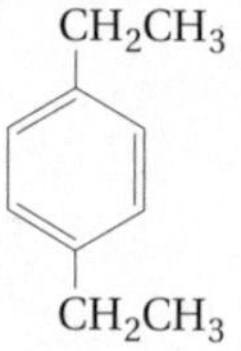

b.

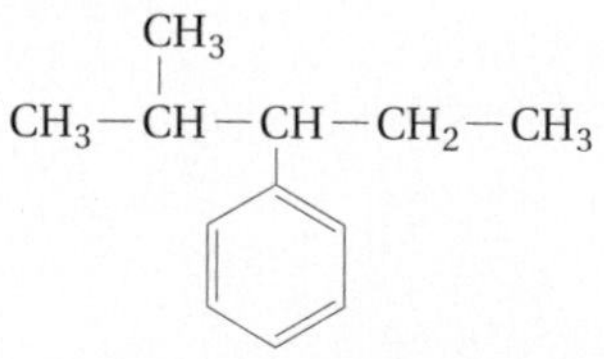

c.

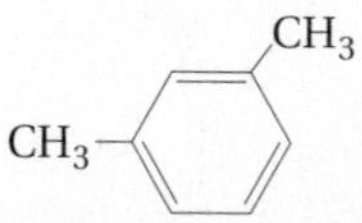

50. Two different structural formulas are possible because a benzene ring exhibits resonance.

51. Catalysts are used during cracking to produce more short-chain components.

52. peat, lignite, bituminous coal, anthracite coal

53. When coal that contains a high percentage of sulfur burns, the major air pollutants SO_2 and SO_3 are by-products.

Understanding Concepts

54. a. The *di-* indicates two methyl groups, but only one location is given; 2,2-dimethylpentane.

   b. Alkyl groups on end carbons are part of the chain; pentane.

   c. The chain wasn't numbered so the substituent has the lowest possible number; 2-methylbutane.

   d. The methyl group on carbon 4 is part of the chain; 3-methylpentane

55. a. Ethyne has one triple C–C bond and two single C–H bonds.

   b. All bonds in propane are single bonds.

   c. In methylbenzene, there are hybrid bonds within the ring and single bonds within substituents and between substituents and the ring.

56. a. $CH \equiv C - CH_3$

   b.

   c. $CH_3 - CH - CH_3$

   d.

57. propane, butane, pentane

58. Gemoetric isomers differ in the arrangement of substituent groups attached to each carbon in a double bond. In optical isomers, there is at least one asymmetric carbon.

59. a.

   b.

   c. $H{:}C{::}C{:}H$

   d.

60. $2C_8H_{18} + 25O_2 \rightarrow 16CO_2 + 18H_2O$

61. The middle structure is most stable due to resonance within the ring.

62. a. 9.6 billion   **b.** 81%

63. No, the structures are identical; one has been flipped over.

64. a. (3)
   b. (1)
   c. (5)
   d. (4)
   e. (2)

Critical Thinking

65. The amount of heat per carbon is higher for methane (–890 kJ/mol of carbon burned) than for benzene (–545 kJ/mol of carbon burned). Methane undergoes complete combustion if sufficient air is present:. Burning aromatic compounds produces more soot.

66. *Meth-* implies one carbon atom; *ene* implies a double bond, which requires two carbon atoms.

67. The methyl and ethyl groups can be on the same side of the bond or opposite sides.

   trans-2-pentene   *cis*-2-pentene

68. Students may infer that the ring structures in cyclic hydrocarbons produce stronger van der Waals attractions, which increase the energy required for vaporization.

69. $H_2C = C = CH_2$

70. The cycloalkene would be most unstable because the bond angles are 90° instead of the 120° predicted by VSEPR theory.

   $C \equiv C - C - C$ (alkyne)
   ▢ (cycloalkene)
   $C = C - C = C$ (alkadiene)

71. a.

   b.

72. b.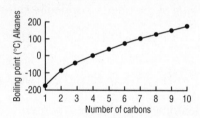

    c. $CH_3 - C \equiv C - CH_2 - CH_3$

    d. $CH_2 = CH - CH_2 - CH_3$

73. Alkanes contain only single bonds. Alkenes contain at least one double bond. Aromatic hydrocarbons contain a benzene ring or a similar ring. Cycloalkanes contain aliphatic chains linked end-to-end.

74. an alkyne, because it contains a triple bond

Concept Challenge

75. The graph isn't a straight line. The estimated bp should be greater than 150°C. The boiling point of undecane is 196°C.

Boiling point (°C) Alkanes vs *Number of carbons*

76. Answers will vary, but should reflect that fossil fuels are not renewable.

77. a. $C_6 = 5$, $C_7 = 9$, $C_8 = 18$, $C_9 = 35$, $C_{10} = 75$

    b. The more carbon atoms, the more possible ways to arrange them.

78. a.

$$CH_3$$
$$|$$
$$CH_3CH_2CHCH_2CH_2CH_3$$

3-methylhexane

b.

CH_2CH_3 (on ring)

CH_2CH_3

c.

$$CH_3 \quad CH_2CH_3$$
$$|\quad\quad |$$
$$CH_3CH_2 - C - CHCH_2CH_2CH_2CH_3$$
$$|$$
$$CH_3$$

3,3-dimethyl-4-ethyloctane

Cumulative Review

79. a. 13.9 L
    b. 1 L
    c. 20 kPa

80. 3.04×10^2 calories

81. 1.13 mol KNO_3; 1.14×10^2 g KNO_3

82. 1.67×10^2 J

83. 1 cal = 4.184 J; 4.184×10^3 J

84. a. Smaller particle size speeds up the reaction.
    b. Higher temperature usually speeds up the reaction.

85. a. favors reactants
    b. favors products

86. a. $K_{eq} = \dfrac{[ICl]^2}{[I_2][Cl_2]}$

    b. $K_{eq} = \dfrac{[H_2][Br_2]}{[HBr]^2}$

    c. $K_{eq} = \dfrac{[HCl]^4[S]^3[SO_2]}{[S_2Cl_2]^2[H_2O]^2}$

    d. $K_{eq} = \dfrac{[NH_3]^2}{[N_2][H_2]^2}$

87. a. 10.00   **b.** 7.59
    c. 12.00   **d.** 11.70

88. a. ~8   **b.** Use a pH meter.

89. a. H_3PO_4 **b.** CsOH
    c. H_2CO_3 **d.** $Be(OH)_2$

90. a. $NaOH \rightarrow Na^+ + OH^-$
    b. $Ba(OH)_2 \rightarrow Ba^{2+} + 2OH^-$

91. a. Ca, +2; C, +4; O, –2
    b. Cl, 0
    c. Li, +1; I, +5; O, –2
    d. Na, +1; S, +4; O, –2

92. a. reduction   **b.** reduction
    c. reduction   **d.** oxidation

93. a. +4   **b.** +4   **c.** +3
    d. +5   **e.** +5   **f.** +2

94. a. 2, 9, 6, 8   **b.** 3, 2, 1, 3

95. It is the cell potential when the ion concentrations in the half-cells are $1M$, the temperature is 25°C, and the pressure of any gases present is 101.3 kPa.

96. Reduction occurs in the half-cell with the more positive, or less negative, reduction potential. Ni^{2+} is reduced and Al is oxidized.

Cell reaction: $3Ni^{2+}(aq) + 2Al(s) \rightarrow 3Ni(s) + 2Al^{+3}(aq)$; $E°_{cell} = +1.66$ V

97. The reaction is nonspontaneous.

98. reduction; reduction

Reviewing Content

26. a carbon chain or ring

27. a.

$$ClCH_2\overset{\displaystyle Cl}{\underset{\displaystyle Cl}{C}}CH_2CH_3$$

b.

c.

28. a. 3-chloropropene
b. 1,2-dichloro-4-methylpentane
c. 1,3-dibromobenzene

29. a.

$$\overset{\displaystyle Cl}{\underset{\displaystyle Cl}{CH}}-CH_2-CH_3$$
1, 1-dichloropropane

$$\overset{\displaystyle Cl}{CH_2}-\overset{\displaystyle Cl}{CH}-CH_3$$
1, 2-dichloropropane

$$\overset{\displaystyle Cl}{CH_2}-CH_2-\overset{\displaystyle Cl}{CH_2}$$
1, 3-dichloropropane

$$CH_3-\overset{\displaystyle Cl}{\underset{\displaystyle Cl}{C}}-CH_3$$
2, 2-dichloropropane

b.

$$CH_3-CH_2-CH_2-\overset{\displaystyle Br}{CH_2}$$
1-bromobutane

$$CH_3-CH_2-\overset{\displaystyle Br}{CH}-CH_3$$
2-bromobutane

$$CH_3-\overset{\displaystyle CH_3}{CH}-\overset{\displaystyle Br}{CH_2}$$
1-bromo-2-methylpropane

$$CH_3-\overset{\displaystyle CH_3}{\underset{\displaystyle Br}{C}}-CH_3$$
2-bromo-2-methylpropane

30. a.

b.

c.

$$CH_3-\overset{\displaystyle CH_3}{CH}-OH$$

d.

31. a. 2-propanol   **b.** 1, 2-propanediol

32. a.

$$\overset{\displaystyle Br\ \ Br}{CH_2CHCH_2CH_3}$$

b.

$$\overset{\displaystyle I\ \ \ \ I}{CH_3CHCHCH_3}$$

c.

$$\overset{\displaystyle H\ \ H}{CH_3CHCHCH_3}$$

d.

33. a.

$$\overset{\displaystyle H\ \ \ \ \ Br}{CH_2-CH_2}$$
bromoethane

b.

$$\overset{\displaystyle Cl\ \ \ \ Cl}{CH_2-CH_2}$$
1, 2-dichloroethane

c.

$$\overset{\displaystyle H\ \ \ \ OH}{CH_2-CH_2}$$
ethanol

d.

$$\overset{\displaystyle H\ \ \ \ H}{CH_2-CH_2}$$
ethane

e.

$$\overset{\displaystyle H\ \ \ \ Cl}{CH_2-CH_2}$$
chloroethane

34. a. methylethyl ether
b. ethylphenyl ether
c. divinyl ether or vinyl ether
d. diisopropyl ether or isopropyl ether

35. a. propanone or acetone
b. 3-methylbutanal
c. 2-phenylethanal
d. ethanal or acetaldehyde
e. diphenylmethanone or diphenyl ketone or benzophenone
f. 3-hexanone or ethylpropylketone

36. The properties of polyethylene vary with the length of the chains.

37. a.

$$-CH_2-\overset{\displaystyle CH-}{\underset{\displaystyle \underset{\displaystyle CH_3}{CH_2}}{}}$$

b.

$$-\overset{\displaystyle CH-}{\underset{\displaystyle Cl}{}}\overset{\displaystyle CH-}{\underset{\displaystyle Cl}{}}$$

Understanding Concepts

38. a. $R-X$

b.

$$R-\overset{\displaystyle O}{\overset{\|}{C}}-R$$

c.

$$R-\overset{\displaystyle O}{\overset{\|}{C}}-O-R$$

d.

$$R-\overset{\displaystyle O}{\overset{\|}{C}}-\overset{\displaystyle H}{\underset{\displaystyle }{N}}-R$$

39. b. c, a, b

40. a.

$$CH_3-\overset{\displaystyle O}{\overset{\|}{C}}-OCH_3 + H_2O$$

b.

$$CH_3CH_2CH_2-\overset{\displaystyle O}{\overset{\|}{C}}-O^-Na^+ + CH_3CH_2OH$$

c.

$$CH_3-\overset{\displaystyle O}{\overset{\|}{C}}-H$$

41. Both atoms in a carbon-carbon double bond have the same electronegativity, so the bond is nonpolar. Because oxygen is more electronegative than carbon, a carbon-oxygen bond is very polar.

42. a. $HCOO^-K^+ + H_2O$
b. $CH_3CH_2COO^-Na^+ + H_2O$
c. $CH_3COO^-Na^+ + H_2O$

43. a. phenol
b. ether
c. alcohol
d. phenol
e. alcohol

44. a.
$$\underset{\overset{|}{Cl}}{CH_3CH_2CH}-\underset{}{CH_2}$$

(Cl, Cl)

b.
$$\underset{\overset{|}{Br}}{CH_3CH_2CH}-\underset{}{CH_2}$$

(Br, Br)

c. (cyclohexane with H and Br)

45. a. carboxyl group, ethanoic acid (acetic acid)
b. ketone (carbonyl group), propanone (acetone)
c. ether, diethyl ether (ethyl ether)
d. alcohol (hydroxyl group), ethanol (ethyl alcohol)

46. a. CH_3OH
methanol

b.
$$CH_3-\underset{\overset{|}{OH}}{CH}-CH_3$$
2-propanol

c.
$$CH_3-\underset{\overset{|}{CH_3}}{CH}-\underset{\overset{|}{H}}{C}-OH$$
2-methyl-1-propanol

d. (cyclohexane with OH and H)
cyclohexanol

47. a. $CH_3CH_2COO^-Na^+$, CH_3CH_2OH

b. $CH_3COO^-K^+$, (benzene ring)–OH

c. CH_3CH_2COOH, $CH_3\underset{\overset{|}{CH_3}}{CH}CH_2OH$

Critical Thinking

48. a.
$CH_3COOCH_3 + H_2O \xrightarrow{HCl} CH_3-\overset{\overset{O}{\|}}{C}-OH + CH_3OH$
methyl ethanoate water   ethanoic acid methanol
(methyl acetate)   (acetic acid)

b.
$CH_3CH_2CH_2COOCH_2CH_2CH_3 + H_2O \xrightarrow{NaOH}$
propyl butanoate   water
(propyl butyrate)

$CH_3CH_2CH_2-\overset{\overset{O}{\|}}{C}-O^-Na + CH_3CH_2CH_2OH$
sodium butanoate   1-propanol
(sodium butyrate)

c.
$HCOOCH_2CH_3 + H_2O \xrightarrow{KOH}$
ethyl methanoate water
(ethyl formate)

$H-\overset{\overset{O}{\|}}{C}-O^-K + CH_3CH_2OH$
potassium methanoate ethanol
(potassium formate)

49. The chemical properties (and toxicity) of organic compounds are determined by the compound as a whole. As a substituent in a molecule, a phenyl group ring does not have the same properties as benzene.

50. The oxygen atom in diethyl ether polarizes the small molecule. This enables diethyl ether to dissolve in water, which is also polar. The large dihexyl ether molecule has large nonpolar parts and does not dissolve. Propane is less soluble in water than is diethyl ether because propane is nonpolar.

51. The alcohol molecules form hydrogen bonds with one another, resulting in a higher boiling point. They also form hydrogen bonds with water molecules, causing 1-butanol to be more soluble than diethyl ether. (Although diethyl ether is polar, 1-butanol has greater polarity.)

52. Acetaldehyde is polarized by its carbonyl oxygen forming stronger intermolecular attractions. Nonpolar propane has weak intermolecular attractions. Thus, propane molecules are more easily liberated from the liquid state.

53. The short-chain ethanoic acid has a higher water solubility.

54. Substitution of an alkane by a halogen, for example, usually gives a mixture of products. Addition to a double bond or a triple can give a single addition product.

55. $H_2NCH_2(CH_2)_3CH_2NH_2$ cadaverine; $H_2NCH_2(CH_2)_4CH_2NH_2$ putrescine; both compounds are amines.

56. a. $CH_4 + Cl_2 \xrightarrow[Light]{UV} CH_3Cl + HCl$

b. $C_2H_4 + H_2 \xrightarrow{Pt} C_2H_6$

Concept Challenge

57. Cholesterol is an alcohol with a hydroxyl group on a cycloalkane. It has four nonaromatic rings. It has a double bond on one of its rings, as well as a large alkyl group, making it nonpolar.

58. $CH_2CH_2(g) + Br_2(l) \rightarrow CH_2BrCH_2Br(l)$

$CH_2BrCH_2Br(l) + 2NaOH(aq) \rightarrow$
$CH_2OHCH_2OH(l) + 2NaBr(aq)$

59. Waving lotion reduces —S—S— bonds to —SH bonds. Hair can be placed in curlers to form the hair in the desired shape. The neutralizing agent is an oxidizing agent that reforms —S—S— bonds, locking the hair into its curly shape. Similar steps could be used to straighten curly hair.

60. $CF_2=CF_2$

Cumulative Review

61. b. 3

62. a. $\ddot{F}: + e^- \longrightarrow :\ddot{F}:^-$

    b. $H\cdot + :\underset{..}{O}: + e^- \longrightarrow (:\underset{..}{O}:H)^-$

63. $2.86 \text{ g } SO_2$

64. $1.15 \times 10^2 \text{ kPa}$

65. Anhydrous $Na_2CO_3(s)$ is the better value; the decahydrate is 63.0% water.

66. The amount of dissolved oxygen is greater entering the plant; solubilities of gases tend to decrease with increasing temperature.

67. $0.117M \text{ Ca}(NO_3)_2$

68. At any given moment, the rate of dissolving of solute is equal to the rate of precipitation of solute. As a result, the concentration of the solution remains constant.

69. 71 kJ

70. a. shift toward products
    b. shift toward reactants
    c. shift toward reactants
    d. shift toward products

71. a, c, d, b

72. a. Na +1; N +3; O –2
    b. Co +2; S +6; O –2
    c. Se +2; O –2
    d. Zn +2; O –2; H +1
    e. K +1; Pt +2; Cl –1

73. Oxidized: H of BH_4 Reduced: H of H_2O unaffected: Na, B, O

74. spontaneous redox reactions

75. Reduction always occurs at the cathode. In the electrolytic cell, the cathode is the negative electrode.

76. a.

    b.
$$CH_3CH\!\!\!\underset{\displaystyle |}{\overset{\displaystyle CH_3}{C}}\!\!\!=\!CHCH_2CH_3$$

    c. $CH_3CH\!=\!CHCH_3$

    d. $HC\!\equiv\!CCH_2CH_2CH_3$

77. coal

78. b, c

THE CHEMISTRY OF LIFE

Reviewing Content

37. A eukaryotic cell has a cell membrane and organelles. Prokaryotic cells have a cell membrane, but lack organelles.

38. Photosynthetic organisms use the sun's energy to synthesize carbon compounds from CO_2 and H_2O.

39. $C_6H_{12}O_6 + 6O_2 \rightarrow 6CO_2 + 6H_2O + energy$

40. sample answer: nucleus (cellular reproduction); mitochondria (cellular energy production); lysosomes (digestion of substances)

41. glucose and fructose

42. Glucose is found in blood, corn, and grapes. Fructose is found in honey and many fruits.

43. Glucose is an aldehyde; fructose is a ketone.

44. glucose and fructose

45. **a.** glucose
   b. glucose

46. glucose

47. peptide bond

48. two

49. Peptide chains fold into helixes or into sheets in which peptide chains lie side by side.

50. Both peptides contain alanine, serine, and glycine, but the sequences are different.

51. Enzymes catalyze biological reactions.

52. complex formed when an enzyme and substrate bind to each other

53. At room temperature, animal fats are solid; plant oils are liquid.

54. triester of glycerol and fatty acids

55. alkali metal salt of a fatty acid

56.
$$CH_2OH$$
$$|$$
$$CHOH + 3CH_3(CH_2)_{16}-\overset{\overset{O}{\|}}{C}-O^-Na^+$$
$$|$$
$$CH_2OH$$
Glycerol   Sodium stearate

57.

Hydrophilic head faces water
Hydrophobic tail protected from water
Lipid bilayer

58. long-chain fatty acid and long-chain alcohol

59. protection from water loss and microorganisms in plants; pliability and waterproofing in animals

60. DNA and RNA

61. phosphate group, sugar unit, nitrogen base

62. Ribose has one more oxygen.

63. hydrogen bonding

64. A–T and C–G

65. three

66. gene mutation

67. Each individual's DNA is unique.

68. altered DNA that contains a foreign gene

69. $ADP + H_2O \rightarrow ATP + P_i$

70. foods or existing body tissues

71. In catabolism, molecules are broken down and energy is captured. These products are used to make biomolecules in anabolism.

72. N_2 is converted to NH_3, which is taken up by plants, which are eaten by animals. Decaying organisms return N_2 to the air.

73. products of catabolism

74. Atmospheric nitrogen is reduced to ammonia by industrial processes.

Understanding Concepts

75. Catabolism of 1 mol glucose yields 2.82×10^3 kJ of energy.

76.
$$CH_3(CH_2)_{14}-\overset{\overset{O}{\|}}{C}-O^-Na^+$$
sodium palmitate

77. The negatively charged hydrophilic phosphate heads interact favorably with water.

78. **a.** Arg-Gly-Cys-Asn
    b. Arg-Gly-Cys-Asn

79. **a.** triglyceride   **b.** glucose
    b. dipeptide

80. C-G-x-C-C-x-T-C-A(or G); There are multiple codes for the same amino acid.

81. G-C-T-A-G-G-T

82. **a.** amino acid
    b. monosaccharide (simple sugar)
    c. nucleotide

83. permit passage of nutrients into cells

84. No, three code words specify the termination of a peptide chain.

85. many applications in medicine and agriculture

86. More oxygen is needed for energy-producing processes; it rids the body of excess CO_2.

87. 30.5 kJ/mol × 38 mol/2.82 × 10^3 kJ/ mol × 100% = 41.1%

88. about 275 mol ATP

89. The shape of the cellulose and starch molecules are different; humans lack enzymes necessary to cleave cellulose to glucose monomers.

90. A substrate molecule or molecules binds to the active site of the enzyme to form an enzyme-substrate complex.

91. Coenzymes must be present for an enzyme-catalyzed reaction to occur.

92. evidence from fossilized bacteria

93. **a.** iron(II) ion (Fe^{2+})
    b. iron(III) ion. The consequence is anemia, not enough normal iron.

94. Mutations could occur that would change how the organism constructs a protein.

95. Photosynthesis provides the carbon compounds that plants and animals need to exist.

96. monosaccharides: single simple sugar; glucose, fructose disaccharides: two linked monosaccharide units; sucrose polysaccharide: many linked monosaccharide units; starch, glycogen, cellulose

97. A carboxylic acid group of one amino acid and amino group of another amino acid undergo condensation polymerization to form an amide (peptide) bond.

98. hydrogen bonding between A—T (A—U in RNA) and G—C in DNA; helps hold DNA in double helix

Critical Thinking

99. Blanching the corn destroys most of the enzymes responsible for the conversion of glucose to starch. Freezing the corn slows down the action of any remaining starch-producing enzymes and prevents spoilage.

100. CO_2 cannot produce energy through oxidation. Glucose can be oxidized to CO_2.

101. Inside the helix; strands must unwind

102. Substitution of one base could result in no change in the amino acid sequence of a protein (if there are multiple code words for the amino acid), or a different amino acid, which could be damaging or helpful to the organism. A base added to the start of the gene would result in a nonsense amino acid sequence for the protein produced by the gene. A base added to the end of the gene could make the termination codon untranslatable, and the protein product might not terminate.

103. Bacteria necessary for nitrogen fixation might be killed by sterilization of the soil.

104. **a.** peptides and proteins
     b. polysaccharides
     c. polynucleotides (RNA and DNA)

105

106 A nucleotide consists of a phosphate group, a five-carbon sugar unit, and a nitrogen base. In DNA, the sugar unit is deoxyribose; in RNA, the sugar unit is ribose. In DNA, the bases may be A, G, T, or C; in RNA, the bases may be A, G, U, or C.

107. Sample answer: GTA-ACA-CGA-GCA-GGG; yes, because GGA, GGG, GGT, and GGC all code for proline.

108. Every amino acid consists of a central carbon atom bonded to an amine group, a carboxyl group, a hydrogen atom, and a side chain. Different amino acids have different side chains.

109.

An amide group is formed by the reaction.

Concept Challenge

110. Nutrients supply carbon compounds, ions, and energy needed for growth. The (insufficient) food primarily is used for energy production necessary to sustain the cell.

111. glycerol + a soap

112. Phospholipids have hydrophobic tails that exclude water and polar heads that dissolve in water.

113. hydrogen bonds between adjacent parts of folded chains and covalent bonds between side-chain groups of cysteine

114. A-C-C-T-A-C-T-A-C; no, Leu has 6 possible code words.

Cumulative Review

115. The particles in real gases have volumes and are attracted to one another.

116. a and b are electrolytes. c and d are nonelectrolytes.

117. a. 0.519°C
   b. 0.209°C
   c. 0.238°C
   d. 0.227°C

118. 1.71×10^1 kJ heat absorbed

119. Besides being composed of highly combustible material, the needles have a large surface area that increases their rate of combustion.

120. The equivalents of acid and base must be equal.

121. a. 4.15
   b. 5.26
   c. 12.79
   d. 10.36

122. a. fluorine
   b. oxygen
   c. chlorine

123. Oxidation always occurs at the anode. In the voltaic cell the anode is the negative electrode.

124. The nickel wire would be silver-plated.

125. a. Cu
   b. Ni
   c. Ag
   d. Fe
   e. Cd
   f. Cu

126. a.

b.

c.

d.

127. a. cyclopentane
   b. methylpropane
   c. 3-pentanone

128. **a.** 1-pentene
  b. cyclononane
  c. hexane
  d. decane

129. 1-chlorobutane, 2-chlorobutane,
  1-chloro-2-methylpropane,
  2-chloro-2-methylpropane

130. **a.** $CH_3CO_2CH_3$
  b. $CH_3(CH_2)_2COH$
  c. $CH_3CHOHCOOH$
  d. $CH_3COC_2H_5$

131. **a.** polytetrafluoroethene (non-stick cookware)
  b. polyethylene (plastic bags and containers)
  c. polyvinyl chloride (PVC pipe)
  d. polystyrene (electric insulation)

132.

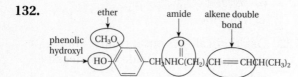

25 NUCLEAR CHEMISTRY

Reviewing Content

25. Each isotope of an element has the same atomic number but a different atomic mass. A radioisotope is an isotope that is radioactive.

26. $^{226}_{88}\text{Ra} \longrightarrow {}^{222}_{86}\text{Rn} + {}^{4}_{2}\text{He}$

27. $^{210}_{82}\text{Pb} \longrightarrow {}^{210}_{83}\text{Bi} + {}^{0}_{-1}\text{e}$

28. a. α, +2
    b. β, -1
    c. γ, 0

29. a. $^{238}_{92}\text{U} \longrightarrow {}^{234}_{90}\text{Th} + {}^{4}_{2}\text{He}$; thorium – 234

    b. $^{230}_{90}\text{Th} \longrightarrow {}^{226}_{88}\text{Ra} + {}^{4}_{2}\text{He}$; radium – 226

    c. $^{235}_{92}\text{U} \longrightarrow {}^{231}_{90}\text{Th} + {}^{4}_{2}\text{He}$; thorium – 231

    d. $^{222}_{86}\text{Rn} \longrightarrow {}^{218}_{84}\text{Po} + {}^{4}_{2}\text{He}$; polonium – 218

30. a. $^{14}_{6}\text{C} \longrightarrow {}^{14}_{7}\text{N} + {}^{0}_{-1}\text{e}$

    b. $^{90}_{38}\text{Sr} \longrightarrow {}^{90}_{39}\text{Y} + {}^{0}_{-1}\text{e}$

    c. $^{40}_{19}\text{K} \longrightarrow {}^{40}_{20}\text{Ca} + {}^{0}_{-1}\text{e}$

    d. $^{13}_{7}\text{N} \longrightarrow {}^{13}_{8}\text{O} + {}^{0}_{-1}\text{e}$

31. a. mass number: unchanged; atomic number: increases by 1
    b. mass number: decreases by 4; atomic number: decreases by 2
    c. Mass number and atomic number are both unchanged.

32. a. $^{234}_{92}\text{U}$ b. $^{206}_{81}\text{Tl}$

    c. $^{206}_{82}\text{Pb}$ d. $^{226}_{88}\text{Ra}$

33. It undergoes radioactive decay.

34. $^{17}_{9}\text{F} \longrightarrow {}^{17}_{8}\text{O} + {}^{0}_{+1}\text{e}$

35. a. $^{13}_{6}\text{C}$ b. $^{1}_{1}\text{H}$

    c. $^{18}_{8}\text{O}$ d. $^{14}_{7}\text{N}$

36. One half-life is the time required for one-half of the atoms of a radioisotope to emit radiation and decay.

37. So the person is exposed to radioactivity for a limited time.

38. 6.3×10^{-1} mg

39. Natural radioactivity comes from elements in nature. Artificial radioactivity comes from elements created in nuclear reactors and accelerators.

40. The elements with an atomic number greater than 92; none occur in nature and all are radioactive.

41. The nuclei of certain isotopes are bombarded with neutrons. The nuclei break into two fragments and release more neutrons. Released neutrons hit other nuclei to start a chain reaction that releases large amounts of energy.

42. A power plant cannot maintain a constant output of electricity with spent fuel rods, which contain depleted fissionable isotopes and fission products. The rods are stored in pools of water.

43. Fusion requires extremely high temperatures, making it difficult to start or contain the reaction.

44. Ionizing radiation, such as X-rays and gamma radiation, has sufficient energy to remove electrons from the atoms it hits.

45. The film badge measures radiation exposure; an exposed film badge indicates how much radiation a worker has received.

46. In diagnosis, the amount of iodine uptake in the thyroid is measured and studied; in treatment the radioactive iodine-131 is concentrated in and by the thyroid.

Understanding Concepts

47. a. $^{30}_{15}\text{P} + {}^{0}_{-1}\text{e} \longrightarrow {}^{30}_{14}\text{Si}$

    b. $^{13}_{6}\text{C} + {}^{1}_{0}\text{n} \longrightarrow {}^{14}_{6}\text{C}$

    c. $^{131}_{53}\text{I} \longrightarrow {}^{131}_{54}\text{Xe} + {}^{0}_{-1}\text{e}$

48. Nuclear fusion takes place in the sun. A nuclear reactor utilizes nuclear fission.

49. a. $^{32}_{16}\text{S}$

    b. $^{14}_{6}\text{C}$

    c. $^{4}_{2}\text{He}$

    d. $^{141}_{57}\text{La}$

    e. $^{185}_{79}\text{Au}$

50. a. $^{90}_{38}\text{Sr} \longrightarrow {}^{90}_{39}\text{Y} + {}^{0}_{-1}\text{e}$

    b. $^{14}_{6}\text{C} \longrightarrow {}^{14}_{7}\text{N} + {}^{0}_{-1}\text{e}$

    c. $^{137}_{55}\text{Cs} \longrightarrow {}^{137}_{56}\text{Ba} + {}^{0}_{-1}\text{e}$

    d. $^{239}_{93}\text{Np} \longrightarrow {}^{239}_{94}\text{Pu} + {}^{0}_{-1}\text{e}$

    e. $^{50}_{22}\text{Ti} \longrightarrow {}^{50}_{23}\text{V} + {}^{0}_{-1}\text{e}$

51. a. about 20%
    b. about 85 g
    c. about 83 days
    d. about 25 days

52. a. $^{222}_{86}\text{Rn} \longrightarrow {}^{218}_{84}\text{Po} + {}^{4}_{2}\text{He}$

    b. $^{234}_{90}\text{Th} \longrightarrow {}^{230}_{88}\text{Ra} + {}^{4}_{2}\text{He}$

    c. $^{210}_{84}\text{Po} \longrightarrow {}^{206}_{82}\text{Pb} + {}^{4}_{2}\text{He}$

53. a. named radioactivity and discovered several radioactive elements
    b. discovered natural radioactivity from uranium ores
    c. discovered the neutron
    d. artificially transmuted elements

54. 1 million

55. $^{215}_{85}\text{At}$

56. a. 27 protons and 33 neutrons
    b. 82 protons and 124 neutrons
    c. 90 protons and 143 neutrons
    d. 1 proton and 2 neutrons

57. 11,460 years

    a. $^{0}_{+1}\text{e}$

    b. $^{238}_{92}\text{U}$

    d. $^{0}_{-1}\text{e}$

59. a. $^{231}_{91}\text{Pa} \longrightarrow {}^{227}_{89}\text{Ac} + {}^{4}_{2}\text{He}$

    b. $^{241}_{95}\text{Am} \longrightarrow {}^{237}_{93}\text{Np} + {}^{4}_{2}\text{He}$

    c. $^{226}_{88}\text{Ra} \longrightarrow {}^{222}_{86}\text{Rn} + {}^{4}_{2}\text{He}$

    d. $^{252}_{99}\text{Es} \longrightarrow {}^{248}_{97}\text{Bk} + {}^{4}_{2}\text{He}$

60. a. $^{3}_{1}\text{H} \longrightarrow {}^{3}_{2}\text{He} + {}^{0}_{-1}\text{e}$

    b. $^{28}_{12}\text{Mg} \longrightarrow {}^{28}_{13}\text{Al} + {}^{0}_{-1}\text{e}$

    c. $^{131}_{53}\text{I} \longrightarrow {}^{131}_{54}\text{Xe} + {}^{0}_{-1}\text{e}$

    d. $^{75}_{34}\text{Se} \longrightarrow {}^{75}_{35}\text{Br} + {}^{0}_{-1}\text{e}$

61. 5730 years

Critical Thinking

62. a. platinum
    b. thorium
    c. francium
    d. titanium
    e. xenon
    f. californium
    g. vanadium
    h. palladium. Thorium (b), francium (c), and californium (f) have no stable isotopes.

63. The organism would be exposed to less harmful radiation.

64. In every round of the tournament, one-half the teams are eliminated; in every half-life one-half the substance decays. In the tournament a single team eventually emerges as the winner and the tournament stops, but radioactive decay continues (almost) indefinitely.

65. An alpha particle is much more likely than other kinds of radiation to collide with another particle and be stopped. At the atomic level, the larger the size of a particle, the greater is the chance of it striking another particle. The greater the magnitude of a particle's charge, the more strongly it will be attracted to particles of opposite charge.

66. Radioactive isotopes of these elements can be incorporated into the body tissue of organisms. When the isotopes decay they can damage tissue very easily.

67. one neutron

68. $^{25}_{12}\text{Mg}$

69. uranium; $^{239}_{94}\text{Pu} \longrightarrow {}^{235}_{92}\text{U} + {}^{4}_{2}\text{He}$

70. 24.6 years

71. $^{18}_{8}\text{O}$

Concept Challenge

72. 2135

73. This graph shows the radioactive decay of carbon-14, along with the increase of the nitrogen product.

74. $^{211}_{83}\text{Bi} \longrightarrow {}^{207}_{81}\text{Tl} + {}^{4}_{2}\text{He}$; thallium – 207

    $^{207}_{81}\text{Tl} \longrightarrow {}^{207}_{82}\text{Pb} + {}^{0}_{-1}\text{e}$; lead – 207

75. Bismuth-214 remains.

76. The reasoning is not sound. Cells other than cancer cells may be fast-growing and therefore killed by radiation as well.

77. $4.2 \times 10^2 \text{ cm}^3$

78. $^{268}_{109}\text{Mt} \longrightarrow {}^{264}_{107}\text{Bh} + {}^{4}_{2}\text{He}$

$^{264}_{107}\text{Bh} \longrightarrow {}^{262}_{105}\text{Db} + {}^{4}_{2}\text{He}$

Cumulative Review

79. **a.** 26 protons and 33 neutrons
b. 2 protons and 143 neutrons
c. 4 protons and 28 neturons

80. Pauli exclusion principle states that no two electrons in an atom can have the same quantum numbers. Hund's rule states that electrons that occupy orbitals of equal energy distribute with unpaired spins as much as possible.

81. **a.** covalent
b. ionic
c. covalent
d. ionic

82. **a.** $\text{Ca(OH)}_2 + 2\text{HCl} \rightarrow \text{CaCl}_2 + 2\text{H}_2\text{O}$
b. $\text{Fe}_2\text{O}_3 + 3\text{H}_2 \rightarrow 2\text{Fe} + 3\text{H}_2\text{O}$
c. $2\text{NaHCO}_3 + \text{H}_2\text{SO}_4 \rightarrow$
$\qquad\qquad \text{Na}_2\text{SO}_4 + 2\text{CO}_2 + 2\text{H}_2\text{O}$
d. $2\text{C}_2\text{H}_6 + 7\text{O}_2 \rightarrow 4\text{CO}_2 + 6\text{H}_2\text{O}$

83. $9.22 \times 10^3 \text{ cm}^3 \text{ H}_2$; 0.412 mol H_2

84. The oxygen atom carries a partial negative charge, and the hydrogen atoms carry partial positive charges. The water molecule's bent shape results in a net polarity, and the negative end of one molecule attracts the positive end of another molecule.

85. 6.7 mL

86. **a.**

b.

c.

d. $\text{CH}_3\text{—C}{\equiv}\text{C—CH}_3$

e.

f.

87. **a.** propanoic acid
b. propanal
c. 1-propanol
d. 1-aminopropane
e. 1-chloropropane
f. ethylmethyl ether

88. **a.** ethanal
b. ethene
c. ethanoic acid
d. ethyne

89. 1-propanol and ethanoic acid

90. They all contain a carbon-oxygen double bond.

91. **a.** (4)
b. (3)
c. (1)
d. (4)
e. (1)
f. (2)
g. (3)
h. (2)
i. (4)
j. (3)

ANSWER KEY

Section Review 1.1

Part A Completion

1. mass
2. space
3. composition
4. changes
5. five
6. carbon
7. carbon
8. organisms
9. Analytical Chemistry
10. physical chemistry
11. energy transfer
12. more than one

Part B True-False

13. NT
14. ST
15. AT
16. ST
17. AT

Part C Matching

18. f
19. i
20. b
21. d
22. h
23. g
24. c
25. a
26. e
27. j

Part D Questions and Problems

28. **a.** physical chemistry
    b. analytical chemistry
    c. biochemistry
    d. organic chemistry

Section Review 1.2

Part A Completion

1. specific
2. microscopic
3. energy
4. conserve
5. batteries
6. productivity
7. crops
8. specific
9. space
10. chemical composition

Part B True-False

9. NT
10. NT
11. AT
12. AT

Part C Matching

13. d
14. a
15. c
16. b
17. f
18. e

Part D Questions and Problems

19. production of chemicals such as insulin; replacement of a gene that is not working properly (gene therapy)
20. Factors include poor soil quality, lack of water, weeds, plant diseases, and pests that eat crops.
21. Data collected by the robotic vehicle *Opportunity* indicated that the landing site was once drenched in water.

Section Review 1.3

Part A Completion

1. alchemists
2. tools
3. techniques
4. measurement
5. systematic
6. scientific method
7. hypothesis
8. experiment
9. theory
10. scientific law

Part B True-False

11. NT
12. NT
13. ST

Part C Matching

14. c
15. b
16. a
17. e
18. d
19. f

Part D Questions and Problems

20. **a.** observation
    b. hypothesis
    c. experiment
    d. observation
    e. scientific law
21. collaboration and communication

Section Review 1.4

Part A Completion

1. plan
2. implementing
3. three
4. analyze
5. unknown
6. plan
7. calculate
8. evaluate
9. sense
10. unit
11. significant figures

Part B True-False

12. ST	**14.** NT	**16.** AT
13. AT	**15.** NT	**17.** AT

Part C Matching

18. b	**20.** d	**22.** c
19. e	**21.** a	

Part D Questions and Problems

23. Step 1: Knowns: length = 10.0 inches
$\qquad\qquad\qquad$ 1 inch = 2.54 cm

Step 2: $10.0 \text{ in.} \times \dfrac{2.54 \text{ cm}}{\text{in.}} = 25.4 \text{ cm}$

Step 3: There are about two and a half centimeters per inch, so the answer 25.4 makes sense.

24. Step 1: Knowns: distance = 5.0 km
$\qquad\qquad\qquad$ 1 km = 0.62 mile

Step 2: $5.0 \text{ km} \times \dfrac{0.62 \text{ mile}}{\text{km}} = 3.1 \text{ mile}$

Step 3: There is a little more than half a mile per kilometer. 3.1 is a little more than half of 5.0.

Practice Problems 1

Section 1.1

1. a. analytical   **d.** organic
$\quad$ **b.** biochemistry   **e.** inorganic
$\quad$ **c.** physical
2. a. applied   **d.** applied
$\quad$ **b.** pure   **e.** pure
$\quad$ **c.** pure

Section 1.2

1. Answers may include development of new methods of energy conservation, such as new types of insulation; development of sources of energy other than fossil fuels, such as biodiesel; and the development of new methods of energy storage, such as improved batteries.

2. a. T   **f.** T
$\quad$ **b.** T   **g.** T
$\quad$ **c.** F   **h.** T
$\quad$ **d.** T   **i.** T
$\quad$ **e.** F

Section 1.3

1. Examples include: The battery could be dead, the car could be out of gas, the spark plugs could be fouled, the wires could be loose.

2. Several experiments were performed to test hypotheses. The experiments disproved some hypotheses, but one experiment resulted in the car starting. Based on the experiment, you could hypothesize that a wire was loose.

3. Check students' answers.

4. Theories are only as reliable as the knowledge on which they are based. Throughout the history of science, theories have been discarded or modified as scientific knowledge has increased.

Section 1.4

1. a. cost of apples = $1.50 a pound
$\qquad$ weight of an apple = 0.50 pound
$\qquad$ dollars available = $16
$\quad$ **b.** cost per apple = $0.75
$\qquad$ number of apples purchased = 8
$\quad$ **c.** Two apples weigh a pound, and a pound costs $1.50. $6.00 is four times $1.50.

2. Figure out how many pounds of apples can be purchased with $6.00. Then figure out how many apples this represents.

Interpreting Graphics 1

1. five		**4.** Component A
2. Component D		**5.** Component E
3. 3.5 minutes		**6.** Component C

Vocabulary Review 1

1. c	**6.** b	**11.** j
2. l	**7.** f	**12.** o
3. a	**8.** i	**13.** h
4. d	**9.** n	**14.** e
5. m	**10.** g	**15.** k

Quiz for Chapter 1

1. T
2. F
3. F
4. T
5. T
6. scientific method
7. hypothesis
8. observations
9. hypothesis
10. communicate
11. **a.** The volume of the test tube is needed.
    b. There is enough information.

Chapter 1 Test A

A. Multiple Choice

1. d
2. c
3. b
4. b
5. b
6. c
7. a
8. b

B. Questions

9. Chemistry is the study of the composition of matter and the changes matter undergoes.
10. Making Observations: Use your senses to obtain information directly.

    Testing Hypotheses: A hypothesis is a proposed explanation for what you observed. Experiments are done to test a hypothesis.

    Developing Theories: A theory is a well-tested explanation for a broad set of observations. A hypothesis may become a theory after repeated experimentation.

C. Essay

11. 1. Analyze. List the knowns and the unknown. A known may be a measurement or an equation that shows a relationship between measurements. Determine what unit, if any, the answer should have. Make a plan for getting from the knowns to the unknown. You might draw a diagram to help visualize the relationship between the knowns and the unknown; or use data from a table or graph; or select an equation.
    2. Calculate. This step can involve converting a measurement from one unit to another or rearranging an equation to solve for an unknown.
    3. Evaluate. Decide if the answer makes sense. Check your work. Make a quick estimate to see whether your answer is reasonable. Make sure the answer is given with the correct number of significant figures. Express the answer in scientific notation, if appropriate.

Chapter 1 Test B

A. Multiple Choice

1. c
2. c
3. c
4. b
5. d
6. b
7. b
8. c
9. c
10. a

B. Problems

11. Organic chemistry is the study of essentially all chemicals containing carbon.

    Inorganic chemistry is the study of essentially all chemicals that do not contain carbon.

    Analytical chemistry is concerned with the composition of chemistry.

    Physical chemistry is concerned with mechanisms, rates, and energy transfer when matter undergoes a change.

    Biochemistry is the study of processes that take place in organisms.

12. Check students' answers.
13. **a.** Hypothesis: The lawn needs water.

    Experiment: Water the lawn every day for one week.

    b. Hypothesis: The lawn needs fertilizer.

    Experiment: Fertilize the lawn as prescribed.

Chapter 1 Small-Scale Lab

Safety goggles should be worn at all times when working in the laboratory. If glassware breaks, tell your teacher and nearby classmates. Dispose of the glass as instructed by the teacher. If you spill water near electrical equipment, stand back, notify your teacher, and warn other students in the area. When working near an open flame, tie back hair and loose clothing. Never reach across a lit burner. Keep flammable materials away from the flame. After cleaning up the work area, wash your hands thoroughly with soap and water. It is not always appropriate to dispose of chemicals by flushing them down the sink. You should follow your teacher's instructions for disposal.

Section Review 2.1

Part A Completion

1. extensive
2. intensive
3. mass
4. volume
5. amount
6. type
7. substance
8. shape or volume
9. shape or volume
10. shape
11. gas

Part B True-False

11. AT
12. NT
13. ST
14. AT

Part C Matching

15. d
16. i
17. c
18. a
19. h
20. e
21. b
22. g
23. f
24. k
25. j

Part D Questions and Problems

26. a. vapor
    b. liquid
    c. liquid
    d. solid
    e. gas
27. a. yes
    b. yes
    c. no
    d. yes

Section Review 2.2

Part A Completion

1. mixture
2. heterogeneous or homogeneous
3. homogeneous or heterogeneous
4. solutions
5. phase
6. physical
7. distillation

Part B True-False

8. ST
9. AT
10. AT
11. ST

Part C Matching

12. f
13. c
14. a
15. e
16. b
17. d
18. g

Part D Questions and Problems

19. a. homogeneous
    b. heterogeneous
    c. homogeneous
    d. heterogeneous
    e. heterogeneous
20. a. substance
    b. mixture
    c. substance
    d. mixture

Section Review 2.3

Part A Completion

1. element or compound
2. compound or element
3. elements
4. ratio or proportions
5. chemical
6. substance
7. mixture
8. symbol
9. C
10. K

Part B True-False

9. ST
10. NT
11. AT
12. AT

Part C Matching

13. d
14. a
15. b
16. c
17. e

Part D Questions and Problems

18. a. compound
    b. element
    c. compound
    d. compound
    e. element
19. a. K
    b. Pb
    c. Na
    d. Cl
    e. S
20. a. copper
    b. hydrogen
    c. silver
    d. iron
    e. nitrogen

Section Review 2.4

Part A Completion

1. chemical
2. physical
3. chemical
4. reactants
5. chemical
6. composition
7. conservation of mass
8. mass

Part B True-False

9. ST
10. AT
11. ST
12. NT
13. NT

Part C Matching

14. e
15. b
16. d
17. c
18. a

Part D Questions and Problems

19. The products of the reaction are gases, which mix with the air.
20. a chemical change
21. 36 grams

Practice Problems 2

Section 2.1

1. b
2. a
3. b
4. d
5. gas   no   no   yes
   liquid   no   yes   no
   solid   yes   yes   no
6. chlorine
7. bromine, ethanol
8. **a.** intensive
   b. extensive
   c. extensive
   d. intensive

Section 2.2

1. distillation, evaporation
2. a mixture with a uniform composition throughout
3. **a.** homogeneous
   b. heterogeneous
   c. heterogeneous

4. **a.** substance
   b. mixture
   c. mixture
   d. substance

Section 2.3

1. nitrogen, hydrogen
2. **a.** lead
   b. potassium
   c. gold
   d. iron
3. **a.** compound
   b. compound
   c. element
   d. mixture
4. **a.** Sn
   b. Na
   c. Ag
   d. C
5. No. It could be a liquid element, a liquid compound, or a mixture of liquids.
6. c

Section 2.4

1. c
2. **a.** physical change
   b. chemical change
   c. chemical change
   d. physical change
3. **a.** carbonic acid **b.** carbon dioxide, water
4. 62 grams
5. 32.4 grams
6. the law of conservation of mass

Interpreting Graphics 2

1. Homogeneous mixture. Since motor oil comes in grades, it has a variable composition.
2. Chemical process. Iron oxide is a compound, while pure iron is an element.
3. **a.** physical separation
   b. chemical separation
   c. physical separation
4. **a.** substance
   b. mixture
   c. mixture
   d. substance

Vocabulary Review 2

1. phase
2. chemical symbol
3. solution
4. elements
5. mass
6. solid
7. mixture
8. gas

Solution: substance

Quiz for Chapter 2

1. a
2. d
3. d
4. b
5. a
6. d
7. d
8. physical blend
9. element
10. vary
11. **a.** potassium
    b. oxygen
    c. hydrogen

Chapter 2 Test A

A. Matching

1. i
2. f
3. g
4. a
5. b
6. e
7. h
8. d
9. j
10. c

B. Multiple Choice

11. d
12. b
13. b
14. b
15. b
16. c
17. d
18. a
19. d
20. d

C. True-False

21. AT
22. NT
23. AT
24. ST
25. NT

D. Completion

26. energy
27. distillation
28. vary
29. chemical
30. physical
31. compounds
32. iron
33. homogeneous
34. conserved
35. products

E. Essay

36. A physical change alters a substance without changing its composition. Melting or boiling are physical changes. In a chemical change, one or more substances change into one or more new substances. Examples of chemical change include the rusting of iron, the reaction between iron and sulfur to produce iron sulfide, and the burning of wood. Some possible clues to chemical change are a transfer of energy, color change, the production of gas, and the formation of a precipitate.

Chapter 2 Test B

A. Matching

1. i
2. d
3. h
4. a
5. j
6. b
7. f
8. e
9. c
10. g

B. Multiple Choice

11. a
12. c
13. d
14. c
15. d
16. c
17. d
18. d
19. d
20. a
21. b
22. b
23. a

C. True-False

24. AT
25. NT
26. ST
27. NT
28. AT

D. Completion

29. liquid
30. vapor
31. heterogeneous
32. N
33. reactants
34. chemical
35. physical
36. substance

E. Essay

37. Salt dissolves in water; iron filings are attracted to a magnet; sawdust floats in water. To separate the mixture, skim the sawdust directly off the surface of the water, then expose the resulting mixture to a magnet to remove the iron filings. Boil off the water, recapturing the water through distillation. Solid salt remains at the bottom of the flask.

Chapter 2 Small-Scale Lab

Section 2.4 1 + 2 + 3 = BLACK!, page 56

Analysis

	NaClO	H₂O₂	CuSO₄
KI	yellow	yellow	brown ppt
KI + Starch	black	black	black
KI + Paper	black	black	black
KI + Cereal	black	black	black

Figure A

1. yellow
2. the mixture turns a blue-black color.
3. They all turn a mixture of Kl and starch black.
4. Starch; both turn blue-black, which suggests the presence of starch.
5. The results may be the same in reactions that are simnilar to the one with Kl and starch, but different in other reactions.

You're The Chemist

1. Add Kl + NaClO to various foods. A black color indicates the presence of starch.
2. Most table salt contains 0.01% Kl. Wet only a portion of a small pile of salt with starch. Add CuSO₄ or H₂O₂. A black color indicates the presence of Kl.
3. If an antacid tablet contains starch, it will turn black whenn treated with Kl + NaClO.
4. The color in the ink becomes bleached. A picture can be drawn with colored ink. Certain areas can be treated with NaClO to bleach parts of the picture.

Section Review 3.1

Part A Completion

1. accuracy		6. absolute value
2. precision		7. 100%
3. experimental value		8. scientific notation
4. error		9. known
5. accepted value		10. estimated

Part B True-False

11. ST
12. AT
13. AT

Part C Matching

14. b	16. a	18. d
15. e	17. f	19. c

Part D Questions and Problems

20. **a.** 3   **c.** 2
    b. 4
21. **a.** 4.35×10^2 mL   **c.** 2.1×10^2
    b. 8.4 cm³

Section Review 3.2

Part A Completion

1. metric		6. gram
2. seven		7. Celsius
3. meter		8. kelvin
4. liter		9. joule/calorie
5. weight		10. calorie/joule

Part B True-False

11. NT
12. NT
13. AT
14. NT

Part C Matching

15. k	20. l	25. j
16. e	21. d	26. f
17. m	22. c	27. b
18. g	23. h	
19. a	24. i	

Part D Questions and Problems

28. Volume = 1.8 cm × 8.8 cm × 30.5 cm
$$= 4.8 \times 10^2 \text{ cm}^3$$

29. °C = K − 273 = 20 − 273 = −253°C

30. a. p; 10^{-12} **c.** μ; 10^{-6}
   b. k; 10^3 **d.** c; 10^{-2}

Section Review 3.3

Part A Completion

1. one (unity)
2. conversion factor
3. remains the same
4. dimensional analysis
5. known
6. steps
7. conversion factor
8. denominator
9. units
10. unknown

Part B True-False

11. NT **13.** AT **15.** AT
12. ST **14.** NT

Part C Questions and Problems

16. a. $125 \text{ g} \times \dfrac{1 \text{ kg}}{1000 \text{ g}} = 0.125 \text{ kg}$

$= 1.25 \times 10^{-1} \text{ kg}$

b. $0.12 \text{ L} \times \dfrac{1000 \text{ mL}}{1 \text{ L}} = 1.2 \times 10^2 \text{ mL}$

17. $\dfrac{1.0 \text{ in}}{1500 \text{ cells}} \times \dfrac{2.54 \text{ cm}}{1 \text{ in}} \times \dfrac{1 \text{ m}}{100 \text{ cm}} \times \dfrac{10^6 \text{ }\mu\text{m}}{1 \text{ m}}$

$= 17 \text{ }\mu\text{m/cell}$

18. $\dfrac{186\,000 \text{ miles}}{1 \text{ s}} \times \dfrac{1 \text{ s}}{10^6 \text{ }\mu\text{s}} \times \dfrac{1.61 \text{ km}}{1 \text{ mile}}$

$= \dfrac{2.99 \times 10^{-1} \text{ km}}{1 \mu\text{s}}$

Section Review 3.4

Part A Completion

1. density
2. intensive
3. composition

Part B True-False

4. ST **5.** ST

Part C Questions and Problems

6. $32.1 \text{ mL} \times \dfrac{1 \text{ cm}^3}{1 \text{ mL}} = 3.21 \text{ cm}^3$

$\text{Density} = \dfrac{\text{mass}}{\text{volume}} = \dfrac{127 \text{ g}}{32.1 \text{ cm}^3} = 3.96 \text{ g/cm}^3$

7. $1.00 \text{ L} \times \dfrac{1000 \text{ cm}^3}{1 \text{ L}} = 1000 \text{ cm}^3$

$1.58 \text{ kg} \times \dfrac{1000 \text{ g}}{\text{kg}} = 1580 \text{ g}$

$\text{Density} = \dfrac{\text{mass}}{\text{volume}} = \dfrac{1580 \text{ g}}{1000 \text{ cm}^3} = 1.58 \text{ g/cm}^3$

Practice Problems 3

Section 3.1

1. 20 cm
2. 21.0 cm
3. $4.2 \times 10^2 \text{ cm}^2$
4. Pete's
5. Bruce's
6. 1 cm
7. 5%
8. 6.0 m

Section 3.2

1. 20 cm
2. 400 mm
3. 24 liters
4. 12,000 g
5. 50 lb
6. 6×10^{10}
7. 293 K
8. 4°C

Section 3.3

1. $\text{pop. density} = \dfrac{750{,}000 \text{ people}}{49 \text{ mi}^2} \times \dfrac{1 \text{ mi}^2}{640 \text{ acres}}$

$= 24 \text{ people/acre}$

2. $\text{cost} = \dfrac{1 \text{ can}}{50.2 \text{ g}} \times \dfrac{454 \text{ g}}{1 \text{ lb}} \times 2.99 \dfrac{\text{dollars}}{\text{can}}$

$= 27.0 \dfrac{\text{dollars}}{\text{lb}}$

3. $60 \dfrac{\text{mi}}{\text{h}} \times \dfrac{1.609 \text{ km}}{\text{mi}} = 96.54 \text{ km/h}$

4. The chicken costs \$2.14/lb, the beef steak costs \$1.82/lb. The beef steak is less expensive per pound.

5. $1 \text{ day} \times \dfrac{24 \text{ h}}{1 \text{ day}} \times \dfrac{60 \text{ min}}{1 \text{ h}} \times \dfrac{60 \text{ s}}{1 \text{ min}} = 86{,}400 \text{ s}$

6. $72 \dfrac{\text{km}}{\text{h}} \times \dfrac{1000 \text{ m}}{1 \text{ km}} \times \dfrac{100 \text{ cm}}{1 \text{ m}} \times \dfrac{1 \text{ h}}{60 \text{ min}} \times \dfrac{1 \text{ min}}{60 \text{ s}}$

$= 2.0 \times 10^3 \text{ cm/s}$

7. $1 \text{ m}^3 \times 19.3 \dfrac{\text{g}}{\text{cm}^3} \times \left(\dfrac{100 \text{ cm}}{1 \text{ m}}\right)^3 \times \dfrac{1 \text{ kg}}{1000 \text{ g}}$

$= 1.93 \times 10^4 \text{ kg}$

8. $40.0 \dfrac{\text{mi}}{\text{gal}} \times \dfrac{0.264 \text{ gal}}{1 \text{ L}} \times \dfrac{1.61 \text{ km}}{1 \text{ mi}} = 17.0 \text{ km/L}$

9. $1.00 \text{ dollar} \times \dfrac{1 \text{ oz}}{375 \text{ dollars}} \times \dfrac{1 \text{ lb}}{16 \text{ oz}}$

$\times \dfrac{454 \text{ g}}{1 \text{ lb}} \times \dfrac{1000 \text{ mg}}{1 \text{ g}} = 75.7 \text{ mg}$

Section 3.4

1. 6.00 grams
2. The balloon will float. Air is less dense than carbon dioxide.
3. 1.09 liters
4. 27 g

Interpreting Graphics 3

1. Two significant figures
2. Three significant figures
3. cylinder B
4. either cylinder A or B
5. the Celsius scale
6. the Kelvin scale
7. No, 20 °C is known. Another significant figure could be estimated.
8. liquid

Vocabulary Review 3

1. g	6. j	11. c
2. i	7. l	12. d
3. h	8. b	13. e
4. f	9. a	
5. k	10. m	

Quiz for Chapter 3

1. no
2. 1×10^{-3} kg/ 1 g
3. 4
4. a. 0.083 m
   b. 20°C
   c. 6900 km
5. a. 8.3×10^{-2} m
   b. 2.0×10^{1} °C
   c. 6.9×10^{3} km
6. b
7. c
8. $K = -55°C + 273 = 218$
9. Percent Error
$$= \frac{5.10 \text{ g/cm}^3 - 4.80 \text{ g/cm}^3}{5.10 \text{ g/cm}^3} \times 100 = 5.88\%$$

Chapter 3 Test A

A. Matching

1. i	5. f	8. a
2. b	6. c	9. d
3. j	7. e	10. h
4. g		

B. Multiple Choice

11. d	16. b	21. d
12. d	17. a	22. a
13. b	18. c	23. d
14. a	19. b	24. d
15. c	20. a	25. b

C. True-False

26. ST	29. AT	32. ST
27. ST	30. ST	33. AT
28. ST	31. NT	34. NT

D. Problems

35. Density $= \dfrac{\text{mass}}{\text{volume}} = \dfrac{980 \text{ g}}{64 \text{ cm}^3} = 15$ g/cm³; no

36. a. $4.15 \text{ cm} \times 1.8 \text{ cm} = 7.5 \text{ cm}^2$
    b. $13.00 \text{ m} - 0.54 \text{ m} = 12.46 \text{ m}$
    c. $(1.7 \times 10^{-5} \text{ m}) \times (3.72 \times 10^{-4} \text{ m})$
       $= 6.3 \times 10^{-9} \text{ m}^2$

37. Density $= \dfrac{\text{mass}}{\text{volume}} = \dfrac{14.0 \text{ g}}{18.0 \text{ cm}^3}$
    $= 0.778$ g/cm³

E. Essay

38. Density is the ratio of the mass of an object to its volume. Density is an intensive property that depends only on the composition of a substance, not on the size of the sample. Volume is a measure of the space occupied by an object. Volume is an extensive property that depends on the amount of matter in a sample. The density of water at a given temperature does not vary with the size of the sample; the volume of the water, however, does vary with the size of the sample.

Chapter 3 Test B

A. Matching

1. e	5. c	8. a
2. i	6. b	9. h
3. g	7. j	10. d
4. f		

B. Multiple Choice

11. c	18. d	25. a
12. d	19. d	26. a
13. a	20. c	27. b
14. c	21. d	28. d
15. a	22. b	29. c
16. d	23. a	30. a
17. c	24. c	31. d

C. True-False

32. AT	35. AT	38. NT
33. ST	36. AT	39. NT
34. ST	37. NT	

D. Problems

40. a. 36.47 cm + 2.721 cm + 15.1 cm
= 54.291 cm = 54.3 cm

b. 148.576 g − 35.41 g = 113.166 g
= 113.17 g

c. $(5.6 \times 10^7 \text{ m}) \times (3.60 \times 10^{-2} \text{ m})$
$= 20.16 \times 10^5 \text{ m}^2 = 2.016 \times 10^6 \text{ m}^2$
$= 2.0 \times 10^6 \text{ m}^2$

d. $\dfrac{8.74 \times 10^9 \text{ m}}{4.2 \times 10^{-6}} = 2.08 \times 10^{15} \text{ m}$
$= 2.1 \times 10^{15} \text{ m}$

41. a. $V = \left(0.60 \text{ m} \times \dfrac{100 \text{ cm}}{\text{m}}\right) \times 10.0 \text{ cm} \times$
$\left(50.0 \text{ mm} \times \dfrac{1 \text{ cm}}{10 \text{ mm}}\right) = 3000 \text{ cm}^3$
$= 3.0 \times 10^3 \text{ cm}^3$

$3.0 \times 10^3 \text{ cm}^3 \times \dfrac{1 \text{ L}}{1000 \text{ cm}^3} = 3.0 \text{ L}$

b. $3.0 \text{ L} \times \dfrac{1 \text{ kg H}_2\text{O}}{\text{L}} = 3.0 \text{ kg H}_2\text{O}$

42. density $= \dfrac{\text{mass}}{\text{volume}} = \dfrac{750.0 \text{ g}}{65.0 \text{ cm}^3} = 11.5 \text{ g/cm}^3$

The metal is not pure silver.

E. Essay

43. To find the volume of the box in liters, you must first express the volume of the box in cubic units, based on the linear dimensions given, and then select a conversion factor that will allow you to convert the cubic units into liters.

Thus, since $V = L \times W \times H$,

$V = 25 \text{ cm} \times 10 \text{ cm} \times 8 \text{ cm} = 2000 \text{ cm}^3$

To convert the cm^3 into liters, you must select a conversion factor so that relates cm^3 to liters, that the cm^3 units cancel and the liter units remain.

Thus, since $1 \text{ L} = 1000 \text{ cm}^3$

$2000 \text{ cm}^3 \times \dfrac{1 \text{ L}}{1000 \text{ cm}^3} = 2 \text{ L}$

Chapter 3 Small-Scale Lab

Section 3.4 Now What Do I Do?, page 94

Analysis

Answers are based on the following sample data:

average mass of water drop = 0.019 g
mass of pre-1982 penny = 3.11 g
mass of post-1982-penny = 2.50 g

1. $x \text{ mg} = 0.019 \text{ g} \times 1000 \text{ mg/g} = 19 \text{ mg}$

2. $V = \dfrac{0.019 \text{ g}}{1.00 \text{ g/cm}^3} = 0.019 \text{ cm}^3$

$x \text{ mL} = 0.019 \text{ cm}^3 \times \dfrac{1 \text{ mL}}{1 \text{ cm}^3} = 0.019 \text{ mL}$

$x \text{ } \mu\text{L} = 0.019 \text{ mL} \times \dfrac{1000 \text{ } \mu\text{L}}{1 \text{ mL}} = 19 \text{ } \mu\text{L}$

3. $x \text{ mg/cm}^3 = 1.00 \text{ g/cm}^3 \times 1000 \text{ mg/g}$
$= 1000 \text{ mg/cm}^3;$
$1000 \text{ mg/cm}^3 \times 1 \text{ cm}^3/1 \text{ mL} = 1000 \text{ mg/mL}$

4. $\text{g Cu} = 3.11 \text{ g penny} \times \dfrac{95.0 \text{ g Cu}}{100 \text{ g penny}}$
$= 2.95 \text{ g Cu}$

$\text{g Zn} = 3.11 \text{ g penny} \times \dfrac{5.0 \text{ g Zn}}{100 \text{ g penny}}$
$= 0.16 \text{ g Zn}$

5. $x \text{ g Cu} = 2.50 \text{ g penny} \times \dfrac{2.4 \text{ g Cu}}{100 \text{ g penny}}$
$= 0.060 \text{ g Cu}$

$x \text{ g Zn} = 2.50 \text{ g penny} \times \dfrac{97.6 \text{ g Zn}}{100 \text{ g penny}}$
$= 2.44 \text{ g Zn}$

6. The new penny is lighter because it is mostly zinc which has a lower density than copper.

You're The Chemist

1. at 90°, mass of 1 drop: 0.019 g

at 45°, mass of 1 drop: 0.0218 g

at 0°, mass of 1 drop: 0.0242 g

Pipets give different results.

2. The best angle is 90° because the pipet is easiest to control. Expel the air bubble so that the first drop will be the same size as the rest.

3. Find mass of can and divide by density of aluminum. Sample answer:

mass of one can: 14.77 g;

density of Al: 2.70 g/cm^3; $V = 5.47$ cm^3

4. (1) Measure the mass before and after you fill the can with water. Use the mass and density of water to find the volume.

(2) Measure the height and radius and calculate volume.

$V = \pi r^2 h$

(Can is not a perfect cylinder.)

(3) Read label: 12 oz = 355 mL

5. Sample answer:

$V = 16.5$ m $\times$ 3.0 m $\times$ 12.8 m

$= 630$ m^3 $\times$ 1000 L/m^3

$= 630\ 000$ L

Assume 30 people with an average weight of 130 lb (1 kg = 2.2 lb) and a density of about 1.0 kg/L.

Volume of 30 people

$V = 30 \times 130$ lb $\times$ 1 kg/2.2 lb $\times$ 1 L/1.0 kg

$= 1800$ L

The volume of 30 chairs, 15 tables, and 2 desks is about that of 30 people or 1800 L. The volume of people and furniture is 3600 L.

% error = (3600 L/630,000 L)(100%)

$= 0.57\%$.

6. If die measures 1.55 cm on a side:

$V = (1.55$ cm$)^3 = 3.72$ cm^3

A die has 21 holes that are hemispheres with a radius of 0.20 cm.

Volume of hemisphere: $2/3\pi r^3$

$V = 2/3\pi r^3 = 0.017$ cm^3

Volume of 21 hemispheres: 0.36 cm^3

Volume of die:

$V = 3.72$ cm$^3 - 0.36$ cm^3

$= 3.36$ cm^3

Error $= 0.36$ cm^3

Percent error

$= (0.36$ cm$^3/3.36$ cm$^3)(100\%) = 11\%$

Note: The holes in some dice are cones. The volume of a cone is $1/3\ \pi r2h$.

7. Find weight in pounds and convert to kg. Assume the density is about 1.00 kg/L.

$V = weight \times 1$ kg/2.2 lb $\times$ 1L/1.00 kg

Section Review 4.1

Part A Completion

1. atoms

2. different

3. compounds

4. separated, joined, or rearranged

Part B True-False

5. NT   **6.** ST   **7.** AT

Part C Matching

8. c   **10.** d

9. a   **11.** b

Part D Questions and Problems

12. simple whole-number ratios

13. $\dfrac{1 \times 10^8 \text{ atoms}}{\cancel{cm}} \times \dfrac{100 \cancel{cm}}{m} = 10^{10}$ atoms/m

Section Review 4.2

Part A Completion

1. subatomic

2. negative

3. protons

4. neutrons

5. nucleus

6. Ernest Rutherford

7. positive

8. electrons

Part B True-False

9. NT   **11.** NT

10. AT   **12.** AT

Part C Matching

13. c   **15.** e   **17.** b

14. a   **16.** d

Part D Questions and Problems

18. protons, neutrons

19. protons, electrons
20. Atoms are mostly empty space. The relatively massive protons and neutrons are concentrated in a small region called the nucleus; electrons are found outside the nucleus. Most alpha particles pass through the empty space without deflection. The few that come near the nucleus are deflected or bounce straight back.

Section Review 4.3

Part A Completion

1. protons
2. number
3. electrons
4. protons
5. neutrons
6. isotopes
7. atomic mass
8. 1
9. no
10. 1

Part B True-False

11. NT
12. AT
13. ST
14. AT
15. AT

Part C Matching

16. e
17. f
18. c
19. g
20. a
21. d
22. b
23. h

Part D Questions and Problems

24. oxygen-16:16 amu $\times$ 0.9976 = 15.96 amu
    oxygen-17:17 amu $\times$ 0.00037 = 0.0063 amu
    oxygen-18:18 amu $\times$ 0.00204 = 0.0367 amu
    16.00 amu = 16 amu

Practice Problems 4

Section 4.1

1. $(1 \times 10^7 \text{ atoms}) \times \dfrac{1 \text{ cm}}{1 \times 10^8 \text{ atoms}} \times \dfrac{10 \text{ mm}}{1 \text{ cm}}$

    = 1 mm

Section 4.2

1. mass of e^- is negligible;
   $16(1.67 \times 10^{-24} \text{ g}) + 16(1.67 \times 10^{-24})$
   $= 5.33 \times 10^{-23} \text{ g}$
2. approximately 6×10^{23} neutrons
3. b

Section 4.3

1. **a.** 5
   b. 16
   c. 10
   d. 3
2. Number of protons: 11; 39; 33; 89
   Number of electrons: 25; 35; 39; 89
   Number of neutrons: 50; 42; 138
   Atomic number: 25; 11; 35; 33; 89
   Mass number: 55; 23; 80
3. **a.** 12
   b. 146
   c. 46
   d. 10
4. 12.011 amu
5. 75% X−100, 25% X−104

Vocabulary Review 4

1. f
2. h
3. g
4. b
5. j
6. c
7. e
8. d
9. a
10. i

Quiz for Chapter 4

1. simple whole-number
2. chemical reaction
3. Electrons
4. neutrons
5. proton
6. atomic
7. 8
8. mass
9. 156
10. 30
11. periods
12. atomic number

Chapter 4 Test A

A. Matching

1. j
2. g
3. a
4. c
5. f
6. e
7. d
8. b
9. h
10. i

B. Multiple Choice

11. c	16. a	21. c
12. d	17. b	22. d
13. c	18. a	23. c
14. c	19. b	
15. d	20. b	

C. Problems

24. $63.929 \text{ amu} \times 0.4889 = 31.25 \text{ amu}$
$65.926 \text{ amu} \times 0.2781 = 18.33 \text{ amu}$
$66.927 \text{ amu} \times 0.0411 = 2.75 \text{ amu}$
$67.925 \text{ amu} \times 0.1857 = 12.61 \text{ amu}$
$69.925 \text{ amu} \times 0.0062 = \underline{0.43 \text{ amu}}$
$\text{atomic mass} = 65.37 \text{ amu}$

25. Atomic number: 7; 20; 26
Mass number: 19; 41
Number of protons: 9; 7; 20; 13
Number of neutrons: 14; 30
Number of electrons: 9; 7; 13; 26

26. $^{13}_{6}\text{C}$: 6; 7; 6
$^{10}_{4}\text{Be}$: 4; 6; 4
$^{20}_{10}\text{Ne}$: 10; 10; 10
$^{11}_{5}\text{B}$: 5; 6; 5
$^{33}_{16}\text{S}$: 16; 17; 16

D. Essay

27. Atoms of different elements have a unique number of protons and electrons. Isotopes of the same element differ in the number of neutrons in the nuclei.

C. Problems

25. Ar-36 $35.978 \text{ amu} \times 0.00337 = 0.121 \text{ amu}$
Ar-38 $37.963 \text{ amu} \times 0.00063 = 0.024 \text{ amu}$
Ar-40 $39.962 \text{ amu} \times 0.99600 = \underline{39.802 \text{ amu}}$
$\text{atomic mass} = 39.947 \text{ amu}$

26. $^{19}_{9}\text{F}$: 9; 10; 9
$^{27}_{13}\text{Al}$: 13; 14; 13
$^{40}_{18}\text{Ar}$: 18; 22; 18
$^{65}_{30}\text{Zn}$: 30; 35; 30
$^{108}_{47}\text{Ag}$: 47; 61; 47

27. Atomic number: 19; 26; 35; 79
Mass number 24; 56; 80; 197
Number of protons: 12; 19; 26; 35
Number of neutrons: 12; 45
Number of electrons: 12; 19; 35; 79
Symbol: $^{39}_{19}\text{K}$; $^{56}_{26}\text{Fe}$; $^{197}_{79}\text{Au}$

D. Essay

28. Isotopes of the same element are alike in that they have the same atomic number, and thus, the same number of protons and electrons. Isotopes of the same element are different in that they have different numbers of neutrons, and thus, different mass numbers.

Chapter 4 Test B

A. Matching

1. c	5. h	8. j
2. i	6. a	9. e
3. b	7. f	10. d
4. g		

B. Multiple Choice

11. a	16. c	21. b
12. c	17. c	22. b
13. d	18. b	23. a
14. d	19. a	24. d
15. a	20. c	

Chapter 4 Small-Scale Lab

Section 4.3 The Atomic Mass of Candium, page 120

Analysis

Sample data provided.

	A	B	C	Totals
Total mass (grams)	13.16 g	13.83 g	15.40 g	42.39 g
Total Number	15	13	20	48
Average mass (grams)	0.8773 g	1.064 g	0.7700 g	0.8831 g
Relative abundance	0.3125	0.2708	0.4167	100.0
Percent abundance	31.25	27.08	41.67	1.000
Relative mass	0.2742 g	0.2883 g	0.3208 g	0.8833 g

Figure A

1. See row 3 in Figure A.
2. See row 4 in Figure A.
3. See row 5 in Figure A.
4. See row 6 in Figure A.
5. 0.2742 g + 0.2883 g + 0.3208 g = 0.8833 g
6. Percent abundance is parts per hundred. Relative abundance is parts per one or the decimal form of percent. The individual percent abundances add up to 100. The individual relative abundances add up to 1.
7. Relative abundance tells you the decimal fraction of particles.
8. The total in row 3 is an average that ignores the relative abundances of particles. The total in row 6 is a weighted average because it considers differences in mass and abundance among the particles.
9. Another student might not have had the same relative abundance of each candy. A larger sample would provide a greater sampling of all isotopes.

You're The Chemist

1. Any differences are probably due to small variations in the numbers of each kind of candy in the samples, which affect the relative abundances.
2. The larger the samples, the better the results with any of the methods. Mass is likely to provide better results than volume.

Section Review 5.1

Part A Completion

1. electrons
2. John Dalton
3. J.J. Thomson
4. plum-pudding
5. nucleus
6. circular
7. quantum mechanical
8. probability

Part B True/False

9. AT
10. ST
11. NT
12. AT
13. AT
14. AT

Part C Matching

15. c
16. b
17. a
18. d

Part D Questions and Problems

19. Dalton proposed that matter was made of indestructible particles called atoms. Thomson proposed an atomic model in which negatively charged electrons were embedded in a positively charged mass. Rutherford discovered that atoms are mainly empty space. He proposed that electrons surround a dense nucleus. Bohr proposed that electrons are arranged in concentric circular paths around the nucleus. According to Bohr, the electrons in a particular orbit have a fixed energy, which prevents them from falling into the nucleus. In the modern atomic theory, the locations of electrons are not fixed; they are described in terms of probability.

20. **a.** 3 orbitals   **c.** 7 orbitals
    b. 5 orbitals   **d.** 1 orbital

Section 5.2

Part A Completion

1. electron configurations
2. Aufbau principle
3. equal
4. Pauli exclusion
5. two
6. opposite
7. a single electron
8. superscripts
9. electrons
10. Chromium

Part B True/False

11. ST	13. NT	15. AT
12. NT	14. AT	16. NT

Part C Matching

17. e	19. b	21. c
18. d	20. a	

Part D Questions and Problems

22. **a.** $1s^2 2s^2 2p^2$
    b. $1s^2 2s^2 2p^6 3s^2 3p^4$
    c. $1s^2 2s^2 2p^6 3s^2 3p^6 4s^1$
    d. $1s^2 2s^2 2p^6 3s^2 3p^6$

23. **a.** Ar **b.** B

Section 5.3

Part A Completion

1. waves
2. inversely
3. light
4. atomic emission spectrum
5. light radiation
6. photoelectric
7. frequency

Part B True/False

8. NT	10. AT	12. NT
9. NT	11. NT	

Part C Matching

13. c	15. e	17. b
14. a	16. d	

Part D Questions and Problems

18. $v = \dfrac{3.00 \times 10^{10}\ \text{cm/s}}{2.40 \times 10^{-5}\ \text{cm}}$

    $v = 1.25 \times 10^{15}\ \text{s}^{-1}$

19. The photoelectric effect will not occur unless the frequency of the light striking a metal is high enough to cause an electron to be ejected from the metal. The frequency of the light must be above the threshold frequency that will provide the necessary quanta of energy.

Practice Problems 5

Section 5.1

1. **a.** 1   **d.** 4
   b. 2   **e.** 5
   c. 3   **f.** 6

2. **a.** 1   **e.** 1
   b. 1   **f.** 3
   c. 5   **g.** 16
   d. 7   **h.** 5

3. **a.** 1s, 1 orbital
   b. 2s, 1 orbital; 2p, 3 orbitals
   c. 3s, 1 orbital; 3p, 3 orbitals; 3d, 5 orbitals
   d. 4s, 1 orbital; 4p, 3 orbitals; 4d, 5 orbitals; 4f, 7 orbitals
   e. 5s, 1 orbital; 5p, 3 orbitals; 5d, 5 orbitals; 5f, 7 orbitals

Section 5.2

1. **a.** $1s^1$
   b. $1s^2 2s^2 2p^6 3s^2 3p^6 3d^3 4s^2$
   c. $1s^2 2s^2 2p^6 3s^2$
   d. $1s^2 2s^2 2p^6 3s^2 3p^6 3d^{10} 4s^2 4p^6 4d^{10} 5s^2 5p^6 6s^2$
   e. $1s^2 2s^2 2p^6 3s^2 3p^6 3d^{10} 4s^2 4p^5$
   f. $1s^2 2s^2 2p^6 3s^2 3p^4$
   g. $1s^2 2s^2 2p^6 3s^2 3p^6 3d^{10} 4s^2 4p^6$
   h. $1s^2 2s^2 2p^6 3s^2 3p^6 3d^{10} 4s^2 4p^3$
   i. $1s^2 2s^2 2p^6 3s^2 3p^6 3d^{10} 4s^2 4p^6 4d^{10} 4f^{14} 5s^2 5p^6$ $5d^{10} 6s^2 6p^6$

Section 5.3

1. $\lambda = \dfrac{c}{v} = \dfrac{3.00 \times 10^{10}\ \text{cm/s}}{5.00 \times 10^{15}\ \text{s}^{-1}}$

   $\lambda = 6.00 \times 10^{-6}$ cm; ultraviolet

2. $v = \dfrac{c}{\lambda} = \dfrac{3.00 \times 10^{8}\ \text{m/s}}{6.70 \times 10^{-7}\ \text{m}}$

   $v = 4.48 \times 10^{14}\ \text{s}^{-1}$

The laser emits red light.

3. $E = h \times v = 6.6262 \times 10^{-34} \text{ J s} \times 2.22 \times 10^{14} \text{ s}^{-1}$
   $E = 1.47 \times 10^{-19} \text{ J}$

4. $v = \dfrac{E}{h} = \dfrac{6.00 \times 10^{-15} \text{ J}}{6.6262 \times 10^{-34} \text{ J s}}$
   $v = 9.05 \times 10^{18} \text{ s}^{-1}$

5. radio waves, microwaves, infrared, visible light, ultraviolet, gamma rays

6. $\lambda = \dfrac{c}{v} = \dfrac{3.00 \times 10^8 \text{ m/s}}{1600 \times 10^3 \text{ s}^{-1}}$
   $\lambda = 1.88 \times 10^2 \text{ m}$

Interpreting Graphics 5

1. $v \text{ (s}^{-1}\text{)}$: 4.01×10^{13}; 1.14×10^{14}; 2.75×10^{14}; 7.30×10^{14}; 3.20×10^{15}; 7.41×10^{13}; 2.34×10^{14}; 6.88×10^{14}; 3.15×10^{15}; 1.60×10^{14}; 6.17×10^{14}; 3.08×10^{15}; 4.57×10^{14}; 2.93×10^{15}; 2.48×10^{15}

2. λ: 7.48×10^{-6} m; 2.63×10^{-6} m; 1.09×10^{-6} m; 4.11×10^{-7} m; 9.38×10^{-8} m; 4.05×10^{-6} m; 1.28×10^{-6} m; 4.36×10^{-7} m; 9.52×10^{-8} m; 1.88×10^{-6} m; 4.86×10^{-7} m; 9.74×10^{-8} m; 6.56×10^{-7} m; 1.02×10^{-7} m; 1.21×10^{-7} m

3. **type of radiation:** infrared; infrared; infrared; visible light; ultraviolet light; infrared; infrared; visible light; ultraviolet light; infrared; visible light; ultraviolet light; visible light; ultraviolet light; ultraviolet light

4. $6 \to 2$
   $5 \to 2$
   $4 \to 2$
   $3 \to 2$

5. $6 \to 2$ blue
   $5 \to 2$ blue
   $4 \to 2$ green
   $3 \to 2$ red

6. All of the transitions end at the $n = 2$ energy level.

7. The Bohr model is adequate for explaining the emission spectra of atoms with a single electron. Li^{2+} and He^+ each have a single electron surrounding the nucleus and should, thus, behave according to the Bohr model.

Vocabulary Review 5

1. Hund's rule
2. photons
3. hertz
4. Pauli exclusion principle
5. quantum
6. quantum mechanical model
7. aufbau principle
8. wavelength
9. atomic emission spectrum
10. photoelectrons

Quiz for Chapter 5

1. ST
2. NT
3. AT
4. ST
5. AT
6. NT
7. Planck's constant
8. ground state
9. photons
10. photoelectric
11. wavelike

Chapter 5 Test A

A. Matching

1. b
2. g
3. e
4. c
5. h
6. j
7. i
8. d
9. f
10. a

B. Multiple Choice

11. b
12. c
13. a
14. d
15. a
16. c
17. b
18. d
19. d
20. a

C. Problems

21. a.

3p

3s

2p

2s

1s

$1s^2 2s^2 2p^6 3s^2 3p^4$

b.

3s

2p

2s

1s

$1s^2 2s^2 2p^6 3s^1$

22. $v = \dfrac{3.00 \times 10^{10}\,\text{cm/s}}{2.40 \times 10^{-5}\,\text{cm}} = 1.25 \times 10^{15}\,\text{s}^{-1}$

23. a. aluminum   **c.** cobalt

    b. krypton

24. a. phosphorus   **c.** bromine

    b. neon

25. Energy level 1 = 2
Energy level 2 = 8
Energy level 3 = 18
Energy level 4 = 32
Energy level 5 = 50

D. Essay

26. Electrons occupy orbitals in a definite sequence, filling orbitals with lower energies first. Generally, orbitals in a lower principal energy level have lower energies than those in a higher principal energy level, but in the fourth level the energy ranges of the principal energy levels begin to overlap. As a result, the 5s sublevel is lower in energy than the 4d sublevel.

E. Additional Matching

27. b	**29.** f	**31.** c
28. a	**30.** e	**32.** d

F. True/False

33. AT	**36.** ST	**39.** AT
34. NT	**37.** NT	**40.** ST
35. AT	**38.** AT	**41.** AT

Chapter 5 Test B

A. Matching

1. h	**5.** d	**8.** j
2. c	**6.** g	**9.** a
3. f	**7.** b	**10.** i
4. e		

B. Multiple Choice

11. c	**16.** a	**21.** c
12. c	**17.** c	**22.** d
13. c	**18.** b	**23.** c
14. b	**19.** d	**24.** b
15. b	**20.** b	

C. Problems

25. a. $1s^2 2s^2 2p^6 3s^2$
    b. $1s^2 2s^2 2p^6 3s^2 3p^3$
    c. $1s^2 2s^2 2p^6 3s^2 3p^6 4s^2 3d^{10} 4p^5$
    d. $1s^2 2s^2 2p^6 3s^2 3p^6 4s^2 3d^{10} 4p^6 5s^2 4d^{10} 5p^6$

26. a. S   **e.** Sr
    b. Ne   **f.** P
    c. Sc   **g.** Mn
    d. Br   **h.** Fr

27. $c = v\lambda$
$v = c/\lambda$
$v = \dfrac{3.00 \times 10^{10}\,\text{cm/s}}{6.25 \times 10^{-5}\,\text{cm}}$
$v = 4.80 \times 10^{14}\,\text{s}^{-1}$

28. $E = h \times v$
$E = (6.6262 \times 10^{-34}\,\text{Js}) \times (5.2 \times 10^{15}\,\text{s}^{-1})$
$E = 3.4 \times 10^{-18}\,\text{J}$

D. Essay

29. According to the Bohr model, electrons travel around the nucleus along fixed paths much as planets orbit the sun. The quantum mechanical model, explains the positions of electrons in terms of probability clouds within which the electrons are most likely to be found. The Bohr model places electrons at specific distances from the nucleus. The quantum mechanical model allows electrons to be at virtually any distance from the nucleus, but describes the locations of greatest probability in terms of specified orbital shapes.

E. Additional Matching

30. c	**32.** a	**34.** e
31. d	**33.** f	**35.** b

F. True/False

36. AT	**39.** NT	**42.** ST
37. NT	**40.** AT	**43.** AT
38. AT	**41.** AT	**44.** AT

Chapter 5 Small-Scale Lab

See Teacher's Edition, p. 137 for answers.

Section Review 6.1

Part A Completion

1. properties
2. groups
3. periods or rows
4. atomic number
5. group
6. Metals
7. gases
8. metalloids
9. less
10. more

Part B True-False

10. NT	**12.** AT
11. NT	**13.** NT

Part C Matching

14. b	**16.** a	**18.** d
15. e	**17.** c	

Part D Questions and Problems

19. nitrogen and phosphorus are nonmetals; arsenic and antimony are metalloids; bismuth is a metal.

20. good conductors of heat and electric current; high luster; ductile; malleable; solids at room temperature

21. fluorine, bromine, iodine

Section Review 6.2

Part A Completion

1. names
2. atoms
3. alkali metals
4. alkaline earth metals
5. representative elements
6. halogens
7. noble gases
8. transition metals
9. inner transition metals
10. p
11. not filled

Part B True-False

12. ST	**14.** NT
13. NT	**15.** AT

Part C Matching

16. f	**19.** d	**21.** c
17. e	**20.** b	**22.** a
18. g		

Part D Questions and Problems

23. Na, $3s^1$; Mg, $3s^2$; Al, $3s^23p^1$; Si, $3s^23p^2$; P, $3s^23p^3$; S, $3s^23p^4$; Cl, $3s^23p^5$; Ar, $3s^23p^6$

24. Oxygen: nonmetal, gas;
Sulfur: nonmetal, solid;
Selenium: nonmetal, solid;
Tellurium: metalloid, solid;
Polonium: metal, solid

Section Review 6.3

Part A Completion

1. decrease	6. increases
2. increases	7. electrons
3. energy levels	8. smaller
4. charge	9. electronegativity
5. ionization	10. increases

Part B True-False

11. ST	**13.** AT
12. AT	**14.** NT

Part C Matching

15. d	**17.** f	**19.** e
16. c	**18.** a	**20.** b

Part D Questions and Problems

21. **a.** Al   **d.** Na
    b. S   **e.** O
    c. Br

22. **a.** gallium   **c.** chlorine
    b. oxygen   **d.** bromine

Practice Problems

Section 6.1

1. c

2. **a.** nonmetal   **d.** nonmetal
   b. metalloid   **e.** metal
   c. metal

3. a

4. Li, Na, Rb, Cs, Fr

5. The three classes are as follows.
   1) The metals: good conductors of heat and electric current; high luster when clean; malleable; ductile.
   2) The nonmetals: poor conductors of heat and electric current; nonlustrous. Solid metals tend to be brittle.
   3) The metalloids: elements that have properties similar to those of metals and nonmetals depending on the conditions.

Section 6.2

1. Silicon is in the third period. Its first and second energy levels are full ($1s^2 2s^2 2p^6$). It is the fourth element in the period; so its electron configuration must end in $3s^2 3p^2$. The complete configuration is $1s^2 2s^2 2p^6 3s^2 3p^2$.

2. Iodine is located in period 5. Its first four energy levels are full. It is Group 4A; so its electron configuration must end in $5s^2 5p^5$. The complete configuration is $1s^2 2s^2 2p^6 3s^2 3p^6 3d^{10} 4s^2 4p^6 4d^{10} 5s^2 5p^5$.

3. The configuration $s^2 p^3$ indicates 5 electrons in the highest occupied energy level, which is a feature of Group 5A.

4. **a.** Elements in Group 5A have 5 electrons in their highest occupied energy level. The third period element in Group 5A is phosphorus.
   b. $4s^2 4p^5$ represents the Group 7A element in period 4; this element is bromine.
   c. selenium.

5. **a.** The period 2 element with six electrons is oxygen.

b. The period 4 element with 2 electrons is calcium.

c. The element in period 4 with 2 electrons in the 4s sublevel and 10 electrons in the 3d sublevel is zinc.

6. Both Ne and Ar have a completely filled highest occupied energy level. They are in Group 8A, which is also known as the noble gases.
   Ne: $1s^2 2s^2 2p^6$
   Ar: $1s^2 2s^2 2p^6 3s^2 3p^6$

7. The chemical and physical properties are largely determined by their electron configurations. Lithium in Group 1A has only 1 electron in its highest occupied energy level. Sulfur in Group 6A has 6 electrons in its highest occupied energy level.

8. Transition metals are elements whose highest occupied s sublevel and a nearby d sublevel contain electrons. The electron configurations for Ag and Fe are:
   Ag $1s^2 2s^2 2p^6 3s^2 3p^6 4s^2 4p^6 4d^{10} 5s^1$
   Fe $1s^2 2s^2 2p^6 3s^2 3p^6 3d^6 4s^2$

Section 6.3

1. A magnesium atom is smaller than a sodium atom because the shielding effect is constant for elements in the same period, but the nuclear charge is greater in magnesium. So the electrons are drawn closer to the nucleus. Magnesium and calcium have the same number of electrons in their highest occupied energy level. A magnesium atom is smaller than a calcium atom because there are fewer occupied energy levels.

2. Astatine is in period 6. Tellurium is in period 5. Astatine is in Group 7A; tellurium is in Group 6A. Although atomic size decreases across a period, the additional occupied energy level in astatine significantly increases the size of the astatine atom as compared to the tellurium atom. The prediction is that atoms of astatine are larger than atoms of tellurium.

3. A chlorine atom is smaller than a magnesium atom because atomic size decreases from left to right across a period. When a magnesium atom reacts, it loses electrons from its highest occupied energy level. A magnesium ion has filled first and second levels. When chlorine reacts, it gains an electron in its highest occupied energy level. An ion with three occupied energy levels is larger than an ion with two occupied energy levels.

4. Across a period from left to right the principal energy level remains the same, but the nuclear charge increases. The increasing nuclear charge pulls the electrons closer to the nucleus, resulting in a smaller atomic radius. The trend is less pronounced as the number of electrons increases because the inner electrons shield the electrons in the highest occupied energy level. Atomic size increases as you move down a period because the electrons are added to higher principal energy levels. This enlarging effect is greater than the shrinking effect caused by increasing nuclear charge.

5. When a sulfur atom reacts to form an ion it adds two electrons while chlorine adds one electron. Sulfide and chloride ions have the same number of electrons. Because the chloride ion has the greater nuclear charge, it will be smaller than the sulfide ion.

6. Sodium's first ionization energy is higher than that of potassium because ionization energy tends to decrease from top to bottom within a group.

7. Beryllium's first ionization energy is greater because first ionization energy tends to increase from left to right across a period.

8. Barium is less electronegative than strontium because electronegativity values tend to decrease from top to bottom within a group.

9. Because magnesium has a relatively low first and second ionization energy, the removal of two electrons from magnesium is likely. The relatively high third ionization energy indicates the difficulty of removing a third electron from the filled second energy level. Magnesium normally forms an ion with a 2+ charge.

10. Because electronegativity decreases from top to bottom within a group, sulfur is less electronegative than oxygen. Because electronegativity increases from left to right across a period, fluorine is more electronegative than oxygen. The correct order for increasing electronegativity is then sulfur < oxygen < fluorine.

Interpreting Graphics 6

1. 42
2. table A
3. atomic weight
4. 0.53 g/cm^3
5. 2617 °C
6. table B
7. 4

8. physical state at room temperature; general class, e.g. transition metal; whether an element is not found in nature

9. In the periodic table elements with similar chemical and physical properties are grouped together in vertical columns. This organization helps scientists predict and explain similarities and differences in the properties of elements based on their underlying atomic structure. Listing the elements, in alphabetical order, makes it possible to quickly find information about the properties of a particular element without having to know the location of the element in the periodic table.

10. a. Li: Group 1A (or Group 1), period 2
   Mo: Group 6B (or Group 6), period 5

   b. No, because they are not located in the same group or family.

   c. Lithium, Li, is an alkali metal.
   Molybdenum, Mo, is a transition metal.

   d. Answers may include sodium, potassium, rubidium, cesium, and francium.

11. Check students' work. Their keys need to include the color, mp, and bp, of the element (and the state if the square is not color coded for style).

Vocabulary Review 6

1. a
2. n
3. m
4. c
5. k
6. b
7. l
8. g
9. o
10. i
11. e
12. f
13. h
14. d
15. p
16. j

Quiz for Chapter 6

1. number
2. seven
3. group (column or family)
4. six
5. two less
6. ST
7. AT
8. NT
9. AT
10. NT

Chapter 6 Test A

A. Matching

1. d
2. f
3. j
4. b
5. c
6. i
7. a
8. g
9. e
10. h

B. Multiple Choice

11. d
12. c
13. d
14. a
15. a
16. c
17. c
18. d
19. a
20. d
21. a
22. c
23. d
24. b
25. b

C. Questions

26. a. period 5, Group 2A (or Group 2)
     b. period 4, Group 6A (or Group 16)
     c. period 6, Group 4A (or Group 14)
27. a. $1s^2$
     b. $4s^1$
     c. $3s^2\,3p^1$
     d. $4s^2\,4p^6$
     e. $2s^2\,2p^4$
28. a. Li, K, Cs
     b. Ar, Cl P, Si
     c. Be, Ca, Sr, Ba
29. a. alkaline earth metal, period 4, Group 2A (or Group 2)
     b. alkali metal, period 6, Group 1A (or Group 1)
     c. halogen, period 2, Group 7a (or Group 17)
     d. transition metal, period 4, Group 6B (or Group 6)
     e. noble gas, period 2, Group 8A (or Group 18)
     f. transition metal, period 5, Group 1B (or Group 11)
30. a. Mg   b. I   c. Cl

D. Essay

31. Two factors influence the size of an atom as the atomic number increases within a group. There is an increase in nuclear charge, which draws the electrons closer to the nucleus. There is an increase in the number of occupied energy levels, which shields the electrons in the highest occupied energy level from the attraction of protons in the nucleus. The net effect is a decrease in the attraction of the nucleus on the electrons in the highest occupied energy level and an increase in atomic radius. From left to right across a period, electrons are being added to the same energy level. The increasing charge on the nucleus tends to pull the electrons closer and atomic radius decreases.

Chapter 6 Test B

A. Matching

1. c
2. i
3. b
4. g
5. h
6. a
7. j
8. d
9. f
10. e

B. Multiple Choice

11. b
12. d
13. d
14. a
15. d
16. c
17. d
18. c
19. d
20. a
21. d
22. d
23. b
24. a
25. c
26. c
27. a
28. b
29. b
30. c

C. Questions

31. a. 2; 2A(2); alkaline earth metal; Be
     b. 3; 5A(15); P
     c. 3; 8A(18); noble gas; Ar
     d. 4; 1A(1); alkali metal; K
     e. 4; 4B(4); transition metal; Sc
     f. 4; 7A(17); halogen; Br
32. a. Cs, K, Li, C, F
     b. Cs, K, Li, C, F
     c. F, C, Li, K, Cs

33. a. K; Li; K

b. C; F; C

c. Ca; Mg; Ca

d. S; O; S

34. a. B   **d.** B

b. C   **e.** B

c. D

D. Essay

35. Ionization energy and electronegativity are properties that reflect an atom's ability to attract and retain electrons. A high ionization energy indicates that an atom has a tight hold on its electrons. A high electronegativity value indicates an ability to attract electrons.

Chapter 6 Small-Scale Lab

Analyze and Conclude

1. Fluorine

2. Electronegativity generally increases from left to right along a period.

3. Metals, which are on the left side of the table, have lower electronegativity values than nonmetals, which are on the right.

4. Electronegativity generally increases from bottom to top within a group. Except for boron, the rest of Group 3A shows a reverse in this trend.

5. Although hydrogen is placed in Group 1A based on its electron configuration, hydrogen is classified as a nonmetal.

You're The Chemist

1. Students divide the values of first ionization energies by 300 and measure the appropriate length of straws.

2. Students must determine their own scale before they begin. Students often use two wells to represent both ionic and atomic radii. Other students cut a straw to a length that represents the larger radius of an atom and mark the straw to show the smaller radius of the corresponding cation.

3. The value for xenon is similar to iodine, which is consistent with the general trend. Based on this value, xenon appears to have the ability to attract electrons and form compounds.

Section Review 7.1

Part A Completion

1. valence electrons
2. group
3. electron dot structures
4. octet rule
5. cations
6. anions
7. 1+
8. Halide ions
9. gain
10. charges

Part B True/False

| 11. NT | 13. ST | 15. AT |
| 12. AT | 14. NT | 16. NT |

Part C Matching

17. b	20. g	22. a
18. d	21. f	23. c
19. e		

Part D Questions and Problems

24. a. ·Ṡi·   **c.** ·Ba·

b. Rb·

25 a. 2 electrons lost; magnesium ion; cation

b. 2 electrons lost; calcium ion; cation

c. 1 electron gained; bromide ion, anion

d. 1 electron lost; silver ion; cation

26. Nonmetals attain stable noble gas configurations by gaining electrons and forming anions with 8 outer electrons in the existing energy level. Metals attain noble gas configurations by losing electrons and forming cations with a complete octet in the next-lowest energy level.

Section 7.2

Part A Completion

1. electrostatic forces
2. oppositely
3. ionic bonds
4. neutral
5. formula unit
6. crystals
7. high
8. large
9. stable
10. molten

Part B True-False

11. AT   13. AT   15. NT
12. ST   14. ST

Part C Matching

16. b   18. c   20. a
17. e   19. d

Part D Questions and Problems

21. Ionic bonds are the electrostatic forces of attraction that bind oppositely charged ions together. In an ionic compound, the positive charges of the cations equal the negative charges of the ions.

22. When ionic compounds are melted, the orderly crystal structure breaks down. Each ion is then free to move throughout the molten mass. If a voltage is applied, cations will migrate to one electrode, and anions will migrate to the other. This movement of ions means that there is a flow of electricity between the two electrodes. When ionic compounds dissolve in water, their ions are free to move. Thus, aqueous solutions of ionic compounds also conduct electricity.

Section 7.3

Part A Completion

1. cations
2. electrons
3. metallic
4. electrical
5. malleable/ductile
6. ductile/malleable
7. body-centered/face-centered
8. face-centered/body-centered
9. hexagonal close-packed
10. alloy

Part B True-False

11. NT   13. NT   15. AT
12. ST   14. AT

Part C Matching

16. d   18. b   20. a
17. e   19. c

Part D Questions and Problems

21. Solid metals consist of closely packed cations surrounded by free-moving valence electrons, which make metals good conductors of electric current. As electrons enter one end of a bar of metal, an equal number leave the other end. Metal cations are insulated from one another by electrons. When a metal is subjected to pressure, the metal cations easily slide past one another. This behavior makes the metal malleable and ductile.

22. The superior properties of alloys result from the cumulative properties of all the constituents of the alloy. For example, an alloy can be more durable than one constituent but more malleable than another.

Practice Problems 7

Section 7.1

1. **a.** (i) 2 (ii) Ba$\cdot$ (iii) Ba^{2+}
   b. (i) 7 (ii) $:\overset{..}{I}\cdot$ (iii) I^-
   c. (i) 1 (ii) K$\cdot$ (iii) K^+

2. **a.** 3   **c.** 6
   b. 7

3. **a.** $1s^22s^22p^63s^23p^64s^2$
   b. $1s^22s^22p^63s^23p^5$
   c. $1s^22s^22p^6$
   d. $1s^22s^22p^63s^23p^6$
   e. $1s^22s^22p^6$

4. The number of valence electrons in an atom of a representative element is the same as the group number of the element.

5. **a.** loses 2 electrons; cation
   b. loses 3 electrons; cation
   c. gains 2 electrons; anion
   d. loses 1 electron; cation
   e. gains 1 electron; anion
   f. gains 3 electrons; anion
6. **a.** chloride ion, Cl^-
   b. potassium ion, K^+
   c. oxide ion, O^{2-}
   d. barium ion, Ba^{2+}
7. **a.** 2 lost
   b. 1 gained
   c. 1 lost
   d. 3 lost
8. **a.** cation   **d.** anion
   b. cation   **e.** cation
   c. anion   **f.** cation

Section 7.2

1. **a.** NaBr   **d.** Al_2O_3
   b. Na_2S **e.** $BaCl_2$
   c. CaI_2
2. Ionic compounds are formed when metals react with nonmetals. The combinations in b and c will form ionic compounds
3. The coordination number is the number of ions of the opposite charge that surround an ion in a crystal.
4. The coordination number is determined by using x-ray diffraction crystallography. Patterns are used to calculate the positions of ions in the crystal and to define the structure of the crystal.

Section 7.3

1. A metallic bond is made up of cations that are surrounded by mobile valence electrons.
2. The metallic crystal is thought to consist of an array of metal cations in a "sea" of electrons. Although the electrons are attracted to the metal cations, no individual electron is confined to any specific cation; rather, the electrons are free to move about the crystalline structure. When electrical current is applied to a metal, these mobile electrons can carry charge from one end of the metal to the other.
3. Metals are crystalline. The metal cations are arranged in a very compact and orderly structure or pattern.

4. • Body-centered cubic: every atom (except those at the surface) has 8 neighbors.
   • Face-centered cubic: every atom has 12 neighbors.
   • Hexagonal close-packed: every atom has 12 neighbors, but in a different arrangement than face-centered cubic.
5. An alloy is a mixture of two or more elements, at least one of which is a metal. Alloys have properties of metals.
6. **a.** Brass: copper and zinc
   b. Bronze: copper and tin
   c. Stainless steel: iron, chromium, carbon, and nickel
   d. Sterling silver: silver and copper
   e. Cast iron: iron and carbon
   f. Spring steel: iron, chromium, and carbon

Interpreting Graphics 7

1. sodium $1s^2 2s^2 2p^6 3s^1$
   Sodium has 1 valence electron.
   chlorine $1s^2 2s^2 2p^6 3s^2 3p^5$
   Chlorine has 7 valence electrons.
2. In Step 1, each sodium atom gives up one valence electron to a chlorine atom. In this process, sodium becomes positively charged and chlorine becomes negatively charged. Each ion attains the electron configuration of the nearest noble gas.
3. In Step 2, ionic bonds form between sodium cations and chlorine anions. The ions arrange themselves in an orderly, three-dimensional array characteristic of a crystalline solid. In NaCl, each ion is surrounded by six other ions of opposite charge, which results in a very stable ionic compound.
4. NaCl is typical of many ionic compounds. The large amount of energy released when an ionic lattice is formed (Step 2) compensates for the endothermic nature of the electron transfer (Step 1). To reverse the lattice formation through melting would require enough energy to overcome the multiple atttractions within the crystal lattice.

Vocabulary Review 7

1. j   6. l   11. b
2. i   7. a   12. k
3. f   8. c   13. m
4. g   9. e
5. h   10. d

5. h   **10.** d

Quiz for Chapter 7

1. ST
2. NT
3. AT
4. AT
5. AT
6. valence
7. octet
8. gaining
9. eight
10. pseudo-noble gas
11. metals
12. anion
13. formula unit

Chapter 7 Test A

A. Matching

1. e   **5.** j   **9.** k
2. f   **6.** g   **10.** b
3. h   **7.** a   **11.** d
4. c   **8.** i

B. Multiple Choice

12. c   **16.** c   **20.** a
13. b   **17.** b   **21.** a
14. c   **18.** d   **22.** a
15. b   **19.** b   **23.** c

C. True-False

24. AT   **28.** AT   **31.** AT
25. NT   **29.** NT   **32.** ST
26. NT   **30.** AT   **33.** AT
27. ST

D. Questions

34. **a.** $\cdot$Ca$\cdot$:Ca:$^{2+}$ **c.** $\cdot$Al$\cdot$:Al:$^{3+}$

  b. :Br$\cdot$:Br:$^{-}$

35. **a.** Cl^- anion   **c.** Na^+ cation
  b. Be^{2+} cation   **d.** O^{2-} anion

36. **a.** $1s^2 2s^2 2p^6 3s^2 3p^6$ **c.** $1s^2 2s^2 2p^6$
  b. $1s^2$ **d.** $1s^2 2s^2 2p^6$

37. $\cdot$Al$\cdot$:Cl:

The electron dot formulas show that one atom of Al can give 3 electrons, so 3 atoms of Cl are needed to form the compound $AlCl_3$.

$$\cdot \text{Al} \cdot \; + \; \cdot \text{Cl} : \; \rightarrow \; Al^{3+} + 3 : \text{Cl} :^{-}$$

38.   Na   F
$$1s^2 2s^2 2p^6 3s^1 + 1s^2 2s^2 2p^5 \rightarrow$$
            Na^+ F^-
$$1s^2 2s^2 2p^6 + 1s^2 2s^2 2p^6$$
Both ions have the configuration of neon.

E. Essay

39. Metallic bonds are the result of the attraction of free-floating valence electrons for positively charged metal ions. An electric current is a flow of electrons. As electrons enter one end of a piece of metal, some of the free-floating electrons leave the other end. Thus metals are good conductors of electricity. The cations in a piece of metal are insulated from each other by the free electrons. Thus, when metal is struck, the cations slide past each other easily. This makes the metal malleable.

Chapter 7 Test B

A. Matching

1. f   **5.** b   **9.** h
2. g   **6.** k   **10.** c
3. d   **7.** a   **11.** i
4. e   **8.** j

B. Multiple Choice

12. c   **18.** d   **24.** c
13. b   **19.** c   **25.** d
14. c   **20.** d   **26.** a
15. a   **21.** c   **27.** c
16. a   **22.** d   **28.** d
17. c   **23.** c

C. True-False

D. Questions

40. **a.** $2s^1$; 1; Li·

b. $2s^2 2p^3$; 5; ·N̈·

c. $3s^2 3p^2$; 4; ·S̈i·

d. $4s^2 4p^5$; 7; :B̈r·

41. **a.** Na^+ ; $1s^2 2s^2 2p^6$

b. F^-; $1s^2 2s^2 2p^6$

c. K^+; $1s^2 2s^2 2p^6 3s^2 3p^6$

d. Sr^{2+}; $1s^2 2s^2 2p^6 3s^2 3p^6 4s^2 3d^{10} 4p^6$

42. **a.** Na·; Na^+

b. :C̈l:; :C̈l:⁻

c. ·P̈:; :P̈:³⁻

d. Ca:; Ca^{2+}

43. a. NaF

b. $MgCl_2$

c. CaS

d. Al_2O_3

E. Essay

44. The group number for Ca is 2A, which means that two valence electrons will be lost; the cation Ca^{2+} is produced. The group number for F is 7A, which means that F has seven valence electrons and reacts by gaining one electron to attain the noble gas configuration. The formula for the anion produced is F^-. Thus, when Ca and F react, two atoms of F are required to react with one atom of Ca. The formula of the compound formed is CaF_2.

Chapter 7 Small-Scale Lab

Section 7.2 Analysis of Anions and Cations, page 200

Analyze

Sample data provided.

	Na₂SO₄ (SO_4^{2-})	HNO₃ (NO_3^-)	Na₃PO₄ (PO_4^{3-})
$AgNO_3$	NVR	NVR	Light yellow ppt.
HCl plus 1 piece of Fe(s)	Bubbles	Bubbles w/yellow solution	Bubbles
$Pb(NO_3)_2$	WP	NVR	WP

Figure A
Anion Analysis

	KI (K^+)	CaCl₂ (Ca^{2+})	FeCl₃ (Fe^{3+})
NaOH	NVR	WP	Rust ppt.
KSCN	NVR	NVR	Blood-red soln

Figure B
Cation Analysis

NVR: No Visible Reaction

WP: White Precipitate

1. An intermediate compound, $FeCl_2$, forms, which reacts with the nitrate ion. An orange-brown color forms.

2. Each of the following pairs of ions produces a visible product that can be used to identify the ion in question: PO_4^{3-} and Ag^+, NO_3^- and HCl + Fe, SO_4^{2-} and Pb^{2+}, Ca^{2+} and OH^-, Fe^{3+} and SCN^-.

3. No; neither of the solutions produced a visible product.

You're the Chemist

All designs should include tests that produce unique, observable products.

Section Review 8.1

Part A Completion

1. compound
2. molecular
3. nonmetals
4. diatomic
5. molecular formula
6. low
7. high
8. atoms
9. structure

Part B True-False

10. ST
11. NT
12. AT
13. NT
14. ST

Part C Matching

15. e
16. a
17. d
18. b
19. c

Part D Questions and Problems

20. molecular compound
21. **a.** 4 carbon atoms, 10 hydrogen atoms
    b. 6 carbon atoms, 5 hydrogen atoms, 1 fluorine atom
22. **a.** molecule
    b. atom
    c. molecule
    d. atom
    e. molecule

Section Review 8.2

Part A Completion

1. stable electron
2. covalent
3. shared
4. single
5. unshared pairs
6. double/triple
7. coordinate covalent bond
8. Energy
9. bond dissociation energy
10. resonance structure

Part B True-False

11. NT
12. NT
13. AT
14. AT
15. ST
16. NT

Part C Matching

17. e
18. a
19. b
20. c
21. d

Part D Questions and Problems

22. **a.** :Br:Br:

    b. H:C:::N:

    c.
    $$H:N:H \quad (+)$$
    with H above and H below

Section 8.3

Part A Completion

1. molecular orbitals
2. bonding orbital
3. lower
4. sigma or σ
5. pi or π
6. three-dimensional
7. VSEPR theory
8. orbital hybridization

Part B True-False

9. AT
10. ST
11. NT
12. AT
13. ST
14. AT

Part C Matching

15. d
16. e
17. a
18. b
19. c

Part D Questions and Problems

20. Reading from left to right:
    sp^3 sp^2 sp^2 sp sp sp^3

Section 8.4

Part A Completion

1. equally
2. nonpolar
3. unequally
4. polar
5. electronegativities
6. dipole interactions
7. hydrogen bond
8. electronegative
9. oxygen, nitrogen, or fluorine

Part B True-False

10. NT	**12.** ST	**14.** AT
11. AT	**13.** ST	**15.** AT

Part C Matching

16. b	**18.** e	**20.** a
17. d	**19.** c	

Part D Questions and Problems

21. dispersion forces, dipole interactions, hydrogen bonds

22. a. ionic

  b. polar covalent bonds

  c. polar covalent bonds

  d. nonpolar covalent bonds

Practice Problems 8

Section 8.1

1. a. atom   **d.** molecule

  b. molecule   **e.** atom

  c. molecule

2. a. not diatomic

  b. diatomic

  c. diatomic

  d. not diatomic

  e. diatomic

3. Molecular compounds are usually composed from two or more nonmetallic elements.

4. A molecular structure gives information about the kinds and numbers of atoms present in a molecule.

5. Molecular compounds tend to have lower melting and boiling points that that of ionic compounds

Section 8.2

1. The two atoms share a pair of electrons in order to form a single covalent bond.

$$H\ :\!\ddot{\underset{..}{F}}\!:$$

2. Phosphorous needs 3 more electrons to fill the $3p$ orbitals. Fluorine needs one more electron to fill its second energy level. Since each fluorine atom only needs one electron and phosphorus needs 3 electrons, three fluorine atoms are required to bond with phosphorus.

$$:\!\ddot{F}\!:\!\ddot{P}\!:\!\ddot{F}\!:$$
$$:\!\ddot{F}\!:$$

3. Nitrogen needs 3 more electrons to fill its second energy level. Chlorine needs one more electron to achieve a noble gas configuration. Because each chlorine atom needs only one electron and nitrogen needs 3 electrons, three chlorine atoms are required to bond with nitrogen.

$$:\!\ddot{C}\!l\!:\!\ddot{N}\!:\!\ddot{C}\!l\!:$$
$$:\!\ddot{C}\!l\!:$$

4. Because carbon can form four single covalent bonds, there is an apparent shortage of atoms with which to bond. This is a clue that a carbon-carbon multiple bond exists in this compound. Each carbon atom shares one electron with one of the two hydrogen atoms. The remaining three electrons for each carbon atom form a triple covalent bond. The electron dot structure is:

$$H\!:\!C\!:\!:\!C\!:\!H$$

5. Carbon has 4 valence electrons and each of the oxygens has 6 valence electrons. Two additional electrons are added to account for the ion having a 2− charge. The carbon and oxygen can satisfy the octet rule by having the oxygens bonded to a central carbon. There is one double covalent bond between a carbon and oxygen, which can shift to any one of the carbon-oxygen bonds giving rise to three resonance structures.

Section 8.3

1. The four fluorine atoms are covalently bonded to the central carbon atom. The four shared pairs of electrons repel each other to the corners of a tetrahedron. All four bond angles are 109.5°.

2. The four valence electron pairs repel each other, but the unshared pair is held closer to the phosphorus than the three bonding pairs. The unshared pair repels the shared pairs more strongly. Thus, the angle between bonds is expected to be slightly smaller than the tetrahedral bond angle of 109.5°. The actual bond angle for NH_3, a similar molecule, is 107°.

3. Boron forms three sp^2 orbitals by mixing one $2s$ orbital and two $2p$ orbitals. The three sp^2 orbitals lie in the same plane, 120° apart from one another. Each sp^2 orbital overlaps with an atomic orbital of chlorine to form three equivalent sigma bonds.

4. To form four equivalent bonds, silicon mixes one s orbital and all three of the p orbitals. The hybridization in SiF_4 is sp^3.

5. Oxygen is the central atom in this molecule. It has 6 valence electrons, two of which are bonding electrons. The other 4 electrons are unshared pairs. These 2 unshared pairs repel the two bonding pairs and prevent F_2O from being linear. The molecule is a bent triatomic molecule, with a bond angle of approximately 104.5°. This angle is slightly smaller than the tetrahedral bond angle because the two unshared pairs repel each other more strongly than the two shared pairs.

6. Because each carbon can form single covalent bonds with four other atoms, there exists in this compound an apparent shortage of atoms with which to bond. This is a clue that CH_2CF_2 contains a carbon-carbon multiple bond. The two hydrogen atoms bond with one carbon atom while the two fluorine atoms bond with the other carbon. Each carbon atom has two electrons left over. These electrons form a carbon-carbon double covalent bond. The molecule looks very much like the ethene molecule (C_2H_4). H—C—H and F—C—F bond angles of 120°, the hybridization involved in the carbon-carbon bond is sp^2.

$$\begin{array}{cc} H. & .F \\ :C::C: \\ H. & .F \end{array}$$

7. Carbon 1 mixes one s orbital and three p orbitals to form four sp^3 hybrid orbitals, which form 4 sigma bonds. Carbon 2 mixes one s and two p orbitals to form three sp^2 hybrid orbitals, which overlap with the hybrid orbitals of the carbon and oxygen atoms to form three equivalent sigma bonds. The non-hybridized p carbon orbital overlaps with an oxygen p orbital to form one pi bonding orbital.

Section 8.4

1. a. The difference in electronegativity between Na and O is about 2.4 and the bond is ionic.

   b. With like atoms, the difference is zero and the bond is nonpolar covalent.

   c. The electronegativity difference between P and O is about 1.4 and the bond is polar covalent.

2. For a bond to be classified as nonpolar covalent, like atoms must bond, as in diatomic molecules. Most bonds are between unlike atoms; therefore, they must be ionic or polar covalent.

3. Both carbon dioxide and carbon monoxide contain polar bonds. However, the effect of the polar bond on the polarity of the entire molecule depends on the shape of the molecule. In carbon monoxide, there is a partial positive pole and a partial negative pole. Therefore, the molecule is a dipole. In carbon dioxide, the carbon and oxygens lie along the same axis. The bond polarities cancel, producing a nonpolar molecule.

4. The more electronegative atom in a covalent bond will have the δ− symbol and the less electronegative atom the δ+ symbol.

   a.
   $$\begin{array}{c} \delta+ \\ H \\ \delta+ \ |\delta- \ \delta+ \\ H—N—H \\ \cdot\cdot \end{array}$$

   b.
   $$\begin{array}{c} F\delta- \\ \delta- \ |\delta+ \ \delta- \\ F—C—F \\ | \\ F\delta- \end{array}$$

5. CaO is an ionic compound and CS_2 is a polar covalent compound. Generally, ionic compounds have much higher melting points than molecular compounds.

Interpreting Graphics 8

1. $:\overset{\cdot\cdot}{O}=C=\overset{\cdot\cdot}{O}:$; linear; 180°; none

2. $\begin{array}{cc} H & H \\ \diagdown \diagup \\ C \\ \diagup \diagdown \\ H & H \end{array}$; tetrahedral; 109.5°; none

3. $\begin{array}{cc} :\overset{\cdot\cdot}{O} & \overset{\cdot\cdot}{O}: \\ \diagdown\diagdown \diagup \\ S \\ | \\ :\overset{\cdot\cdot}{O}: \end{array}$; trigonal planar; 120°;

   $$:\overset{\cdot\cdot}{O}: \qquad :\overset{\cdot\cdot}{O}: \qquad :\overset{\cdot\cdot}{O}:$$
   $$\underset{\overset{\cdot\cdot}{O}:}{\overset{\diagdown}{S}}\diagup\overset{\cdot\cdot}{O}: \quad\longleftrightarrow\quad \overset{\cdot\cdot}{O}\overset{S}{\diagdown}\overset{\cdot\cdot}{O}: \quad\longleftrightarrow\quad \overset{\cdot\cdot}{O}\overset{S}{\diagup\diagdown}\overset{\cdot\cdot}{O}:$$

4. $:\overset{\cdot\cdot}{F}—Be—\overset{\cdot\cdot}{F}:$; linear; 180°; none

5. :F̈   F̈:; pyramidal; 96°; none
   ＼ ／
   :P
   |
   :F̈:

6.   :C̈l: ; trigonal bipyramidal;
        | C̈l:
   :C̈l—P⟍
        | C̈l:
      :C̈l:

   90° and 120°; none

7.   Ö   ; bent triatomic; 105°; none
      ／ ＼
    H   H

8. Check students' work.

Vocabulary Review 8

1. coordinate covalent bond
2. bond dissociation energy
3. bonding molecular orbital
4. sigma bond
5. VSEPR theory
6. hybridization
7. polyatomic ion
8. van der Waals forces
9. hydrogen bond
10. molecule

Quiz for Chapter 8

1. a	5. b	9. ST
2. c	6. c	10. ST
3. b	7. ST	11. ST
4. d	8. NT	

Chapter 8 Test A

A. Matching

1. i	5. d	8. c
2. e	6. a	9. g
3. j	7. b	10. h
4. f		

B. Multiple Choice

11. d	17. c	23. b
12. b	18. c	24. a
13. d	19. b	25. d
14. a	20. a	26. c

15. c	21. b	27. c
16. d	22. b	

C. Questions

28. a. :B̈r—B̈r:

   b. :N≡N:

   c. :C≡O:

29. a. K(0.8), F(4.0), difference 3.2; ionic bond

   b. S(2.5), O(3.5), difference 1.0; polar covalent bond

   c. N(3.0), O(3.5), difference 0.5; polar covalent bond

   d. H(2.1), Br(2.8), difference 0.7; polar covalent bond

30. a. H:B̈r:

   b. :Ö:Ö:
       H H

   c. Cl:P̈:Cl
          Cl

D. Essay

31. Network solids are substances in which all of the atoms are covalently bonded to each other. Samples of these solids are thought of as single molecules. Two examples are diamond and silicon carbide.

E. Additional Questions and Problems

32. C—H $5 \text{ mol} \times \dfrac{393 \text{ kJ}}{1 \text{ mol}} = 1965 \text{ kJ}$

   C—O $1 \text{ mol} \times \dfrac{356 \text{ kJ}}{1 \text{ mol}} = 356 \text{ kJ}$

   O—H $1 \text{ mol} \times \dfrac{464 \text{ kJ}}{1 \text{ mol}} = 464 \text{ kJ}$

   C—C $1 \text{ mol} \times \dfrac{347 \text{ kJ}}{1 \text{ mol}} = 347 \text{ kJ}$

   Total = 3132 kJ

33. ∞ + ∞ = ∞∞ sigma bond
   $2p_x$ $2p_x$

   8 + 8 = ⬭ pi bond
   $2p_y$ $2p_y$

   The first $2p$ orbitals lie along the axis connecting the atoms, and so form a sigma bond. The remaining $2p$ orbitals are found in regions above and below the axis, and form pi bonds.

34. From left to right: sp, sp, sp^3, sp^2, sp^3

35.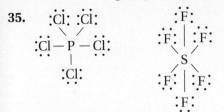

Chapter 8 Test B

A. Matching

1. g	**5.** b	**8.** i
2. e	**6.** d	**9.** a
3. h	**7.** f	**10.** j
4. c		

B. Multiple Choice

11. c	**20.** c	**29.** d
12. a	**21.** b	**30.** c
13. d	**22.** a	**31.** d
14. d	**23.** c	**32.** a
15. d	**24.** b	**33.** a
16. a	**25.** b	**34.** c
17. b	**26.** b	**35.** c
18. d	**27.** c	**36.** a
19. b	**28.** b	**37.** c

C. Questions

38. **a.** H:H; H—H

b. :N: :N:; :N≡N:

c. :O: H; :O—H
  H   H

d.   H   ;   H
   H:N:H   H—N—H

e. :C: :O: ; :C≡O:

39. **a.**
$$\left[\begin{array}{c} H \\ H:N:H \\ H \end{array} \right]^{+}$$

b.
$$\left[\begin{array}{c} :O: \\ :O:P:O: \\ :O: \end{array} \right]^{3-}$$

D. Essay

40. An ionic bond is formed when one or more electrons are transferred from one atom to another. Covalent bonds are formed when atoms share electrons. depends upon The electronegativity difference between two elements is used to predict which type of bonding will occur when specific atoms combine. Differences in excess of 2.0 result in the formation of ionic bonds. Differences of less than 2.0 result in covalent bonding.

E. Additional Questions and Problems

41. **a.** polar covalent; 0.9

  b. polar covalent; 0.4

  c. polar covalent; 0.5

  d. ionic bond; 3.1

  e. nonpolar covalent; 0.2

  f. polar covalent; 1.3

42. $6(C—H) = 6 \times (393 \text{ kJ/mol}) = 2358 \text{ kJ/mol}$
$1(C—C) = 1 \times 347 \text{ kJ/mol} = 347 \text{ kJ/mol}$
Total $= 2705 \text{ kJ or } 2.70 \times 10^3 \text{ kJ/mol}$
$(2.70 \times 10^3 \text{ kJ/mol}) \times (0.25 \text{ mol}) = 675 \text{ kJ}$

Chapter 8 Small-Scale Lab

Section 8.4 Paper Chromatography of Food Dyes, page 245

Analysis

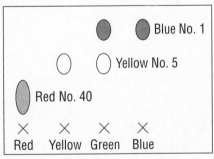

1. Red, yellow, and blue are pure compounds.

2. Green food color is usually a mixture of Yellow No. 5 and Blue No. 1.

3. Red is Red No. 40, Yellow is Yellow No. 5 (or sometimes Yellow No. 6 if it is orange in appearance), and blue is Blue No. 1. (Red #3 has been banned, but sometimes appears, because under the law food manufacturers are allowed to use up their current supplies.)

4. See the above figure.

5. Blue No. 1 is the most polar because it runs the fastest and appears at the top of the chromatogram. Red No. 40 is the least polar.

You're the Chemist

1. Wet a portion of a piece of candy and blot it with a paper towel to remove excess water. Press the wet side of the candy onto the chromatography paper so that it makes a colored spot. Repeat for other colors of candy. Develop in 0.1% NaCl.

2. Make a small spot of each colored marker pen on a piece of chromatography paper and develop in solvent.

3. Use a toothpick to spot a solution of powdered drink on chromatography paper.

4. Rubbing alcohol runs much more slowly and gives slightly better separation than 0.1% NaCl.

5. Some papers cause a reversal of the positions of Blue No. 1 and Yellow No. 5 because of the water content of the paper. Different water content changes variations in the polarity of the stationary phase (the water molecules hydrogen bonded to the paper).

Section Review 9.1

Part A Completion

1. monatomic
2. lose
3. 1+
4. 2+
5. 3+
6. 8
7. 1−
8. transition (Group B) metals
9. Stock
10. classical
11. polyatomic
12. -ite or -ate
13. -ite or -ate

Part B True-False

14. ST
15. AT
16. ST
17. NT
18. AT

Part C Matching

19. b
20. e
21. d
22. a
23. c

Part D Questions and Problems

24. a. 1+   c. 1−
    b. 2−   d. 2+
25. a. hydrogen carbonate
    b. ammonium
    c. permanganate
    d. hydroxide
26. a. loses 2   c. gains 1
    b. gains 2   d. loses 3

Section Review 9.2

Part A Completion

1. cation
2. anion
3. -ide
4. sodium iodide
5. Roman numeral
6. anion
7. oxygen
8. zero

Part B True-False

9. NT
10. AT
11. ST
12. AT

Part C Matching

13. b
14. a
15. d
16. c

Part D Questions and Problems

17. a. iron(III) bromide, binary ionic
    b. potassium hydroxide, ionic with polyatomic ion
    c. sodium dichromate, ionic with polyatomic ion
18. a. $NaClO_3$
    b. $Pb_3(PO_4)_2$
    c. $Mg(HCO_3)_2$

Section Review 9.3

Part A Completion

1. nonmetallic
2. -ide
3. atoms
4. diarsenic pentasulfide

Part B True-False

5. ST
6. NT
7. NT

Part C Matching

8. d
9. a
10. b
11. c

Part D Questions and Problems

12. **a.** phosphorus pentachloride
    b. sulfur dioxide
    c. tetraphosphorus decasulfide
13. **a.** CBr_4 **b.** N_2O_4

Section Review 9.4

Part A Completion

1. hydrogen
2. hydrogen ions
3. hydrobromic
4. nitric
5. ionic
6. hydroxide ions
7. ionic
8. cation
9. anion

Part B True-False

10. ST   11. NT   12. NT

Part C Matching

13. a   14. c   15. b

Part D Questions and Problems

16. **a.** $Mg(OH)_2$ **c.** H_3PO_4
    b. HF   **d.** LiOH
17. **a.** potassium hydroxide
    b. hydroiodic acid
    c. sulfuric acid

Section Review 9.5

Part A Completion

1. definite proportions
2. proportions
3. multiple proportions
4. small whole
5. acid
6. phosphoric acid
7. acid
8. binary
9. molecular
10. carbon tetrachloride
11. acid
12. elements
13. anion
14. 4A
15. lead(II) acetate

Part B True-False

16. ST   18. NT
17. ST   19. AT

Part C Questions and Problems

20. **a.** lead(IV) acetate
    b. hydrofluoric acid
    c. diphosphorus pentoxide
    d. lithium bromide
21. **a.** PCl_5
    b. FeO
    c. HNO_3
    d. KCl
    e. $Ca(NO_3)_2$

Practice Problems 9

Section 9.1

1. **a.** 2−   **d.** 3+
   b. 1−   **e.** 2+
   c. 1+   **f.** 2+
2. **a.** 3 lost   **d.** 2 lost
   b. 3 gained   **e.** 1 gained
   c. 1 lost   **f.** 2 gained
3. **a.** tin(II) or stannous cation
   b. cobalt(III) or cobaltic cation
   c. bromide anion
   d. potassium cation
   e. hydride anion
   f. manganese(II) or manganous cation
4. **a.** CO_3^{2-} **d.** OH^-
   b. NO_2^{2-} **e.** CrO_4^{2-}
   c. SO_4^{2-} **f.** NH_4^+
5. **a.** cyanide anion
   b. hydrogen carbonate anion
   c. phosphate anion
   d. chloride anion
   e. calcium cation
   f. sulfite anion

Section 9.2

1. **a.** MgO   **d.** $AlCl_3$
   b. SnF_2 **e.** Na_2S
   c. KI   **f.** $FeBr_3$
2. **a.** $BaCl_2$ **d.** KBr
   b. AgI   **e.** Al_2O_3
   c. CaS   **f.** FeO
3. **a.** manganese(II) oxide or manganous oxide
   b. lithium nitride
   c. calcium chloride

d. strontium bromide

e. nickel chloride

f. potassium sulfide

g. copper(II) chloride or cupric chloride

h. tin(IV) chloride or stannic chloride

4. a. Na_3PO_4 **d.** KCN

    b. $MgSO_4$ **e.** NH_4Cl

    c. NaOH   **f.** $K_2Cr_2O_7$

5. a. $(NH_4)_2SO_4$ **c.** $Ba(OH)_2$

    b. KNO_3 **d.** Li_2CO_3

6. a. sodium cyanide

    b. iron(III) chloride or ferric chloride

    c. sodium sulfate

    d. potassium carbonate

    e. copper(II) hydroxide or cupric hydroxide

    f. lithium nitrate

7. a. sodium cation, Na^+

    b. nickel cation, Ni^{2+}

    c. calcium cation, Ca^{2+}

    d. potassium cation, K^+

    e. iron(III) cation, Fe^{3+}

    f. copper(I) cation, Cu^+

Section 9.3

1. a. phosphorous pentachloride

    b. carbon tetrachloride

    c. nitrogen dioxide

    d. dinitrogen difluoride

    e. tetraphosphorous hexoxide

    f. xenon difluoride

    g. silicon dioxide

    h. dichlorine heptoxide

2. a. NBr_3 **c.** SO_2

    b. Cl_2O **d.** N_2F_4

Section 9.4

1. a. nitrous acid   **c.** hydrofluoric acid

    b. sulfuric acid   **d.** carbonic acid

2. a. $Ca(OH)_2$ **c.** $Al(OH)_3$

    b. NH_4OH **d.** LiOH

Section 9.5

1. a. K_2S **g.** N_2O_5

    b. $SnCl_4$ **h.** $Fe_2(CO_3)_3$

    c. H_2S **i.** SF_6

    d. CaO   **j.** $MgCl_2$

    e. HBr   **k.** H_3PO_4

    f. AlF_3 **l.** HNO_3

2.

	SO_4^{2-}	NO_3^-	OH^-	PO_4^{3-}
Ca^{2+}	$CaSO_4$	$Ca(NO_3)_2$	$Ca(OH)_2$	$Ca_3(PO_4)_2$
Al^{3+}	$Al_2(SO_4)_3$	$Al(NO_3)_3$	$Al(OH)_3$	$AlPO_4$
Na^+	Na_2SO_4	$NaNO_3$	NaOH	Na_3PO_4
Pb^{4+}	$Pb(SO_4)_2$	$Pb(NO_3)_4$	$Pb(OH)_4$	$Pb_3(PO_4)_4$

3. a. potassium phosphate

    b. aluminum hydroxide

    c. sodium hydrogen sulfate

    d. mercury(II) oxide or mercuric oxide

    e. dinitrogen pentoxide

    f. nitrogen tribromide

    g. phosphorous triiodide

    h. ammonium sulfate

4. The law of definite proportions states that samples of any compound will always contain the constituent elements in the same proportions. The law of multiple proportions states that in two compounds containing the same two elements, the masses of one element that combines with a given mass of the other element will be in the ratio of small whole numbers.

Interpreting Graphics 9

1. 2A   **8.** 10

2. two   **9.** 10

3. 12   **10.** 10

4. 10   **11. a.** 18

5. 7A   **b.** 18

6. one   **c.** 18

7. nine   **d.** 18

Vocabulary Review 9

1. i
2. c
3. g
4. d
5. e
6. f
7. b
8. h
9. j
10. a

Quiz for Chapter 9

1. Metals
2. PCl_5
3. anion
4. definite proportions
5. the group number
6. lose
7. hydroxide
8. $H_2PO_4^-$
9. dinitrogen monoxide
10. $FeCl_2$
11. tin(IV) sulfide (or stannic sulfide)
12. dinitrogen pentoxide
13. sodium hydrogen carbonate (or sodium bicarbonate)
14. $Cu(OH)_2$
15. nitric acid

Chapter 9 Test A

A. Matching

1. f
2. a
3. g
4. h
5. d
6. b
7. c
8. i
9. e

B. Multiple Choice

10. c
11. c
12. a
13. a
14. a
15. a
16. c
17. c
18. d
19. c
20. c
21. c
22. b

C. Completion

23. 4+
24. 1−
25. ions
26. -ide
27. 1−
28. oxygen
29. nonmetallic
30. hydrogen

D. Problems

31. a $Mg(CN)_2$ c. SF_6
    b. $HgBr_2$
32. a. copper(I) chloride
    b. dinitrogen trioxide
    c. potassium acetate

E. Essay

33. Compounds exist in enormous numbers. Common names do not describe the chemical composition of a compound. They may relate to a physical or chemical property, but usually do not reveal what elements are in the compound. The systemic method tells what atoms are in the compound, gives information on the ratio in which the atoms combined to form the compound and promotes efficient and effective communication between chemists.

Chapter 9 Test B

A. Matching

1. i
2. b
3. c
4. h
5. g
6. a
7. f
8. e
9. d

B. Multiple Choice

10. c
11. a
12. a
13. c
14. d
15. d
16. c
17. c
18. b
19. a
20. d
21. c

C. Completion

22. gain
23. lose
24. cation
25. definite proportions
26. 2−
27. NH_4^+
28. magnesium nitrate
29. -ide
30. $Ca_3(PO_4)_2$
31. more

D. Problems

32. a. $Ca(NO_3)_2$, calcium nitrate
    b. Na_2SO_4, sodium sulfate
    c. Fe_2O_3, iron(III) oxide
    d. $Al_2(CO_3)_3$, aluminum carbonate

33. **a.** SiO_2 **e.** HNO_3
    b. CF_4 **f.** $AgNO_3$
    c. $Zn(OH)_2$ **g.** $Fe_2(SO_4)_3$
    d. PBr_3 **h.** $HgCl_2$
34. **a.** carbon disulfide
    b. ammonium carbonate
    c. diarsenic pentoxide
    d. carbon monoxide
    e. tin(IV) hydroxide
    f. sulfuric acid
    g. phosphorus pentiodide
    h. potassium permanganate

E. Essay

35. Ionic compounds consist of a metallic and a nonmetallic ion, whereas molecular compounds consist of nonmetallic elements. Ionic compounds are named from the two ions that comprise them, using a Roman numeral to distinguish between positive ions of the same element that have more than one charge. Molecular compounds are named from the elements that comprise them, using prefixes to denote the numbers of atoms of each element present. No prefix is used if only one atom of the first element is present. The name of the second element always ends in -ide.

Chapter 9 Small-Scale Lab

Section 9.2 Names and Formulas for Ionic Compounds, page 267

Analysis

	$AgNO_3$ (Ag^+)	$Pb(NO_3)_2$ (Pb^{2+})	$CaCl_2$ (Ca^{2+})
Na_2CO_3 (CO_3^{2-})	a milky white ppt	e cloudy tan ppt	i grainy white ppt
Na_3PO_4 (PO_4^{3-})	b cloudy white ppt	f milky white ppt	j milky white ppt
NaOH (OH^-)	c muddy brown ppt	g milky white ppt	k cloudy white ppt
Na_2SO_4 (SO_4^{2-})	d no visible reaction	h milky white ppt	l grainy white ppt

Figure A

1. $Na_2SO_4 + AgNO_3$ did not form a precipitate.
2.

Formula	Name
a. Ag_2CO_3	silver carbonate
b. Ag_3PO_4	silver phosphate
c. AgOH	silver hydroxide

Teacher's note: This is Ag_2O, silver oxide

d. no visible reaction	
e. $PbCO_3$	lead(II) carbonate
f. $Pb_3(PO_4)_2$	lead(II) phosphate
g. $Pb(OH)_2$	lead(II) hydroxide
h. $PbSO_4$	lead(II) sulfate
i. $CaCO_3$	calcium carbonate
j. $Ca_3(PO_4)_2$	calcium phosphate
k. $Ca(OH)_2$	calcium hydroxide
l. $CaSO_4$	calcium sulfate

You're The Chemist

1.

	FeCl$_3$ (Fe^{3+})	MgSO$_4$ (Mg^{2+})	CuSO$_4$ (Cu^{2+})
Na$_2$CO$_3$ (CO$_3{}^{2-}$)	a orange ppt	e white ppt	i blue ppt
Na$_3$PO$_4$ (PO$_4{}^{3-}$)	b orange ppt	f white ppt	j blue ppt
NaOH (OH$^-$)	c orange ppt	g white ppt	k blue ppt
Na$_2$SO$_4$ (SO$_4{}^{2-}$)	d no visible reaction	h no visible reaction	l no visible reaction

Figure B

Formula	Name
a. Fe$_2$(CO$_3$)$_3$	iron(III) carbonate
b. FePO$_4$	iron(III) phosphate
c. Fe(OH)$_3$	iron(III) hydroxide
d. no visible reaction	
e. MgCO$_3$	magnesium carbonate
f. Mg$_3$(PO$_4$)$_2$	magnesium phosphate
g. Mg(OH)$_2$	magnesium hydroxide
h. no visible reaction	
i. CuCO$_3$	copper(II) carbonate
j. Cu$_3$(PO$_4$)$_2$	copper(II) phosphate
k. Cu(OH)$_2$	copper(II) hydroxide
l. no visible reaction	

2. a. $2Fe^{3+} + 3CO_3{}^{2-} \rightarrow Fe_2(CO_3)_3(s)$
b. $Fe^{3+} + PO_4{}^{3-} \rightarrow FePO_4(s)$
c. $Fe^{3+} + 2OH^- \rightarrow Fe(OH)_2(s)$
e. $Mg^{2+} + CO_3{}^{2-} \rightarrow MgCO_3(s)$
f. $3Mg^{2+} + 2PO_4{}^{3-} \rightarrow Mg_3(PO_4)_2(s)$
g. $Mg^{2+} + 2OH^- \rightarrow Mg(OH)_2(s)$
i. $Cu^{2+} + CO_3{}^{2-} \rightarrow CuCO_3(s)$
j. $3Cu^{2+} + 2PO_4{}^{3-} \rightarrow Cu_3(PO_4)_2(s)$
k. $Cu^{2+} + 2OH^- \rightarrow Cu(OH)_2(s)$

Section Review 10.1

Part A Completion

1. mole
2. Avogadro's number
3. atomic masses
4. molar mass
5. 6.02×10^{23}

Part B True-False

6. ST **8.** NT **10.** NT
7. ST **9.** AT

Part C Matching

11. b **13.** d
12. c **14.** c

Part D Questions and Problems

15. 9.3×10^{15} atoms Pb $\times \dfrac{1.0 \text{ mol Pb}}{6.02 \times 10^{23} \text{ atoms Pb}}$

$= 1.5 \times 10^{-8}$ mol Pb

16. $2 \text{ mol C} \times \dfrac{12.0 \text{ g C}}{1 \text{ mol C}} = 24.0 \text{ g C}$

$6 \text{ mol H} \times \dfrac{1.0 \text{ g H}}{1 \text{ mol H}} = 6.0 \text{ g H}$

molar mass of $C_2H_6 = 30.0$ g

17. 3.65×10^{-2} mol K$_2$SO$_4$ $\times \dfrac{174.3 \text{ g K}_2\text{SO}_4}{1.00 \text{ mol K}_2\text{SO}_4}$

$= 636 \times 10^{-2} \text{ g K}_2\text{SO}_4 = 6.36 \text{ g K}_2\text{SO}_4$

18. $2.5 \text{ mol H}_2\text{O}_2 \times$

$\dfrac{6.02 \times 10^{23} \text{ representative particles}}{1 \text{ mol H}_2\text{O}_2}$

$= 1.5 \times 10^{24}$ representative particles

Section Review 10.2

Part A Completion

1. 22.4
2. molar volume
3. 22.4 L SO$_2$/1.00 mol SO$_2$
4. Density
5. mole

Part B True-False

6. ST **8.** NT
7. AT **9.** AT

Part C Matching

10. d   12. a   14. e

11. c   13. b

Part D Questions and Problems

15. Molar mass = 28.0 + 16.0 = 44.0 g

$$\text{Density} = \frac{\text{mass}}{\text{volume}} = \frac{44.0 \text{ g}}{22.4 \text{ L}} = 1.96 \text{ g/L}$$

16. Molar mass NaCl = 23.0 g + 35.5 g
    = 58.5 g/mol

    58.5 g/mol × 2 mol = 117 g

17. Molar mass O_2 = 2(16.0 g/mol)
    = 32.0 g/mol

    16.0 g/32.0 g/mol = 0.500 mol

18. 22.4 L/mol × 0.500 mol = 11.2 L

Section Review 10.3

Part A Completion

1. percent composition

2. 100

3. molar mass

4. empirical

5. whole-number

6. molecular

Part B True-False

7. ST   9. AT

8. AT   10. NT

Part C Matching

11. c   13. a

12. b

Part D Questions and Problems

14. **a.** $\dfrac{104 \text{ g Cr}}{152 \text{ g Cr}_2\text{O}_3} \times 100 = 68.4\%$ Cr

    $\dfrac{48 \text{ g O}}{152 \text{ g Cr}_2\text{O}_3} \times 100 = 31.6\%$ O

    b. $\dfrac{110 \text{ g Mn}}{284 \text{ g Mn}_2\text{P}_2\text{O}_7} \times 100 = 38.7\%$ Mn

    $\dfrac{62 \text{ g P}}{284 \text{ g Mn}_2\text{P}_2\text{O}_7} \times 100 = 21.8\%$ P

    $\dfrac{112 \text{ g O}}{284 \text{ g Mn}_2\text{P}_2\text{O}_7} \times 100 = 39.4\%$ O

    c. $\dfrac{201 \text{ g Hg}}{233 \text{ g HgS}} \times 100 = 86.3\%$ Hg

    $\dfrac{32.1 \text{ g S}}{233 \text{ g HgS}} \times 100 = 13.8\%$ S

d. $\dfrac{40.1 \text{ g Ca}}{164 \text{ g Ca(NO}_3)_2} \times 100 = 24.5\%$ Ca

$\dfrac{28 \text{ g N}}{164 \text{ g Ca(NO}_3)_2} \times 100 = 17.1\%$ N

$\dfrac{96 \text{ g O}}{164 \text{ g Ca(NO}_3)_2} \times 100 = 58.5\%$ O

15. $29.1 \text{ g Na} \times \dfrac{1.00 \text{ mol Na}}{23.0 \text{ g Na}} = 1.27$ mol Na

    1.27 mol Na/1.27 = 1 × 2 = 2

    $40.5 \text{ g S} \times \dfrac{1.00 \text{ mol S}}{32.0 \text{ g S}} = 1.27$ mol S

    1.27 mol S/1.27 = 1 × 2 = 2

    $30.4 \text{ g O} \times \dfrac{1.00 \text{ mol O}}{16.0 \text{ g O}} = 1.90$ mol O

    1.90 mol O/1.27 = 1.5 × 2 = 3

    Empirical formula = $Na_2S_2O_3$

16. molar mass Fe_2O_3 =

    $2 \text{ mol Fe} \times \dfrac{55.8 \text{ g Fe}}{1 \text{ mol Fe}} + 3 \text{ mol O} \times \dfrac{16.0 \text{ g O}}{1 \text{ mol O}}$

    = 112 g Fe + 48 g O = 160 g Fe_2O_3

    $\%\text{Fe} = \dfrac{\text{g Fe}}{\text{g Fe}_2\text{O}_3} \times 100 = \dfrac{112 \text{ g}}{160 \text{ g}} \times 100$

    = 70.0% Fe

    $639 \text{ kg Fe}_2\text{O}_3 \times \dfrac{70.0 \text{ kg Fe}}{100 \text{ kg Fe}_2\text{O}_3} = 447$ kg Fe

Practice Problems

Section 10.1

1. 342.3 g/mol

2. **a.** 208.2 g/mol   **b.** 352.0 g/mol

3. **a.** 158.0 g/mol   **b.** 310.2 g/mol

4. 5.85 mol H_2O

5 3.6×10^{23} atoms

6. 32.0 g

Section 10.2

1. **a.** 180.2 g/mol   **c.** 96.2 g/mol

   b. 84.0 g/mol   **d.** 153.2 g/mol

2. **a.** 1.8×10^3 g

   b. 26 g

   c. 3.20×10^{-2} g

   d. 0.480 g or 4.80×10^{-1} g

   e. 1.43×10^2 g

3. 1.87×10^2 g

4. 204.1 g

5. a. 4.9×10^{-3} mol **d.** 1.98×10^{-5} mol

b. 9.10×10^{-2} mol **e.** 1.97×10^{-5} mol

c. 1.08×10^{-2} mol

6. 5.43 mol

7. 15.1 g

8. 59.6 L CH_4

9. 6.03 mol NH_3

Section 10.3

1. Percent C $= \dfrac{5.34 \text{ g C}}{52.84 \text{ g cpd}} \times 100 = 10.1\%$ C

Percent H $= \dfrac{0.42 \text{ g H}}{52.84 \text{ g cpd}} \times 100 = 0.79\%$ H

Percent Cl $= \dfrac{47.08 \text{ g Cl}}{52.84 \text{ g cpd}} \times 100 = 89.1\%$ Cl

2. Mass of Cl

= total mass of compound − mass of Sn

= 18.35 g of compound − 5.74 g Sn

= 12.61 g Cl

Percent of Sn $= \dfrac{5.74 \text{ g Sn}}{18.35 \text{ g cpd}} \times 100$

= 31.3% Sn

Percent of Cl $= \dfrac{12.61 \text{ g Cl}}{18.35 \text{ g cpd}} \times 100$

= 68.7% Cl

3. Percent C $= \dfrac{3.907 \text{ g C}}{4.781 \text{ g cpd}} \times 100 = 81.7\%$ C

Percent H $= \dfrac{0.874 \text{ g H}}{4.781 \text{ g cpd}} \times 100 = 18.3\%$ H

4. Percent C $= \dfrac{48.0 \text{ g C}}{158.1 \text{ g Ca(C}_2\text{H}_3\text{O}_2)_2} \times 100$

= 30.4% C

Mass C = 30.4% C × 65.3 g = 19.8 g

5. 13.2 g Al

6. 15.11 g Fe

7. a. CCl_4

b. $CHCl_3$

Interpreting Graphics 10

1. 85.7% C

2. $150.0 \text{ g } C_2H_4 \times \dfrac{14.3 \text{ g H}}{100 \text{ g } C_2H_4} = 21.4$ g ethene

3. Some compounds have the same empirical formula but different molecular formulas. Cyclohexane and ethene have the same empirical formula and, therefore, the same percent composition. They are indistinguishable on the basis of percent composition alone.

4. molar mass

5.

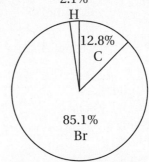

Bromine accounts for the largest percent of the mass of dibromoethane.

6. molar mass of H_2SO_4 = 98.1 g

%H $= \dfrac{2.02 \text{ g}}{98.08 \text{ g}} \times 100\% = 2.06\%$

%S $= \dfrac{32.06 \text{ g}}{98.08 \text{ g}} \times 100\% = 32.69\%$

%O $= \dfrac{64.00 \text{ g}}{98.08 \text{ g}} \times 100\% = 65.25\%$

Acid X represents sulfuric acid, H_2SO_4. Use the same approach to show that Acid Y represents sulfurous acid, H_2SO_3.

Vocabulary Review 10

1. percent composition

2. empirical formula

3. 22.4 L

4. molar mass

5. mole

6. Avogadro's number

7. standard temperature and pressure (0°C, 1 atm)

Quiz for Chapter 10

1. a substance

2. atomic mass

3. molar mass

4. atom

5. $\dfrac{32.0 \text{ g } O_2}{1 \text{ mol } O_2}$

6. AT

7. AT

8. ST

9. NT

10. AT

11. $3.05 \text{ g Ag} \times \dfrac{1.00 \text{ mol}}{108 \text{ g Ag}} \times \dfrac{197 \text{ g Au}}{1.00 \text{ mol}} = 5.56$ g Au

12. $40.7 \text{ g C} \times \dfrac{1.00 \text{ mol C}}{12.0 \text{ g C}} = 3.39 \text{ mol C}$

$54.2 \text{ g O} \times \dfrac{1.00 \text{ mol O}}{16.0 \text{ g O}} = 3.39 \text{ mol O}$

$5.1 \text{ g H} \times \dfrac{1.00 \text{ mol H}}{1.0 \text{ g H}} = 5.1 \text{ mol H}$

5.1 mol H/3.39 = 1.5 mol H
3.39 mol C/3.39 = 1.00 mol C
3.39 mol O/3.39 = 1.00 mol O
1.5 mol H × 2 = 3 mol H
1 mol C × 2 = 2 mol C
1 mol O × 2 = 2 mol O
Empirical formula = $C_2H_3O_2$

Chapter 10 Test A

A. Matching

1. j	**5.** b	**9.** d
2. a	**6.** c	**10.** h
3. g	**7.** i	
4. e	**8.** f	

B. Multiple Choice

11. c	**16.** c	**21.** c
12. a	**17.** a	**22.** b
13. d	**18.** d	**23.** b
14. c	**19.** a	**24.** c
15. c	**20.** c	

C. Problems

25. $5.00 \times 10^{23} \text{ molecules F}_2$

$\times \dfrac{1 \text{ mol F}_2}{6.02 \times 10^{23} \text{ molecules F}_2} \times \dfrac{38.0 \text{ g F}_2}{1 \text{ mol F}_2}$

$= 31.6 \text{ g F}_2$

26. $24.0 \text{ g C} \times \dfrac{1 \text{ mol C}}{12.0 \text{ g C}} = 2 \text{ mol C}$

$76.0 \text{ g F} \times \dfrac{1 \text{ mol F}}{19.0 \text{ g F}} = 4 \text{ mol F}$

The mole ratio of C to F is $\dfrac{2 \text{ mol C}}{4 \text{ mol F}}$.

The lowest whole-number ratio of C to F is CF_2.

27. $364 \text{ g Ar} \times \dfrac{1 \text{ mol Ar}}{39.9 \text{ g Ar}} = 9.12 \text{ mol. Ar}$

D. Essay

28. A mass that has *molar* as a modifier must be the mass of a mole. A mole is a unit that counts all kinds of representative particles, so molar mass can be used for the mass of Avogadro's number of particles of any pure substance.

Chapter 10 Test B

A. Matching

1. f.	**4.** e	**7.** a
2. h	**5.** g	**8.** d
3. b	**6.** c	

B. Multiple Choice

9. d	**15.** a	**21.** d
10. b	**16.** d	**22.** a
11. a	**17.** a	**23.** c
12. c	**18.** c	**24.** b
13. b	**19.** c	**25.** d
14. b	**20.** b	**26.** c

C. Problems

27. $0.25 \text{ mol} \times 6.02 \times 10^{23} \dfrac{\text{atoms}}{\text{mol}}$

$= 1.50 \times 10^{23} \text{ atoms}$

28. $6.25 \text{ mol} \times 98.1 \dfrac{\text{g}}{\text{mol}} = 613 \text{ g}$

29. $15.0 \text{ kg} \times 1000 \dfrac{\text{g}}{\text{kg}} \times \dfrac{1 \text{ mol}}{44.0 \text{ g}} \times \dfrac{22.4 \text{ L}}{\text{mol}} = 7636 \text{ L}$

$= 7640 \text{ L}$

30. $0.650 \dfrac{\text{g}}{\text{L}} \times 22.4 \dfrac{\text{L}}{\text{mol}} = 14.6 \text{ g/mol}$

31. $3.75 \times 10^{15} \text{ atoms} \times \dfrac{1 \text{ mol}}{6.02 \times 10^{23} \text{ atoms}}$

$\times \dfrac{197.0 \text{ g}}{\text{mol}} = 1.23 \times 10^{-6} \text{ g}$

32. $24.3 \text{ g} + 28.0 \text{ g} + 96.0 \text{ g}$

$= 148.3 \text{ g/mol Mg(NO}_3)_2$

Mg: $\dfrac{24.3 \text{ g}}{148.3 \text{ g}} \times 100 = 16.4\%$

N: $\dfrac{28.0 \text{ g}}{148.3 \text{ g}} \times 100 = 18.9\%$

O: $\dfrac{96.0 \text{ g}}{148.3 \text{ g}} \times 100 = 64.7\%$

33. $27.3 \text{ g C} \times \dfrac{1 \text{ mol C}}{12.0 \text{ g C}} = 2.28 \text{ mol C}$

$72.7 \text{ g O} \times \dfrac{1 \text{ mol O}}{16.0 \text{ g O}} = 4.54 \text{ mol O}$

$\dfrac{2.28}{2.28} = 1, \text{ and } \dfrac{4.54}{2.28} = 2$

Thus, the empirical formula is CO_2.

34. $(56.38 \text{ g P}) \times \dfrac{1 \text{ mol P}}{31.0 \text{ g}} = 1.82 \text{ mol P}$

$(43.62 \text{ g O}) \times \dfrac{1 \text{ mol O}}{16.0 \text{ g}} = 2.73 \text{ mol O}$

Empirical formula is P_2O_3
empirical formula mass = 110.0 g, so that

$\text{molecular formula} = \dfrac{219.9 \text{ g}}{110.0 \text{ g}} = 2 \times P_2O_3$

or P_4O_6

D. Essay

35. The mass of a single atom of an element is the atomic mass given on the periodic table, expressed in atomic mass units. The mass of one mole, or Avogadro's number of atoms of that element has the same numerical value as the atomic mass, but expressed in grams.

Chapter 10 Small-Scale Lab

Section 10.2 Counting by Measuring Mass, page 304

Analysis

Student data may vary slightly.

	$H_2O(l)$	$NaCl(s)$	$CaCO_3(s)$
Mass (grams)	4.30	5.09	9.68
Molar Mass (g/mol)	18.0	58.5	100.1
Moles of each compound	0.239	0.0870	0.0967
Moles of each element	0.478 H 0.239 O	0.0870 Na 0.0870 Cl	0.0967 Ca 0.0967 C 0.290 O
Atoms of each element	2.88×10^{23} H 1.44×10^{23} O	5.24×10^{22} Na 5.24×10^{22} Cl	5.82×10^{22} Ca 5.82×10^{22} C 1.75×10^{23} O

Figure A

1. $x \text{ mol NaCl} = 5.09 \text{ g NaCl} \times \dfrac{1 \text{ mol}}{58.5 \text{ g}}$

$= 0.0870 \text{ mol NaCl}$

2. $x \text{ mol } H_2O = 4.30 \text{ g } H_2O \times \dfrac{1 \text{ mol}}{18.0 \text{ g}}$

$= 0.239 \text{ mol } H_2O$

$x \text{ mol } CaCO_3 = 9.68 \text{ g } CaCO_3 \times \dfrac{1 \text{ mol}}{100.1 \text{ g}}$

$= 0.0967 \text{ mol } CaCO_3$

3. $x \text{ mol H} = 0.239 \text{ mol } H_2O \times \dfrac{2 \text{ mol H}}{1 \text{ mol } H_2O}$

$= 0.478 \text{ mol H}$

$x \text{ mol O} = 0.239 \text{ mol } H_2O \times \dfrac{1 \text{ mol O}}{1 \text{ mol } H_2O}$

$= 0.239 \text{ mol O}$

$$x \text{ mol Na} = 0.0870 \text{ mol NaCl} \times \frac{1 \text{ mol Na}}{1 \text{ mol NaCl}}$$
$$= 0.0870 \text{ mol Na}$$
$$x \text{ mol Cl} = 0.0870 \text{ mol NaCl} \times \frac{1 \text{ mol Cl}}{1 \text{ mol NaCl}}$$
$$= 0.0870 \text{ mol Cl}$$
$$x \text{ mol Ca} = 0.0967 \text{ mol CaCO}_3$$
$$\times \frac{1 \text{ mol Ca}}{1 \text{ mol CaCO}_3} = 0.0967 \text{ mol Ca}$$
$$x \text{ mol C} = 0.0967 \text{ mol CaCO}_3$$
$$\times \frac{1 \text{ mol C}}{1 \text{ mol CaCO}_3} = 0.0967 \text{ mol C}$$
$$x \text{ mol O} = 0.0967 \text{ mol CaCO}_3$$
$$\times \frac{3 \text{ mol O}}{1 \text{ mol CaCO}_3} = 0.290 \text{ mol O}$$

4. $x \text{ atoms H} = 0.478 \text{ mol H}$
$$\times \frac{6.02 \times 10^{23} \text{ atoms}}{1 \text{ mol H}}$$
$$= 2.88 \times 10^{23} \text{ atoms H}$$
$x \text{ atoms O} = 0.239 \text{ mol O}$
$$\times \frac{6.02 \times 10^{23} \text{ atoms}}{1 \text{ mol O}}$$
$$= 1.44 \times 10^{23} \text{ atoms O}$$
$x \text{ atoms Na} = 0.0870 \text{ mol Na}$
$$\times \frac{6.02 \times 10^{23} \text{ atoms}}{1 \text{ mol Na}}$$
$$= 5.24 \times 10^{22} \text{ atoms Na}$$
$x \text{ atoms Cl} = 0.0870 \text{ mol Cl}$
$$\times \frac{6.02 \times 10^{23} \text{ atoms}}{1 \text{ mol Cl}}$$
$$= 5.24 \times 10^{22} \text{ atoms Cl}$$
$x \text{ atoms Ca} = 0.09697 \text{ mol Ca}$
$$\times \frac{6.02 \times 10^{23} \text{ atoms}}{1 \text{ mol Ca}}$$
$$= 5.83 \times 10^{22} \text{ atoms Ca}$$
$x \text{ atoms C} = 0.0967 \text{ mol C}$
$$\times \frac{6.02 \times 10^{23} \text{ atoms}}{1 \text{ mol C}}$$
$$= 5.83 \times 10^{22} \text{ atoms C}$$
$x \text{ atoms O} = 0.290 \text{ mol O}$
$$\times \frac{6.02 \times 10^{23} \text{ atoms}}{1 \text{ mol O}}$$
$$= 1.75 \times 10^{23} \text{ atoms O}$$

5. Water has the greatest number of moles in one teaspoon.

6. Water has the greatest total number of atoms.

You're The Chemist

1. Determine the mass of 100 drops of water and then calculate the mass in grams of one drop.

2. Determine the mass of a piece of chalk. Write your name with the chalk and determine the mass of the chalk again. Convert the mass difference to moles and atoms.

Section Review 11.1

A. Completion

1. equation	7. subscripts
2. reactants	8. (*l*)
3. products	9. (*s*)
4. mass	10. (*g*)
5. coefficients	11. (*aq*)
6. element	12. catalyst

B. True-False

13. NT	15. NT
14. AT	16. ST

C. Multiple Choice

17. c	20. g	22. d
18. e	21. a	23. f
19. b		

D. Problems

24. **a.** $2Al(s) + 6HCl(aq) \rightarrow 2AlCl_3(aq) + 3H_2(g)$
     b. $2C_2H_2(g) + 5O_2(g) \rightarrow 4CO_2(g) + 2H_2O(g)$

Section Review 11.2

A. Completion

1. predict
2. combination
3. elements
4. single
5. decomposition
6. single-replacement
7. activity series of metals
8. double-replacement
9. aqueous
10. oxygen
11. carbon dioxide or water
12. water or carbon dioxide

B. True-False

13. AT   **15.** ST   **17.** ST

14. NT   **16.** ST

C. Matching

18. b   **20.** a

19. d   **21.** c

D. Questions and Problems

22. a. combustion

    b. combination

23. $2Li_3PO_4(aq) + 3Zn(NO_3)_2(aq)$
       $\rightarrow Zn_3(PO_4)_2(s) + 6LiNO_3(aq)$

For any double-replacement reaction to occur, one of the products must be a solid (precipitate), or water, or a gas.

Section Review 11.3

A. Completion

1. water

2. aqueous

3. complete ionic equation

4. spectator ions

5. net ionic equation

6. charge

7. atoms

8. precipitate

9. solubility

B. True-False

10. ST   **12.** ST

11. AT   **13.** NT

C. Matching

14. d   **16.** a   **18.** c

15. f   **17.** b   **19.** e

D. Questions and Problems

20. $Cl_2(g) + Na^+(aq) + Br^-(aq)$
       $\rightarrow Br_2(l) + Na^+(aq) + Cl^-(aq)$

The spectator ion is Na^+.
The balanced net ionic equation is
$Cl_2(g) + 2Br^-(aq) \rightarrow Br_2(l) + 2Cl^-(aq)$

21. a. $AgCl(s)$

    b. $CaCO_3(s)$

    c. none

    d. $PbCl_2(s)$

Practice Problem Solutions

Section 11.1

1. $H_2(g) + O_2(g) \rightarrow H_2O(l)$

2. $Fe(s) + S(s) \rightarrow FeS(s)$

3. $MgCO_3(s) \xrightarrow{\Delta} MgO(s) + CO_2(g)$

4. $H_2(g) + Cl_2(g) \rightarrow 2HCl(g)$

5. Hydrochloric acid and solid calcium carbonate react to produce carbon dioxide gas, aqueous calcium chloride, and liquid water.

6. silver + sulfur → silver sulfide

   Silver metal and sulfur react to produce solid silver sulfide. There are 2 silver atoms and 1 sulfur atom on each side of the equation, and the coefficients are in their lowest possible ratio. Thus, the equation is balanced correctly.

7. $H_2O(l) + SO_3(g) \rightarrow H_2SO_4(aq)$

8. $2AgNO_3(aq) + Cu(s) \rightarrow 2Ag(s) + Cu(NO_3)_2(aq)$

9. $4P(s) + 5O_2(g) \rightarrow P_4O_{10}(s)$

Section 11.2

1. Magnesium is a Group 2A metal and forms cations with a 2+ charge. Oxygen is in Group 6A and forms anions with a 2− charge. They combine in a 1:1 ratio to form MgO.

$$Mg + O_2 \rightarrow MgO$$

   The balanced chemical equation is

$$2Mg(s) + O_2(g) \rightarrow 2MgO(s)$$

2. $2Al(s) + 3F_2(g) \rightarrow 2AlF_3(s)$

3. First, determine the formulas for the reactant and products and write them in their proper positions to form a skeleton equation.

$$KClO_3 \rightarrow KCl + O_2$$

   Next, balance the equation.

$$2KClO_3(s) \rightarrow 2KCl(s) + 3O_2(g)$$

4. $Ca(s) + 2HCl(aq) \rightarrow H_2(g) + CaCl_2(aq)$

5. $C_3H_8(g) + 5O_2(g) \rightarrow 3CO_2(g) + 4H_2O(g)$

6. $FeCl_3(aq) + 3NaOH(aq)$
       $\rightarrow Fe(OH)_3(s) + 3NaCl(aq)$

7. combination reactions: 1 and 2
   decomposition reaction: 3
   single-replacement reaction: 4
   double-replacement reaction: 6
   combustion reactions: 1 and 5

8. **a.** no reaction

    b. $Ca(s) + Mg(NO_3)_2(aq)$
         $\rightarrow Ca(NO_3)_2(aq) + Mg(s)$

c. $2K(s) + H_2SO_4(aq) \rightarrow K_2SO_4(aq) + H_2(g)$

d. no reaction

In **a** bromine is less reactive than chlorine so no reaction occurs. In **b** calcium replaces a less reactive magnesium and in **c** potassium replaces the less reactive hydrogen. Because zinc is less reactive than sodium, no reaction occurs in **d**.

Section 11.3

1. This reaction can be described as:

$Ba(NO_3)_2(aq) + Na_2SO_4(aq)$
$\rightarrow BaSO_4(s) + 2NaNO_3(aq)$

The net ionic equation is:

$Ba^{2+}(aq) + SO_4{}^{2-}(aq) \rightarrow BaSO_4(s)$

2. This reaction can be described as:

$Mg(s) + 2HCl(aq) \rightarrow H_2(g) + MgCl_2(aq)$

The net ionic equation is:

$Mg(s) + 2H^+(aq) \rightarrow H_2(g) + Mg^{2+}(aq)$

3. $Pb(NO_3)_2(aq) + 2NH_4Cl(aq)$
$\rightarrow PbCl_2(s) + 2NH_4NO_3(aq)$

$Pb^{2+} + 2Cl^- \rightarrow PbCl_2(s)$

4. **a.** no precipitate   **c.** $CuS(s)$

    b. $AgCl(s)$ **d.** $Al(OH)_3(s)$

Interpreting Graphics 11

nitrous oxide	N_2O
nitric oxide	NO
oxygen	O_2
carbon dioxide	CO_2
water	H_2O
ammonia	NH_3
urea	CH_4N_2O
benzene	C_6H_6
nitrobenzene	$C_6H_5NO_2$
carbonic acid	H_2CO_3
nitric acid	HNO_3

1. $N_2O + O_2 \rightarrow NO$
$2N_2O + O_2 \rightarrow 4NO$

2. $C_6H_6 + O_2 \rightarrow CO_2 + H_2O$
$2C_6H_6 + 15O_2 \rightarrow 12CO_2 + 6H_2O$

3. $NH_3 + CO_2 \rightarrow CH_4N_2O + H_2O$
$2NH_3 + CO_2 \rightarrow CH_4N_2O + H_2O$

4. $C_6H_6 + HNO_3 \rightarrow C_6H_5NO_2 + H_2O$
balanced as written

Vocabulary Review 11

1. combustion
2. decomposition
3. net ionic equation
4. catalyst
5. reactants
6. spectator
7. single replacement
8. balanced equation
9. coefficients

Solution: precipitate

Quiz for Chapter 11

1. skeleton
2. equation
3. formulas
4. balanced
5. **a.** right
   b. left
6. arrow
7. $2HgO(s) \rightarrow 2Hg(l) + O_2(g)$
8. $2Ag^+(aq) + 2Na^+(aq) + 2NO_3^-(aq) + CO_3^{2-}(aq)$
$\rightarrow 2Na^+(aq) + 2NO_3{}^-(aq) + Ag_2CO_3(s)$

net: $2Ag^+(aq) + CO_3{}^{2-}(aq) \rightarrow Ag_2CO_3(s)$
9. $C_4H_8(g) + 6O_2(g) \rightarrow 4CO_2(g) + 4H_2O(g)$
10. $2Na(s) + Br_2(l) \rightarrow 2NaBr(s)$

Chapter 11 Test A

A. Matching

1. e	5. a	8. f
2. g	6. h	9. d
3. j	7. c	10. i
4. b		

B. Multiple Choice

11. a	16. b	21. d
12. c	17. b	22. d
13. b	18. c	23. b
14. c	19. d	24. a
15. a	20. b	25. c

C. Problems

26. **a.** $3Ca(s) + 2H_3PO_4(aq)$
$\rightarrow Ca_3(PO_4)_2(s) + 3H_2(g)$

    b. $2KBrO_3(s) \rightarrow 2KBr(s) + 3O_2(g)$

    c. $(NH_4)_2CO_3(aq) + 2NaOH(aq)$
$\rightarrow Na_2CO_3(aq) + 2NH_3(g) + 2H_2O(l)$

27. **a.** single-replacement

   b. decomposition

   c. double-replacement

28. **a.** $C_5H_{10}(g) + 5O_2(g) \rightarrow 5CO(g) + 5H_2O(g)$
      (incomplete)

   b. $2C_3H_7OH(l) + 9O_2(g) \rightarrow 6CO_2(g) + 8H_2O(g)$
      (complete)

29. **a.** $2K_3PO_4(aq) + 3MgCl_2(aq)$
      $\rightarrow Mg_3(PO_4)_2(s) + 6KCl(aq)$

      net: $3Mg^{2+}(aq) + 2PO_4{}^{3-}(aq)$
      $\rightarrow Mg_3(PO_4)_2(s)$

   b. $2Fe(NO_3)_3(aq) + 3Na_2CO_3(aq)$
      $\rightarrow Fe_2(CO_3)_3(s) + 6NaNO_3(aq)$

      net: $2Fe^{3+}(aq) + 3CO_3{}^{2-}(aq)$
      $\rightarrow Fe_2(CO_3)_3(s)$

D. Essay

30. Whether one metal will replace another is determined by the relative reactivity of the two metals. The activity series of metals lists metals in order of decreasing reactivity. A metal will replace any metal found below it in the activity series.

Chapter 11 Test B

A. Matching

1. g	5. c	8. j
2. h	6. a	9. b
3. i	7. d	10. e
4. f		

B. Multiple Choice

11. d	16. b	21. d
12. b	17. a	22. a
13. c	18. d	23. c
14. b	19. b	24. b
15. a	20. d	25. d

C. Problems

26. $NaCl(aq) + AgNO_3(aq)$
      $\rightarrow NaNO_3(aq) + AgCl(s)$

27. **a.** $CS_2(s) + 3O_2(g) \rightarrow CO_2(g) + 2SO_2(g)$

   b. $2HNO_3(aq) + Mg(OH)_2(aq)$
      $\rightarrow Mg(NO_3)_2(aq) + 2H_2O(l)$

   c. $Fe_2O_3(s) + 3CO(g) \rightarrow 2Fe(s) + 3CO_2(g)$

28. **a.** $Li_2O(s) + H_2O(l) \rightarrow 2LiOH(aq)$

   b. $2H_2O(l) \xrightarrow{\text{electricity}} 2H_2(g) + O_2(g)$

   c. $2Al(s) + 3Fe(NO_3)_2(aq)$
      $\rightarrow 2Al(NO_3)_3(aq) + 3Fe(s)$

   d. $2HNO_3(aq) + Ca(OH)_2(aq)$
      $\rightarrow Ca(NO_3)_2(aq) + 2H_2O(l)$

   e. $C_3H_8(g) + 5O_2(g) \rightarrow 3CO_2(g) + 4H_2O(l)$

29. **a.** $KOH(aq) + HCl(aq) \rightarrow KCl(aq) + H_2O(l)$

      $K^+(aq) + OH^-(aq) + H^+(aq) + Cl^-(aq)$
      $\rightarrow K^+(aq) + Cl^-(aq) + H_2O(l)$

      Spectator ions: $K^+(aq)$ and $Cl^-(aq)$

      Net: $H^+(aq) + OH^-(aq) \rightarrow H_2O(l)$

   b. $Pb(NO_3)_2(aq) + KI(aq)$
      $\rightarrow PbI_2(s) + KNO_3(aq)$

      $Pb^{2+}(aq) + 2NO_3{}^-(aq) + K^+(aq) + I^-(aq)$
      $\rightarrow PbI_2(s) + K^+(aq) + NO_3{}^-(aq)$

      Spectator ions: $K^+(aq)$ and $NO_3{}^-(aq)$

      Net: $Pb^{2+}(aq) + 2I^-(aq) \rightarrow PbI_2(s)$

   c. $ZnI_2(aq) + NaOH(aq)$
      $\rightarrow NaI(aq) + Zn(OH)_2(s)$

      $Zn^{2+}(aq) + 2I^-(aq) + Na^+(aq) + OH^-(aq)$
      $\rightarrow Na^+(aq) + I^-(aq) + Zn(OH)_2(s)$

      Spectator ions: $Na^+(aq)$ and $I^-(aq)$

      Net: $Zn^{2+}(aq) + 2OH^-(aq) \rightarrow Zn(OH)_2(s)$

D. Essay

30. $AB + CD \rightarrow AD + CB$; double-replacement reaction; the cations have exchanged positions such that two new compounds are formed.

   $E + FG \rightarrow EG + F$; single-replacement reaction; the metal E has replaced the metal F so that a new compound and a different element are produced.

Chapter 11 Small-Scale Lab

Section 11.3 Precipitation Reactions: Formation of Solids, page 345

Analysis

	AgNO$_3$ (Ag$^+$)	Pb(NO$_3$)$_2$ (Pb^{2+})	CaCl$_2$ (Ca^{2+})
Na$_2$CO$_3$ (CO$_3^{2-}$)	a white ppt	f white ppt	k white ppt
Na$_3$PO$_4$ (PO$_4^{3-}$)	b tan ppt	g white ppt	l white ppt
NaOH (OH$^-$)	c brown ppt	h white ppt	m white ppt
Na$_2$SO$_4$ (SO$_4^{2-}$)	d no visible reaction	i white ppt	n no visible reaction
NaCl (Cl$^-$)	e white ppt	j white ppt	o no visible reaction

1. **a.** $Na_2CO_3 + 2AgNO_3$
   $\rightarrow 2NaNO_3 + Ag_2CO_3(s)$

   b. $2Na_3PO_4 + 3Pb(NO_3)_2$
   $\rightarrow 6NaNO_3 + Pb_3(PO_4)_2(s)$

2. Sodium hydroxide reacts with calcium chloride to form sodium chloride and solid calcium hydroxide.

3. Mixings **d, n,** and **o** all gave no visible reaction so it is not necessary to write an equation.

4. **b.** $Na_3PO_4 + 3AgNO_3$
   $\rightarrow 3NaNO_3 + Ag_3PO_4(s)$

   c. $NaOH + AgNO_3 \rightarrow NaNO_3 + AgOH(s)$

   Teacher's note:
   The students will write the above reaction but this is what really happens:
   $2NaOH + 2AgNO_3$
   $\rightarrow 2NaNO_3 + Ag_2O(s) + H_2O$

   e. $NaCl + AgNO_3 \rightarrow NaNO_3 + AgCl(s)$

   f. $Na_2CO_3 + Pb(NO_3)_2$
   $\rightarrow 2NaNO_3 + PbCO_3(s)$

   h. $2NaOH + Pb(NO_3)_2$
   $\rightarrow 2NaNO_3 + Pb(OH)_2(s)$

   i. $Na_2SO_4 + Pb(NO_3)_2$
   $\rightarrow 2NaNO_3 + PbSO_4(s)$

   j. $2NaCl + Pb(NO_3)_2 \rightarrow 2NaNO_3 + PbCl_2(s)$

   k. $Na_2CO_3 + CaCl_2 \rightarrow 2NaCl + CaCO_3(s)$

   l. $2Na_3PO_4 + 3CaCl_2$
   $\rightarrow 6NaCl + Ca_3(PO_4)_2(s)$

   m. $2NaOH + CaCl_2 \rightarrow 2NaCl + Ca(OH)_2(s)$

5. **a.** $2Ag^+ + CO_3^{2-} \rightarrow Ag_2CO_3(s)$

   b. $3Ag^+ + PO_4^{3-} \rightarrow Ag_3PO_4(s)$

   c. $Ag^+ + OH^- \rightarrow AgOH(s)$

   e. $Ag^+ + Cl^- \rightarrow AgCl(s)$

   f. $Pb^{2+} + CO_3^{2-} \rightarrow PbCO_3(s)$

   g. $3Pb^{2+} + 2PO_4^{3-} \rightarrow Pb_3(PO_4)_2(s)$

   h. $Pb^{2+} + 2OH^- \rightarrow Pb(OH)_2(s)$

   i. $Pb^{2+} + SO_4^{2-} \rightarrow PbSO_4(s)$

   j. $Pb^{2+} + 2Cl^- \rightarrow PbCl_2(s)$

   k. $Ca^{2+} + CO_3^{2-} \rightarrow CaCO_3(s)$

   l. $3Ca^{2+} + 2PO_4^{3-} \rightarrow Ca_3(PO_4)_2(s)$

   m. $Ca^{2+} + 2OH^- \rightarrow Ca(OH)_2(s)$

You're the Chemist

1. $KI + AgNO_3 \rightarrow KNO_3 + AgI(s)$
   Silver iodide is pale green.
   $Ag^+ + I^- \rightarrow AgI(s)$
   $2KI + Pb(NO_3)_2 \rightarrow 2KNO_3 + PbI_2(s)$
   Lead(II) iodide is bright yellow.
   $Pb^{2+} + 2I^- \rightarrow PbI_2(s)$

2. Adding one drop of lead nitrate to a few grains of table salt causes white crystals to grow on the salt. Silver nitrate produces a similar result.

3. Place one drop of lead nitrate on a small pile of dry table salt. Be sure to keep part of the pile dry and look carefully for signs of yellow lead iodide.

Section Review 12.1

Part A Completion

1. moles/molecules
2. balanced equation
3. mass/atoms
4. atoms/mass
5. moles
6. STP (standard temperature and pressure)

Part B True-False

7. AT	**9.** AT	**11.** AT
8. ST	**10.** ST	**12.** ST

Part C Matching

13. b	**15.** e	**17.** c
14. d	**16.** a	

Part D Questions and Problems

18. moles $N_2 = 2$
moles $O_2 = 3$
moles $N_2O_3 = 2$
molecules $N_2 = 2$
molecules $O_2 = 3$
molecules $N_2O_3 = 2$
volume $N_2 = 2 \times 22.4$ L $= 44.8$ L
volume $O_2 = 3 \times 22.4$ L $= 67.2$ L
volume $N_2O_3 = 2 \times 22.4$ L $= 44.8$ L

$\begin{array}{rl} 2 \text{ mol } N_2 = & 56 \text{ g} \\ 3 \text{ mol } O_2 = & \underline{96 \text{ g}} \end{array}$

mass reactants $= 152$ g
2 mol $N_2O_3 = 152$ g
mass product $= 152$ g

19. $14 \cancel{\text{ mol FeCl}_3} \times \dfrac{3 \text{ mol } Cl_2}{2 \cancel{\text{ mol FeCl}_3}} = 21 \text{ mol } Cl_2$

Section Review 12.2

Part A Completion

1. representative particles
2. volumes
3. coefficients
4. mole ratios
5. product/reactant
6. reactant/product
7. moles

Part B True-False

8. AT	**11.** ST	**13.** NT
9. NT	**12.** NT	**14.** AT
10. AT		

Part C Matching

15. c	**17.** d	**19.** a
16. b	**18.** e	

Part D Questions and Problems

20. $4.8 \cancel{\text{ g } O_2} \times \dfrac{1 \cancel{\text{ mol } O_2}}{32.0 \cancel{\text{ g } O_2}} \times \dfrac{2 \cancel{\text{ mol CO}}}{1 \cancel{\text{ mol } O_2}}$

$\times \dfrac{22.4 \text{ L CO}}{1 \cancel{\text{ mol CO}}} = 6.7 \text{ L CO}$

21. $2.1 \times 10^{24} \cancel{\text{ molecules } O_2}$

$\times \dfrac{1 \cancel{\text{ mol } O_2}}{6.02 \times 10^{23} \cancel{\text{ molecules } O_2}} \times \dfrac{4 \cancel{\text{ mol } NH_3}}{7 \cancel{\text{ mol } O_2}}$

$\times \dfrac{17.0 \text{ g } NH_3}{1 \cancel{\text{ mol } NH_3}} = 33.9 \text{ g } NH_3$

Section 12.3

Part A Completion

1. limiting reagent	4. theoretical yield
2. used up	5. maximum
3. product	6. actual yield

Part B True-False

7. AT	**9.** NT	**11.** AT
8. NT	**10.** ST	**12.** AT

Part C Matching

13. b	**15.** e	**17.** d
14. c	**16.** a	

Part D Questions and Problems

18. a. $3.1 \cancel{\text{ mol } SO_2} \times \dfrac{1 \text{ mol } O_2}{2 \cancel{\text{ mol } SO_2}}$

$= 1.6 \text{ mol } O_2$ needed
SO_2 is the limiting reagent.

b. $3.1 \cancel{\text{ mol } SO_2} \times \dfrac{2 \text{ mol } SO_3}{2 \cancel{\text{ mol } SO_2}}$

mol SO_3 can be formed
2.7 mol $O_2 - 1.6$ mol O_2
$= 1.1$ mol O_2 in excess

Practice Problems 12

Section 12.1

1. $10A + 2C + Ci \rightarrow A_{10}C_2Ci$

$25 \cancel{A_{10}C_2Ci} \times \dfrac{10A}{\cancel{A_{10}C_2Ci}} = 250 \text{ apples}$

2. $2KClO_3(s) \rightarrow 2KCl(s) + 3O_2(g)$

$12 \cancel{\text{ mol } KClO_3} \times \dfrac{3 \text{ mol } O_2}{2 \cancel{\text{ mol } KClO_3}} = 18 \text{ mol } O_2$

3. $14 \text{ mol } \cancel{KClO_3} \times \dfrac{3 \text{ mol } O_2}{2 \text{ mol } \cancel{KClO_3}} = 21 \text{ mol } O_2$

4. $2H_2(s) + O_2(g) \rightarrow 2H_2O(g)$

$2.0 \times 10^{23} \cancel{\text{molecules } O_2} \times \dfrac{2 \text{ molecules } H_2O}{1 \cancel{\text{molecule } O_2}}$

$= 4.0 \times 10^{23} \text{ molecules } H_2O$

$22.5 \cancel{\text{mol } O_2} \times \dfrac{2 \text{ mol } H_2O}{1 \cancel{\text{mol } O_2}} = 45.0 \text{ mol } H_2O$

Section 12.2

1. $10 \cancel{\text{mol } H_2} \times \dfrac{2 \text{ mol } HCl}{1 \cancel{\text{mol } H_2}} = 20 \text{ mol } HCl$

2. $14 \cancel{\text{mol } FeCl_3} \times \dfrac{3 \text{ mol } Cl_2}{2 \cancel{\text{mol } FeCl_3}} = 21 \text{ mol } Cl_2$

3. $4 \cancel{\text{mol } NO} \times \dfrac{2 \cancel{\text{mol } NO_2}}{2 \cancel{\text{mol } NO}} \times \dfrac{46 \text{ g } NO_2}{1 \cancel{\text{mol } NO_2}}$

$= 184 \text{ g } NO_2$

4. $75.0 \text{ g } \cancel{KClO_3} \times \dfrac{1 \cancel{\text{mol } KClO_3}}{122.6 \text{ g } \cancel{KClO_3}}$

$\times \dfrac{3 \cancel{\text{mol } O_2}}{2 \cancel{\text{mol } KClO_3}} \times \dfrac{32.0 \text{ g } O_2}{1 \cancel{\text{mol } O_2}} = 29.4 \text{ g } O_2$

5. $2Ag(s) + Cl(g) \rightarrow 2AgCl(s)$

$84 \text{ g } \cancel{AgCl} \times \dfrac{1 \cancel{\text{mol } AgCl}}{43.5 \text{ g } \cancel{AgCl}} \times \dfrac{2 \cancel{\text{mol } Ag}}{2 \cancel{\text{mol } AgCl}}$

$\times \dfrac{108 \text{ g } Ag}{1 \cancel{\text{mol } Ag}} = 63 \text{ g } Ag$

6. $4.80 \text{ g } \cancel{O_2} \times \dfrac{1 \cancel{\text{mol } O_2}}{32.0 \text{ g } \cancel{O_2}} \times \dfrac{2 \cancel{\text{mol } CO}}{1 \cancel{\text{mol } O_2}}$

$\times \dfrac{22.4 \text{ L } CO}{1 \cancel{\text{mol } CO}} = 6.72 \text{ L } CO$

7. $15.0 \text{ L } \cancel{N_2O_3} \times \dfrac{3 \text{ L } O_2}{2 \text{ L } \cancel{N_2O_3}} = 22.5 \text{ L } O_2$

8. $Zn(s) + 2HNO_3 \rightarrow H_2(g) + Zn(NO_3)_2$

$7.5 \text{ L } \cancel{H_2} \times \dfrac{1 \cancel{\text{mol } H_2}}{22.4 \text{ L } \cancel{H_2}} \times \dfrac{1 \cancel{\text{mol } Zn}}{1 \cancel{\text{mol } H_2}}$

$\times \dfrac{65.4 \text{ g } Zn}{1 \cancel{\text{mol } Zn}} = 22 \text{ g } Zn$

Section 12.3

1. $2H_2(g) + O_2(g) \rightarrow 2H_2O(g)$

$4 \cancel{\text{mol } O_2} \times \dfrac{2 \text{ mol } H_2}{1 \cancel{\text{mol } O_2}} = 8 \text{ mol } H_2$

$16 \cancel{\text{mol } H_2} \times \dfrac{1 \text{ mol } O_2}{2 \cancel{\text{mol } H_2}} = 8 \text{ mol } O_2$

Oxygen is the limiting reagent.

$4 \cancel{\text{mol } O_2} \times \dfrac{2 \text{ mol } H_2O}{1 \cancel{\text{mol } O_2}} = 8 \text{ mol } H_2O \text{ formed}$

2. $2H_2(g) + O_2(g) \rightarrow 2H_2O(g)$

$160.0 \text{ g } \cancel{O_2} \times \dfrac{1 \cancel{\text{mol } O_2}}{32.0 \text{ g } \cancel{O_2}} \times \dfrac{2 \text{ mol } H_2}{1 \cancel{\text{mol } O_2}}$

$= 10.0 \text{ mol } H_2 \text{ needed}$

Oxygen is the limiting reagent.

$5.00 \cancel{\text{mol } O_2} \times \dfrac{2 \cancel{\text{mol } H_2O}}{1 \cancel{\text{mol } O_2}} \times \dfrac{18.0 \text{ g } H_2O}{1 \cancel{\text{mol } H_2O}}$

$= 180 \text{ g } H_2O$

3. $C(s) + O_2(g) \rightarrow CO_2(g)$

$18.0 \text{ g } \cancel{C} \times \dfrac{1 \cancel{\text{mol } C}}{12.0 \text{ g } \cancel{C}} \times \dfrac{1 \cancel{\text{mol } CO_2}}{1 \cancel{\text{mol } C}}$

$\times \dfrac{44.0 \text{ g } CO_2}{1 \cancel{\text{mol } CO_2}} = 66.0 \text{ g } CO_2$

$\text{percent yield} = \dfrac{55.0 \text{ g } CO_2}{66.0 \text{ g } CO_2} \times 100\% = 83.3\%$

4. $2HCl(g) \rightarrow H_2(g) + Cl_2(g)$

$25.8 \text{ g } \cancel{HCl} \times \dfrac{1 \cancel{\text{mol } HCl}}{36.5 \text{ g } \cancel{HCl}} \times \dfrac{1 \cancel{\text{mol } Cl_2}}{2 \cancel{\text{mol } HCl}}$

$\times \dfrac{71.0 \text{ g } Cl_2}{1 \cancel{\text{mol } Cl_2}} = 25.1 \text{ g } Cl_2$

$\text{percent yield} = \dfrac{13.6 \text{ g } Cl_2}{25.1 \text{ g } Cl_2} \times 100\% = 54.2\%$

5. $100.0 \text{ g } \cancel{AgCl} \times \dfrac{1 \cancel{\text{mol } AgCl}}{143.5 \text{ g } \cancel{AgCl}} \times \dfrac{2 \cancel{\text{mol } Ag}}{2 \cancel{\text{mol } AgCl}}$

$\times \dfrac{108 \text{ g } Ag}{1 \cancel{\text{mol } Ag}} = 75.3 \text{ g } Ag$

$\text{mass of } Ag(s) \text{ reclaimed} = 0.946 \times 75.3 \text{ g } Ag$

$= 71.2 \text{ g } Ag$

6. $42.8 \text{ g } \cancel{Mg} \times \dfrac{1 \cancel{\text{mol } Mg}}{24.3 \text{ g } \cancel{Mg}} \times \dfrac{2 \cancel{\text{mol } MgO}}{2 \cancel{\text{mol } Mg}}$

$\times \dfrac{40.3 \text{ g } MgO}{1 \cancel{\text{mol } MgO}} = 71.0 \text{ g } MgO$

$\text{actual yield} = 71.0 \text{ g } MgO \times 0.817$

$= 58.0 \text{ g } MgO$

Interpreting Graphics 12

1. **a.** 102.1 g/mol **c.** 180.1 g/mol

   b. 138.1 g/mol

2. Student 1: 0.0155 moles SA
   Student 2: 0.0147 moles SA

3. Student 1: 5.25 g acetic anhydride
            0.0514 moles
   Student 2: 5.25g acetic anhydride
            0.0514 moles

4. salicylic acid

5. Student 1: 2.79 g
   Student 2: 2.65 g

6. Student 1: 1.745 g
   Student 2: 2.509 g
7. Student 1: 62.5%
   Student 2: 94.7%
8. Student 2 exhibited much better lab technique, which is reflected by a higher percent yield than that obtained by Student 1. Student 2 should receive the higher grade.

Vocabulary Review 12

1. d	5. g	8. i
2. h	6. j	9. e
3. f	7. b	10. c
4. a		

Quiz for Chapter 12

1. coefficients	6. NT
2. reactant	7. NT
3. moles	8. NT
4. atoms	9. NT
5. 44.8	10. ST

Chapter 12 Test A

A. Matching

1. b	3. e	5. a
2. c	4. f	6. d

B. Multiple Choice

7. b	11. b	15. c
8. c	12. c	16. a
9. b	13. b	17. c
10. d	14. a	18. c

C. Problems

19. There is no limiting reagent, because the mole ratio of the reactants is 1 mol N_2 to 3 mol H_2.

20. $558 \text{ g Fe} \times \dfrac{1 \text{ mol Fe}}{55.8 \text{ g Fe}} \times \dfrac{3 \text{ mol CO}}{2 \text{ mol Fe}}$
    $\times \dfrac{28.0 \text{ g CO}}{1 \text{ mol CO}} = 4.20 \times 10^2 \text{ g CO}$

21. $15.0 \text{ g CO}_2 \times \dfrac{1 \text{ mol CO}_2}{44 \text{ g CO}_2} \times \dfrac{2 \text{ mol C}_4\text{H}_{10}}{8 \text{ mol CO}_2} \times$
    $\dfrac{58 \text{ g C}_4\text{H}_{10}}{1 \text{ mol C}_4\text{H}_{10}} = 4.94 \text{ g C}_4\text{H}_{10}$

22. **a.** Theoretical yield:
    $$4.0 \text{ g H}_2 \times \frac{1 \text{ mol H}_2}{2.0 \text{ g H}_2} \times \frac{1 \text{ mol CH}_3\text{OH}}{2 \text{ mol H}_2}$$
    $$\times \frac{32.0 \text{ g CH}_3\text{OH}}{1 \text{ mol CH}_3\text{OH}} = 32.0 \text{ g CH}_3\text{OH}$$
    b. Percent yield: $\dfrac{28.0 \text{ g}}{32.0 \text{ g}} \times 100\% = 87.5\%$

D. Essay

23. The coefficients of a balanced chemical equation describe the relative number of moles of reactants and products. From this information, the amounts of reactants and products can be calculated. The number of moles may be converted to mass, volume, or number of representative particles.

E. Additional Problems

24. **a.** $5.00 \times 10^2 \text{ g Al}_2(\text{SO}_4)_3 \times \dfrac{1 \text{ mol Al}_2(\text{SO}_4)_3}{342 \text{ g Al}_2(\text{SO}_4)_3}$
    $\times \dfrac{3 \text{ mol CaSO}_4}{1 \text{ mol Al}_2(\text{SO}_4)_3} \times \dfrac{136 \text{ g CaSO}_4}{1 \text{ mol CaSO}_4}$
    $= 596 \text{ g CaSO}_4$

    $5.00 \times 10^2 \text{ g Al}_2(\text{SO}_4)_3 \times \dfrac{1 \text{ mol Al}_2(\text{SO}_4)_3}{342 \text{ g Al}_2(\text{SO}_4)_3}$
    $\times \dfrac{3 \text{ mol Ca(OH)}_2}{1 \text{ mol Al}_2(\text{SO}_4)_3} \times \dfrac{74.1 \text{ g Ca(OH)}_2}{1 \text{ mol Ca(OH)}_2}$
    $= 325 \text{ g Ca(OH)}_2$

    $Al_2(\text{SO}_4)_3$ is the limiting reagent.

    b. $450 \text{ g} - 325 \text{ g} = 125 \text{ g excess Ca(OH)}_2$
    $125 \text{ g Ca(OH)}_2 \times \dfrac{1 \text{ mol Ca(OH)}_2}{74.1 \text{ g Ca(OH)}_2}$
    $= 1.69 \text{ mol Ca(OH)}_2 \text{ remaining}$

25. $10.0 \text{ L H}_2\text{S} \times \dfrac{3 \text{ mol O}_2}{2 \text{ mol H}_2\text{S}} = 15.0 \text{ L O}_2$

26. $5.00 \text{ L O}_2 \times \dfrac{1 \text{ mol O}_2}{22.4 \text{ L O}_2} \times \dfrac{2 \text{ mol KClO}_3}{3 \text{ mol O}_2}$
    $\times \dfrac{122.6 \text{ g KClO}_3}{1 \text{ mol KClO}_3} = 18.2 \text{ g KClO}_3$

27. $\dfrac{4.80 \text{ L}}{5.00 \text{ L}} \times 100\% = 96.0\%$

Chapter 12 Test B

A. Matching

1. b	3. d	5. f
2. e	4. a	6. c

B. Multiple Choice

7. d	**12.** b	**17.** c
8. d	**13.** c	**18.** d
9. b	**14.** b	**19.** a
10. d	**15.** a	**20.** b
11. d	**16.** c	**21.** c

C. Problems

22. $\dfrac{2 \text{ mol NH}_3}{3 \text{ mol H}_2} \times 12.0 \text{ mol H}_2 = 8.00 \text{ mol NH}_3$

23. $\dfrac{1 \text{ mol SnF}_2}{2 \text{ mol HF}} \times \dfrac{1 \text{ mol HF}}{20.0 \text{ g HF}} \times 45.0 \text{ g HF}$

$\times \dfrac{156.7 \text{ g SnF}_2}{1 \text{ mol SnF}_2} = 176 \text{ g SnF}_2$

24. $\dfrac{1 \text{ mol CH}_4}{1 \text{ mol CO}_2} \times 150 \text{ mol CO}_2 \times \dfrac{16.0 \text{ g CH}_4}{1 \text{ mol CH}_4}$

$= 2.4 \times 10^3 \text{ g CH}_4$

25. $\dfrac{2 \text{ mol Al}_2\text{O}_3}{3 \text{ mol O}_2} \times \dfrac{1 \text{ mol O}_2}{22.4 \text{ L O}_2} \times \dfrac{1 \text{ L}}{1000 \text{ mL}}$

$\times 625 \text{ mL O}_2 \times \dfrac{102 \text{ g Al}_2\text{O}_3}{1 \text{ mol Al}_2\text{O}_3}$

$= 1.90 \text{ g Al}_2\text{O}_3$

26. $50.8 \text{ g CaCO}_3 \times \dfrac{1 \text{ mol CaCO}_3}{100.1 \text{ g CaCO}_3}$

$\times \dfrac{1 \text{ mol CaO}}{1 \text{ mol CaCO}_3} \times \dfrac{56.1 \text{ g CaO}}{1 \text{ mol CaO}}$

$= 28.5 \text{ g CaO}$

$\% \text{ yield} = \dfrac{\text{actual}}{\text{theoretical}} \times 100\%$

$= \dfrac{26.4 \text{ g CaO}}{28.5 \text{ g CaO}} \times 100\%$

$= 92.6\% \text{ yield}$

D. Essay

27. Based on the 2:3 molar ratio between A and B, the 1.0 mol of A requires only 1.5 mol of B in order to react completely. The maximum amount of A_2B_3 that can be produced (0.50 mol) is thus limited by the amount of A that is available, with 0.50 mol of B remaining in excess.

E. Additional Problems

28. $6CO_2 + 6H_2O \xrightarrow{\text{energy}} C_6H_{12}O_6 + 6O_2$

$\dfrac{1 \text{ mol C}_6\text{H}_{12}\text{O}_6}{6 \text{ mol H}_2\text{O}} \times 4.50 \text{ mol H}_2\text{O}$

$\times \dfrac{180 \text{ g C}_6\text{H}_{12}\text{O}_6}{1 \text{ mol C}_6\text{H}_{12}\text{O}_6} = 135 \text{ g C}_6\text{H}_{12}\text{O}_6$

29. $\dfrac{4 \text{ mol CO}_2}{2 \text{ mol C}_2\text{H}_2} \times 5.00 \times 10^4 \text{ g C}_2\text{H}_2$

$\times \dfrac{1 \text{ mol C}_2\text{H}_2}{26.0 \text{ g C}_2\text{H}_2} \times \dfrac{44.0 \text{ g CO}_2}{1 \text{ mol CO}_2}$

$= 1.69 \times 10^5 \text{ g CO}_2$

30. $\dfrac{2 \text{ mol H}_3\text{PO}_4}{3 \text{ mol H}_2\text{SO}_4} \times 1.25 \times 10^5 \text{ kg H}_2\text{SO}_4$

$\times \dfrac{1 \text{ mol H}_2\text{SO}_4}{98.1 \text{ g H}_2\text{SO}_4} \times \dfrac{1000 \text{ g}}{1 \text{ kg}} \times \dfrac{98.0 \text{ g H}_3\text{PO}_4}{1 \text{ mol H}_3\text{PO}_4}$

$\times \dfrac{1 \text{ kg}}{1000 \text{ g}} = 8.32 \times 10^4 \text{ kg H}_3\text{PO}_4$

31. a. $\dfrac{3 \text{ mol CuO}}{2 \text{ mol NH}_3} \times \dfrac{1 \text{ mol NH}_3}{17.0 \text{ g NH}_3} \times 57.0 \text{ g NH}_3$

$= 5.03 \text{ mol CuO needed}$

$290.0 \text{ g CuO} \times \dfrac{1 \text{ mol CuO}}{79.5 \text{ g CuO}}$

$= 3.65 \text{ mol CuO present}$

Thus, CuO is the limiting reagent.

b. $\dfrac{2 \text{ mol NH}_3}{3 \text{ mol CuO}} \times 3.65 \text{ mol CuO}$

$= 2.43 \text{ mol NH}_3 \text{ react}$

Since $57.0 \text{ g NH}_3 \times \dfrac{1 \text{ mol NH}_3}{17.0 \text{ g NH}_3}$

$= 3.35 \text{ mol NH}_3 \text{ present}$

$NH_3 \text{ excess} = 3.35 \text{ mol} - 2.43 \text{ mol}$

$= 0.92 \text{ mol}$

c. $\dfrac{1 \text{ mol N}_2}{3 \text{ mol CuO}} \times 3.65 \text{ mol CuO} \times \dfrac{28.0 \text{ g N}_2}{1 \text{ mol N}_2}$

$= 34.1 \text{ g N}_2$

32. $\dfrac{4 \text{ mol NO}}{4 \text{ mol NH}_3} \times 10.0 \text{ kg NH}_3 \times \dfrac{1000 \text{ g}}{1 \text{ kg}}$

$\times \dfrac{1 \text{ mol NH}_3}{17.0 \text{ g NH}_3} \times \dfrac{30.0 \text{ g NO}}{1 \text{ mol NO}} \times \dfrac{1 \text{ kg}}{1000 \text{ g}}$

$\times 0.80 = 14.1 \text{ kg NO}$

Chapter 12 Small-Scale Lab

Section 12.2 Analysis of Baking Soda, page 367

Procedure

Sample answers are given.

A. 2.83 g

B. 3.28 g

C. 10.70 g

D. 4.29 g

E. If the mixture does not turn red when thymol blue is added, have students add just enough HCl from a third pipet to turn the mixture red. Students must measure the mass lost by the pipet to add to the total mass of HCl used.

F. 10.53 g

G. 8.78 g

Analysis

1. $HCl + NaHCO_3(s) \rightarrow CO_2(g) + H_2O + NaCl$

2. $3.28 \text{ g} - 2.83 \text{ g} = 0.45$ g baking soda

3. $(10.70 - 4.29) \text{ g HCl} \times 1.00$ mmol HCl/g HCl
   $= 6.41$ mmol HCl

4. $(10.53 - 8.78) \text{ g NaOH}$
   $\times 0.500$ mmol NaOH/g NaOH
   $= 0.875$ mmol NaOH
   (0.875 mmol HCl unreacted)

5. 6.41 mmol HCl total
   $- 0.875$ mmol HCl unreacted
   $= 5.53$ mmol HCl neutralized
   (5.53 mmol $NaHCO_3$)

6. $(0.0840 \text{ g } NaHCO_3/\text{mmol } NaHCO_3)$
   $\times 5.53 \text{ mmol } NaHCO_3 = 0.46$ g $NaHCO_3$

7. $100\% \times (0.46 \text{ g} - 0.45 \text{ g})/0.45 \text{ g} = 2.2$ % error (assuming baking soda is 100% $NaHCO_3$).

You're the Chemist

1. (See Steps 2–7.)

2. Repeat Steps A–G and 1–7 except use baking powder instead of baking soda. The % error is the % of baking soda in baking powder assuming no other errors.

Section Review 13.1

Part A Completion

1. motion
2. empty space
3. far apart
4. independently
5. random or rapid
6. collisions
7. kinetic energy
8. atmospheric
9. 0°C
10. 101.3 kPa or 1 atm

Part B True-False

11. ST
12. AT
13. NT
14. AT
15. NT
16. AT

Part C Matching

17. b
18. c
19. d
20. e
21. a

Part D Questions and Problems

22. $4.30 \text{ atm} \times \dfrac{101.3 \text{ kPa}}{1 \text{ atm}} = 436$ kPa

    $4.30 \text{ atm} \times \dfrac{760 \text{ mm Hg}}{1 \text{ atm}} = 3.27 \times 10^3$ mm Hg

23. According to the kinetic theory, the motion of the particles in a gas is constant and random. Because the particles are relatively far apart, no attractive or repulsive forces exist between the particles. They move independently of each other and travel in straight line paths until they collide with one another or other objects.

24. Odors travel long distances from their sources.

Section 13.2

Part A Completion

1. denser
2. condensed
3. vaporization
4. boiling
5. cooling
6. surface
7. vapor pressure
8. manometer
9. vapor pressure
10. 101.3 kPa or 1 atm

Part B True-False

11. ST
12. ST
13. NT
14. AT
15. ST
16. AT

Part C Matching

17. a
18. e
19. c
20. d
21. b

Part D Questions and Problems

22. At the boiling point, particles throughout the liquid have enough kinetic energy to vaporize.

23. Liquid B would evaporate faster because it has a higher vapor pressure, which indicates that it is more volatile.

24. Evaporation leads to cooling of a liquid because the particles with the highest kinetic energy tend to escape first. The remaining particles have a lower average kinetic energy and a lower temperature.

Section 13.3

Part A Completion

1. compress
2. fixed
3. melts
4. melting point
5. freezing point
6. high
7. crystalline
8. lattice
9. unit cell
10. amorphous

Part B True-False

11. AT	13. NT	15. AT
12. ST	14. ST	

Part C Matching

16. e	19. a	22. d
17. c	20. b	
18. f	21. g	

Part D Questions and Problems

24. When a solid is heated, its particles vibrate more rapidly as their kinetic energy increases. Eventually, the disruptive vibrations of the particles are strong enough to overcome the attractions that hold them in fixed positions. The organization of the particles within the solid breaks down and the solid becomes a liquid.

Section 13.4

Part A Completion

1. sublimation
2. vapor pressure
3. carbon dioxide
4. phase
5. equilibrium
6. triple point
7. 0.016°C
8. 0.61 kPa

Part B True-False

9. NT	11. NT	13. NT
10. AT	12. AT	14. NT

Part C Matching

15. b	17. d	19. a
16. c	18. e	20. f

Part D Questions and Problems

21. Solids that have a vapor pressure that exceeds atmospheric pressure at or near room temperature can change directly to a vapor. This process is called sublimation.

22. The temperature of the system remains constant while the change of state is occurring.

Practice Problems 13

Section 13.1

1. Gas pressure is the result of collisions between between rapidly moving particles in a gas and an object. Because there are no particles of matter in a vacuum, there can be no collisions or pressure.

2. Setting aside fluctuations due to changes in the weather, you would notice that the pressure reading on the barometer would decrease as you climbed in altitude.

3. $754.3 \text{ mm Hg} \times \dfrac{1 \text{ atm}}{760 \text{ mm Hg}} = 0.9925 \text{ atm}$

   $754.3 \text{ mm Hg} \times \dfrac{101.3 \text{ kPa}}{760 \text{ mm Hg}} = 100.5 \text{ kPa}$

4. The average kinetic energy of the particles of a substance is directly proportional to the Kelvin Temperature.

   $-100.0 \,°C + 273 = 173 \text{ K}$

   $73 \,°C + 273 = 346 \text{ K}$

   Because the Kelvin temperature increases by a factor of two, the average kinetic energy increases by a factor of two.

Section 13.2

1. According to kinetic theory, there are no attractions between the particles in a gas, but there are attractions between particles of a liquid.

2. For a dynamic equilibrium to be established, the beaker must be sealed so that the rate of condensation can equal the rate of evaporation.

3. The fastest runner corresponds to the particles in a liquid with the greatest kinetic energy. When these particles vaporize, the remaining particles have a lower average kinetic energy.

4. Ethanol must have the greater vapor pressure because 75°C is very close to the boiling point of ethanol and the vapor pressure is equal to the external pressure at a liquid's boiling point.

Section 13.3

1. The carbon atoms in graphite are arranged in widely-spaced sheets. In diamond, each carbon atom is strongly bonded to four other carbon atoms in a rigid three-dimensional array.

2. Allotropes are two or more different molecular forms of the same element in the same physical state. Carbon has multiple allotropes, including diamond, graphite, and buckminsterfullerene. The carbon atoms are arranged differently in each allotrope.

3. Peanut brittle is an amorphous solid.

4. A molecular solid. In general, ionic solids have higher melting points because the forces that hold particles together in an ionic solid are usually stronger than the forces that hold particles together in a molecular solid.

5. One example of a crystalline solid is sodium chloride. In crystal atoms, ions, or molecules are arranged in an orderly, repeating, three-dimensional pattern called a crystal lattice.

Section 13.4

1. The melting point of water decreases as the pressure increases.

2. This line represents the set of all temperature–pressure values at which the solid and vapor phases of water are in equilibrium.

3. This line represents the set of all temperature–pressure values at which the liquid and gas phases of water are in equilibrium.

4. 101.3 kPa (1 atm)

Interpreting Graphics 13

1.

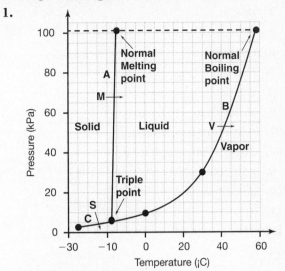

2. Normal melting point = −7.0°C
Normal boiling point = 59°C
Triple point = −8°C and 6 kPa

3. See answer to 1.

4. The melting-point curve leans slightly to the right (has a positive slope) indicating that, as pressure is increased, the melting point of bromine increases. Higher pressures favor the denser phase of a substance. Solid bromine is more dense than liquid bromine.

5. 50°C

6. The triple point is the temperature and pressure at which solid, liquid, and vapor phases of a substance are in equilibrium.

7. See answer to 1.

8. condenses

9. freezes

Vocabulary Review 13

1. kinetic energy

2. gas pressure

3. evaporation

4. boiling point

5. crystal

6. allotropes

7. melting point

8. pascal

Solution: barometer

Quiz for Chapter 13

1. kinetic
2. decreases
3. temperature
4. kinetic
5. elastic
6. condensed
7. minimum kinetic energy
8. external (atmospheric) pressure
9. unit cell
10. amorphous
11. ST
12. AT
13. AT

Chapter 13 Test A

A. Matching

1. i	6. d	11. k
2. f	7. b	12. h
3. g	8. n	13. l
4. j	9. e	14. a
5. c	10. m	

B. Multiple Choice

15. a	20. c	24. b
16. d	21. a	25. b
17. d	22. b	26. c
18. c	23. a	27. c
19. b		

C. True-False

28. AT	31. ST
29. NT	32. AT
30. AT	

D. Problems

33. $3.70 \text{ atm} \times \dfrac{101.3 \text{ kPa}}{1 \text{ atm}} = 375 \text{ kPa}$

34. $3.70 \text{ atm} \times \dfrac{760 \text{ mm Hg}}{1 \text{ atm}} = 2.81 \times 10^3 \text{ mm Hg}$

E. Essay

35. Because the Kelvin temperature is directly proportional to the average kinetic energy of the particles in a substance, it doesn't matter how many particles there are in the sample.

F. Additional Problems

36. $610.0 \text{ mm Hg} \times \dfrac{1 \text{ atm}}{760 \text{ mm Hg}} = 0.803 \text{ atm}$

37. $0.803 \text{ atm} \times \dfrac{101.3 \text{ kPa}}{1 \text{ atm}} = 81.3 \text{ kPa}$

G. Additional Questions

38. The additional energy is being used to change the liquid water to water vapor. The temperature of the water will not rise until all of the water is in the gaseous state.

39. When water boils at standard atmospheric pressure, it cannot be heated above 100°C. Only water at pressures of more than one atmosphere will boil at higher temperatures. The pressure must be increased to the point at which water boils at 150°C or higher to kill bacteria.

Chapter 13 Test B

A. Matching

1. j	6. k	11. a
2. n	7. b	12. m
3. h	8. g	13. c
4. e	9. f	14. i
5. d	10. l	

B. Multiple Choice

15. d	21. a	26. a
16. b	22. a	27. a
17. d	23. a	28. c
18. d	24. b	29. d
19. c	25. b	30. b
20. b		

C. True-False

31. AT	34. AT	36. ST
32. ST	35. NT	37. AT
33. AT		

D. Essay

38. The boiling point of a liquid is the temperature at which the vapor pressure of the liquid is equal to atmospheric pressure. The normal boiling point is the boiling point of the liquid when the atmospheric pressure is 101.3 kPa. If atmospheric pressure is less than 101.3 kPa, then the boiling point of a liquid will be lower than its normal boiling point. Conversely, if atmospheric pressure is

greater than 101.3 kPa, the boiling point of the liquid will be higher than its normal boiling point.

E. Additional Questions

39. The particles of a gas are relatively far apart and there are no attractive or repulsive forces among them. The volume of the particles is insignificant and their collisions are perfectly elastic. In a liquid, the particles are attracted to each other, which is why liquids have a definite volume. Because the particles are closer together, liquids are denser than gases. In solids, the particles are closely packed together, usually in an organized array. The particles in a solid vibrate around fixed points. Solids are dense and difficult to compress.

40. a. As more energy is added to a boiling liquid, more particles of the liquid acquire enough kinetic energy to escape. As a result, all the liquid boils away at a constant temperature.

    b. If the mixture is heated, more ice melts but the temperature of the mixture remains the same as long as ice is present. If the mixture is cooled, more liquid freezes, but the temperature of the mixture remains the same as long as liquid water is present.

Chapter 13 Small-Scale Lab

Section 13.3 The Behavior of Liquids and Solids, page 400

Analyze and Conclude

1. Water in the dish evaporates and condenses into a cloud when it contacts the cold surface under the ice.

2. The drop of water on top of the dish provides enough cooling to cause cloud formation.

3. Water beads up and alcohol spreads out due to stronger intermolecular attractions in water.

4. Calcium chloride absorbs water from the environment in the dish.

5. The calcium chloride removes water vapor from the atmosphere.

You're the Chemist

1. The water drop increases in diameter over time as the alcohol evaporates and is captured by the water drop. The attractions in the resulting mixture are weaker overall.

2. The BTB turns from green to yellow in the presence of vinegar.

3. Place a drop of vinegar and a drop of BTB about 3 cm apart in a Petri dish. Cover and observe. The BTB slowly changes from green to yellow even though there is no mixing of the drops. Ethanoic acid that evaporates is "captured" by the BTB.

4. Place a drop of ammonia and a drop of BTB about 3 cm apart in a Petri dish. Cover and observe. The BTB slowly changes from green to blue even though there is no mixing of the drops. Ammonia thatt evaporates is captured by the BTB.

Section 14.1

Part A Completion

1. compressed	6. kinetic
2. spare	7. doubles
3. volume	8. reducing
4. temperature	9. pressure
5. moles	

Part B True-False

10. AT	12. NT	14. AT
11. ST	13. ST	

Part C Matching

15. c	17. e	19. b
16. d	18. a	

Part D Questions and Problems

20. The motion of particles in a gas is constant and random. The particles travel in straight paths until they collide with other particles or the walls of their container. There are no significant attractive or repulsive forces between particles in a gas, which is why a gas can expand to take the shape and volume of its container. The volume of the particles in a gas is small compared the overall volume of a gas, which is why a gas can be compressed.

Section 14.2

Part A Completion

1. inversely
2. increases
3. Boyle's
4. mass
5. Kelvin
6. Charles's
7. Gay-Lussac's
8. directly
9. combined
10. amount

Part B True-False

11. NT
12. AT
13. ST
14. NT
15. NT
16. AT

Part C Matching

17. c
18. b
19. e
20. a
21. d

Part D Questions and Problems

22. $P_2 = \dfrac{P_1 \times T_2}{T_1} = \dfrac{55 \text{ kPa} \times 473 \text{ K}}{173 \text{ K}}$

$= 1.5 \times 10^2 \text{ kPa}$

23. $V_2 = \dfrac{P_1 \times V_1 \times T_2}{T_1 \times P_2}$

$= \dfrac{91 \text{ kPa} \times 0.075 \text{ L} \times 273 \text{ K}}{303 \text{ K} \times 101.3 \text{ kPa}}$

$= 0.061 \text{ L} = 61 \text{ mL}$

Section 14.3

Part A Completion

1. number of moles
2. $PV = nRT$
3. n
4. ideal gas constant
5. $8.31 \times \dfrac{(\text{L} \cdot \text{kPa})}{(\text{K} \cdot \text{mol})}$
6. ideal
7. real
8. attractions
9. volume

Part B True-False

10. AT
11. ST
12. NT
13. NT
14. AT

Part C Matching

15. d
16. c
17. b
18. a

Part D Questions and Problems

19. $n = \dfrac{P \times V}{R \times T} = \dfrac{25{,}325 \text{ kPa} \times 12.5 \text{ L}}{8.31 \frac{\text{L} \times \text{kPa}}{\text{K} \times \text{mol}} \times 295 \text{ K}}$

$= 1.29 \times 10^2 \text{ mol O}_2(g)$

20. $n = \dfrac{P \times V}{R \times T} = \dfrac{240.0 \text{ kPa} \times 0.275 \text{ L}}{8.31 \frac{\text{L} \times \text{kPa}}{\text{K} \times \text{mol}} \times 301 \text{ K}}$

$= 2.64 \times 10^{-2} \text{ mol NO}_2$

mass of NO_2

$= 2.64 \times 10^{-2} \text{ mol NO}_2 \times \dfrac{46.0 \text{ g NO}_2}{1 \text{ mol NO}_2}$

$= 1.21 \text{ g NO}_2$

Section 14.4

Part A Completion

1. total
2. sum
3. lower
4. uniform
5. diffusion
6. effusion
7. hole
8. inversely
9. molar mass
10. Graham's law

Part B True-False

11. AT
12. NT
13. ST
14. AT

Part C Matching

15. a
16. b
17. c

Part D Questions and Problems

18. The kinetic energy of a molecule is equal to $\dfrac{\frac{1}{2}}{\text{mv}^2}$ where m is the mass and v is the velocity of the molecule. At a given temperature, molecules all have the same average kinetic energy. If two molecules with different masses have the same kinetic energy, the less massive molecule must have a higher velocity.

Practice Problems

Section 14.1

1. On average, temperatures are higher in the summer than in the winter. The motion of the tires causes the air in the tires to heat up. At higher temperatures, the particles inside the tire have a greater average kinetic energy. So, the frequency and force of the collisions between the particles and the walls of the tire are greater, resulting in a greater pressure inside the tire.

2. Overnight the air in the mattress cools down; the average kinetic energy of the particles in the air decreases. Thus, they collide less frequently and less forcefully with the walls of the mattress. Consequently, the pressure inside the mattress decreases, as does the volume.

Section 14.2

1. $P_2 = \dfrac{P_1 \times V_1}{V_2} = \dfrac{155.0 \text{ kPa} \times 22.0 \text{ L}}{10.0 \text{ L}}$
   $= 341 \text{ kPa}$

2. No, the balloon will only expand until internal pressure is equal to the external pressure, which in this case is about half the initial pressure.

3. $V_2 = \dfrac{V_1 \times T_2}{T_1} = \dfrac{10.0 \text{ L} \times 373 \text{ K}}{248 \text{ K}} = 15.0 \text{ L}$

4. $P_2 = \dfrac{P_1 \times V_1 \times T_2}{T_1 \times V_2}$
   $= \dfrac{501 \text{ kPa} \times 5.2 \text{ L} \times 373 \text{ K}}{298 \text{ K} \times 7.00 \text{ L}} = 466 \text{ kPa}$

5. $P_1 = \dfrac{P_2 \times V_2 \times T_1}{T_2 \times V_1}$
   $= \dfrac{105.4 \text{ kPa} \times 55.0 \text{ L} \times 323 \text{ K}}{248 \text{ K} \times 105 \text{ L}} = 71.9 \text{ kPa}$

Section 14.3

1. $n = \dfrac{P \times V}{R \times T} = \dfrac{1.24 \times 10^4 \text{ kPa} \times 25 \text{ L}}{8.31 \frac{L \times kPa}{K \times mol} \times 297 \text{ K}}$
   $= 1.3 \times 10^2 \text{ mol argon}$

2. $T = \dfrac{P \times V}{n \times R} = \dfrac{500.0 \text{ kPa} \times 35.0 \text{ L}}{7.00 \text{ mol} \times 8.31 \frac{L \times kPa}{K \times mol}}$
   $= 3.01 \times 10^2 \text{ K}$

3. $n = \dfrac{P \times V}{R \times T} = \dfrac{102.0 \text{ kPa} \times 25.0 \text{ L}}{8.31 \frac{L \times kPa}{K \times mol} \times 297 \text{ K}}$
   $= 1.03 \text{ mol He}$
   mass of He $= 1.03 \text{ mol He} \times \dfrac{4.00 \text{ g He}}{1 \text{ mol He}}$
   $= 4.12 \text{ g He}$

4. $V = \dfrac{n \times R \times T}{P}$
   $= \dfrac{2.25 \text{ mol} \times 8.31 \frac{L \times kPa}{K \times mol} \times 273 \text{ K}}{101.3 \text{ kPa}}$
   $=$
   50.4 L

5. $V_2 = \dfrac{V_1 \times T_2}{T_1} = \dfrac{10.5 \text{ L} \times 300 \text{ K}}{473 \text{ K}} = 6.66 \text{ L}$

6. $V = \dfrac{n \times R \times T}{P}$
   $= \dfrac{0.355 \text{ mol} \times 8.31 \frac{L \times kPa}{K \times mol} \times 273 \text{ K}}{101.3 \text{ kPa}}$
   $= 7.95 \text{ L}$

7. $n = 25.0 \text{ g} \times 1 \text{ mol} \backslash 44.0 \text{ g} = 0.568 \text{ mol}$
   $V = \dfrac{n \times R \times T}{P}$
   $= \dfrac{0.568 \text{ mol} \times 8.31 \frac{L \times kPa}{K \times mol} \times 273 \text{ K}}{101.3 \text{ kPa}}$
   $= 12.7 \text{ L}$

Section 14.4

1. $P_{O_2} = P_{total} - (P_{N_2} + P_{Ar})$
   $= 98.5 \text{ kPa} - (22.0 \text{ kPa} + 50.0 \text{ kPa})$
   $= 26.5 \text{ kPa}$
   $n = \dfrac{P \times V}{R \times T} = \dfrac{26.5 \text{ kPa} \times 3.5 \text{ L}}{8.31 \frac{L \times kPa}{K \times mol} \times 298 \text{ K}}$
   $= 3.75 \times 10^{-2} \text{ mol } O_2(g)$

2. $\dfrac{Rate_{O_2}}{Rate_{N_2}} = \sqrt{\dfrac{molar\ mass_{O_2}}{molar\ mass_{N_2}}} = \sqrt{\dfrac{28.0 \text{ g}}{32.0 \text{ g}}}$
   $= \sqrt{0.875} = 0.935$

   Oxygen effuses slightly slower than nitrogen.

Interpreting Graphics 14

1. **a.** 0.41 g   **b.** 0.43 g
2. 0.267 L
3. **a.** 372 K   **b.** 372 K
4. **a.** 103 kPa   **b.** 108 kPa

5. a. $n = \dfrac{103 \text{ kPa} \times 0.267 \text{ L}}{8.31 \frac{\text{L} \times \text{kPa}}{\text{K} \times \text{mol}} \times 372 \text{ K}}$

$= 8.90 \times 10^{-3} \text{ mol}$

b. $n = \dfrac{108 \text{ kPa} \times 0.267 \text{ L}}{8.31 \frac{\text{L} \times \text{kPa}}{\text{K} \times \text{mol}} \times 372 \text{ K}}$

$= 9.33 \times 10^{-3} \text{ mol}$

6. a. molar mass $= \dfrac{0.41 \text{ g}}{8.90 \times 10^{-3} \text{ mol}}$

$= 46 \text{ g/mol}$

b. molar mass $= \dfrac{0.43 \text{ g}}{9.33 \times 10^{-3} \text{ mol}}$

$= 46 \text{ g/mol}$

7. 46 g/mol

8. C_2H_6O (ethanol)

Vocabulary Review 14

1. g   5. d   8. a
2. i   6. e   9. h
3. j   7. c   10. b
4. f

Quiz for Chapter 14

1. collisions
2. doubles
3. small
4. real
5. diffusion

6. $P_2 = P_1 \times \dfrac{T_1}{T_2} = 388 \text{ kPa} \times \dfrac{273 \text{ K}}{713 \text{ K}} = 149 \text{ kPa}$

7. $T_1 = 27°C + 273 = 300 \text{ K}$ $P_1 = 115 \text{ kPa}$
$T_2 = -10°C + 273 = 263 \text{ K}$ $P_2 = 99 \text{ kPa}$

$V_2 = V_1 \times \dfrac{P_1}{P_2} \times \dfrac{T_2}{T_1}$

$= 3.5 \times 10^5 \text{ m}^3 \times \dfrac{115 \text{ kPa}}{99 \text{ kPa}} \times \dfrac{263 \text{ K}}{300 \text{ K}}$

$= 3.6 \times 10^5 \text{ m}^3$

8. $P_{O_2} = P_{\text{total}} - (P_{N_2} + 2P_{CO_2})$

$= 145.0 \text{ kPa} - (28.5 \text{ kPa} + 76.0 \text{ kPa})$

$= 40.5 \text{ kPa}$

Chapter 14 Test A

A. Matching

1. c   4. g   7. e
2. h   5. f   8. d
3. b   6. a

B. Multiple Choice

9. d   14. b   19. d
10. b   15. c   20. b
11. a   16. b
12. c   17. c
13. d   18. c

C. Problems

21. $\dfrac{P_1}{T_1} = \dfrac{P_2}{T_2}$

$P_2 = \dfrac{T_2 \times P_1}{T_1}$

$T_1 = 227°C + 273 = 500 \text{ K}$
$T_2 = 27°C + 273 = 300 \text{ K}$

$P_2 = \dfrac{300 \text{ K} \times 655 \text{ kPa}}{500 \text{ K}}$

$= 393 \text{ kPa}$

22. $P_1 \times V_1 = P_2 \times V_2$

$P_2 = \dfrac{P_1 \times V_1}{V_2}$

$V_2 = \dfrac{156 \text{ kPa} \times 15.0 \text{ L}}{215 \text{ kPa}}$

$= 10.9 \text{ L}$

23. $T_1 = 35.0°C + 273 = 308 \text{ K}$
$T_2 = 0.0°C + 273 = 273 \text{ K}$

$V_2 = \dfrac{P_1 \times V_1 \times T_2}{T_1 \times P_2}$

$= \dfrac{95.9 \text{ kPa} \times 180 \text{ mL} \times 273 \text{ K}}{308 \text{ K} \times 101.3 \text{ kPa}} = 151 \text{ mL}$

24. $V_2 = V_1 \times \dfrac{T_2}{T_1}$

$T_1 = -55.0°C + 273 = 218 \text{ K}$
$T_2 = 30.0°C + 273 = 303 \text{ K}$

$V_2 = 550 \text{ mL} \times \dfrac{303 \text{ K}}{218 \text{ K}} = 764 \text{ mL}$

D. Essay

25. An ideal gas is one that follows the gas laws at all conditions of pressure and temperature. The behavior of a real gas deviates from the behavior of an ideal gas, especially at low temperatures and high pressures. Also, kinetic theory assumes that the particles of an ideal gas have no volume and are not attracted to each other. This is not true for real gases, which can be liquefied and sometimes solidified by cooling and applying pressure.

E. True-False
26. NT   **28.** ST
27. AT   **29.** AT

F. Additional Problems
30. $n = \dfrac{P \times V}{R \times T} = \dfrac{216 \text{ kPa} \times 25.0 \text{ L}}{8.31 \frac{\text{L} \times \text{kPa}}{\text{K} \times \text{mol}} \times 300 \text{ K}}$

$= 2.17 \text{ mol}$

$\dfrac{96.0 \text{ g}}{2.17 \text{ mol}} = 44.2 \text{ g/mol formula mass}$

31. $\sqrt{\dfrac{\text{Rate}_{235}}{\text{Rate}_{238}}} = \sqrt{\dfrac{352.0}{349.0}} = \sqrt{1.009} = 1.004$

UF_6 containing U-235 diffuses 1.004 times faster.

Chapter 14 Test B

A. Matching
1. g   **5.** d   **8.** a
2. i   **6.** e   **9.** h
3. j   **7.** c   **10.** b
4. f

B. Multiple Choice
11. d   **17.** a   **23.** c
12. c   **18.** c   **24.** b
13. b   **19.** a   **25.** a
14. d   **20.** b   **26.** b
15. d   **21.** b
16. b   **22.** d

C. Problems
27. $P_1 V_1 = P_2 V_2$

$V_2 = \dfrac{P_1 \times V_1}{P_2}$

$V_2 = \dfrac{(425 \text{ kPa})(1.20 \text{ L})}{615 \text{ kPa}}$

$V_2 = 0.829 \text{ L}$

28. $\dfrac{V_1}{T_1} = \dfrac{V_2}{T_2}$

$V_2 = \dfrac{V_1 \times T_2}{T_1}$

$V_2 = \dfrac{(0.650 \text{ L})(313 \text{ K})}{(293 \text{ K})}$

$V_2 = 0.694 \text{ L}$

29. $\dfrac{P_1}{T_1} = \dfrac{P_2}{T_2}$

$T_2 = \dfrac{P_2 \times T_1}{P_1}$

$T_2 = \dfrac{(98.0 \text{ kPa})(310 \text{ K})}{(85.0 \text{ kPa})}$

$T_2 = 357 \text{ K or } 84.4°\text{C}$

31. $\dfrac{P_1 V_1}{T_1} = \dfrac{P_2 V_2}{T_2}$

$V_2 = \dfrac{P_1 \times V_1 \times T_2}{T_1 \times V_2}$

$V_2 = \dfrac{(80.0 \text{ kPa})(3.50 \text{ L})(273 \text{ K})}{(330 \text{ K})(101.3 \text{ kPa})}$

$V_2 = 2.29 \text{ L}$

31. $PV = nRT$

$n = \dfrac{P \times V}{R \times T} = \dfrac{152 \text{ kPa} \times 8.0 \text{ L}}{8.31 \frac{\text{L} \times \text{kPa}}{\text{K} \times \text{mol}} \times 300 \text{ K}}$

$n = 0.49 \text{ mol}$

$0.49 \text{ mol CO}_2 \times \dfrac{44.0 \text{ g CO}_2}{1 \text{ mol CO}_2} = 22 \text{ g CO}_2$

D. Essay
32. If all gases behaved ideally, the individual particles that make up each gas could never exert the attractive forces on each other that are necessary for them to condense to liquids and solids.

E. True-False
33. ST   **35.** AT
34. AT   **36.** NT

F. Additional Problems
37. $\dfrac{V_1}{T_1} = \dfrac{V_2}{T_2}$

$T_2 = \dfrac{V_2 \times T_1}{V_1}$

$T_2 = \dfrac{(0.925 \text{ L})(250 \text{ K})}{(1.25 \text{ L})}$

$T_2 = 185 \text{ K or } -88°\text{C}$

38. $PV = nRT$

$$n = \frac{P \times V}{R \times T} = \frac{50.6 \text{ kPa} \times 10.0 \text{ L}}{8.31 \frac{L \times kPa}{K \times mol} \times 200 \text{ K}}$$

$n = 0.304$ mol

Chapter 14 Small-Scale Lab

Section 14.4 Diffusion, page 437

Analyze and Conclude

1. The drops near the center change immediately. As the gas diffuses, all the drops change color. The color change begins at the outer edge of each drop.

2. The first picture should show one edge turning yellow. Succeeding pictures should show the yellow area gradually increasing until the entire dot is yellow.

3. The particles of gas produced are in motion. As the particles diffuse from the center, they collide and react with molecules of BTB.

4. $NaHSO_3 + HCl \rightarrow SO_2 + H_2O + NaCl$

You're the Chemist

1. As ammonia diffuses, BTB changes from yellow to blue.

   $NH_4Cl + NaOH \rightarrow NH_3 + H_2O + NaCl$

2. Vary the size of the BTB drops from "pin-heads" to "puddles." Tiny drops are better able to detect small quantities of gas.

3. The KI turned orange in the same manner as the BTB turned yellow. $3NaNO_2 + 2HCl \rightarrow 2NO + H_2O + NaNO_3 + 2NaCl$

Section Review 15.1

Part A Completion

1. polar
2. negative
3. positive
4. polar
5. hydrogen
6. low
7. high
8. surface
9. spherical
10. surfactant
11. Ice
12. dense
13. hydrogen bonding

Part B True-False

14. NT
15. NT
16. AT
17. AT
18. ST

Part C Matching

19. a
20. c
21. b

Part D Question

22. **a.** lower
    b. higher

Section Review 15.2

Part A Completion

1. solvent
2. homogeneous
3. "like dissolves like"
4. electrolytes
5. strong
6. partially
7. conduct
8. nonelectrolyte
9. hydrates
10. efflorescence

Part B True-False

11. AT
12. AT
13. ST
14. AT

Part C Matching

15. d
16. a
17. h
18. b
19. f
20. g
21. c
22. e

Part D Questions and Problems

23. molar mass $Na_2SO_4 \cdot 10H_2O = 322$ g
    Mass of $10H_2O = 180.0$ g
    $$\frac{180.0 \text{ g}}{322 \text{ g}} \times 100\% = 55.9\%$$

24. b and c

Section Review 15.3

Part A Completion

1. larger
2. filtration
3. Colloids
4. Tyndall effect
5. Brownian
6. molecules/ions
7. ions/molecules
8. Emulsions
9. stability
10. emulsions

Part B True-False

11. NT   **13.** AT   **15.** NT

12. ST   **14.** ST

Part C Matching

16. e   **18.** d   **20.** f

17. b   **19.** a   **21.** c

Part D Questions and Problems

22. b   **23.** a

Practice Problems 15

Section 15.1

1. Hydrogen bonds are attractive forces in which a hydrogen atom that is covalently bonded to a very electronegative atom is also weakly bonded to an unshared electron pair of an electronegative atom in the same molecule or in a nearby molecule.

2.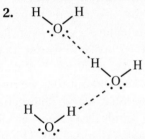

3. Hydrogen bonds hold the water molecules in place in the solid phase. The structure of ice is a regular, open, framework like a honeycomb.

Section 15.2

1. The solute is potassium chloride (KCl). The solvent is water.

2. $NH_3(g) + H_2O(l) \rightleftharpoons NH_4^+(aq) + OH^-(aq)$

3. Possible answers include glucose ($C_6H_{12}O_6$) and ethyl alcohol (C_2H_6O).

4. Hygroscopic compounds are those compounds that remove moisture from air.

5. a. soluble   **c.** soluble

b. insoluble   **d.** soluble

6. a. $NH_4NO_3(s) \rightarrow NH_4^+(aq) + NO_3^-(aq)$

b. $KOH(s) \rightarrow K^+(aq) + OH^-(aq)$

7. a. $CaSO_4 \cdot 2H_2O$

b. $CoCl_2 \cdot 6H_2O$

8. Molar mass of $NiCl_2 \cdot 6H_2O = 237.7$ g/mol
Mass of $6H_2O = 108.0$ g

$$\text{Percent } H_2O = \frac{\text{mass of water}}{\text{mass of hydrate}} \times 100\%$$

$$= \frac{108.0 \text{ g}}{237.7 \text{ g/mol}} \times 100\% = 45.44\%$$

Section 15.3

1. Colloids and suspensions exhibit the Tyndall effect and have larger particles than solutions. The particles in a suspension are retained on a filter and will settle out slowly upon standing.

2. Brownian motion refers to the chaotic movement of colloidal particles caused by the collisions of water molecules with the small, dispersed colloidal particles.

3. a. colloid   **e.** suspension

b. colloid   **f.** colloid

c. solution   **g.** solution

d. colloid

Vocabulary Review 15

1. desiccants

2. hydrogen bonding

3. suspension

4. aqueous solution

5. solvent

6. surfactant

7. strong electrolyte

8. water of hydration

9. Brownian motion

SOLUTION: **1.** WATER VAPOR

2. ICE

3. LIQUID WATER

Quiz for Chapter 15

1. a   **3.** c

2. a   **4.** b

5. solute

6. solvent

7. aqueous solutions

8. like dissolves like

Chapter 15 Test A

A. Completion

1. nonelectrolyte
2. deliquescent
3. suspension
4. solvent
5. effloresce
6. Brownian motion
7. Emulsions
8. hydrate
9. Tyndall effect
10. Surface tension

B. Multiple Choice

11. c
12. d
13. a
14. d
15. a
16. a
17. a
18. c
19. c
20. a
21. b
22. c

C. True-False

23. ST
24. ST
25. ST
26. NT

D. Problems

27. Molar Mass of hydrate = 238 g
    1 mol H_2O = 18.0 g
    6 mol H_2O = 108 g

$$\frac{108 \text{ g}}{238 \text{ g}} \times 100\% = 45.4\% \text{ } H_2O$$

E. Essay

28. Because polar water molecules can attract charged particles, they cause solute ions to break away from the surface of the solid. As the solute dissolves, the ions are surrounded by molecules of solvent

Chapter 15 Test B

A. Completion

1. hygroscopic
2. solvation
3. solute
4. surfactants
5. dessicants
6. colloids
7. aqueous
8. hydrogen
9. nonelectrolytes
10. effloresce

B. Multiple Choice

11. a
12. a
13. b
14. c
15. c
16. d
17. c
18. c
19. c
20. d
21. a

C. True-False

22. AT
23. ST
24. AT
25. AT
26. AT
27. NT
28. AT
29. AT

D. Problem

30. $\%H_2O = \dfrac{\text{mass of } H_2O}{\text{mass of hydrate}} \times 100\%$

$= \dfrac{180.0 \text{ g}}{322.1 \text{ g}} \times 100\% = 55.9\% \text{ } H_2O$

E. Essay

31. Soaps and detergents are surfactants that reduce the surface tension of water by interfering with the hydrogen bonding between water molecules. With surface tension reduced, the beads of water that would normally have formed collapse, allowing the water to spread out to cover and penetrate the fabric. Soaps and detergents also are emulsifying agents that allow oils and greases to form colloidal dispersions. The oil and grease particles, which are normally insoluble in water, are removed from the surface of the fabric.

Chapter 15 Small-Scale Lab

Section 15.2 Electrolytes, page 458

Analysis

NaCl(s) Aqueous conducts	MgSO$_4$(s) Aqueous conducts
Na$_2$CO$_3$(s) Aqueous conducts	Sugar Aqueous does not conduct
NaHCO$_3$(s) Aqueous conducts	Corn Starch Aqueous does not conduct
KCl(s) Aqueous conducts	KI(s) Aqueous conducts

1. These are electrolytes: NaCl, MgSO$_4$, Na$_2$CO$_3$, NaHCO$_3$, KCl, KI.

   These are nonelectrolytes: sugar, corn starch.

2. None of the electrolytes conduct electricity in the solid form because the ions are locked in a crystal lattice and cannot move.

3. Table sugar and cornstarch are covalent compounds. NaCl, MgSO$_4$, Na$_2$CO$_3$, NaHCO$_3$, KCl, KI are ionic compounds. In general, to be an electrolyte a compound must dissociate into ions in solution.

You're the Chemist

1. $MgSO_4(s) \rightarrow Mg^{2+}(aq) + SO_4^{2-}(aq)$

   $NaHCO_3(s) \rightarrow Na^+(aq) + HCO_3^-(aq)$

   $KCl(s) \rightarrow K^+(aq) + Cl^-(aq)$

   $KI(s) \rightarrow K^+(aq) + I^-(aq)$

2. Test a drop of each solution with a conductivity device.

   Strong electrolytes (bright light): HCl, H$_2$SO$_4$, HNO$_3$, NaOH

   Weak electrolytes (dim light) CH$_3$COOH, NH$_3$

   Nonelectrolytes (no light): rubbing alcohol, distilled water

3. Strong electrolytes: soft drinks, pickle juice
   Weak electrolytes: orange juice, coffee

Section Review 16.1

Part A Completion

1. particle size
2. rate
3. pressure
4. Henry's
5. temperature
6. saturated
7. miscible
8. solubility
9. increases
10. supersaturated

Part B True-False

11. AT
12. ST
13. AT
14. NT
15. AT

Part C Matching

16. c
17. a
18. f
19. e
20. g
21. d
22. b

Part D Problem

23. $\dfrac{1.6 \text{ g/L}}{1.0 \text{ atm}} = \dfrac{S_2}{2.5 \text{ atm}}$

   $S_2 = \dfrac{1.6 \text{ g/L} \times 2.5 \text{ atm}}{1.0 \text{ atm}} = 4.0 \text{ g/L}$

Section Review 16.2

Part A Completion

1. solvent
2. solution
3. dilute
4. moles
5. liter
6. diluting
7. solute
8. solvent

Part B True-False

9. NT
10. AT
11. NT
12. NT

Part C Matching

13. b
14. c
15. e
16. a
17. d

Part D Problem

18. molar mass C$_{12}$H$_{22}$O$_{11}$ = 342.3
    $M \times V$ = mol solute needed

    $\dfrac{0.50 \text{ mol}}{1 \text{ L}} \times 0.3000 \text{ L} = 0.15 \text{ mol}$

    $\dfrac{342.3 \text{ g}}{1 \text{ mol}} \times 0.15 \text{ mol} = 51 \text{ g}$

Section Review 16.3

Part A Completion

1. solute
2. colligative properties
3. freezing
4. lowering/depression
5. elevation
6. directly
7. solution
8. particles
9. twice
10. twice

Part B True/False

11. NT
12. ST
13. NT
14. AT

Part C Matching

15. d **17.** c
16. a **18.** b

Part D Questions and Problems

19. a. two **c.** four
  b. one **d.** two
20. a. K_2CO_3 **c.** NaCl
  b. NaCl

Section Review 16.4

Part A Completion

1. solute
2. solvent
3. kilogram
4. mole fraction
5. molal boiling point
6. depression
7. molal
8. elevation

Part B True-False

9. ST **11.** AT
10. NT **12.** AT

Part C Matching

13. b **15.** d **17.** c
14. e **16.** a

Part D Problem

18. molality $= \dfrac{2.0 \text{ mol CaCl}_2}{800.0 \text{ g H}_2\text{O}} \times \dfrac{1000 \text{ g}}{1 \text{ kg}}$

  $= 2.5m$

  molality of total particles $= 3 \times 2.5m = 7.5m$

  $\Delta T_f = K_f \times m = \dfrac{1.86°C}{m} \times 7.5m = 14°C$

  freezing point of solution $= 0°C - 14°C$
    $= -14°C$

Practice Problems 16

Section 16.1

1. $S_2 = \dfrac{S_1 \times P_2}{P_1} = \dfrac{0.54 \text{ g/L} \times 1.86 \text{ atm}}{1.22 \text{ atm}}$

  $= 0.82 \text{ g/L}$

2. $\dfrac{34.0 \text{ g KCl}}{100 \text{ g H}_2\text{O}} \times 500.0 \text{ g H}_2\text{O} = 1.7 \times 10^2 \text{ g KCl}$

3. Solubility of $AgNO_3$ at 20°C
   $= 222.0 \text{ g}/100 \text{ g H}_2\text{O}$
  Solubility of $AgNO_3$ at 50°C
   $= 455.0 \text{ g}/100 \text{ g H}_2\text{O}$
  $455.0 \text{ g} - 222.0 \text{ g} = 233.0 \text{ g}$
  Add 233.0 g to maintain saturation at 50°C.

Section 16.2

1. a. $\dfrac{0.40 \text{ mol NaCl}}{1.6 \text{ L}} = 0.25M$

  b. $\dfrac{20.2 \text{ g KNO}_3}{250.0 \text{ mL}} \times \dfrac{1 \text{ mol KNO}_3}{101.1 \text{ g KNO}_3} \times \dfrac{1000 \text{ mL}}{1 \text{ L}}$
   $= 0.799M$

2. a. moles KOH $= 2500.0 \text{ mL} \times \dfrac{1 \text{ L}}{1000 \text{ mL}}$

   $\times \dfrac{3.0 \text{ mol KOH}}{1 \text{ L}} = 7.5 \text{ mol KOH}$

  mass of KOH $= 7.5 \text{ mol KOH}$

   $\times \dfrac{56.1 \text{ g KOH}}{1 \text{ mol KOH}} = 4.2 \times 10^2 \text{ g KOH}$

  b. moles $HNO_3 = 2.0 \text{ L} \times \dfrac{2.0 \text{ mol HNO}_3}{L}$

   $= 4.0 \text{ mol HNO}_3$

  mass of $HNO_3 = 4.0 \text{ mol HNO}_3$

   $\times \dfrac{63 \text{ g HNO}_3}{1 \text{ mol HNO}_3}$

   $= 2.5 \times 10^2 \text{ g HNO}_3$

3. moles $NaNO_3 = 212.5 \text{ g} \times \dfrac{1 \text{ mol}}{85.0 \text{ g}} = 2.50 \text{ mol}$

  molarity $= \dfrac{2.50 \text{ mol}}{3.0 \text{ L}} = 0.83M$

4. $M_1V_1 = M_2V_2$
  $0.750M \times 300.0 \text{ mL} = 2.00M \times V_2$
  $V_2 = \dfrac{0.75M \times 300.0 \text{ mL}}{2.0M} = 113 \text{ mL}$

5. $V_2 = \dfrac{M_1 \times V_1}{M_2} = \dfrac{6.00M \times 1.0 \text{ L}}{0.500M} = 12 \text{ L}$
  The final volume should be 12 L. Therefore,
  add 11 L of H_2O.

6. a. $\%\text{ (v/v)} = \dfrac{60.0 \text{ mL methanol}}{500.0 \text{ mL solution}} \times 100\%$

   $= 12.0\% \text{ methanol (v/v)}$

  b. $\%\text{ (v/v)} = \dfrac{25.0 \text{ mL C}_3\text{H}_7\text{OH}}{200.0 \text{ mL solution}} \times 100\%$

   $= 12.5\% \text{ C}_3\text{H}_7\text{OH (v/v)}$

7. a. $1.00 \text{ L} \times \dfrac{10^3 \text{ mL}}{1 \text{ L}} \times \dfrac{3.00 \text{ g}}{100 \text{ mL}} = 30.0 \text{ g NaCl}$

b. $2.00 \text{ L} \times \dfrac{10^3 \text{ mL}}{1 \text{ L}} \times \dfrac{5.00 \text{ g}}{100 \text{ mL}} =$

$= 1.00 \times 10^2 \text{ g KNO}_3$

Section 16.3

1. Colligative properties of solutions are the physical properties of solutions that depend on the concentration of solute particles in solution but not on the chemical identity of the solute. Three important colligative properties are vapor-pressure lowering, boiling-point elevation, and freezing-point depression.

2. Each formula unit of K_2CO_3 produces three particles in solution.

3. Three moles of Na_2SO_4, when dissolved in water, produce 9 mol of particles because each formula unit of Na_2SO_4 dissociates into three ions.

4. The boiling point of water increases by 0.512 °C for every mole of particles that the solute forms when dissolved in 1000 g of water. When 2 mol of $MgCl_2$ dissolve in water, 6 mol of particles are produced because each formula unit of $MgCl_2$ dissociates into three ions. Thus, the boiling point of the solution increases by $6 \times 0.512°C = 3.07°C$. The boiling point of the solution is $100 °C + 3.07°C = 103.07°C$.

5. Vapor-pressure lowering is a colligative property.

6. a. The solution containing calcium chloride has a lower freezing point.

b. The solution containing calcium chloride has a lower vapor pressure.

c. The solution containing sodium chloride has a lower boiling point.

Section 16.4

1. a. $X_{\text{LiBr}} = \dfrac{n_{\text{LiBr}}}{n_{\text{LiBr}} + n_{\text{H}_2\text{O}}} = \dfrac{3.0 \text{ mol}}{3.0 \text{ mol} + 6.0 \text{ mol}}$

$= 0.33$

b. $X_{\text{KNO}_3} = \dfrac{n_{\text{KNO}_3}}{n_{\text{KNO}_3} + n_{\text{H}_2\text{O}}}$

$= \dfrac{\left(125 \text{ g} \times \frac{1 \text{ mol}}{101.1 \text{ g}}\right)}{\left(125 \text{ g} \times \frac{1 \text{ mol}}{101.1 \text{ g}}\right) + \left(800.0 \text{ g} \times \frac{1 \text{ mol}}{18.0 \text{ g}}\right)}$

$= 0.0271$

2. $750.0 \text{ g H}_2\text{O} \times \dfrac{0.50 \text{ mol NaCl}}{1000 \text{ g H}_2\text{O}}$

$\times \dfrac{58.4 \text{ g NaCl}}{1 \text{ mol NaCl}} = 22 \text{ g NaCl}$

3. $1600.0 \text{ g H}_2\text{O} \times \dfrac{2.0 \text{ mol Li}_2\text{S}}{1000 \text{ g H}_2\text{O}}$

$\times \dfrac{45.9 \text{ g Li}_2\text{S}}{1 \text{ mol Li}_2\text{S}} = 1.5 \times 10^2 \text{ g Li}_2\text{S}$

4. a. $\dfrac{2.3 \text{ mol glucose}}{500.0 \text{ g H}_2\text{O}} \times \dfrac{10^3 \text{ g}}{1 \text{ kg}} = 4.6m \text{ glucose}$

b. moles $Ba(NO_3)_2 = 131 \text{ g Ba(NO}_3)_2$

$\times \dfrac{1 \text{ mol Ba(NO}_3)_2}{261.3 \text{ g Ba(NO}_3)_2}$

$= 0.501 \text{ mol Ba(NO}_3)_2$

$\dfrac{0.501 \text{ mol Ba(NO}_3)_2}{750.0 \text{ g H}_2\text{O}} \times \dfrac{10^3 \text{ g}}{1 \text{ kg}}$

$= 0.668m \text{ Ba(NO}_3)_2$

5. a. $\Delta T_b = K_b \times m$

$= 0.512°C/m \times 2.00m \times 2$

$= 2.05°C$

The boiling point of this solution is $100 °C + 2.05°C = 102.05 °C$.

b. $\Delta T_b = K_b \times m$

$= 0.512°C/m \times 1.50m \times 3$

$= 2.30°C$

The boiling point of this solution is $100°C + 2.30°C = 102.30°C$.

6. a. molality of solute particles

$= 2 \times \dfrac{0.35 \text{ mol NaCl}}{900.0 \text{ g H}_2\text{O}} \times \dfrac{10^3 \text{ g}}{1 \text{ kg}}$

$= 0.78m \text{ NaCl}$

$\Delta T_f = K_f \times m$

$= 1.8°C/m \times 0.78m$

$= 1.45°C$

The freezing point of this solution is $0 °C - 1.45°C = -1.45°C$.

b. moles $C_{12}H_{22}O_{11} = 126.0 \text{ g } C_{12}H_{22}O_{11}$

$\times \dfrac{1 \text{ mol } C_{12}H_{22}O_{11}}{342.3 \text{ g } C_{12}H_{22}O_{11}}$

$= 0.3681 \text{ mol } C_{12}H_{22}O_{11}$

molality of solute particles

$= \dfrac{0.3861 \text{ mol } C_{12}H_{22}O_{11}}{2500.0 \text{ g H}_2\text{O}} \times \dfrac{10^3 \text{ g}}{1 \text{ kg}}$

$= 0.1472m \text{ } C_{12}H_{22}O_{11}$

$\Delta T_f = K_f \times m$

$= 1.86 °C/m \times 0.1472m$

$= 0.274 °C$

The freezing point of this solution is
$0°C - 0.274°C = -0.274°C$.

Interpreting Graphics 16

1. b, c

2. Solubility KCl at 20°C = 34.0 g/100 g H_2O
   Solubility KCl at 50°C = 42.6 g/100 g H_2O
   = 42.6 g - 34.0 g = 8.6 g

3. Solubility of sucrose at 100°C
   = 487 g/100 g H_2O
   Solubility of sucrose at 20°C
   = 230.9 g/100 g H_2O
   (487 g/100 g H_2O × 1000.0 g H_2O)
   − (230.9 g/100 g H_2O × 1000.0 g H_2O)
   = 4870 g − 2309 g = 2561 g

4.

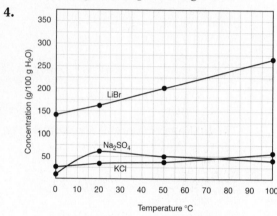

a. LiBr   b. Na_2SO_4

Vocabulary Review 16

1. Molarity. All others are qualitative terms used to describe solutions.

2. Concentration. The other terms are used to describe mixtures of liquids.

3. Henry's Law. All others are units of concentration.

4. Colligative properties. All others are associated with the solubility of gases.

5. Saturated solution. All others are associated with colligative properites of solutions.

6. Molarity. All others are related to freezing-point depression

7. Mole fraction. All others are factors affecting the rate at which a substance dissolves.

8. Boiling-point elevation. All others are associated with the preparation of solutions.

Quiz for Chapter 16

1. b	4. a	7. c
2. d	5. b	8. b
3. a	6. c	

Chapter 16 Test A

A. Matching

1. b	5. f	8. a
2. i	6. d	9. h
3. g	7. j	10. e
4. c		

B. Multiple Choice

11. c	15. c	19. a
12. d	16. b	20. b
13. a	17. a	21. d
14. c	18. b	

C. True-False

22. ST	26. NT	29. AT
23. AT	27. NT	30. ST
24. AT	28. NT	31. NT
25. AT		

D. Problems

32. $V_2 = 250$ mL, $M_2 = 0.60M$, $M_1 = 2.0M$
    $M_1V_1 = M_2V_2$

    $$V_1 = \frac{M_2 \times V_2}{M_1}$$

    $$V_1 = \frac{0.60M \times 250 \text{ mL}}{2.0M} = 75 \text{ mL}$$

    Add 75 mL of $2.0M$ $Al_2(SO_4)_3$ to enough distilled water to make 250 mL of solution.

33. Molar mass KNO_3:
    K: 1 × 39.1 = 39.1 g
    N: 1 × 14.0 = 14.0 g
    O: 3 × 16.0 = 48.0 g
    ───────
    101.1 g

    $$\text{mol } KNO_3 = \frac{95.5 \text{ g}}{101.1 \text{ g/mol}} = 0.945 \text{ mol}$$

    $$\text{molarity} = \frac{0.945 \text{ mol}}{0.750 \text{ L}} = 1.26M$$

34. $\dfrac{S_1}{P_1} = \dfrac{S_2}{P_2}$

    $$S_2 = \frac{S_1 \times P_2}{P_1} = \frac{16.9 \text{ g/L} \times 606 \text{ kPa}}{505 \text{ kPa}}$$

    $$= 20.3 \text{ g/L}$$

E. Essay

35. Boiling-point elevation, and freezing-point and vapor-pressure lowering are colligative properties. They depend solely on the number of particles in the solution.

Boiling-point elevation: Additional attractive forces exist between solute and solvent that must be overcome for the solution to boil.

Freezing-point depression: The solute particles interfere with the formation of the orderly pattern that the solvent particles assume as the solvent changes from liquid to solid.

Vapor-pressure lowering: The formation of solvent shells around the solute particles reduces the number of solvent particles that have sufficient kinetic energy to vaporize.

F. Additional Problems

36. $\dfrac{mol\ K_3PO_4}{1000\ g\ H_2O}$

$= \dfrac{0.900\ mol\ K_3PO_4}{2750\ g\ H_2O} \times \dfrac{1000\ g\ H_2O}{1\ kg\ H_2O}$

$= 0.327m$

$K_3PO_4 \rightarrow 3K^+ + PO_4^{3-} = 4$ particles

4 particles $\times\ 0.327m = 1.31m$

$\Delta T_b = K_b \times m$

$= 0.512\dfrac{°C}{m} \times 1.31m$

$= 0.671°C$

The boiling point of the solution is $100°C + 0.671°C = 100.671°C$.

37. Molar mass KNO_3:

K: $1 \times 39.1 = $ 39.1 g
N: $1 \times 14.0 = $ 14.0 g
O: $3 \times 16.0 = $ 48.0 g
                  101.1 g

$175\ g\ KNO_3 \times \dfrac{1\ mol}{101.1\ g\ KNO_3}$

$= 1.73\ mol\ KNO_3$

$molality = \dfrac{mol\ solute}{1000\ g\ solvent}$

$= \dfrac{1.73\ mol\ KNO_3}{1250\ g\ H_2O} \times \dfrac{10^3\ g\ H_2O}{1\ kg\ H_2O}$

$= 1.38m$

A. Matching

1. g	**5.** d	**8.** i
2. c	**6.** a	**9.** j
3. h	**7.** f	**10.** b
4. e		

B. Multiple Choice

11. d	**17.** a	**22.** a
12. a	**18.** b	**23.** c
13. b	**19.** d	**24.** a
14. b	**20.** b	**25.** b
15. c	**21.** d	**26.** a
16. a		

C. True-False

27. AT	**31.** ST	**34.** AT
28. NT	**32.** NT	**35.** NT
29. NT	**33.** NT	**36.** AT
30. NT		

D. Problems

37. $\dfrac{100.0\ g\ H_2O}{216\ g\ AgNO_3} \times (725\ g\ AgNO_3) = 336\ g\ H_2O$

38. $\dfrac{S_1}{P_1} = \dfrac{S_2}{P_2}$

$P_2 = \dfrac{S_2 \times P_1}{S_1}$

$P_2 = \dfrac{6.25\ g/L \times 0.750\ atm}{2.45\ g/L}$

$P_2 = 1.91\ atm$

39. $\dfrac{50.0\ g\ Mg(NO_3)_2}{225\ mL} \times 1000\ \dfrac{mL}{L}$

$\times \dfrac{1\ mol\ Mg(NO_3)_2}{148.3\ g\ Mg(NO_3)_2} = 1.50M$

40. $\dfrac{0.250\ mol\ AgNO_3}{1\ kg} \times \dfrac{1\ kg}{1000\ g} \times 125\ g$

$\times \dfrac{169.9\ g\ AgNO_3}{1\ mol\ AgNO_3} = 5.31\ g\ AgNO_3$

E. Essay

41. Salt is often used on bridges and sidewalks because it dissolves in an ice/ice water mixture to produce a solution with a lower freezing point than that of water alone. This causes any ice that was initially present to melt, and prevents additional ice from forming down to temperatures below 0 °C. The salt causes the freezing point of water to be depressed because it interferes with the crystallization process.

F. Additional Problems

42.
$$\frac{0.15 \text{ mol } H_2SO_4}{1 \text{ L}} \times \frac{1 \text{ L}}{1000 \text{ mL}} \times 750 \text{ mL}$$
$$\times \frac{98.1 \text{ g } H_2SO_4}{1 \text{ mol } H_2SO_4} = 11 \text{ g } H_2SO_4$$

43. $\Delta T_f = K_f \times m$
$$= 1.86 \,°C/m \times \frac{27.5 \text{ g } CH_3OH}{250.0 \text{ g}}$$
$$\times \frac{1 \text{ mol } CH_3OH}{32.0 \text{ g } CH_3OH} \times \frac{1000 \text{ g}}{1 \text{ kg}}$$
$$= 6.39 \,°C$$

freezing point $= 0°C - 6.39°C = -6.39°C$

44. molality of total particles
$$= \frac{62.5 \text{ g } Ba(NO_3)_2}{750.0 \text{ g}} \times \frac{1 \text{ mol } Ba(NO_3)_2}{261 \text{ g } Ba(NO_3)_2}$$
$$\times \frac{1000 \text{ g}}{1 \text{ kg}} \times \frac{3 \text{ moles particles}}{1 \text{ mol } Ba(NO_3)_2}$$
$$= 0.958m$$

$\Delta T_b = K_b \times m = 0.512 \,°C/m \times 0.958m$
$$= 0.490 \,°C$$

boiling point $= 100°C + 0.490°C$
$$= 100.490°C$$

Chapter 16 Small-Scale Lab

Section 16.4 Making a Solution, page 497

Analysis

Sample answers are given.

mass of dry flask $= 15.98$ g

mass of flask + NaCl $= 22.88$ g

mass of flask + NaCl + water $= 69.09$ g

1. a. mass of the solute (NaCl)
$$= 22.88 \text{ g} - 15.98 \text{ g} = 6.90 \text{ g}$$

b. mass of the solvent (water)
$$= 69.09 \text{ g} - 22.88 \text{ g} = 46.21 \text{ g}$$

c. % by mass of NaCl
$$= \frac{6.90 \text{ g}}{(6.90 + 46.21) \text{ g}} \times 100 = 13.0\% \text{ NaCl}$$

2. a. moles of NaCl solute $= \dfrac{6.90 \text{ g}}{58.5 \text{ g/mol}}$
$$= 0.118 \text{ mol}$$

b. moles of water $= \dfrac{46.21 \text{ g}}{18.0 \text{ g/mol}} = 2.57 \text{ mol}$

c. mole fraction $= \dfrac{0.118 \text{ mol}}{(0.118 + 2.57) \text{ mol}}$
$$= 0.0439.$$

3. Molality $= \dfrac{0.118 \text{ mol NaCl}}{0.04621 \text{ kg } H_2O} = 2.55m$

4. a. liters of solution $= 50 \text{ mL} \times \dfrac{1 \text{ L}}{1000 \text{ mL}}$
$$= 0.050 \text{ L}$$

b. Molarity $= \dfrac{0.118 \text{ mol NaCl}}{0.050 \text{ L}} = 2.4M$

5. Density $= \dfrac{6.90 \text{ g} + 46.21 \text{ g}}{50 \text{ mL}} = 1.1 \text{ g/mL}$

Notice that because the flask measures less accurately than the balance, molarity and density have fewer significant figures than molality, mass percent and mole fraction.

You're the Chemist

Sample answers are given.

1. Sample data:

dry flask $= 15.98$ g

flask + NaCl solution $= 22.88$ g

flask + NaCl solution + water $= 69.09$ g

mass of NaCl solution $= 6.90$ g

mass of water $= 46.21$ g

mass of NaCl $= 0.897$ g

percent mass of NaCl = 1.69%

moles NaCl = 1.54×10^{-2} mol

mass of water = 46.21 g

moles of water = 2.57 mol

mole fraction = 5.96×10^{-3}

molality = $0.333m$

density = 1.1 g/mL

2. mass of dry flask = 16.72 g

   mass of flask + sugar = 20.85 g

   mass of flask + sugar + water = 69.53 g

   mass of the sugar = 20.85 g − 16.72 g
   $$= 4.13 \text{ g}$$

   mass of the solvent (water)
   $$= 69.53 \text{ g} - 20.85 \text{ g} = 48.68 \text{ g}$$

   % by mass of sugar $= \dfrac{4.13 \text{ g}}{(4.13 + 48.68) \text{ g}} \times 100$
   $$= 7.82\%$$

   moles of sugar ($C_{12}H_{22}O_{11}$) =

   $48.68 \text{ g} \times \dfrac{1 \text{ mol}}{18.0 \text{ g}} = 0.0121$ mol

   moles of water $= 4.13 \text{ g} \times \dfrac{1 \text{ mol}}{342 \text{ g}}$

   $$= 2.70 \text{ mol}$$

   Mole fraction $= \dfrac{0.0121 \text{ mol}}{(0.0121+2.70) \text{ mol}}$
   $$= 0.00446$$

   Molality $= \dfrac{0.0121 \text{ mol sugar}}{0.04868 \text{ kg H}_2\text{O}} = 0.249m$

   Molarity $= \dfrac{0.0121 \text{ mol NaCl}}{0.050 \text{ L}} = 0.242M$

   density $= \dfrac{4.13 \text{ g} + 48.68 \text{ g}}{50 \text{ mL}} = 1.1$ g/mL

Section Review 17.1

Part A Completion

1. heat
2. potential energy
3. thermochemistry
4. calorie
5. joule
6. specific heat or specific heat capacity
7. metals
8. water

Part B True-False

9. NT
10. AT
11. NT
12. AT
13. AT

Part C Matching

14. c
15. e
16. b
17. d
18. a

Part D Questions and Problems

19. Chemical potential energy is energy *stored* within the structural units of chemical substances. Work is done when a force moves an object. Heat is energy that is *transfered* because of a temperature difference.

20. $C = \dfrac{124.2 \text{ J}}{18.0 \text{ g} \times 15.0\,°\text{C}} = 0.460 \text{ J/(g} \cdot °\text{C})$

    The unknown metal is iron.

Section 17.2

Part A Completion

1. calorimeter
2. enthalpy
3. ΔH
4. initial or final
5. final or initial
6. mass

Part B True-False

7. ST
8. AT
9. AT
10. NT
11. AT
12. AT

Part C Matching

13. e
14. a
15. b
16. c
17. d

Part D Questions and Problems

18. $2NO + O_2 \rightarrow 2NO_2$ $\Delta H = -113.04$ kJ

19. $34.8 \text{ g CH}_4 \times \dfrac{1 \text{ mol CH}_4}{16.0 \text{ g CH}_4} \times \dfrac{890.2 \text{ kJ}}{1 \text{ mol CH}_4}$
    $$= 1.94 \times 10^3 \text{ kJ}$$

Section 17.3

Part A Completion

1. molar heat of fusion
2. molar heat of solidification
3. equal
4. 3.16 kJ/mol
5. molar heat of vaporization
6. Condensation

7. molar heat of condensation

Part B True-False

8. AT **10.** ST **12.** NT
9. NT **11.** NT

Part C Matching

13. a **15.** b **17.** d
14. e **16.** c

Part D Questions and Problems

18. a. endothermic **d.** endothermic
b. endothermic **e.** exothermic
c. exothermic **f.** exothermic

19. $\Delta H = 28.3 \text{ g H}_2\text{O}(s) \times \dfrac{1 \text{ mol H}_2\text{O}(s)}{18.0 \text{ g H}_2\text{O}(s)}$

$\times \dfrac{6.01 \text{ kJ}}{1 \text{ mol H}_2\text{O}(s)} = 9.45 \text{ kJ}$

20. $\Delta H = 5.53 \text{ mol NH}_4\text{NO}_3(s)$

$\times \dfrac{25.7 \text{ kJ}}{1 \text{ mol NH}_4\text{NO}_3(s)} = 142 \text{ kJ}$

Section 17.4

Part A Completion

1. sum
2. enthalpy
3. indirectly
4. changed (reversed)
5. standard heat of formation
6. change
7. one
8. ΔH_f^0
9. zero
10. subtracting

Part B True-False

11. NT **13.** AT **15.** NT
12. NT **14.** NT

Part C Matching

16. b **18.** a **20.** e
17. c **19.** d

Part D Questions and Problems

21.
$$\text{CuO}(s) \rightarrow \text{Cu}(s) + \tfrac{1}{2}\text{O}_2 \quad \Delta H = +155 \text{ kJ}$$
$$\underline{\text{H}_2(g) + \tfrac{1}{2}\text{O}_2(g) \rightarrow +\text{H}_2\text{O}(g) \quad \Delta H = -242 \text{ kJ}}$$
$$\text{CuO}(s) + \text{H}_2(g) \rightarrow \text{Cu}(s) + \text{H}_2\text{O}(g) \quad \Delta H_{\text{rxn}} = -87 \text{ kJ}$$

22. ΔH_f^0 (products)

$= 3 \text{ mol CO}_2(g) \times \dfrac{-393.5 \text{ kJ}}{1 \text{ mol CO}_2(g)}$

$= -1181 \text{ kJ}$

ΔH_f^0 (reactants)

$= 3 \text{ mol CO}(g) \times \dfrac{-110.5 \text{ kJ}}{1 \text{ mol CO}(g)} + (-822.1 \text{ kJ})$

$= -1154 \text{ kJ}$

$\Delta H^0 = \Delta H_f^0$ (products) $- \Delta H_f^0$ (reactants)

$= -1181 \text{ kJ} - (-1154 \text{ kJ})$

$= -27 \text{ kJ}$

Practice Problems

Section 17.1

1. $200.0 \text{ Cal} \times \dfrac{1000 \text{ cal}}{1 \text{ Cal}} \times \dfrac{4.184 \text{ J}}{1 \text{ cal}} \times \dfrac{1 \text{ kJ}}{10^3 \text{ J}}$

$= 836.8 \text{ kJ}$

2. $C = \dfrac{525.0 \text{ cal}}{25.0 \text{ g} \times 15.0°\text{C}} = 1.40 \text{ cal}/(\text{g} \times °\text{C})$

3. $\Delta T = \dfrac{1255.0 \text{ J}}{100.0 \text{ g} \times 2.1 \text{ J}/(\text{g} \times °\text{C})} = 6.0°\text{C}$

4. $q = 100.0 \text{ g} \times 120.0°\text{C} \times 0.90 \dfrac{\text{J}}{\text{g} \times °\text{C}}$

$= 1.1 \times 10^3 \text{ J}$

Section 17.2

1. $\Delta H = 150.0 \text{ g} \times 4.18 \dfrac{\text{J}}{\text{g} \times °\text{C}} \times 10°\text{C}$

$= 6.3 \times 10^3 \text{ J} = 6.3 \text{ kJ}$

2. $\Delta H = 15.0 \text{ g Ca(OH)}_2(s) \times \dfrac{1 \text{ mol Cu(OH)}_2(s)}{74.1 \text{ g Ca(OH)}_2(s)}$

$\times \dfrac{-65.2 \text{ kJ}}{1 \text{ mol Ca(OH)}_2(s)} = -13.2 \text{ kJ}$

3. $\Delta H = 52.4 \text{ g CH}_4(g) \times \dfrac{1 \text{ mol CH}_4(g)}{16.0 \text{ g CH}_4(g)}$

$\times \dfrac{-890.2 \text{ kJ}}{1 \text{ mol CH}_4(g)} = 2.93 \times 10^3 \text{ kJ}$

4. $4\text{NH}_3 + 5\text{O}_2(g) \rightarrow 4\text{NO}(g) + 6\text{H}_2\text{O}(g)$

$\Delta H = \dfrac{-226 \text{ kJ}}{1 \text{ mol NH}_3(g)} \times 4 \text{ mol NH}_3(g)$

$= -904 \text{ kJ}$

Section 17.3

1. $\Delta H = 35.0 \text{ g } \cancel{H_2O(s)} \times \dfrac{1 \text{ mol } \cancel{H_2O(s)}}{18.0 \text{ g } \cancel{H_2O(s)}}$

$\times \dfrac{6.01 \text{ kJ}}{1 \text{ mol } \cancel{H_2O(s)}}$

$= 11.7 \text{ kJ}$

2. Step 1: $H_2O(l)$ at $18\,°C \rightarrow H_2O(l)$ at $100\,°C$

$\Delta H = 190.0 \cancel{\text{ g}} \times 4.18 \dfrac{J}{\cancel{\text{g}} \times \cancel{°C}} \times 82 \cancel{°C}$

$= 6.512 \times 10^3 \text{ J} = 6.512 \text{ kJ}$

Step 2: $H_2O(l)$ at $100\,°C \rightarrow H_2O(g)$ at $100\,°C$

$\Delta H = 190.0 \cancel{\text{ g}} \times \dfrac{1 \text{ mol}}{18.0 \cancel{\text{ g}}} \times \dfrac{40.7 \text{ kJ}}{1 \text{ mol}}$

$= 429.6 \text{ kJ}$

$\Delta H_{total} = 6.512 \text{ kJ} + 429.6 \text{ kJ} = 436.1 \text{ kJ}$

3. $\Delta H = 2.543 \text{ mol NaOH}(s) \times \dfrac{-445.1 \text{ kJ}}{1 \text{ mol NaOH}(s)}$

$= 1.132 \times 10^3 \text{ kJ}$

4. Step 1: $H_2O(s)$ at $-24\,°C \rightarrow H_2O(s)$ at $0\,°C$

$\Delta H = 96 \cancel{\text{ g}} \times 2.1 \dfrac{J}{\cancel{\text{g}} \times \cancel{°C}} \times 24\,°C = 4.8 \times 10^3 \text{ J}$

Step 2: $H_2O(s)$ at $0\,°C \rightarrow H_2O(l)$ at $0\,°C$

$\Delta H = 96 \cancel{\text{ g}} \times \dfrac{1 \text{ mol}}{18.0 \cancel{\text{ g}}} \times \dfrac{6.01 \text{ kJ}}{1 \text{ mol}} = 32 \text{ kJ}$

Step 3: $H_2O(l)$ at $0\,°C \rightarrow H_2O(l)$ at $28\,°C$

$\Delta H = 96 \cancel{\text{ g}} \times 4.18 \dfrac{J}{\cancel{\text{g}} \times \cancel{°C}} \times 28\,°C$

$= 1.1 \times 10^4 \text{ J} = 11 \text{ kJ}$

$\Delta H_{total} = 4.8 \text{ kJ} + 32 \text{ kJ} + 11 \text{ kJ} = 47.8 \text{ kJ}$

Section 17.4

1. ΔH_f^0 (products)

$= \left[2 \cancel{\text{ mol } SO_2(g)} \times \dfrac{-296.8 \text{ kJ}}{1 \cancel{\text{ mol } SO_2(g)}} \right]$

$+ \left[2 \cancel{\text{ mol } H_2O(g)} \times \dfrac{-241.8 \text{ kJ}}{1 \cancel{\text{ mol } H_2O(g)}} \right]$

$= -593.6 \text{ kJ} + (-483.6 \text{ kJ})$

$= -1077 \text{kJ}$

ΔH_f^0 (reactants)

$= 2 \cancel{\text{ mol } H_2S(g)} \times \dfrac{-20.1 \text{ kJ}}{1 \cancel{\text{ mol } H_2S(g)}}$

$= -40.2 \text{ kJ}$

$\Delta H_f^0 = -1077 \text{ kJ} - (-40.2 \text{ kJ}) = 1.04 \times 10^3 \text{ kJ}$

2. ΔH_f^0(reactants) $= -635.1 \text{ kJ} + (-393.5 \text{ kJ})$

$= -1028.6 \text{ kJ}$

$\Delta H^0 = -1207.0 \text{ kJ} - (-1028.6 \text{ kJ})$

$= -178.4 \text{ kJ}$

The reaction is exothermic.

3. $N_2(g) + 2H_2O(l) \rightarrow N_2H_4(l) + O_2(g)$

$\Delta H = 622.2 \text{ kJ}$

$\dfrac{2[H_2(g) + \frac{1}{2}O_2(g) \rightarrow H_2O(l)] \quad \Delta H = -571.6 \text{ kJ}}{2H_2(g) + N_2(g) \rightarrow N_2H_4(l) \quad \Delta H = 50.6 \text{ kJ}}$

Interpreting Graphics 17

1. a. $27.0\,°C$ **b.** $26.5\,°C$

2. a. $-73.0\,°C$ **b.** $-73.5\,°C$

3. a. $5\,°C$ **b.** $5.5\,°C$

4. a. $\Delta H = (4.184)(39.100)(5.0) = 8.2 \times 10^2 \text{ J}$

    b. $\Delta H = (4.184)(39.452)(5.5) = 9.1 \times 10^2 \text{ J}$

5. heat gained by H_2O = heat lost by metal

    a. $-8.2 \times 10^2 \text{ J}$

    b. $-9.1 \times 10^2 \text{ J}$

6. a. specific heat $= \dfrac{-8.2 \times 10^2}{(50.33)(-73.0)}$

$= 0.22 \text{ J}/(g \times °C)$

    b. specific heat $= -9.1 \times 10^2 \backslash (50.35)(-73.5)$

$= 0.25 \text{ J}/(g \times °C)$

7. b; see Table 17.1.

Vocabulary Review 17

1. a	**5.** b	**8.** d
2. h	**6.** e	**9.** j
3. f	**7.** i	**10.** c
4. g		

Quiz for Chapter 17

1. b	**6.** a
2. c	**7.** is reversed
3. a	**8.** zero
4. d	**9.** minus
5. b	

Chapter 17 Test A

A. Matching

1. e
2. i
3. g
4. f
5. j
6. h
7. c
8. b
9. a
10. d

B. Multiple Choice

11. c
12. b
13. c
14. a
15. d
16. a
17. c
18. b
19. d
20. b
21. b
22. c
23. a
24. d
25. b

C. Essay

26. Endothermic processes absorb heat, while exothermic processes release heat. Endothermic examples include the melting of ice, the evaporation of a puddle, the sublimation of mothballs, and the heat used to cook food. Exothermic examples include the combustion of fossil fuels such as gasoline, the cooling of skin as perspiration evaporates, and the freezing of water.

D. Problems

27. $\text{Specific heat} = \dfrac{96\,\text{J}}{12\,\text{g} \times 20°\text{C}}$

    $= 0.40\,\text{J}/(\text{g} \times °\text{C})$

28. $\Delta H = m \times C \times \Delta T$

    $= \left(60.0\ \cancel{\text{mL}} \times 1.00\ \dfrac{\text{g}}{\cancel{\text{mL}}}\right) \times \left(4.18\ \dfrac{\text{J}}{\text{g} \times °\text{C}}\right)$

    $\times (35.0°\text{C} - 27.0°\text{C})$

    $= \dfrac{60.0\ \cancel{\text{g}} \times 4.18\,\text{J}}{\cancel{\text{g}} \times \cancel{°\text{C}}} \times 8.0°\cancel{\text{C}}$

    $= 2.0 \times 10^3\,\text{J or } 2.0\,\text{kJ}$

29. $56.0\,\text{g}\,\cancel{\text{CO}} \times \dfrac{1\ \cancel{\text{mol CO}}}{28.0\ \text{g}\,\cancel{\text{CO}}} \times \dfrac{24.7\,\text{kJ}}{3\ \cancel{\text{mol CO}}}$

    $= 16.5\,\text{kJ}$

30. $55.0\ \cancel{\text{kJ}} \times \dfrac{1\ \cancel{\text{mol}}}{6.01\ \cancel{\text{kJ}}} \times \dfrac{18.0\,\text{g H}_2\text{O}}{1\ \cancel{\text{mol H}_2\text{O}}} = 165\,\text{g}$

31. $2[\text{Mg}(s) + \text{Cl}_2(g) \rightarrow \text{MgCl}_2(s)]\ 2(\Delta H = -641\,\text{kJ})$
    $\text{SiCl}_4(l) \rightarrow \text{Si}(s) + 2\text{Cl}_2(g)\ \ \Delta H = +687\,\text{kJ}$
    $2\text{Mg}(s) + \text{SiCl}_4(l) \rightarrow \text{Si}(s) + 2\text{MgCl}_2(s)$
    $\quad\quad\quad \Delta H = -1282\,\text{kJ} + 687\,\text{kJ} = -595\,\text{kJ}$

32. $\text{C}_2\text{H}_6 + \frac{7}{2}\text{O}_2(g) \rightarrow 2\text{CO}_2(g) + 3\text{H}_2\text{O}(l)$
    $\Delta H^0 = ?$
    $\Delta H^0 = \Delta H^0_f\,(\text{products}) - \Delta H^0_f\,(\text{reactants})$
    $= [2(-393.5\,\text{kJ}) + 3(-285.8\,\text{kJ})]$
    $\quad\quad\quad\quad - [(-84.68\,\text{J}) + (0.0\,\text{kJ})]$
    $= -1559.7\,\text{kJ}$

Chapter 17 Test B

A. Matching

1. g
2. f
3. h
4. c
5. j
6. d
7. e
8. i
9. b
10. a

B. Multiple Choice

11. c
12. b
13. a
14. d
15. b
16. b
17. d
18. b
19. c
20. a
21. b
22. d
23. c
24. b
25. d

C. Essay

26. In vaporizing, steam absorbs the heat required for vaporization (40.7 kJ/mol). Thus, steam at 100 °C contains more energy than boiling water at the same temperature.

D. Problems

27. $\text{Specific heat} = \dfrac{75\,\text{J}}{18\,\text{g} \times 25°\text{C}}$

    $= 0.17\,\text{J}/(\text{g} \times °\text{C})$

28. $\Delta H = m \times C \times \Delta T$

    $= \left(55.0\ \cancel{\text{mL}} \times 1.00\ \dfrac{\text{g}}{\cancel{\text{mL}}}\right) \times \left(4.18\ \dfrac{\text{J}}{\text{g} \times °\text{C}}\right)$

    $\times (33.0°\text{C} - 24.0°\text{C})$

    $= 55.0\ \cancel{\text{g}} \times 4.18\ \dfrac{\text{J}}{\cancel{\text{g}} \times \cancel{°\text{C}}} \times 9.0°\cancel{\text{C}}$

    $= 2.1 \times 10^3\,\text{J} = 2.1\,\text{kJ}$

29. $8.00\,\text{g}\,\cancel{\text{O}_2} \times \dfrac{1\ \cancel{\text{mol O}_2}}{32.0\,\text{g}\,\cancel{\text{O}_2}} \times \dfrac{1411\,\text{kJ}}{3\ \cancel{\text{mol O}_2}} = 118\,\text{kJ}$

30. $75.0\ \cancel{\text{kJ}} \times \dfrac{1\ \cancel{\text{mol}}}{6.01\ \cancel{\text{kJ}}} \times \dfrac{18.0\,\text{g H}_2\text{O}}{1\ \cancel{\text{mol H}_2\text{O}}} = 225\,\text{g}$

31. $2[\text{C}(s) + \text{O}_2(g) \rightarrow \text{CO}_2(g)]\ 2(\Delta H = -393.5\,\text{kJ})$
    $2\text{CO}_2(g) \rightarrow 2\text{CO}(g) + \text{O}_2(g)\ \ \Delta H = +565.7\,\text{kJ}$
    $2\text{C}(s) + \text{O}_2(g) \rightarrow 2\text{CO}(g)$
    $\quad\quad\quad \Delta H = -787.0\,\text{kJ} + 565.7\,\text{kJ} = -221.3\,\text{kJ}$

32. $C_6H_6 + 15/2O_2(g) \rightarrow 6CO_2(g) + 3H_2O(l)$

$\Delta H = ?$

$\Delta H^0 = \Delta H_f^0$ (products) $- \Delta H_f^0$ (reactants)

$= [6(-393.5 \text{ kJ}) + 3(-285.8 \text{ kJ})]$
$\qquad - [(48.50 \text{ kJ}) + (0.0 \text{ kJ})]$

$= -3266.9 \text{ kJ}$

Chapter 17 Small-Scale Lab

Section 17.4 Heat of Combustion of a Candle, page 533

Analysis

1.

2. The wax burns but many students will say the wick.

3. The wick draws melted wax to the flame. Those who think the wick burns may suggest that the wax slows the rate of burning.

4. The hot gases expand and rise.

5. The candle flame might be round in zero gravity.

6. Depending on the candle and the time burned, the wick loses a few millimeters and the candle a few tenths of a gram. The mass loss is consistent with the wax burning.

7. Heat from the combustion melts the wax, which is drawn up into the wick, evaporated, and burned. Wick, as a verb, means to draw a liquid from one place to another by capillary action.

8. $C_{20}H_{42} + \frac{61}{2}O_2 \rightarrow 20CO_2 + 21H_2O$

9. C: $20 \times 12 = 240$

H: $42 \times 1 = \underline{42}$

282

$0.50 \text{ g} \times 1 \text{ mol}/282 \text{ g} = 0.0018 \text{ mol}$

10. $\Delta H = 20(-394) + 21(-242)$
$\qquad\qquad\qquad -(-2230) - 61/2(0)$

$= -10,700 \text{ kJ/mol}$

11. $10,700 \text{ kJ/mol} \times 0.0018 \text{ mol} = 19 \text{ kJ}$

You're the Chemist

1. Black soot will appear on a glass Petri dish held over the flame.

2. Liquid water will form on the underside of a glass Petri dish filled with ice held over the flame.

Section Review 18.1

Part A Completion

1. Rates
2. react
3. kinetic energy
4. activation
5. minimum
6. products
7. slower
8. temperature
9. catalyst
10. increasing

Part B True-False

11. ST
12. NT
13. AT
14. AT

Part C Matching

15. b
16. d
17. f
18. a
19. e
20. c

Part D Questions and Problems

21. $120 \text{ kg}/24 \text{ h} = 5.0 \text{ kg/h}$
22. b, d

Section Review 18.2

Part A Completion

1. reversible
2. products
3. forward
4. reactants
5. reverse
6. reactants
7. products
8. equilibrium
9. equilibrium constant
10. ratio
11. Le Châtelier's

Part B True-False

12. NT **14.** NT
13. ST **15.** AT

Part C Matching

16. d **18.** b **20.** e
17. a **19.** c

Part D Questions and Problems

21. $K_{eq} = \dfrac{[SO_2]^2 \, [O_2]}{[SO_3]^2}$

$= \dfrac{(0.42)^2(0.21)}{(0.072)^2} = 7.145 = 7.1$

Section Review 18.3

Part A Completion

1. solubility product constant
2. common ion effect
3. addition
4. precipitate

Part B Matching

5. a
6. c
7. b

Part C Problem

8. $[CO_3{}^{2-}] = 0.00070M$
$[Ba^{2+}] = 0.0015M$
$[CO_3{}^{2-}] \times [Ba^{2+}]$
$= (7.0 \times 10^{-4}M) \times (1.5 \times 10^{-3}M)$
$= 1.1 \times 10^{-6}$

Precipitation occurs because the ion product (1.1×10^{-6}) is greater than the K_{sp} of $BaCO_3$ (5.0×10^{-9}).

Section Review 18.4

Part A Completion

1. spontaneous
2. nonspontaneous
3. energy
4. work
5. free energy
6. energy
7. greater
8. entropy
9. disorder
10. law of disorder
11. maximum

Part B True-False

12. ST **14.** AT **16.** ST
13. AT **15.** AT

Part C Matching

17. c **19.** e **21.** d
18. f **20.** a **22.** b

Part D Questions

23. **a.** a heap of loose stamps
b. ice cubes in a bucket
c. 10 mL of steam at 100°C
d. the people watching the parade
24. b
25. d

Section 18.5

Part A Completion

1. rate
2. concentration
3. rate law
4. specific rate constant
5. order
6. first-order
7. second order
8. experiment
9. elementary reaction
10. mechanism

Part B True-False

11. NT   **13.** AT

12. ST   **14.** AT

Part C Matching

15. d   **17.** b   **19.** e

16. f   **18.** a   **20.** c

Part D Questions

21. This diagram represents a reaction that takes place in two elementary steps. The reaction is exothermic. Points A and C represent the energy level of the activated complexes. Point B represents the energy level of the intermediate product. Point D represents the energy level of the final product.

Practice Problems 18

Section 18.1

1. Rates of chemical reactions can usually be increased by (1) increasing the temperature, (2) increasing the concentration of the reactants, (3) decreasing the reactant particle size, and (4) using of a catalyst.

2. 2 mol/4 h = 0.5 mol/h

3. a. decrease the rate

    b. increase the rate

4. increase the rate

Section 18.2

1. $K_{eq} = \dfrac{[NO_2]^4 \times [O_2]}{[N_2O_5]^2}$

2. $K_{eq} = \dfrac{[0.80]^4 \times [0.20]}{[0.50]^2}$

    $= 0.33$

3. a. shift left

    b. shift right

4.

$\dfrac{[N_2O_4]}{[NO_2]^2} = 5.6$

$[NO_2]^2 = \dfrac{[N_2O_4]}{5.6}$

$[NO_2]^2 = \sqrt{\dfrac{0.66}{5.6}} = 0.3$

5. a. $K_{eq} = \dfrac{[N_2O_4]^2}{[NO]^4 \times [O_2]^2}$

    b. $K_{eq} = \dfrac{[NOBr]^2}{[NO]^2 \times [Br_2]}$

    c. $K_{eq} = \dfrac{[CH_3OH]}{[CO] \times [H_2]^2}$

    d. $K_{eq} = \dfrac{[SO_3] \times [NO]}{[SO_2] \times [NO_2]}$

6. a. shift right

    b. shift right

    c. shift right

    d. no shift

7. $K_{eq} = 1 \times 10^{12}$

8. $K_{eq} = \dfrac{[H_2]^2 \times [S_2]}{[H_2S]^2}$

$K_{eq} = \dfrac{(0.014)^2 \times (0.035)}{(0.18)^2} = 2.1 \times 10^{-4}$

Section 18.3

1. a. $Ca(OH)_2(s) \rightleftharpoons Ca^{2+}(aq) + 2OH^-(aq)$

    $K_{sp} = [Ca^{2+}] \times [OH^-]^2$

    b. $Ag_2CO_3(s) \rightleftharpoons 2Ag^+(aq) + CO_3^{2-}(aq)$

    $K_{sp} = [Ag^+]^2 \times [CO_3^{2-}]$

2. $Ag_2CO_3(s) \rightleftharpoons 2Ag^+(aq) + CO_3^{2-}(aq)$

$K_{sp} = [Ag^+]^2 \times [CO_3^{2-}]$

Let $x = [CO_3^{2-}]$; $2x = Ag^+$

$K_{sp} = (2x)^2(x) = 8.1 \times 10^{-12}$

$4x^3 = 8.1 \times 10^{-12}$

$x^3 = 2.0 \times 10^{-12}$

$x = 1.3 \times 10^{-4} M = [CO_3^{2-}]$

$[Ag^+] = 2x = 2.6 \times 10^{-4} M$

3. $Fe(OH)_2(s) \rightleftharpoons Fe^{2+}(aq) + 2OH^-(aq)$

$K_{sp} = [Fe^{2+}] \times [OH^-]^2$

$[Fe^{2+}] = 0.5[OH^-] = 6.0 \times 10^{-6}$

$K_{sp} = (6.0 \times 10^{-6})(1.2 \times 10^{-5})^2$

$K_{sp} = 8.6 \times 10^{-16}$

4. $SrCO_3 \rightleftharpoons Sr^{2+}(aq) + CO_3^{2-}(aq)$

$K_{sp} = [Sr^{2+}] \times [CO_3^{2-}]$

Let $x = [Sr^{2+}] = [CO_3^{2-}]$

$K_{sp} = x^2 = 9.3 \times 10^{-10}$

$x = [Sr^{2+}] = 3.0 \times 10^{-5} M$

5. $K_{sp} = [Ag^+]^2 \times [CO_3^{2-}]$

Let $[Ag^+] = 2x$; $[CO_3^{2-}] = x + 0.20$

assume $x \ll 0.20$ mol; $[CO_3^{2-}] = 0.20$

$K_{sp} = (2x)^2(0.20) = 8.1 \times 10^{-12}$

$x^2 = 1.0 \times 10^{-11}$

$x = 3.2 \times 10^{-6} M = [CO_3^{2-}]$

$[Ag^+] = 6.4 \times 10^{-6} M$

6. $K_{sp}(PbSO_4) = 6.3 \times 10^{-7} = [Pb^{2+}] \times [SO_4^{2-}]$

$$[SO_4^{2-}] = 0.0050M = \frac{400.0 \text{ mL}}{1000.0 \text{ mL}} = 0.0020M$$

$$[Pb^{2+}] = 0.0020M = \frac{600.0 \text{ mL}}{1000.0 \text{ mL}} = 0.0012M$$

$$[Pb^{2+}] \times [SO_4^{2-}] = (0.0012)(0.0020)$$
$$= 2.4 \times 10^{-6}$$

Because this product exceeds the K_{sp} value, precipitation will occur.

7. $K_{sp}(CaCO_3) = 4.5 \times 10^{-9} = [Ca^{2+}] \times [CO_3^{2-}]$
The total volume is 1000 mL, so
$[Ca^{2+}] = 0.0021 \text{ mol/L} = 0.0021M$
$[CO_3^{2-}] = 0.0013 \text{ mol/L} = 0.0013M$
$[Ca^{2+}] \times [CO_3^{2-}] = (0.0021)(0.0013)$
$$= 2.7 \times 10^{-6}$$

Because this product exceeds the K_{sp} value, precipitation will occur.

8. NaCl has no ion in common with $Mg(OH)_2$.

Section 18.4

1. increase
2. decrease
3. **a.** increasing **c.** increasing
   b. increasing
4. **a.** D **c.** D
   b. N **d.** A

Section 18.5

1. $2.4 \text{ mol}/(L \bullet s) \div 8 = 0.30 \text{ mol}/(L \bullet s)$
2. rate $= k[HgCl_2][Na_2C_2O_4]^2$
3. rate $= k[J][K]$
   The reaction is first order in both J and K.
4. rate $= k[H_2O_2]$; $k = \text{rate}/[H_2O_2]$
   $k = 0.00842 \text{ mol}/(L \bullet s) \div 0.500 \text{ mol/L}$
   $= 0.0168 \text{ s}^{-1}$
5. three elementary reactions
6. 1.0; 0.020
7. **a.** two elementary reactions
   b. $C_3H_8O_3$
   c. rate $= k[C_2H_4O_2][CH_4O]$

Interpreting Graphics 18

1. **a.** negative **d.** positive
   b. negative **e.** positive
   c. negative **f.** positive
2. greater
3. less
4. Example a
5. yes

Vocabulary Review 18

1. e 5. b 8. d
2. g 6. f 9. c
3. i 7. j 10. h
4. a

Quiz for Chapter 18

1. b 4. b 7. NT
2. d 5. d 8. AT
3. a 6. b 9. NT

Chapter 18 Test A

A. Matching

1. i 5. g 8. d
2. a 6. e 9. f
3. j 7. h 10. b
4. c

B. Multiple Choice

11. b 16. c 20. a
12. b 17. d 21. b
13. c 18. b 22. a
14. d 19. c 23. d
15. d

C. Problems

24. $K_{eq} = \dfrac{[NO]^2 \times [Cl_2]}{[NOCl]^2} = \dfrac{(1.2)^2 \times (0.60)}{(0.30)^2} = 9.6$

25. $\dfrac{[CH_3OH]}{[CO] \times [H_2]^2} = 2.2 \times 10^2$

$[CH_3OH] = 2.2 \times 10^2 \times [CO] \times [H_2]^2$

$= 2.2 \times 10^2 \times (0.020)(0.60)^2$

$[CH_3OH] = 1.58 \text{ mol/L}$

26. **a.** favors products

  b. favors reactants

  c. favors products

  d. favors reactants

D. Essay

27. Spontaneous reactions are reactions that, under the conditions specified, are known to favor the formation of products.

Nonspontaneous reactions do not favor the formation of products under the specified conditions. Some spontaneous reactions apprear to be nonspontaneous because their rates are slow.

E. Additional Problem

28. Doubling A doubles the rate—first order in A. Doubling B increases the rate 8 times ($2^3 = 8$) —third order in B. First order + third order = fourth order overall.

Chapter 18 Test B

A. Matching

1. j	**5.** f	**8.** e
2. g	**6.** c	**9.** b
3. h	**7.** d	**10.** a
4. i		

B. Multiple Choice

11. d	**16.** c	**21.** c
12. a	**17.** d	**22.** b
13. d	**18.** b	**23.** c
14. b	**19.** d	**24.** b
15. c	**20.** a	

C. Problems

25. **a.** shifts left; decreases

  b. shifts left; decreases

  c. shifts right; increases

  d. shifts right; increases

  e. shifts right; increases

  f. shifts left; decreases

26. $K_{eq} = \dfrac{[H_2O]^2 \times [Cl_2]^2}{[HCl]^4 \times [O_2]}$

$= \dfrac{(5.8 \times 10^{-2})^2 \times (5.8 \times 10^{-2})^2}{(1.2 \times 10^{-3})^4 \times (3.8 \times 10^{-4})}$

$= 1.4 \times 10^{10}$

27. PbF_2

D. Essay

28. **a.** The addition of more reactant causes an increase in the rate of the forward reaction, which consumes that reactant.

  b. An increase in temperature causes the endothermic reaction to speed up in an effort to consume the additional heat.

  c. An increase in pressure (for a gaseous system with an unequal number of molecules) causes the reaction that produces the fewest number of molecules to speed up.

E. Additional Problem

29. $K_{eq} = \dfrac{[NH_3]^2}{[N_2] \times [H_2]^3}$

$[N_2] = \dfrac{[NH_3]^2}{K_{eq} \times [H_2]^3}$

$= \dfrac{(1.23 \times 10^{-4})^2}{(6.59 \times 10^{-3}) \times (2.75 \times 10^{-6})^3}$

$= 1.10 \times 10^{11} \text{ mol/L}$

Chapter 18 Small-Scale Lab

Section 18.4 Enthalpy and Entropy, page 574

Analyze

Sample data are provided.

1.

Mixture	T_1	T_2	ΔT
a. $NaCl + H_2O(l)$	21°C	21°C	0°C
b. $NH_4Cl + H_2O(l)$	21°C	5°C	−16°C
c. $CaCl_2 + H_2O(l)$	21°C	53°C	+32°C

2. $NH_4Cl + H_2O$ is endothermic. ΔH is positive. $CaCl_2 + H_2O$ is exothermic. ΔH is negative.

3. $NaCl + H_2O(l)$ did not change much in temperature. ΔH is close to 0.

4. heat + $NH_4Cl(s) \rightarrow NH_4^+(aq) + Cl^-(aq)$

$CaCl_2(s) \rightarrow Ca^{2+}(aq) + 2Cl^-(aq) + $ heat

5. All of the solids dissolved rapidly. Entropy usually increases in the dissolving process. ΔS is positive in each case.

6. $\Delta G = \Delta H - T\Delta S$.
   $\Delta G = (0) - T(+)$ for $NaCl(s)$
   ΔG is $-$.
   $\Delta G = (+) - T(+)$ for $NH_4Cl(s)$
   ΔG is $+$ or $-$.
   $\Delta G = (-) - T(+)$ for $CaCl_2(s)$
   ΔG is $-$.

You're the Chemist

1. The temperature of the NaCl and ice dropped dramatically.
   Sample data:

Mixture	T_1	T_2	ΔT
$NaCl + H_2O(s)$	$0°C$	$-15°C$	$-15°C$

2. Melting ice is endothermic. Endothermic reactions absorb heat, cooling the environment. This explains the drop in temperature of the NaCl and ice mixture.

3. Both $CaCl_2$ and NH_4Cl depress the freezing point of ice and cause a drop in temperature.

4. Many salts such as KCl, $NaHCO_3$, Na_2CO_3 and Na_3PO_4 dissolve endothermically or with little or no change in temperature.

Section Review 19.1

Part A Completion

1. three
2. Arrhenius
3. hydroxide ions
4. proton
5. acceptor
6. electron-pair
7. donor
8. monoprotic
9. diprotic
10. conjugate acid–base pair
11. amphoteric

Part B True-False

12. NT	14. AT	16. AT
13. NT	15. ST	

Part C Matching

17. g	20. h	23. c
18. d	21. e	24. f
19. a	22. i	25. b

Part D Problems

26. Dimethyl ether is a Lewis base because it donates an electron pair to form a bond. Boron trifluoride is a Lewis acid because it accepts an electron pair from dimethyl ether.

Section Review 19.2

Part A Completion

1. self-ionize
2. 1×10^{-7}
3. 0 to 14
4. hydrogen ion
5. acidic
6. basic
7. neutral
8. 7
9. ion-product
10. hydronium/hydroxide
11. hydroxide/hydronium

Part B True-False

12. AT	14. AT	16. NT
13. ST	15. NT	

Part C Matching

17. c	20. a	22. g
18. f	21. b	23. d
19. e		

Part D Problems

24. $K_w = [H^+][OH^-]$
$$[OH^-] = \frac{K_w}{[H^+]} = \frac{1 \times 10^{-14}}{1 \times 10^{-10}} = 1 \times 10^{-4}$$
The solution is basic.

25. a. $pH = -\log[H^+]$
   $[H^+] = 1 \times 10^{-3}M$

   b. $pH = -\log[H^+]$
   $[H^+] = 1 \times 10^{-6}M$

   c. $pH = -\log[H^+]$
   $[H^+] = 1 \times 10^{-10}$

Section Review 19.3

Part A Completion

1. degree of ionization
2. K_a
3. larger
4. pH
5. completely
6. strong
7. weak
8. bases
9. water
10. acid
11. strong

Part B True-False

12. ST
13. NT
14. AT
15. ST

Part C Matching

16. c
17. e
18. a
19. b
20. d
21. f

Part D Problem

22. $HX \rightleftharpoons H^+ + X^-$

$[H^+] = [X^-] = 4.1 \times 10^{-2}$

$[HX] = 0.35 - 4.1 \times 10^{-2} = 0.35 - 0.041$

$\qquad = 0.309$

$$K_a = \frac{[H^+][X^-]}{[HX]} = \frac{(4.1 \times 10^{-2})(4.1 \times 10^{-2})}{0.309}$$

$\qquad = 5.4 \times 10^{-3}$

Section Review 19.4

Part A Completion

1. acid
2. hydroxide
3. water
4. neutralization
5. titration
6. end point
7. equivalence

Part B True-False

8. AT
9. AT
10. AT
11. NT

Part C Matching

12. c
13. e
14. a
15. b
16. d

Part D Problem

17. **a.** $H_3PO_4 + Al(OH)_3 \rightarrow AlPO_4 + 3H_2O$
    b. $2HI + Ca(OH)_2 \rightarrow CaI_2 + 2H_2O$

Section Review 19.5

Part A Completion

1. salt
2. acidic
3. basic
4. neutral
5. hydrolyze
6. strong
7. weak
8. buffer
9. capacity

Part B True-False

10. NT
11. NT
12. ST
13. AT

Part C Matching

14. a
15. d
16. b
17. c

Part D Questions and Problems

18. **a.** acidic
    b. neutral
    c. basic

Practice Problems

Section 19.1

1. H_2SO_4 and H_3O^+ are proton donors and H_2O and HSO_4^- are the proton acceptors. The conjugate acid–base pairs are H_2SO_4/HSO_4^- and H_3O^+/H_2O.

   $H_2SO_4 + H_2O \rightleftharpoons H_3O^+ + HSO_4^-$

2. H_3PO_4 is a triprotic acid able to ionize three hydrogens. All ions formed are shown in the following chemical equations.

   $H_3PO_4 + H_2O \rightleftharpoons H_3O^+ + H_2PO_4^-$
   $H_2PO_4^- + H_2O \rightleftharpoons H_3O^+ + HPO_4^{2-}$
   $HPO_4^{2-} + H_2O \rightleftharpoons H_3O^+ + PO_4^{3-}$

3. Only hydrogens bonded to highly electronegative atoms are ionizable.

   a. monoprotic
   b. monoprotic
   c. diprotic
   d. triprotic

4. Like other alkali metals, lithium reacts violently with water to produce hydrogen and the base lithium hydroxide.

$$2Li(s) + 2H_2O \rightarrow H_2(g) + 2LiOH(aq)$$

5. BF_3 can accept a pair of electrons to form a covalent bond and is therefore a Lewis acid. Since F^- donates the pair of electrons, it is a Lewis base.

6. Acids have a tart or sour taste and cause indicators to change color. Acids react with compounds containing hydroxide ions to produce a salt and water.

7. Aqueous solutions of bases taste bitter and feel slippery. They react with acids to produce a salt and water. Bases cause indicators to change colors.

Section 19.2

1. $pH = -\log[H^-]$
   $= -\log(1 \times 10^{-6})$
   reminder: the $\log(a \times b) = \log a + \log b$
   $= -(0.0 + (-6))$
   reminder: the $\log 1 = 0.0$
   $= 6.0$

2. $pH = -\log[H^-]$
   $= -\log(7.2 \times 10^{-9})$
   $= -(0.86) - (-9.00)$
   Use log tables or your calculator to find the log of 7.2.
   $= 9.00 - 0.86$
   $= 8.14$

3. $pOH = -\log[OH^-]$
   $= -\log(3.5 \times 10^{-2})$
   $= -(0.54) - (-2.00)$
   $= 2.00 - 0.54$
   $= 1.46$

4. $pOH = 14.0 - pH$
   $= 14.0 - 3.4$
   $= 10.6$

5. a. basic   d. neutral
   b. acidic   e. acidic
   c. acidic

6. a. 5.0   c. 7.34
   b. 10.36   d. 12.6

7. a. acidic   c. basic
   b. basic   d. basic

8. Most acidic solutions of interest have a hydrogen ion concentration of less than $1M$. The log of this concentration would always be a negative number. Taking the negative log (minus sign in the pH definition) ensures that the pH values will usually be positive.

9. $pH + pOH = 14.0$
   $pH = 14.0 - pOH = 14.0 - 12.4 = 1.6$

10. $pH = -\log[H^+]$
    $= -\log(1 \times 10^{-3}) = -(0.0 + (-3)) = 3.0$

Section 19.3

1. strong base, weak base, weak acid, strong acid

2. $HF(aq) \rightleftharpoons H^+(aq) + F^-(aq)$
   $$K_a = \frac{[H^+][F^-]}{[HF]}$$

3. $N_2H_4(aq) + H_2O(l) \rightleftharpoons N_2H_5^+(aq) + OH^-(aq)$
   $$K_b = \frac{[N_2H_5^+][OH^-]}{[N_2H_4]}$$

4. The weakest acid has the smallest K_a.
   $HCO_3^- < H_2PO_4^- < HCOOH < H_2C_2O_4$

5. a. $H_2S(aq) \rightleftharpoons H^+(aq) + HS^-(aq)$
   $$K_a = \frac{[H^+][HS^-]}{[H_2S]}$$
   b. $NH_4^+(aq) \rightleftharpoons NH_3(aq) + H^+(aq)$
   $$K_a = \frac{[NH_3][H^+]}{[NH_4^+]}$$
   c. $C_6H_5COOH(aq) \rightleftharpoons$
   $$C_6H_5COO^-(aq) + H^+(aq)$$
   $$K_a = \frac{[C_6H_5COO^-][H^+]}{[C_6H_5COOH]}$$

6. a. (4)   d. (5)
   b. (2)   e. (3)
   c. (1)

7. $$K_b = \frac{[C_6H_5NH_3^+][OH^-]}{[C_6H_5NH_2]}$$

8. $$K_a = \frac{(4.2 \times 10^{-3}M)(4.2 \times 10^{-3}M)}{0.096M}$$
   $$= 1.8 \times 10^{-4}M$$

9. At equilibrium, $[H^+] = x = [C_6H_5COO^-]$
   $[C_6H_5COOH] = 0.20M - x = 0.20M$
   (since $x << 0.20M$)
   $$K_a = \frac{x^2}{0.20M} = 6.3 \times 10^{-5}M$$
   $x = 3.5 \times 10^{-3}M = [H^+]$

10. At equilibrium, $[H^+] = [CN^-] = 6.3 \times 10^{-6}M$
    $$K_a = \frac{[H^+][CN^-]}{[HCN]}$$
    $$= \frac{(6.3 \times 10^{-6}M)^2}{0.10M} = 4.0 \times 10^{-10}M$$

Section 19.4

1. $2NaOH(aq) + H_2SO_4(aq)$
$$\rightarrow Na_2SO_4(aq) + 2H_2O(l)$$

$0.014 \text{ L } H_2SO_4 \times \dfrac{0.75 \text{ mol } H_2SO_4}{1 \text{ L } H_2SO_4}$

$\times \dfrac{2 \text{ mol NaOH}}{1 \text{ mol } H_2SO_4} = 0.021 \text{ mol NaOH}$

$\text{Molarity} = \dfrac{\text{moles}}{\text{liters}} = \dfrac{0.021 \text{ mol NaOH}}{0.038 \text{ L NaOH}}$

$= 0.55M \text{ NaOH}$

2. $Ca(OH)_2(aq) + 2HC_2H_3O_2(aq)$
$$\rightarrow Ca(C_2H_3O_2)_2(aq) + 2H_2O(l)$$

$0.0142 \text{ L } HC_2H_3O_2 \times \dfrac{0.0140 \text{ mol } HC_2H_3O_2}{1 \text{ L } HC_2H_3O_2}$

$\times \dfrac{1 \text{ mol } Ca(OH)_2}{2 \text{ mol } HC_2H_3O_2}$

$= 9.94 \times 10^{-5} \text{ mol } Ca(OH)_2$

$= 9.94 \times 10^{-5} \text{ mol } Ca(OH)_2$

$\text{Molarity} = \dfrac{9.94 \times 10^{-5} \text{ mol } Ca(OH)_2}{0.0246 \text{ L } Ca(OH)_2}$

$= 0.00404M$

3. $Ca(OH)_2(aq) + H_2SO_4(aq)$
$$\rightarrow CaSO_4(aq) + 2H_2O(l)$$

$0.0198 \text{ L } Ca(OH)_2 \times \dfrac{0.0100 \text{ mol } Ca(OH)_2}{1 \text{ L } Ca(OH)_2}$

$\times \dfrac{1 \text{ mol } H_2SO_4}{1 \text{ mol } Ca(OH)_2} = 0.000198 \text{ mol } H_2SO_4$

$= 0.000198 \text{ mol } H_2SO_4$

$\text{Molarity} = \dfrac{\text{moles}}{\text{liters}} = \dfrac{0.000198 \text{ mol } H_2SO_4}{0.0124 \text{ L } H_2SO_4}$

$= 0.0160M \text{ } H_2SO_4$

4. $Ba(OH)_2(aq) + 2HCl(aq)$
$$\rightarrow BaCl_2(aq) + 2H_2O(l)$$

$0.0122 \text{ L } HCl \times \dfrac{0.25 \text{ mol } HCl}{1 \text{ L } HCl}$

$\times \dfrac{1 \text{ mol } Ba(OH)_2}{2 \text{ mol HC}}$

$= 0.0015 \text{ mol } Ba(OH)_2$

$\text{liters} = \dfrac{\text{moles}}{\text{molarity}} = \dfrac{0.0015 \text{ mol } Ba(OH)_2}{0.12M \text{ } Ba(OH)_2}$

$= 0.0125 \text{ L } Ba(OH)_2 = 13 \text{ mL } Ba(OH)_2$

5. $Al(OH)_3(aq) + 3HCl(aq)$
$$\rightarrow AlCl_3(aq) + 3H_2O(l)$$

$0.0550 \text{ g } Al(OH)_3 \times \dfrac{1 \text{ mol } Al(OH)_3}{78.0 \text{ g } Al(OH)_3}$

$\times \dfrac{3 \text{ mol HCl}}{1 \text{ mol } Al(OH)_3} = 0.00212 \text{ mol HCl}$

$\text{liters} = \dfrac{\text{moles}}{\text{molarity}} = \dfrac{0.00212 \text{ mol HCl}}{0.200M \text{ HCl}}$

$= 0.0106 \text{ L HCl} = 10.6 \text{ mL HCl}$

Section 19.5

1. $CHO_2^- + H^+ \rightleftharpoons HCHO_2$
$HCHO_2 + OH^- \rightleftharpoons CHO_2^- + H_2O$

2. **a.** neutral solution

b. acidic solution

c. basic solution

Interpreting Graphics 19

1. $C_6H_5COOH + NaOH \rightarrow C_6H_5COONa + H_2O$
One mole of sodium hydroxide will neutralize one mole of benzoic acid.

2. To determine the equivalence point, find the area of the titration curve where the pH changes abruptly when a small volume of NaOH is added. Locate the point on this steep portion of the curve equidistant between the two plateaus. The pH at the equivalence point is approximately 8.5; the solution is slightly basic.

3. Benzoic acid is a weak acid. The neutralization of a weak acid with a strong base, such as NaOH, produces a basic solution at the equivalence point.

4. $0.025 \text{ L} \times 0.10 \text{ mol/L NaOH}$
$= 0.0025 \text{ mol NaOH}$

5. The equivalence point occurs when the number of moles of NaOH added equals the number of moles of C_6H_5COOH originally present. Because NaOH is a strong base, each mole of NaOH added reacts with each mole of C_6H_5COOH present. Thus, at the equivalence point,
$[C_6H_5COOH] = [NaOH] = 0M$ and

$[C_6H_5COONa] = \dfrac{0.0025 \text{ mol}}{0.050 \text{ L}} = 0.050M.$

6. Based on the answers to questions 4 and 5, $0.0025 \text{ mol } C_6H_5COOH$ were originally present in a volume of 25 mL.

Thus, $[C_6H_5COOH] = \dfrac{0.0025 \text{ mol}}{0.025 \text{ L}} = 0.10M$

7. Because the equivalence point occurs between pH 6 and pH 11, phenolphthalein would be a good choice. A faint pink color should be detected at the equivalence point. Thymol blue might also be a good candidate. Students should draw a horizontal band on the graph encompassing the pH range 8-10 to show the region of the curve where phenolphthalein would be an effective indicator of neutralization.

8. $C_6H_5COO^- + H_2O \rightleftharpoons C_6H_5COOH + OH^-$

   At the equivalence point, the benzoate ion establishes the equilibrium shown. The resulting solution is slightly basic because $[OH^-] > [H^+]$.

9. $K_b = \dfrac{[C_6H_5COOH][OH^-]}{[C_6H_5COO^-]}$

10. $pH + pOH = 14$

    $8.5 + pOH = 14$

    $pOH = 5.5$

    $[OH^-] = 3.2 \times 10^{-6} M$

    At the equivalence point $[OH^-] =$
    $[C_6H_5COOH] = 3.2 \times 10^{-6} M$

    $[C_6H_5COO^-] = 0.050 M$

    $K_b = \dfrac{(3.2 \times 10^{-6})^2}{(0.050)} = 2.0 \times 10^{-10}$

Vocabulary Review 19

1. Hydronium ion. The other terms describe aqueous solutions based on their pH.

2. Acidic solution. Alkaline is another name for a basic solution and basic solutions would have a high hydroxide ion concentration.

3. Amphoteric. The other terms are theories used to classify acids and bases.

4. Lewis acid. The other terms refer to ways of describing acids and bases according to the Brønsted-Lowry theory.

5. Strong acids. Weak acids and bases are only partially ionized in aqueous solution. The dissociation constant reflects the fraction of a weak base or weak acid that is in ionized form.

6. hydrolyzing salt
7. neutral
8. equivalence point
9. buffer

Quiz for Chapter 19

1. b	4. c	7. c
2. b	5. c	8. b
3. a	6. d	

Chapter 19 Test A

A. Matching

1. i	5. h	8. e
2. a	6. g	9. c
3. j	7. d	10. b
4. f		

B. Multiple Choice

11. b	18. d	25. a
12. d	19. a	26. d
13. d	20. b	27. a
14. a	21. d	28. c
15. c	22. d	29. b
16. d	23. d	
17. c	24. a	

C. Problems

30. **a.** $pH = -\log[H^+] = 9$, basic
    b. $[H^+] = 1 \times 10^{-4}$, pH = 4, acidic
    c. pH = 7, neutral

31. $K_w = [H^+] \times [OH^-]$

    $[H^+] = \dfrac{K_w}{[OH^-]} = \dfrac{1 \times 10^{-14}}{1 \times 10^{-12}}$
    $= 1 \times 10^{-2}$ acidic

32. **a.** $H_2SO_3 \rightleftharpoons H^+ + HSO_3^-$
    $K_a = \dfrac{[H^+] \times [HSO_3^-]}{[H_2SO_3]}$

    b. $HNO_3 \rightleftharpoons H^+ + NO_3^-$
    $K_a = \dfrac{[H^+] \times [NO_3^-]}{[HNO_3]}$

33. **a.** $2HBr + Mg(OH)_2 \rightarrow MgBr_2 + 2H_2O$

    b. $3H_2SO_4 + 2Al(OH)_3 \rightarrow Al_2(SO_4)_3 + 6H_2O$

34. **a.** basic   **c.** acidic
    b. neutral   **d.** basic

D. Essay

35. Both acids and base, cause indicators to change colors and react with each other to form water and a salt. Acids taste sour; bases taste bitter. Bases feel slippery.

Chapter 19 Test B

A. Matching

1. b	**5.** f	**9.** i
2. g	**6.** c	**10.** j
3. d	**7.** h	**11.** e
4. a	**8.** k	

B. Multiple Choice

12. b	**17.** b	**22.** c
13. d	**18.** d	**23.** a
14. a	**19.** a	**24.** b
15. b	**20.** d	**25.** a
16. c	**21.** a	**26.** a

C. Problems

27. $K_w = [H^+][OH^-] = 1.0 \times 10^{-14} \, (\text{mol/L})^2$

$[OH^-] = K_w/[H^+]$

$$[OH^-] = \frac{1.0 \times 10^{-14} \, (\text{mol/L})^2}{1.0 \times 10^{-9} \, \text{mol/L}}$$

$= 1.0 \times 10^{-5} \, \text{mol/L}$

The solution is basic.

28. a. $[OH^-] = 1 \times 10^{-11}$; 3; acidic

b. $[H^+] = 1 \times 10^{-6}$; 6; acidic

c. $[H^+] = 1 \times 10^{-7}$; 7; neutral

29. a. $K_a = \dfrac{[H^+][I^-]}{[HI]}$

b. $K_a = \dfrac{[H^+][HSO_4^-]}{[H_2SO_4]}$

30. a. $HF(aq) + KOH(aq) \rightarrow KF(aq) + H_2O(l)$

b. $H_2SO_4(aq) + 2LiOH(aq)$
$\rightarrow Li_2SO_4(aq) + 2H_2O(l)$

31. $H_2SO_4(aq) + 2KOH(aq) \rightarrow K_2SO_4(aq) + 2H_2O(l)$
   1 mol   2 mol   1 mol   2 mol

$\dfrac{1 \, \text{mol} \, H_2SO_4}{2 \, \text{mol KOH}} \times 0.35 \, \text{mol KOH}$

   $= 0.18 \, \text{mol} \, H_2SO_4$

32. $CuCl(s) \rightarrow Cu^+(aq) + Cl^-(aq)$

$K_{sp} = [Cu^+][Cl^-]$

$3.2 \times 10^{-7} = [Cu^+][Cu^+]$

$3.2 \times 10^{-7} = [Cu^+]^2$

$5.7 \times 10^{-4} M = [Cu^+]$

D. Essay

33. The Brønsted-Lowry theory defines acids as proton donors and bases as proton acceptors. According to the Lewis theory, acids are electron-pair acceptors, whereas bases are electron-pair donors.

E. Additional Problems

34. $pH = -\log[H^+]$
$= -\log[3.4 \times 10^{-4}]$
$= -(\log 3.4 + \log 10^{-4})$
$= -[(0.53) + (-4)]$
$= -[-3.47]$
$= 3.47$

The solution is acidic.

35. a. $HF(aq)$; $H_2O(l)$; $H_3O^+(aq)$; $F^-(aq)$

b. $HCl(g)$; $H_2O(l)$; $H_3O^+(aq)$; $Cl^-(aq)$

c. $HC_2H_3O_2(aq)$; $H_2O(l)$; $H_3O^+(aq)$; $C_2H_3O_2^-(aq)$

36. a. H^+; I^-

b. BCl_3; NH_3

37. $HC_2H_3O_2(aq) \rightleftharpoons H^+(aq) + C_2H_3O_2^-(aq)$

$[H^+] = [C_2H_3O_2^-] = 2.25 \times 10^{-3} M$

$[HC_2H_3O_2] = 0.1000M - 0.00225M$
$= 0.09775M$

$K_a = \dfrac{[H^+][C_2H_3O_2^-]}{[HC_2H_3O_2]}$

$= \dfrac{[0.00225][0.00225]}{[0.09775]}$

$= 5.18 \times 10^{-5}$

Chapter 19 Small-Scale Lab

Section 19.4 Ionization Constants of Weak Acids, page 617

Analysis

1 Yellow	2 Yellow	3 Yellow
4 Green	5 Blue	6 Blue
7 Blue	8 Blue	9 Blue
10 Blue	11 Blue	12 Blue

Figure A

1. The pH solutions 1-3 are yellow.
2. The pH solutions 5-12 are blue.
3. The pH solution 4 is green, an intermediate between yellow and blue.
4. The conjugate acid, HBCG is yellow.
5. The conjugate base, BCG⁻ is blue.
6. An equal mixture of HBCG and BCG⁻ is green at pH = 4.

You're the Chemist

1. Results will vary depending on the indicator chosen.
2. To measure the K_a of a colored weak acid, mix one drop of the weak acid with one drop of each pH 1-12 buffer solution. Look for the pH of the color change. This pH is the K_a of the acid.

Section Review 20.1

Part A Completion

1. redox
2. away
3. toward
4. reduction
5. oxidizing
6. reduced
7. reducing
8. oxidized

Part B True-False

9. AT
10. AT
11. NT
12. NT

Part C Matching

13. e
14. b
15. f
16. c
17. a
18. d

Part D Questions and Problems

19. Oxidation is the complete or partial loss of electrons. Reduction is the complete or partial gain of electrons.
20. The zinc metal, Zn, was oxidized and is the reducing agent. The copper ion, Cu^{2+}, was reduced and is the oxidizing agent.
21. When oxygen and water attack iron, the iron atoms lose electrons as the iron begins to be oxidized. Since aluminum and zinc are better reducing agents than iron and are more easily oxidized, they immediately transfer electrons to the iron ions, reducing them back to neutral iron atoms.

Section Review 20.2

Part A Completion

1. zero
2. sign
3. charge
4. zero
5. charge on the ion
6. electron
7. oxidation
8. decrease

Part B True-False

9. AT
10. AT
11. NT
12. NT
13. NT
14. NT
15. AT
16. AT

Part C Matching

17. e
18. h
19. d
20. a
21. g
22. c
23. f
24. i
25. b

Part D Questions and Problems

26. An increase in the oxidation number of an atom indicates oxidation. A decrease in the oxidation number indicates reduction.

27. N is reduced (+5 to +2);
Br is oxidized (−1 to 0)

Mn is reduced (+7 to +2);
Cl is oxidized (−1 to 0)

N is reduced (+5 to +2);
Sb is oxidized (0 to +5)

S is reduced (+6 to +4);
C is oxidized (0 to +4)

Section Review 20.3

Part A Completion

1. oxidation number
2. half-reaction
3. balanced
4. ionic
5. two
6. added
7. ionic

Part B True-False

8. AT
9. AT
10. AT
11. NT
12. NT
13. NT

Part C Matching

14. c
15. a
16. f
17. b
18. e
19. d
20. g

Part D Questions and Problems

21. a. $HNO_3 \rightarrow NO$; N changes +5 to +2, a gain of $3e^-$; multiply by 2

$2HI \rightarrow I_2$; I changes from −1 to 0, a loss of $2e^-$ for I_2; multiply by 3

$2HNO_3 + 6HI \rightarrow 2NO + 3I_2 + 4H_2O$

b. $HNO_3 \rightarrow NO_2$; N changes +5 to +4, a gain of $1e^-$; multiply by 10

$I_2 \rightarrow 2HIO_3$; I changes from 0 to +5, a loss of $10e^-$ for I_2

$10HNO_3 + I_2 \rightarrow 2HIO_3 + 10NO_2 + 4H_2O$

22. a. $S^{2-} \rightarrow S + 2e^-$ and
$3e^- + 4H^+ + NO_3^- \rightarrow NO + 2H_2O$;
Multiply the oxidation reaction by 3 and the reduction reaction by 2.

$3H_2S + 2HNO_3 \rightarrow 3S + 2NO + 4H_2O$

b. $Fe^{2+} \rightarrow Fe^{3+} + e^-$ and $6e^- + 14H^+ + Cr_2O_7^{2-} \rightarrow 2Cr^{3+} + 7H_2O$; multiply the oxidation reaction by 6

$14H^+ + 6Fe^{2+} + Cr_2O_7^{2-} \rightarrow 6Fe^{2+} + 2Cr^{3+} + 7H_2O$

Practice Problems

Section 20.1

1. Sr: oxidized (reducing agent)
   O_2: reduced (oxidizing agent)
2. Li: oxidized (reducing agent)
   S: reduced (oxidizing agent)
3. Cs: oxidized (reducing agent)
   Br_2: reduced (oxidizing agent)
4. Mg: oxidized (reducing agent)
   N_2: reduced (oxidizing agent)
5. Fe: oxidized (reducing agent)
   O_2: reduced (oxidizing agent)
6. Br^-: oxidized (reducing agent)
   Cl_2: reduced (oxidizing agent)
7. Si: oxidized (reducing agent)
   F_2 reduced (oxidizing agent)
8. Ca: oxidized (reducing agent)
   O_2 reduced (oxidizing agent)
9. Mg: oxidized (reducing agent)
   H^+: reduced (oxidizing agent)
10. Na: oxidized (reducing agent)
    H_2O: reduced (oxidizing agent)

Section 20.2

1. a. Sn is tin in an uncombined state. The oxidation number is 0.

b. The ionic charge on potassium is 1+, thus the oxidation number is +1.

c. The ionic charge on sulfur is 2−, thus the oxidation number is −2.

d. The ionic charge on iron is 3+, thus the oxidation number is +3.

e. Se is selenium in an uncombined state. The oxidation number is 0

f. The ionic charge on magnesium is 2+, thus the oxidation number is +2.

g. The ionic charge on tin is 4+, thus the oxidation number is +4.

h. The ionic charge on bromine is $1-$, thus the oxidation number is -1.

2. a. $+3$ **c.** $+2$

    b. $+6$ **d.** $+6$

3. a. $\overset{0}{C} + \overset{+1\ +6\ -2}{H_2SO_4} \rightarrow \overset{+4\ -2}{CO_2} + \overset{+4\ -2}{SO_2} + \overset{+1\ -2}{H_2O}$

Carbon is oxidized ($0 \rightarrow +4$).
Sulfur is reduced ($+6 \rightarrow +4$).

    b. $\overset{+1\ +5\ -2}{HNO_3} + \overset{+1\ -1}{HI} \rightarrow \overset{+2\ -2}{NO} + \overset{0}{I_2} + \overset{+1\ -2}{H_2O}$

Nitrogen is reduced ($+5 \rightarrow +2$).
Iodide ion is oxidized ($-1 \rightarrow 0$).

    c. $\overset{+1\ +7\ -2}{KMnO_4} + \overset{+1\ -1}{HCl} \rightarrow \overset{+2\ -1}{MnCl_2} + \overset{0}{Cl_2} + \overset{+1\ -2}{H_2O} + \overset{+1\ -1}{KCl}$

Manganese is reduced ($+7 \rightarrow +2$).
Chloride ion is oxidized ($-1 \rightarrow 0$).

    d. $\overset{0}{Sb} + \overset{+1\ +5\ -2}{HNO_3} \rightarrow \overset{+5\ -2}{Sb_2O_5} + \overset{+2\ -2}{NO} + \overset{+1\ -2}{H_2O}$

Antimony is oxidized ($0 \rightarrow +5$).
Nitrogen is reduced ($+5 \rightarrow +2$).

4. a. Oxidizing agent is sulfur;
Reducing agent is carbon.

    b. Oxidizing agent is nitrogen;
Reducing agent is iodine.

    c. Oxidizing agent is manganese;
Reducing agent is chlorine.

    d. Oxidizing agent is nitrogen;
Reducing agent is antimony.

Section 20.3

1. a. Increase in oxidation number of carbon $= +4$; decrease in oxidation number of sulfur $= -2$.

$C + 2H_2SO_4 \rightarrow CO_2 + 2SO_2 + 2H_2O$

    b. Increase in oxidation number of sulfur $= +2$; decrease in oxidation number of nitrogen $= -3$.

$3H_2S + 2HNO_3 \rightarrow 3S + 2NO + 4H_2O$

    c. Increase in oxidation number of iodine ion $= +1$; decrease in oxidation number of nitrogen $= -3$.

$2HNO_3 + 6HI \rightarrow 2NO + 3I_2 + 4H_2O$

    d. Increase in oxidation number of antimony $= +5$; decrease in oxidation number of nitrogen $= -3$.

$6Sb + 10HNO_3 \rightarrow 3Sb_2O_5 + 10NO + 5H_2O$

    e. Increase in oxidation number of chlorine ion $= +1$; decrease in oxidation number of manganese $= -5$.

$2KMnO_4 + 16HCl$
$\rightarrow 2MnCl_2 + 5Cl_2 + 8H_2O + 2KCl$

---

f. Increase in oxidation number of iodine ion $= +1$; decrease in oxidation number of iodine $= -7$.

$KIO_4 + 7KI + 8HCl \rightarrow 8KCl + 4I_2 + 4H_2O$

g. Increase in oxidation number of zinc $= +2$; decrease in oxidation number of chromium $= -3$.

$3Zn + 2Cr_2O_7{}^{2-} + 28H^+$
$\rightarrow 3Zn^{2+} + 4Cr^{3+} + 14H_2O$

2. a. $Fe^{2+} \rightarrow Fe^{3+} + e^-$

$5e^- + 8H^+ + MnO_4{}^- \rightarrow Mn^{2+} + 4H_2O$

    b. $Sn^{2+} \rightarrow Sn^{4+} + 2e^-$

$6H^+ + 6e^- + IO_3{}^- \rightarrow I^- + 3H_2O$

    c. $S^{2-} \rightarrow S + 2e^-$

$3e^- + 4H^+ + NO_3{}^- \rightarrow NO + 2H_2O$

    d. $4OH^- + Mn^{2+} \rightarrow MnO_2 + 2H_2O + 2e^-$

$2e^- + H_2O + H_2O_2 \rightarrow H_2O + 2OH^-$

3. a. $2OH^- + Zn + HgO \rightarrow ZnO_2{}^{2-} + Hg + H_2O$

    b. $8H^+ + 5Fe^{2+} + MnO_4{}^-$
$\rightarrow 5Fe^{3+} + Mn^{2+} + 4H_2O$

    c. $6H^+ + 3Sn^{2+} + IO_3{}^- \rightarrow 3Sn^{4-} + I^- + 3H_2O$

    d. $8H^+ + 3S^{2-} + 2NO_3{}^- \rightarrow 3S + 2NO + 4H_2O$

    e. $2OH^- + Mn^{2+} + H_2O_2 \rightarrow MnO_2 + 2H_2O$

    f. $2OH^- + CrO_2 + ClO^-$
$\rightarrow CrO_4{}^{2-} + Cl^- + H_2O$

Interpreting Graphics 20

1. a. 3   **d.** 2

    b. 2   **e.** 4

    c. 3   **f.** 1

2. $MnO_4{}^- + 8H^+ + 5Fe^{2+}$
$\rightarrow Mn^{2+} + 4H_2O + 5Fe^{3+}$

3. The end point occurs when the number of equivalents of $MnO_4{}^-$ added equals the number of equivalents of Fe^{2+} originally present in the reaction flask. One equivalent is the amount of reducing agent (or oxidizing agent) that can give (or accept) one mole of electrons. When all the Fe^{2+} in the flask is oxidized, the next drop of $MnO_4{}^-$ remains unreacted, and the solution in the flask turns light purple, signaling the end point of the titration.

4. Volume $KMnO_4$ = Initial Volume − Final Volume = 48.65 mL − 23.35 mL = 25.30 mL

$$\text{Moles } MnO_4{}^- = 0.02530 \cancel{L} \times \frac{0.0200 \text{ mol}}{\cancel{L}}$$

$$= 5.06 \times 10^{-4} \text{ mol } MnO_4{}^-$$

$$\text{Moles iron(II)} = 5.06 \times 10^{-4} \; \cancel{\text{mol MnO}_4^-}$$
$$\times \frac{5 \; \text{mol Fe}^{2+}}{1 \; \cancel{\text{mol MnO}_4^-}} = 2.53 \times 10^{-3} \; \text{mol Fe}^{2+}$$
$$\text{Mass Fe} = 2.53 \times 10^{-3} \; \cancel{\text{mol Fe}^{2+}}$$
$$\times \frac{55.85 \; \text{g Fe}^{2+}}{1 \; \cancel{\text{mol Fe}^{2+}}} = 0.141 \; \text{g}$$
$$\% \text{ Fe in ore} = \frac{0.141 \; \text{g}}{2.938 \; \text{g}} \times 100\% = 4.80\%$$

Vocabulary Review 20

1. oxidizing agent
2. oxidation-number-change method
3. reduction
4. half-reaction method
5. oxidation number
6. reducing agent
7. half-reaction
8. oxidation-reduction reaction
9. oxidation
10. redox reaction

Quiz for Chapter 20

1. b	4. b	7. c
2. a	5. a	8. d
3. b	6. a	

Chapter 20 Test A

A. Matching

1. d	5. i	9. c
2. j	6. g	10. h
3. f	7. e	
4. a	8. b	

B. Multiple Choice

11. b	17. c	23. d
12. d	18. c	24. c
13. c	19. a	25. c
14. b	20. a	26. c
15. a	21. c	
16. b	22. b	

C. Questions

27. **a.** Na oxidized, reducing agent; Br_2 reduced, oxidizing agent
    b. S reduced, oxidizing agent; K oxidized, reducing agent
28. $2Cr + 3Br_2 \rightarrow 2Cr^{3+} + 6Br^-$
29. **a.** Li $+1$, Al $+3$, F -1
    b. Na $+1$, O -2
    c. S 0 (element)
30. Oxidation-number change method:

$$\overset{\overbrace{\hspace{4em}}^{2 \times (-3) = -6}}{\overset{+3 \; -2 \quad +2 \; -2 \quad\quad 0 \quad\quad +4 \; -2}{Fe_2O_3 + CO \rightarrow Fe + CO_2}}$$
$$\underset{3 \times (+2) = +6}{\underbrace{\hspace{7em}}}$$

$$Fe_2O_3 + 3CO \rightarrow 2Fe + 3CO_2$$

Half-reaction method:
$$6H^+ + Fe_2O_3 + 6e^- \rightarrow 2Fe + 3H_2O$$
$$\underline{3(H_2O + CO \rightarrow CO_2 + 2H^+ + 2e^-)}$$
$$6H^+ + Fe_2O_3 + 6e^- + 3H_2O + 3CO$$
$$\rightarrow 2Fe + 3H_2O + 3CO_2 + 6H^+ + 6e^-$$
$$Fe_2O_3 + 3CO \rightarrow 2Fe + 3CO_2$$

D. Essay

31. An oxidation number is assigned to an element in a compound according to a set of arbitrary rules. The oxidation number of an element in an uncombined state is zero. The oxidation number of a monatomic ion is the same in magnitude and sign as the ionic charge. The sum of the oxidation numbers of the elements in a neutral compound is zero. In a polyatomic ion, however, the sum is equal to the charge on the ion. Oxidation numbers help keep track of electrons in redox reactions. An oxidation-number increase is oxidation. A decrease is reduction.

Chapter 20 Test B

A. Matching

1. e	5. i	9. b
2. f	6. a	10. j
3. d	7. c	
4. g	8. h	

B. Multiple Choice

11. d	17. a	23. d
12. a	18. b	24. c
13. a	19. c	25. d
14. d	20. c	26. b
15. d	21. b	27. b
16. b	22. b	28. a

C. Questions

29. **a.** K; I; I_2; K

  b. Na; H; H_2O; Na

  c. H; Cu; CuO; H_2

  d. Mg; Cu; $Cu(NO_3)_2$; Mg

30. **a.** $K_2SO_4 = +1, +6, -2$

  b. $Cu(NO_3)_2 = +2, +5, -2$

  c. $HAsO_3 = +1, +5, -2$

  d. $MnO_4^- = +7, -2$

31. **a.**
$$\overset{3 \times (+1) = +3}{\overbrace{}}$$
$$4HNO_3 + 3Ag \rightarrow 3AgNO_3 + NO + 2H_2O$$
$$\underset{1 \times (-3) = -3}{\underbrace{}}$$

  b.
$$\overset{1 \times (+2) = +2}{\overbrace{}}$$
$$Br_2 + SO_2 + 2H_2O \rightarrow H_2SO_4 + 2HBr$$
$$\underset{2 \times (-1) = -2}{\underbrace{}}$$

32. **a.** $HNO_2 + HI \rightarrow I_2 + NO + H_2O$

  $H^+(aq) + NO_2^-(aq) + H^+(aq) + I^-(aq)$
  $\quad\quad \rightarrow I_2(aq) + NO(g) + H_2O(l)$

  Oxidation: $2I^-(aq) \rightarrow I_2 + 2e^-$

  Reduction: $2[2H^+(aq) + NO_2^-(aq) + 1e^-$
  $\quad\quad\quad\quad \rightarrow NO + H_2O]$

  $\dfrac{4H^+ + 2NO_2^- + 2e^- \rightarrow 2NO + 2H_2O}{4H^+ + 2I^- + 2NO_2^- \rightarrow I_2 + 2NO + H_2O}$

  Final: $2HNO_2 + 2HI \rightarrow I_2 + 2NO + 2H_2O$

  b. $K_2Cr_2O_7 + FeCl_2 + HCl \rightarrow$
  $\quad\quad\quad CrCl_3 + KCl + FeCl_3 + H_2O$

  $2K^+(aq) + Cr_2O_7^{2-}(aq) + Fe^{2+}(aq) + 2Cl^-$
  $\quad\quad + H^+(aq) + Cl^-(aq)$
  $\rightarrow Cr^{3+}(aq) + 3Cl^-(aq) + K^+(aq) + Cl^-(aq)$
  $\quad\quad + Fe^{3+}(aq) + 3Cl^-(aq) + H_2O$

  Oxidation: $6[Fe^{2+} \rightarrow Fe^{2+} + 1e^-]$

  Reduction: $2Cr^{6+} + 6e^- \rightarrow 2Cr^{3+}$

  $\overline{6Fe^{2+} + 2Cr^{6+} \rightarrow 6Fe^{3+} + 2Cr^{3+}}$

  Final: $K_2Cr_2O_7 + 6FeCl_2 + 14HCl$
  $\quad\quad \rightarrow 2CrCl_3 + 2KCl + 6FeCl_3 + 7H_2O$

D. Essay

33. Since oxidation is the loss of electrons, it can only occur in the presence of another substance that will accept the lost electrons. The accepting substance gains electrons, and thus, undergoes reduction. In other words, a loss of electrons can only occur if a gain takes place concurrently.

Chapter 20 Small-Scale Lab

Section 20.3 Half Reactions, page 655

Analysis

	HCl	HNO$_3$	H$_2$SO$_4$
Zn	Bubbles	Bubbles	Bubbles
Mg	Bubbles	Bubbles	Bubbles
Cu	No visible reaction	No visible reaction	No visible reaction
Fe	Bubbles	Bubbles	Bubbles

Figure A

1. Mg is most reactive because it bubbles most vigorously. Cu did not react. The order of reactivity is Mg > Zn > Fe > Cu.

2. $H_2(g)$ is the gas produced all the reactions.

3. $Mg(s) + 2HCl(aq) \rightarrow H_2(g) + MgCl_2(aq)$

  $Mg(s) + 2H^+(aq) \rightarrow H_2(g) + Mg^{2+}(aq)$

  $Fe(s) + 2HCl(aq) \rightarrow H_2(g) + FeCl_2(aq)$

  $Fe(s) + 2H^+(aq) \rightarrow H_2(g) + Fe^{2+}(aq)$

  All are redox reactions because the oxidation number of reactants change.

4. $Mg(s) \rightarrow Mg^{2+}(aq) + 2e^-$

  $Fe(s) \rightarrow Fe^{2+}(aq) + 2e^-$

5. $2H^+ + 2e^- \rightarrow H_2(g)$.

  $Mg(s) \rightarrow Mg^{2+}(aq) + 2e^-$

$$Mg(s) + 2H^+(aq) \rightarrow H_2(g) + Mg^{2+}(aq)$$

You're the Chemist

1. Add a drop of any acid to the damaged part of the penny and notice that only the zinc interior reacts.

2. Many toilet-bowl cleaners and vinegar dissolve metals. Keep products containing acids away from metal pipes and fixtures.

Section Review 21.1

Part A Completion

1. electrochemical process
2. electrons
3. voltaic cells
4. salt bridge
5. ions
6. anode
7. cathode

Part B True-False

8. NT
9. AT
10. NT
11. ST

Part C Matching

12. g
13. f
14. d
15. b
16. c
17. e
18. a

Part D Problem

19. The shorthand notation $Mg(s) \mid MgSO_4(aq) \parallel PbSO_4(aq) \mid Pb(s)$ represents a magnesium-lead voltaic cell. The single vertical lines indicate boundaries of phases that are in contact, and the double vertical lines represent the salt bridge that separates the anode compartment from the cathode compartment. In this electrochemical cell, Mg is oxidized to Mg^{2+} at the anode (the negative electrode) and Pb^{2+} is reduced to Pb at the cathode (the positive electrode). Electrons flow from the anode, through an external circuit (connected to a light bulb or voltmeter), to the cathode. To complete the circuit, sulfate (SO_4^{2-}) anions move from the cathode compartment to the anode compartment, and magnesium and sodium cations move from the anode compartment to the cathode compartment. Check students' diagrams.

Section Review 21.2

Part A Completion

1. electric potential
2. electrons
3. cell potential
4. standard hydrogen electrode
5. 0.00 V
6. less
7. spontaneous

Part B True-False

8. NT
9. ST
10. NT
11. NT

Part C Matching

12. b
13. d
14. f
15. c
16. a
17. e

Part D Problem

18. Oxidation: $Mg \rightarrow Mg^{2+} + 2e^-$

Reduction: $\underline{ 2e^- + Cl_2 \rightarrow 2Cl^-}$

Redox: $Mg + Cl_2 \rightarrow Mg^{2+} + 2Cl^-$

$$\begin{aligned} E^0_{cell} &= E^0_{red} - E^0_{oxid} \\ &= E^0_{Cl_2} - E^0_{Mg} \\ &= +1.36\,V - (-2.37\,V) \\ &= +3.73\,V \end{aligned}$$

Section Review 21.3

Part A Completion

1. electrolysis
2. electrolytic cell
3. electrons
4. battery
5. electrolyte
6. hydrogen/oxygen
7. oxygen/hydrogen
8. hydrogen gas

Part B True-False

9. NT
10. ST
11. ST
12. AT

Part C Matching

13. b
14. d
15. e
16. c
17. a

Part D Questions and Problems

18. In electrolytic cells, electrical energy is used to bring about a normally nonspontaneous chemical reaction. In a voltaic cell, chemical energy is converted to electrical energy by a spontaneous redox reaction. Electrolytic cells are used in electroplating, in refining metals, and in the production of substances such as sodium hydroxide, aluminum, sodium, and chlorine. Voltaic cells are used in pacemakers, hearing aids, and cameras.

19.

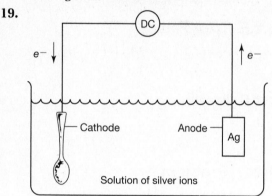

Anode (oxidation): $Ag(s) \rightarrow Ag^+(aq) + e^-$
Cathode (reduction): $Ag^+(aq) + e^- \rightarrow Ag(s)$

Practice Problems

Section 21.2

1. a. $Cl_2(g) + Mg(s) \rightarrow 2Cl^-(aq) + Mg^{2+}(aq)$
$E^0_{cell} = 1.36\,V - (-2.37\,V) = 3.73\,V$
cathode: $Cl_2(g) + 2e^- \rightarrow 2Cl^-(aq)$

b. $2Ag^+(aq) + Ni(s) \rightarrow Ni^{2+}(aq) + 2Ag(s)$
$E^0_{cell} = 0.80\,V - (-0.25\,V) = 1.05\,V$
cathode: $Ag^+(aq) + e^- \rightarrow Ag(s)$

c. $2MnO_4^-(aq) + 16H^+(aq) + 5Cd(s)$
$\rightarrow 5Cd^{2+}(aq) + 2Mn^{2+}(aq) + 8H_2O(l)$
$E^0_{cell} = 1.51\,V - (-0.40\,V) = 1.91\,V$
cathode: $MnO_4^-(aq) + 8H^+(aq) + 5e^-$
$\rightarrow Mn^{2+}(aq) + 4H_2O(l)$

d. $Br_2 + 2Na(s) \rightarrow 2Na^+(aq) + 2Br^-(aq)$
$E^0_{cell} = 1.07\,V - (-2.71\,V) = 3.78\,V$
cathode: $Br_2(l) + 2e^- \rightarrow 2Br^-(aq)$

e. $MnO_2(s) + 4H^+(aq) + H_2(g)$
$\rightarrow 2H^+(aq) + Mn^{2+}(aq) + 2H_2O(l)$
$E^0_{cell} = 1.28\,V - 0.00\,V = 1.28\,V$
cathode: $MnO_2(s) + 4H^+(aq) + 2e^-$
$\rightarrow Mn^{2+}(aq) + 2H_2O(l)$

2. a. $E^0_{cell} = -0.14\,V - (-2.90\,V) = +2.76\,V$; spontaneous

b. $E^0_{cell} = +0.80\,V - 1.36\,V = -0.56\,V$; nonspontaneous

c. $E^0_{cell} = +2.87\,V - (-0.76\,V) = +3.63\,V$; spontaneous

d. $E^0_{cell} = -0.28\,V - (-3.05\,V) = +2.77\,V$; spontaneous

e. $E^0_{cell} = -2.93\,V - 0.54\,V = -3.47\,V$; nonspontaneous

Interpreting Graphics 21

1. anode(+)

2. cathode(−)

3. electrorefining

4. a. The anode(+) of the electrolytic cell should be connected to the positive(+) terminal of the battery. The cathode(−) of the electrolytic cell should be connected to the negative(−) terminal of the battery.

b. The anode of the electrolytic cell is connected to the cathode of the battery. The cathode of the electrolytic cell is connected to the anode of the battery.

5. Oxidation occurs at the anode, labeled number 1 in the diagram. Reduction occurs at the cathode, labeled number 2 in the diagram.

6. Students should indicate the flow of electrons out of the anode(+) and into the cathode(−).

7. The voltage should be great enough to oxidize copper metal at the anode and reduce copper(II) ions at the cathode, but not high enough to oxidize other metals at the anode and reduce them at the cathode. The voltage should be greater than 0.34 V but less than 0.44 V.

8. a. gold, silver, and platinum

b. Zn^{2+} and Fe^{2+}

c. copper

Vocabulary Review 21

1. voltaic cell

2. fuel cell

3. electrochemical cell

4. electrochemical process

5. cathode

6. reduction potential

Solution: aluminum

Quiz for Chapter 21

1. NT	**7.** NT	**13.** NT
2. AT	**8.** AT	**14.** AT
3. NT	**9.** AT	**15.** NT
4. AT	**10.** ST	**16.** AT
5. ST	**11.** NT	**17.** AT
6. NT	**12.** AT	**18.** NT

Chapter 21 Test A

A. Matching

1. b	**5.** j	**9.** f
2. h	**6.** g	**10.** a
3. d	**7.** i	
4. c	**8.** e	

B. Multiple Choice

11. d	**16.** a	**21.** c
12. b	**17.** d	**22.** c
13. c	**18.** c	**23.** a
14. c	**19.** a	**24.** a
15. c	**20.** a	**25.** c

C. True-False

26. NT	**28.** AT	**30.** NT
27. NT	**29.** NT	

D. Question

31.

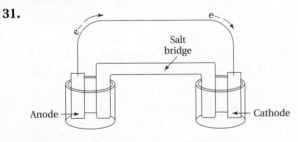

E. Essay

32. In both voltaic and electrolytic cells, oxidation occurs at the anode and reduction occurs at the cathode. In the voltaic cell, the cathode is positive and the anode is negative. In the electrolytic cell, the anode is positive and the cathode is negative.

F. Additional Questions

33. The negative value means that the tendency for zinc ions to be reduced is less than that of hydrogen ions to be reduced, so zinc metal is oxidized when paired with the standard hydrogen half-cell.

34. The reduction potential of a half-cell is a measure of the tendency of a given half-reaction to occur as a reduction.

35. **a.**
$$Ni^{2+}(aq) + 2e^- \rightarrow Ni(s) \qquad E^0 = -0.25\,V$$
$$Zn^{2+}(aq) + 2e^- \rightarrow Zn(s) \qquad E^0 = -0.76\,V$$
$$E^0_{cell} = E^0_{red} - E^0_{oxid}$$
$$= -0.76\,V - (-0.25\,V)$$
$$= -0.51\,V$$

This reaction is not spontaneous.

b.
$$2[Al^{3+}(aq) + 3e^- \rightarrow Al(s)] \qquad E^0 = -1.66\,V$$
$$3[Co^{2+}(aq) + 2e^- \rightarrow Co(s)] \qquad E^0 = -0.28\,V$$
$$E^0_{cell} = E^0_{red} - E^0_{oxid}$$
$$= -1.66\,V - (-0.28\,V)$$
$$= -1.38\,V$$

This reaction is not spontaneous.

Chapter 21 Test B

A. Matching

1. h	**5.** c	**9.** b
2. d	**6.** g	**10.** a
3. f	**7.** j	
4. i	**8.** e	

B. Multiple Choice

11. c	**17.** d	**23.** b
12. d	**18.** a	**24.** a
13. b	**19.** d	**25.** b
14. c	**20.** c	**26.** c
15. d	**21.** b	**27.** d
16. a	**22.** c	

C. True-False

28. NT	**30.** AT	**32.** AT
29. NT	**31.** AT	**33.** ST

D. Question

34.

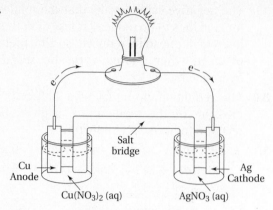

Cu Anode — Salt bridge — Ag Cathode
$Cu(NO_3)_2$ (aq) — $AgNO_3$ (aq)

35. $Cu(s) \rightarrow Cu^{2+}(aq) + 2e^-$

$2Ag^+(aq) + 2e^- \rightarrow 2Ag(s)$

Net: $Cu(s) + 2Ag^+(aq) \rightarrow Cu^{2+}(aq) + 2Ag(s)$

$E^0_{cell} = E^0_{red} - E^0_{oxid}$

$\qquad = +0.80\,V - (+0.34\,V)$

$\qquad = +0.46\,V$

E. Essay

36. In both voltaic and electrolytic cells, electrons flow from the anode to the cathode through the external circuit, reduction occurs at the cathode, and oxidation occurs at the anode. However, while the flow of electrons in a voltaic cell is caused by a spontaneous chemical reaction, in an electrolytic cell the flow of electrons is being pushed by an outside source such as a battery. Additionally, while the anode is the negative electrode and the cathode is the positive electrode in a voltaic cell, the reverse is true in an electrolytic cell—the anode in an electrolytic cell is the positive electrode and the cathode is negative.

F. Additional Questions

37. Since Al is above Pb in the reduction potential table, Al is oxidized and Pb is reduced. Thus, the two half-cell reactions are as follows:

$2[Al(s) \rightarrow Al^{3+}(aq) + 3e^-]$

$3[Pb^{2+}(aq) + 2e^- \rightarrow Pb(s)]$

Net: $2Al(s) + 3Pb^{2+}(aq) \rightarrow 2Al^{3+}(aq) + 3Pb(s)$

$E^0_{cell} = E^0_{red} - E^0_{oxid}$

$\qquad = -0.13\,V - (-1.66\,V)$

$\qquad = +1.53\,V$

38. a. The half-reactions are:

Oxidation: $Na(s) \rightarrow Na^+(aq) + e^-$

$E^0 = -2.71\,V$

Reduction: $Cu^{2+}(aq) + 2e^- \rightarrow Cu(s)$

$E^0 = +0.34\,V$

$E^0_{cell} = E^0_{red} - E^0_{oxid}$

$E^0_{cell} = +0.34\,V - (-2.71\,V)$

$E^0_{cell} = +3.05\,V$

Since the standard cell potential is positive, the redox reaction will be spontaneous.

b. The half-reactions are:

Oxidation: $Ag(s) \rightarrow Ag^+(aq) + e^-$

$E^0 = +0.80\,V$

Reduction: $Mg^{2+}(aq) + 2e^- \rightarrow Mg(s)$

$E^0 = -2.37\,V$

$E^0_{cell} = E^0_{red} - E^0_{oxid}$

$\qquad = -2.37\,V - (+0.80\,V)$

$\qquad = -3.17\,V$

Since the standard cell potential is negative, the redox reaction will be nonspontaneous.

c. The half-reactions are:

Oxidation: $Al(s) \rightarrow Al^{3+}(aq) + 3e^-$

$E^0 = -1.66\,V$

Reduction: $Zn^{2+}(aq) + 2e^- \rightarrow Zn(s)$

$E^0 = -0.76\,V$

$E^0_{cell} = E^0_{red} - E^0_{oxid}$

$\qquad = -0.76\,V - (-1.66\,V)$

$\qquad = +0.90\,V$

Since the standard cell potential is positive, the redox reaction will be spontaneous.

39. Reaction 1: since Z is oxidized and X^{2+} is reduced, Z appears above X in the activity series.

Reaction 2: since W is not oxidized in the presence of X^{2+}, W should appear below X.

Reaction 3: since Y is oxidized and Z^{2+} is reduced, Y appears above Z.

The elements should be listed as follows: Y, Z, X, and W.

Chapter 21 Small-Scale Lab

Section 21.3 Electrolysis of Water, page 684

Analysis

H$_2$O	Na$_2$SO$_4$	Na$_2$SO$_4$ + BTB
No visible reaction	Bubbles at both the anode and cathode	Anode area turns yellow, cathode area turns blue

Figure A

1. Pure water has too few ions to carry an electric current.

2. Sodium sulfate is an electrolyte. It dissociates into ions in solution, which carry an electric current through the solution.

3. The bubbles are H$_2$(g) and the blue BTB solution indicates the presence of OH$^-$ ions.

4. The bubbles are O$_2$(g) and H$^+$ ions in solution impart the yellow color to the BTB solution.

5.
$$2H_2O + 2e^- \rightarrow H_2(g) + 2OH^-$$
$$\underline{H_2O \rightarrow \tfrac{1}{2}O_2(g) + 2H^+ + 2e^-}$$
$$3H_2O \rightarrow H_2(g) + \tfrac{1}{2}O_2(g) + 2OH^- + 2H^+$$
$$3H_2O \rightarrow H_2(g) + \tfrac{1}{2}O_2(g) + 2H_2O$$
$$H_2O \rightarrow H_2(g) + \tfrac{1}{2}O_2(g)$$

You're the Chemist

1.

KI	KI + starch	KI + BTB
Bubbles at the cathode. Yellow soln at the anode.	Bubbles at the cathode. Black solution at the anode.	Bubbles and blue soln at the cathode. Yellow soln at the anode.

Figure B

The bubbles are H$_2$(g) and the blue solution indicates of the presence of OH$^-$ ions. The yellow solution is I$_2$(aq), which is black in the presence of starch.

2. NaCl:
Cathode: $2H_2O + 2e^- \rightarrow H_2(g) + 2OH^-$
Bubbles, blue BTB
Anode: $2Cl^- \rightarrow Cl_2(aq) + 2e^-$
Yellow solution.

KBr:
Cathode: $2H_2O + 2e^- \rightarrow H_2(g) + 2OH^-$
Bubbles, blue BTB
Anode: $2Br^- \rightarrow Br_2(aq) + 2e^-$
Yellow solution.

CuSO$_4$:
Cathode: $Cu^{2+} + 2e^- \rightarrow H_2(g) + 2OH^-$
Copper plates out.
Anode: $H_2O \rightarrow \tfrac{1}{2}O_2(g) + 2H^+ + 2e^-$
Bubbles, yellow BTB

3.
	E^o
$2H_2O + 2e^- \rightarrow H_2(g) + 2OH^-$	0.00 V
$H_2O \rightarrow \tfrac{1}{2}O_2(g) + 2H^+ + 2e^-$	-0.82 V
$2I^- \rightarrow I_2(aq) + 2e^-$	-0.54 V

I$^-$ is more likely to oxidize (lose electrons) than H$_2$O because it has a more favorable (more positive) E^o value.

Section Review 22.1

Part A Completion

1. carbon	6. straight
2. organic	7. branches
3. hydrocarbons	8. alkyl
4. four	9. longest
5. single	10. parent

Part B True-False

11. NT	13. AT	15. AT
12. ST	14. ST	

Part C Matching

16. d	18. e	20. b
17. a	19. f	21. c

Part D Questions and Problems

22. 2,2-dimethylbutane

23. **a.** 16   **b.** 16

24.

$$CH_3-\overset{\overset{\displaystyle CH_3}{|}}{\underset{\underset{\displaystyle CH_3}{|}}{C}}-\overset{\overset{\displaystyle CH_2}{|}\atop\overset{\displaystyle CH_3}{}}{CH}-CH_2-\overset{\overset{\displaystyle CH_3}{|}}{CH}-CH_2-CH_2-CH_3$$

Section 22.2

Part A Completion

1. unsaturated
2. double
3. triple
4. longest
5. double
6. alkane
7. *-ene*
8. double bond
9. *-yne*

Part B True-False

10. NT
11. ST
12. AT
13. ST

Part C Matching

14. c
15. d
16. a
17. b

Part D Questions and Problems

18. 3-methyl-2-hexene
19. 2,3,4,5-tetramethylnonane
20. 4-methyl-1-hexene
21.

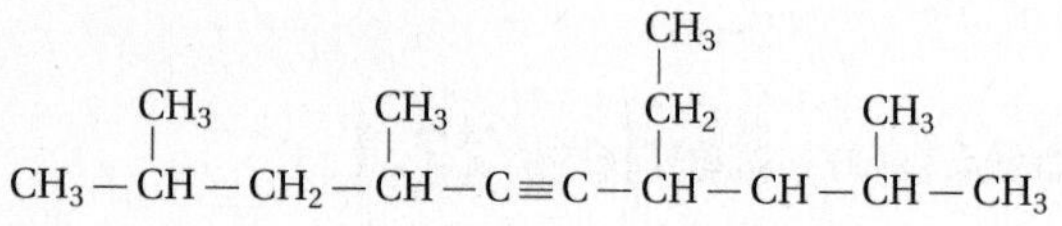

$$CH_3-CH-CH_2-CH-C\equiv C-CH-CH-CH-CH_3$$

with substituents: CH_3, CH_3, CH_2 (CH_3), CH_3

Section 22.3

Part A Completion

1. molecular
2. structures
3. butane
4. properties
5. Geometric
6. *cis*
7. *trans*
8. stereoisomer
9. asymmetric
10. optical
11. mirror
12. superimposed

Part B True-False

13. NT
14. ST
15. NT
16. AT

Part C Matching

17. h
18. e
19. d
20. c
21. f
22. b
23. a
24. g

Part D Problems

25. $CH_3-CH_2-CH_2-CH_2-CH_3$

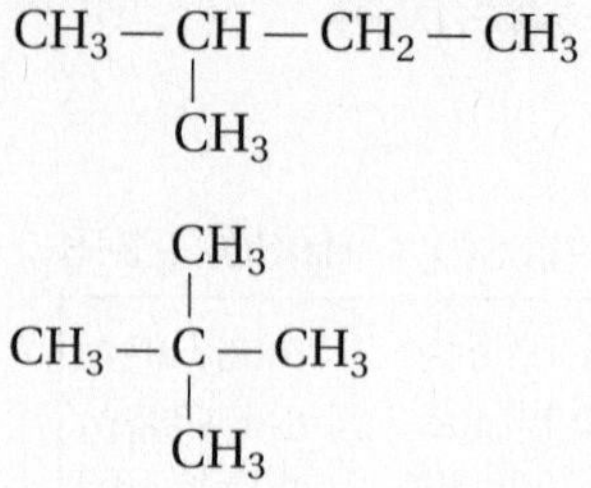

$$CH_3-CH-CH_2-CH_3$$
with CH_3

$$CH_3-\underset{CH_3}{\overset{CH_3}{C}}-CH_3$$

26. Carbon 2 is the asymmetric carbon.

27.

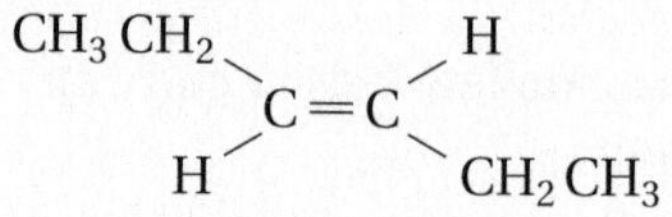

$$\underset{H}{\overset{CH_3CH_2}{>}}C=C\underset{CH_2CH_3}{\overset{H}{<}}$$

trans-3-hexene

$$\underset{H}{\overset{CH_3CH_2}{>}}C=C\underset{H}{\overset{CH_2CH_3}{<}}$$

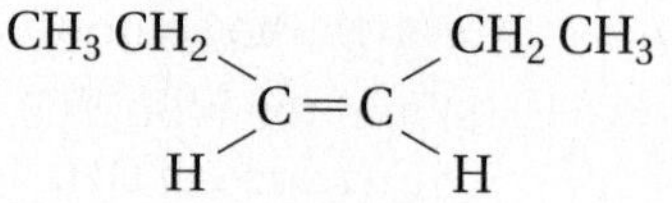

cis-3-hexene

Section 22.4

Part A Completion

1. cyclic
2. aromatic
3. six
4. hydrogen
5. double
6. resonance
7. Methylbenzene
8. xylenes
9. *ortho, o*
10. *meta, m*
11. *para, p*

Part B True-False

12. ST
13. AT
14. ST
15. AT
16. ST

Part C Matching

17. d
18. a
19. c
20. b

Part D Questions and Problems

21. ⬡ — $CH_2CH_2CH_3$

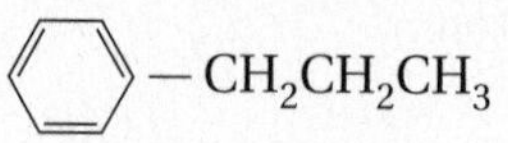

22. $CH_2=CH-CH-CH_3$ with ⬡

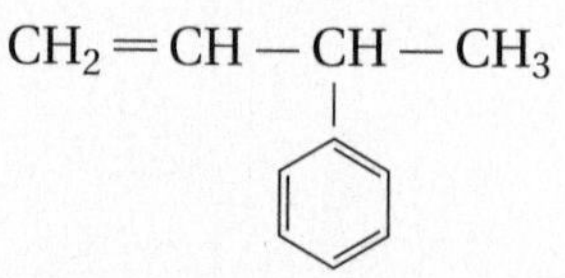

23. a. cyclooctane

    b. 1,3-diethylbenzene or *m*-diethylbenzene

Section 22.5

Part A Completion

1. natural gas
2. coal
3. methane
4. aliphatic
5. distillation
6. boiling point
7. lignite
8. bituminous
9. anthracite
10. aromatic

Part B True-False

11. NT
12. NT
13. AT
14. ST

Part C Matching

15. b
16. d
17. e
18. c
19. a

Part D Problems

20. $2C_5H_{12}(l) + 11O_2(g) \rightarrow 10CO(g) + 12H_2O(g)$
21. $2C_6H_6 + 15O_2 \rightarrow 12CO_2 + 6H_2O$

Practice Problems

Section 22.1

1. 5-ethyl-3,3,5-trimethyloctane
2. 3-ethyl-2,3,5,5-tetramethylheptane
3. **a.**

$$CH_3-CH-\underset{\underset{CH_2}{\underset{|}{CH_3}}}{\overset{\overset{CH_3}{\overset{|}{C}}}{C}}-CH_2-CH_3$$
$$CH_3$$

  b. $CH_3-CH_2-\underset{\underset{CH_3}{\underset{|}{CH_2}}}{CH}-\underset{\underset{CH_3}{\underset{|}{CH_2}}}{CH}-CH_2-CH_3$

  c. $CH_3-\underset{\underset{CH_3}{|}}{CH}-\underset{\underset{CH_3}{|}}{CH}-\underset{\underset{CH_3}{|}}{CH}-\underset{\underset{CH_3}{|}}{CH}-CH_2-CH_2-CH_2-CH_3$

4. heptane:
$$CH_3-CH_2-CH_2-CH_2-CH_2-CH_2-CH_3$$
octane:
$$CH_3-CH_2-CH_2-CH_2-CH_2-CH_2-CH_2-CH_3$$

5. 19

Section 22.2

1. 2,4-dimethyl-2-hexene
2. 3,4-dimethyl-1-pentyne
3. 1-pentyne: $CH\equiv C-CH_2-CH_2-CH_3$
   2-pentyne: $CH_3-C\equiv C-CH_2-CH_3$
   3-methyl-1-butyne:
$$CH\equiv C-\underset{\underset{CH_3}{|}}{CH}-CH_3$$

4. **a.** $CH_2=CH-\underset{\underset{CH_3}{|}}{CH}-CH_2-\underset{\underset{CH_3}{|}}{CH}-CH_3$

  b. $CH_2=CH-CH_2-\underset{\underset{CH_3}{|}}{CH}-CH_3$

  c.
$$CH\equiv C-\underset{\underset{CH_3}{\underset{|}{C}}}{\overset{\overset{CH_3}{\overset{|}{}}}{C}}-CH_3$$

Section 22.3

1. *cis*-2-pentene
2. *trans*-6-methyl-3-heptene
3.
$$\underset{H}{\overset{CH_3}{\diagdown}}C=C\underset{CH_2-CH_2-CH_2-CH_3}{\overset{H}{\diagup}}$$

4. a, d
5. Carbon 3 is the asymmetric carbon.
6. a, c

Section 22.4

1. 1-ethyl-3-methylbenzene
2. 5-phenyl-2-hexene
3. **a.**

$$\underset{\underset{CH_2}{|}}{CH_2}\overset{\overset{CH}{|}}{}\underset{}{CH_2}$$

  b.
$$\underset{\bigcirc}{\overset{H}{\diagdown}}C=C\underset{\bigcirc}{\overset{H}{\diagup}}$$

  c.
$$CH_3-CH_2-\bigcirc-CH_2-CH_3$$

Section 22.5

1. $2C_8H_{18} + 25O_2 \rightarrow 16CO_2 + 18H_2O$

2. The refining process yields fractions that differ with respect to the length of the carbon chains. Natural gas contains mainly low molar mass, straight-chain alkanes—methane, ethane, propane, and butane. Gasoline is composed of alkanes with five to twelve carbon atoms. Kerosene is composed of alkanes with twelve to fifteen carbon atoms.

Interpreting Graphics 22

1. A

2. C

3. 3,3-dimethylpentane

4. D and F; *cis*-2-pentene and *trans*-2-pentene

5. E; 2-phenylbutane; C-2 is asymmetric

6. 22

7. 10

8. Compounds A (2-phenylpropane) and E (2-phenylbutane) are aromatic compounds.

9. Compounds D and F are geometric isomers. Like all isomers, they are different compounds with different properties. Thus, the boiling points of compounds D and F are not expected to be the same. (In fact, the boiling points of *trans*-2-pentene and *cis*-2-pentene are 36.3°C and 36.9°C respectively, a small but measurable difference.)

Vocabulary Review 22

1. alkynes

2. substituent

3. *cis* configuration

4. homologous series

5. cracking

6. arene

7. stereoisomers

8. saturated compounds

Solution: hydrocarbons

Chapter 22 Quiz

1. ST
2. NT
3. NT
4. AT
5. NT
6. NT
7. NT
8. AT
9. ST
10. AT

11. 2,5,7-trimethyl-3-octene

12.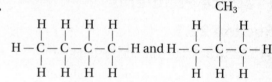

Chapter 22 Test A

A. Matching

1. g
2. i
3. a
4. h
5. d
6. c
7. f
8. e
9. j
10. b

B. Multiple Choice

11. c
12. c
13. a
14. b
15. d
16. c
17. c
18. d
19. a
20. a
21. c
22. c
23. b

C. Problems

24. 2-methyl-2-phenylbutane

25.

$$H-\overset{\overset{\displaystyle H}{|}}{\underset{\underset{\displaystyle H}{|}}{C}}-\overset{\overset{\displaystyle H}{|}}{\underset{\underset{\displaystyle H}{|}}{C}}-\overset{\overset{\displaystyle H}{|}}{\underset{\underset{\displaystyle H}{|}}{C}}-\overset{\overset{\displaystyle H}{|}}{\underset{\underset{\displaystyle H}{|}}{C}}-H \text{ and } H-\overset{\overset{\displaystyle H}{|}}{\underset{\underset{\displaystyle H}{|}}{C}}-\overset{\overset{\displaystyle CH_3}{|}}{\underset{\underset{\displaystyle H}{|}}{C}}-\overset{\overset{\displaystyle H}{|}}{\underset{\underset{\displaystyle H}{|}}{C}}-H$$

26.

$$CH_3-\overset{\overset{\displaystyle CH_3}{|}}{C}=CH-\overset{\overset{\displaystyle CH_2}{|}}{C}-CH_2-\overset{\overset{\displaystyle CH_3}{|}}{CH}-CH_3$$

27. $2C_6H_{14}(l) + 19O_2(g) \rightarrow 12CO_2(g) + 14H_2O(l)$

D. Essay

28. 1. Find the root word (ending in -*ane*) in the hydrocarbon name. Then draw the longest carbon chain to form the parent structure. 2. Number the carbons in the chain. 3. Identify the substituent groups. Attach the substituents to the numbered chain at the proper positions. 4. Add hydrogens as needed so that each carbon added has four bonds.

E. Additional Problems

29. Carbon 3 is asymmetric.

30.

$$CH_3\text{—}\underset{\displaystyle \underset{|}{C}=\underset{\displaystyle \underset{|}{H}}{C}}{H}\overset{\overset{CH_3}{|}}{CH}-CH_2-CH_3$$

$$\underset{H}{\overset{CH_3}{\diagdown}}C=C\underset{\overset{|}{CH_3}}{\overset{H}{\diagup}}CH-CH_2-CH_3$$

F. True-False

31. AT **33.** AT
32. AT **34.** NT

Chapter 22 Test B

A. Matching

1. b   **5.** h   **8.** c
2. i   **6.** a   **9.** j
3. f   **7.** d   **10.** e
4. g

B. Multiple Choice

11. d   **17.** b   **23.** c
12. c   **18.** d   **24.** d
13. b   **19.** d   **25.** a
14. b   **20.** d   **26.** d
15. c   **21.** b   **27.** b
16. d   **22.** c   **28.** d

C. True-False

29. AT   **33.** AT   **36.** NT
30. AT   **34.** AT   **37.** NT
31. NT   **35.** AT   **38.** ST
32. AT

D. Problems

39. a.

$$CH_3-\overset{\overset{CH_3}{|}}{CH}-\overset{\overset{CH_3}{|}}{CH_2}-CH_2-CH_3$$

b.

$$CH_3-\overset{\overset{CH_3}{|}}{C}=\overset{\overset{CH_3}{|}}{C}-\underset{\underset{\underset{CH_3}{|}}{CH_2}}{C}-CH_2-CH_3$$

c.

$$CH_3-C\equiv C-\overset{\overset{CH_2CH_3}{|}}{CH}-\underset{\underset{\underset{CH_3}{|}}{CH_2}}{\overset{\overset{CH_3}{|}}{C}}-\overset{\overset{CH_3}{|}}{CH}-\overset{\overset{CH_3}{|}}{CH}-CH_3$$

40. a. 3,5-diethyl-4-methylheptane
b. 3-ethyl-2,4,4-trimethyl-2-pentene
c. 6,7-diethyl-2,8-dimethyl-5-propyl-3-decyne

41. a. CH_3—CH_2—CH_2—CH_2—CH_3 pentane
b.

$$CH_3-\overset{\overset{CH_3}{|}}{CH}-CH_2-CH_3$$

2-methylbutane

c.

$$CH_3-\overset{\overset{CH_3}{|}}{\underset{\underset{CH_3}{|}}{C}}-CH_3$$

2,2-dimethylpropane

42.

$$\underset{H}{\overset{CH_3}{\diagdown}}C=C\underset{H}{\overset{CH_3}{\diagup}} \qquad \underset{H}{\overset{CH_3}{\diagdown}}C=C\underset{CH_3}{\overset{H}{\diagup}}$$

cis-2-butene   *trans*-2-butene

E. Essay

43. a. hexane C_6H_{14}
CH_3—CH_2—CH_2—CH_2—CH_2—CH_3
b. 2-hexene C_6H_{12}
CH_3—$CH=CH$—CH_2—CH_2—CH_3
c. 2-hexyne C_6H_{10}
CH_3—$C\equiv C$—CH_2—CH_2—CH_3

The number of hydrogen atoms decreases when carbon atoms form double or triple bonds in the alkene and alkyne, respectively. The number of hydrogen atoms is at a maximum in the unsaturated alkane.

F. Additional Problems

44. Carbon 3 is asymmetric because there are four different groups attached to it—a methyl, an ethyl, propyl groups, plus a 3-carbon branched chain.

45. a. ethylbenzene
b. 2,3-dimethyl-3-phenylhexane

Chapter 22 Small-Scale Labs

Section 22.3 Hydrocarbon Isomers, page 708

Analyze

1.

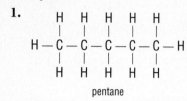

pentane

H H H H
$H-C-C-C-C-H$
H | H H
$H-C-H$
H

2-methylbutane

H
$H-C-H$
$H-C-C-C-H$
$H-C-H$
H

2, 2-dimethylpropane

2. To find the number of hydrogen atoms on any carbon of a line-angle formula, count the number of lines drawn to any point and subtract from four.

3. $CH_3CH_2CH_2CH_3$

butane

CH_3CHCH_3
CH_3

methylpropane

You're the Chemist

1.

hexane

2-methylpentane

3-methylpentane

2,3-dimethylbutane

2,2-dimethylbutane

2.

H H
$C=C$
H $CH_2CH_2CH_3$

1-pentene

CH_3 H
$C=C$
H CH_2CH_3

trans-2-pentene

CH_3 CH_2CH_3
$C=C$
H H

cis-2-pentene

CH_3 H
$C=C$
CH_3CH_2 H

2-methyl-1-butene

CH_3 H
C
CH_3 $C=C$
H H

3-methyl-1-butene

CH_3 CH_3
$C=C$
H CH_3

3-methyl-2-butene

Section Review 23.1

Part A Completion

1. functional
2. reactive/functional
3. alkenes
4. alkynes
5. Halocarbons
6. substitution
7. hydrogen
8. bromine
9. alcohol
10. salt

Part B True-False

11. AT
12. NT
13. ST
14. AT

Part C Matching

15. d
16. b
17. a
18. c

Part D Problems

19. **a.** hydroxyl
    b. carbonyl
    c. carbonyl
    d. carboxyl

20. **a.**

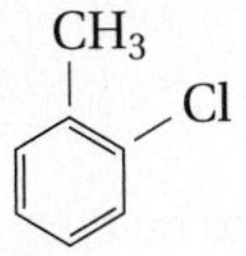

   b.

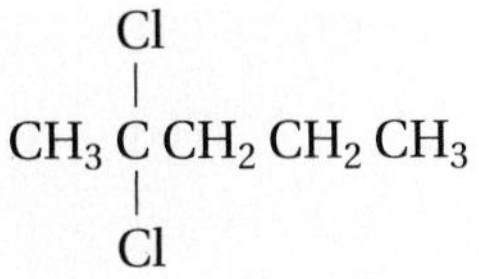

Section Review 23.2

Part A Completion

1. Alcohols
2. primary
3. secondary
4. tertiary
5. secondary
6. hydrogen bonding
7. hydration
8. water
9. hydrogenation
10. alkane
11. ethers
12. lower

Part B True-False

13. AT
14. NT
15. AT
16. NT

Part C Matching

17. e
18. a
19. d
20. b
21. c

Part D Problems

22. **a.** tertiary
    b. primary

23. **a.**

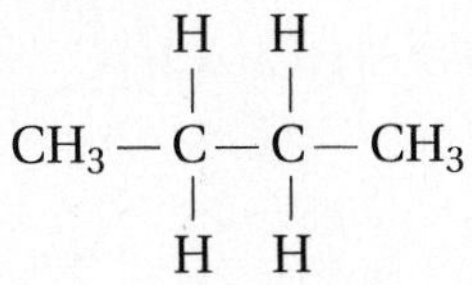

   b.

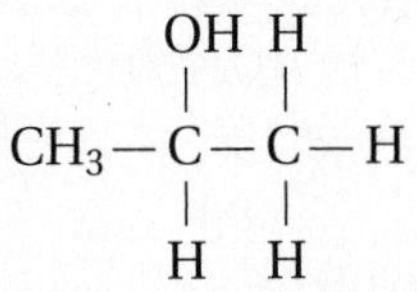

Section Review 23.3

Part A Completion

1. oxygen
2. double
3. ketones/carboxylic acids
4. ketones/carboxylic acids
5. aldehyde
6. carboxylic acid
7. formaldehyde
8. carboxylic acids
9. esters
10. propanol
11. oxidation–reduction
12. potassium dichromate

Part B True-False

14. AT
15. NT
16. NT
17. AT

Part C Matching

18. c
19. d
20. e
21. b
22. a

Part D Questions and Problems

23.

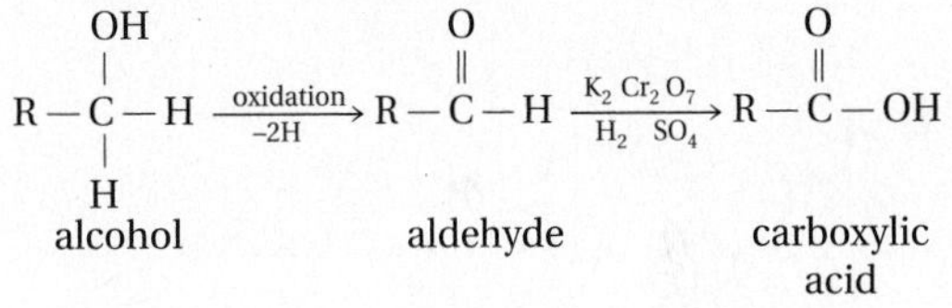

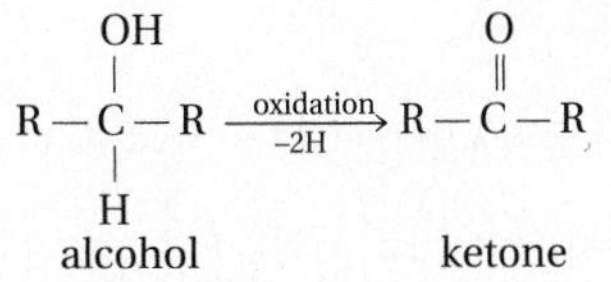

24. 3–hexanone

Section Review 23.4

Part A Completion

1. polymer
2. Addition
3. Condensation
4. Polyethylene
5. polyesters
6. length

Part B True-False

7. ST
8. AT
9. NT
10. AT
11. AT

Part C Matching

Part D Questions and Problems

17.

$$x \;\; \begin{array}{c} H \\ \diagdown \\ \diagup \\ H \end{array} C = C \begin{array}{c} H \\ \diagup \\ \diagdown \\ H \end{array} \longrightarrow H \left(CH_2 - CH_2 \right)_x H$$

18. Polyesters are polymers consisting of many repeating units of dicarboxylic acids and dihydroxy alcohols joined by ester bonds. Dacron™ is one example of a polyester.

Practice Problems

Section 23.1

1. a. ether   **c.** halogen

    b. carboxyl   **d.** hydroxyl

2. They are all halocarbons.

    a. *m*-bromobenzene

    b. 1-bromo-1-chloroethane

    c. chloroethene (vinyl chloride)

3. a.

$$\begin{array}{c} CH_3 \\ \diagdown \\ CH_3 \diagup \end{array} CH - CH_2 - CH_2 - OH + NaBr$$

    b. $CCl_4 + 4HCl$

4. a.

(structure: benzene ring with Br and CH_2CH_3)

    b. $CH_3 CH_2 CH_2 - CH - CH - CH_2 CH_2 Br$ with CH_3 CH_3 substituents

Section 23.2

1. a. 2-butanol; secondary

    b. ethylphenyl ether

    c. 3-methyl-1-butanol; primary

    d. 1-pentanol; primary

2. dipropyl ether:

$$CH_3 CH_2 CH_2 - O - CH_2 CH_2 CH_3$$

2-methyl-1-butanol:

$$\begin{array}{c} CH_3 \\ | \\ CH_3 CH_2 \; C \; CH_2 OH \\ | \\ H \end{array}$$

2,3-butanediol:

$$\begin{array}{c} CH_3 - CH - CH - CH_3 \\ \quad | \quad\quad | \\ \quad OH \quad OH \end{array}$$

2,3-butanediol is expected to be most soluble due to its two —OH groups, which can form hydrogen bonds with water.

3. a. $CH_3 CH_2 CH = CH_2 + HCl \longrightarrow CH_3 CH_2 CH CH_3$ with Cl substituent

    b. (benzene) $+ Br_2 \xrightarrow{\text{catalyst}}$ (benzene with Br) $+ HBr$

4. a. addition   **b.** substitution

Section 23.3

1. a. benzaldehyde

    b. 2-butanone

    c. 3-methylpentanoic acid

    d. ethyl butanoate

    e. 3-phenyl-2-propenal

2. a. ethanal (acetaldehyde)

    b. propane

    c. 1-butanol

3. a. 2-pentanone

    b. octanoic acid

    c. 1-butene or 2-butene

4. a.

$$\begin{array}{c} CH_3 \\ \diagdown \\ CH_3 \diagup \end{array} CH - OH + CH_3 CH_2 CH_2 \; \overset{\displaystyle O}{\overset{\|}{C}} _{OH}$$

$$\xrightarrow{H^+} CH_3 CH_2 CH_2 \; \overset{\displaystyle O}{\overset{\|}{C}} \begin{array}{c} \\ O - CH \diagup \end{array} \begin{array}{c} CH_3 \\ \diagdown \\ CH_3 \end{array} + H_2O$$

    b. $CH_3 CH_2 CH_2 CH_2 OH \xrightarrow[H_2SO_4]{K_2Cr_2O_7} CH_3 CH_2 CH_2 \; \overset{\displaystyle O}{\overset{\|}{C}} _{OH}$

5. a. esterification

    b. oxidation-reduction; 1–butanol is oxidized to butanoic acid.

Section 23.4

1. propene (propylene)

$$x\text{CH}_2 \!=\! \underset{\underset{\text{CH}_3}{|}}{\text{CH}}$$

polypropylene

$$\left(\!\!\begin{array}{c}\\ \text{CH}_2 - \underset{\underset{\text{CH}_3}{|}}{\text{CH}}\\ \end{array}\!\!\right)_{\!\!x}$$

tetrafluoroethene

$$x\text{CF}_2 \!=\! \text{CF}_2$$

polytetrafluoroethene (PTFE)

$$\left(\!\text{CF}_2 - \text{CF}_2\!\right)_{\!\!x}$$

Polypropylene is used extensively in utensils and containers. Polytetrafluoroethene, also known as Teflon™, is used to coat nonstick cookware and to make bearings and bushings in chemical reactors.

2.

$$\left(\!\!\begin{array}{c} \overset{O}{\overset{\|}{\text{C}}}-\!\!\!\!\bigcirc\!\!\!\!-\overset{O}{\overset{\|}{\text{C}}}-\text{O}-\text{CH}_2\,\text{CH}_2-\text{O} \end{array}\!\!\right)_{\!\!x}$$

Polyethylene terephthalate (PET) is formed from the condensation of terephthalic acid and ethylene glycol. One molecule of water is lost for each bond formed. Because the repeating units are joined by ester bonds, PET is a polyester.

Interpreting Graphics 23

1. Only primary and secondary alcohols are oxidized by dichromate ion. Tertiary alcohols, such as 2-methyl-2-propanol, are not expected to react. Table 1 shows a change in absorbance values with time, which indicates a reaction between ethanol, a primary alcohol, and the oxidizing agent. The data in Table 2 show no change even after five minutes. (The slight fluctuation is due to random electronic noise in the instrument.)

2. This tertiary alcohol serves as a negative control Investigators use negative and positive controls to check that a chemical assay is functioning properly.

3. **a.** $\text{CH}_3\text{CH}_2\text{OH} \xrightarrow{\underset{\text{H}_2\text{SO}_4}{\text{K}_2\text{Cr}_2\text{O}_7}} \text{CH}_3\text{CHO}$

   b. $\text{Rate} = \dfrac{\Delta[\text{CH}_3\text{CH}_2\text{OH}]}{\Delta t} = k \times [\text{CH}_3\text{CH}_2\text{OH}]$

4. **a.** 0.000; 0.140; 0.304; 0.465; 0.627; 0.766

b.

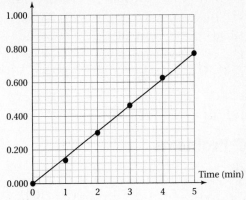

Log (absorbance)

c. Answers will vary slightly.

slope $= 0.157 \text{ min}^{-1}$

$$0.157 \text{ min}^{-1} = \frac{k}{2.303}$$

$$k = 0.362 \text{ min}^{-1}$$

Vocabulary Review 23

1. functional group
2. aryl halides
3. substitution reaction
4. alcohols
5. hydration reactions
6. hydrogenation
7. ketones

Solution: aspirin

Quiz for Chapter 23

1.

$$\underset{\underset{\text{H}}{|}}{\bigcirc} + \text{I}_2 \rightarrow \underset{\underset{\text{I}}{|}}{\bigcirc} + \text{HI}$$

2. NT	7. NT	12. AT
3. AT	8. NT	13. AT
4. ST	9. AT	14. AT
5. AT	10. NT	15. AT
6. AT	11. ST	16. ST

Chapter 23 Test A

A. Matching

1. e	5. d	8. j
2. i	6. h	9. a
3. f	7. c	10. b
4. g		

B. Multiple Choice

11. b	17. c	23. d
12. c	18. d	24. c
13. a	19. d	25. c
14. b	20. c	26. c
15. d	21. c	27. c
16. a	22. a	

C. Problems

28. **a.**

$$H-\underset{\underset{H}{|}}{\overset{\overset{H}{|}}{C}}-\underset{}{\overset{\overset{H}{|}}{C}}=\underset{}{\overset{\overset{H}{|}}{C}}-\underset{\underset{H}{|}}{\overset{\overset{H}{|}}{C}}-H + HOH$$

$$\rightarrow H-\underset{\underset{H}{|}}{\overset{\overset{H}{|}}{C}}-\underset{\underset{H}{|}}{\overset{\overset{H}{|}}{C}}-\underset{\underset{OH}{|}}{\overset{\overset{H}{|}}{C}}-\underset{\underset{H}{|}}{\overset{\overset{H}{|}}{C}}-H$$

b.

⬡ + Cl₂ →(catalyst) ⬡Cl + HCl

29. **a.** 2-butanol
    b. chlorobenzene/phenyl chloride
30. **a.** R—X
    b. R—O—R
    c.
$$R-\overset{\overset{\textstyle O}{\|}}{C}-O-R$$
    d.
$$R-\overset{\overset{\textstyle O}{\|}}{C}-OH$$

D. Essay

31. Polymers are large, chain-like molecules formed by the covalent bonding of repeating smaller molecules, called monomers. In addition polymerization, unsaturated monomers, such as alkenes, are joined to one another. In condensation polymerization, monomers with two functional groups, such as dicarboxylic acids and dihydroxy alcohols, react in a head-to-tail fashion. Because of their malleability, high strength-to-weight ratio, and durability, polymers have many commercial uses such as packaging, insulation, and synthetic fibers.

Chapter 23 Test B

A. Matching

1. i	5. j	8. d
2. a	6. b	9. e
3. g	7. f	10. c
4. h		

B. Multiple Choice

11. c	17. d	23. d
12. a	18. d	24. a
13. b	19. c	25. c
14. c	20. b	26. c
15. c	21. c	27. c
16. c	22. b	28. b

C. Problems

29. **a.** 3–chloro–2–methylpentane
    b. 2,3–dimethyl–2–butanol
    c. butanal
    d. 2–hexanone
    e. propyl ethanoate
30. **a.** aldehyde   **d.** carboxylic acid
    b. ester   **e.** ether
    c. alcohol   **f.** ketone
31. **a.** $CH_3CH_2I + KOH \rightarrow CH_3CH_2OH + KI$
    ethanol
    b. $CH_3-CH_2-CH = CH-CH_2-CH_2-CH_3 + HBr$
    $\rightarrow CH_3-CH_2-CHBr-CH_2-CH_2-CH_2-CH_3$
    3–bromohexane
    c.

⬡ + I₂ → ⬡I + HI
iodobenzene

D. Essay

32. Ethylene glycol is an alcohol with both a high boiling point and a low freezing point due to intermolecular hydrogen bonding. Ethylene glycol is soluble in water. When ethylene glycol is added to the water in a car radiator, the resulting mixture boils at a temperature higher than water alone, and freezes at a temperature lower than water alone. Thus, ethylene glycol protects against boiling in summer and freezing in winter.

Chapter 23 Small-Scale Lab

Section 23.4 Polymers, page 753

Analysis

1. The polymer is a gel-like liquid which is very viscous. It will not hold its shape like a solid and will flow slowly if left to stand. It wiggles, squirms, and oozes.

2–3.

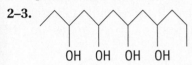

4.

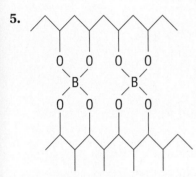

5.

You're the Chemist

1. Through experimentation, students are able to produce an amazing variety of polymers with different properties.

2. The chain is like a polymer because it contains many repeating units linked end to end. The rings that link two chains together are like the borate ion that cross links polymer chains.

Section Review 24.1

Part A Completion

1. prokaryotic/eukaryotic
2. prokaryotic/eukaryotic
3. bacteria
4. green plants
5. organelles
6. Mitochondria
7. lysosomes
8. nucleus
9. Sunlight
10. Photosynthesis
11. oxygen

Part B True-False

| 12. NT | 14. AT | 16. NT |
| 13. AT | 15. AT | |

Part C Matching

| 17. b | 19. a |
| 18. c | 20. d |

Part D Question

21. Chloroplasts contain the biological molecules necessary for the conversion of solar energy into chemical energy. Plants store the excess chemical energy in carbon compounds. Like animals, they meet their energy demands by breaking down these stored compounds. These oxidation reactions take place in mitochondria.

Section Review 24.2

Part A Completion

1. Carbohydrates
2. energy
3. cellulose
4. monosaccharides
5. disaccharides
6. polysaccharide
7. starch
8. glucose
9. Glycogen
10. liver

Part B True-False

| 11. NT | 13. AT | 15. ST |
| 12. AT | 14. AT | |

Part C Matching

| 16. e | 18. c | 20. d |
| 17. b | 19. a | |

Part D Questions

21. Starches are a source of energy for plants. Cellulose is used by plants to construct cell walls that are hard and rigid.

22. glucose and fructose

23. The hydroxyl group, $-OH$.

Section Review 24.3

Part A Completion

1. amino acid
2. side-chain group
3. side-chain group
4. peptide
5. peptide
6. water
7. protein
8. catalysts
9. enzymes

Part B True-False

10. ST
11. NT
12. AT
13. AT

Part C Matching

14. b
15. a
16. c

Part D Problem

17.

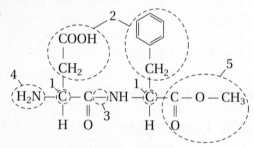

Section Review 24.4

Part A Completion

1. lipid
2. not soluble/insoluble
3. triglycerides
4. Triglycerides
5. Saponification
6. glycerol
7. Phospholipids
8. hydrophilic/polar
9. hydrophobic/nonpolar
10. lipid bilayer
11. Cell membranes

Part B True-False

12. AT
13. NT
14. AT
15. AT
16. ST

Part C Matching

17. d
18. b
19. c
20. a

Part D Questions

21. Wax coats on the surface of plant leaves protect against water loss and attack by microorganisms. In animals, waxes coat the skin, hair, and feathers, which keep these structures pliable and waterproof.

22. The molecules of both types of lipids have hydrophilic and hydrophobic ends. Thus, both types of lipids can interact with polar and nonpolar phases simultaneously. The cleansing action of soaps relies on this physical property.

Section Review 24.5

Part A Completion

1. nucleotide
2. deoxyribonucleic acid
3. ribonucleic acid
4. proteins
5. nitrogen base
6. adenine, guanine, thymine, or cytosine
7. adenine, guanine, thymine, or cytosine
8. adenine, guanine, thymine, or cytosine
9. adenine, guanine, thymine, or cytosine
10. uracil
11. double helix
12. hydrogen bonds
13. thymine
14. cytosine

Part B True-False

15. AT
16. AT
17. ST
18. AT

Part C Matching

19. b
20. e
21. c
22. a
23. d

Part D Question

24. Mutations are random changes in the sequence of nucleotides in a DNA molecule. Mutations may arise from additions, deletions, or substitutions of one or more of the nucleotides. When a mutation occurs within a gene, it may stop production of the specified protein or cause production of a protein with an altered amiono acid sequence. Sometimes the change is beneficial; more often, the ability of the

protein to function is seriously impaired. For example, a mutation in the peptide chain of hemoglobin reduces its ability to transport oxygen. People with this mutation have a molecular disease called sickle cell anemia, which is named for the distorted shape of the defective red blood cells.

Section Review 24.6

Part A Completion

1. adenosine triphosphate
2. adenosine diphosphate -ADP
3. oxidation
4. 30.5 kJ
5. nonspontaneous
6. catabolic or anabolic
7. catabolic or anabolic
8. metabolism
9. catabolism
10. anabolism

Part B True-False

11. AT   13. NT   15. NT
12. AT   14. AT

Part C Matching

16. d   18. c
17. b   19. a

Part D Question

21. The free energy of ATP hydrolysis is used to drive many nonspontaneous biological reactions. ATP hydrolysis provides the extra energy needed to shift the equilibrium of a nonspontaneous reaction in favor of the products. ATP captures energy from catabolism reactions to drive anabolism reactions.

Interpreting Graphics 24

Part A

1. cytoplasm
2. cell membrane
3. cell wall
4. nucleus
5. cytoplasm
6. cell membrane

Part B

1. The cell in panel **a** represents a prokaryotic cell. It lacks a nucleus and organelles, which are present in eukaryotic cells such as the one depicted in panel **b**. Prokaryotic cells are the cells of bacteria. The cells of all other organisms are eukaryotic.

2. Figure 1a: 0.0001 to 0.001 mm, 0.1 to 1.0 μm, 100 to 1000 nm.
   Figure 1b: 0.001 to 0.01 mm, 1.0 to 10.0 μm, 1000 to 10,000 nm.

3. All of the organelle types labeled in Figure 1b are found in a typical plant cell. Plant cells are eukaryotic.

4. Plant cells contain chloroplasts, structures that enable plants to produce carbohydrates through photosynthesis. Plant cells have cell walls.

5. ATP is produced in the mitochondrion and transported out to the cytoplasm, where it is used to fuel nonspontaneous processes.

6. Mitochondria produce energy needed for cellular activities. Muscle cells are highly active cells, which require many mitochondria to meet their energy demands. Skin cells are less active. They contain significantly fewer mitochondria.

7. Carbohydrates are found in the cytoplasm and are attached to the extracellular surfaces of membrane-bound proteins. They comprise the cell walls, which provide structure and rigidity to plant cells. Because proteins catalyze metabolic reactions, they are found throughout the cell. Proteins embedded in cell membranes help to transport molecules and ions across this barrier. Lipids are found mainly in cell and organelle membranes where they form a barrier to the free flow of ions and molecules into and out of the membrane-enclosed compartments. DNA, a molecule that stores the information needed to make proteins, is found primarily in the nucleus of eukaryotic cells and in the cytoplasm of prokaryotic cells. RNA, a molecule that participates in the transfer of information between DNA and protein, is found in the cytoplasm of all cells.

Vocabulary Review 24

1. c	5. k	9. i
2. f	6. h	10. d
3. b	7. e	11. a
4. g	8. j	

Quiz for Chapter 24

1. NT	4. AT	7. b
2. AT	5. ST	8. b
3. NT	6. d	9. d

Chapter 24 Test A

A. Matching

1. e	5. c	8. d
2. b	6. f	9. h
3. g	7. a	10. j
4. i		

B. Multiple Choice

11. d	16. d	21. d
12. b	17. a	22. d
13. b	18. c	23. c
14. d	19. c	24. a
15. b	20. b	25. c

C. True-False

26. AT	30. ST	33. NT
27. AT	31. AT	34. AT
28. NT	32. NT	35. AT
29. ST		

D. Questions and Problems

36. Trp-Arg-Ala-Leu-Asn-end

37. **a.** $ATP + H_2O \rightarrow ADP + P_i$

    b. $K_{eq} = \dfrac{[ADP][P_i]}{[ATP]} > 1$

    c. spontaneous

38. Phosphorus is essential for the synthesis of phospholipids, nucleic acids, and energy-rich molecules such as ATP. Phosphorus is found in the bloodstream as HPO_4^{2-} and $H_2PO_4^-$, which together form an important buffer. Nitrogen is required for the synthesis of amino acids and nitrogen-containing bases of nucleic acids.

39. Test the aqueous solubility of the substance. Many carbohydrates are soluble in water, whereas lipids are not.

40. Eukaryotic cells contain a nucleus and other membrane-enclosed structures called organelles. Prokaryotic cells do not contain a nucleus or organelles. Eukaryotic cells are typically much larger than prokaryotic cells.

41. **a.** A membrane protein that acts as a channel must have contacts inside and outside the cell membrane. To span the entire bilayer, membrane proteins must have dimensions similar to the observed thickness of the lipid bilayer. The length along the transmembrane axis of the protein must be approximately 5 to 10 nm.

    b. Because the lipid bilayer is composed of two sheets of phospholipid molecules arranged tail to tail, each phospholipid molecule must be approximately 2.5 to 5 nm long from head to tail.

E. Essay

42. Nucleic acids are polymers found primarily in cell nuclei. They are composed of nucleotides that contain a phosphate group, a five-carbon sugar, and a nitrogen-containing base. There are two types: DNA and RNA. DNA stores the information needed to make proteins. DNA governs the reproduction and growth of cells. RNA has a key role in the transmission of the information stored in DNA.

Chapter 24 Test B

A. Matching

1. c	5. b	8. e
2. d	6. a	9. h
3. g	7. f	10. j
4. i		

B. Multiple Choice

11. c	16. d	21. d
12. d	17. d	22. b
13. b	18. c	23. c
14. a	19. c	24. c
15. d	20. b	25. d

C. True-False

26. NT	**30.** ST	**33.** AT
27. AT	**31.** AT	**34.** AT
28. AT	**32.** AT	**35.** NT
29. ST		

D. Questions and Problems

36. More than one answer is possible due to the redundancy of the genetic code. One possibility: ACAGTTGGTACT

37. An enzyme catalyzes the conversion of a substrate to product. Doubling and tripling the number of enzyme molecules in the reaction mixture is equivalent to doubling and tripling the number of active sites to which substrate can bind. Thus, when all other conditions are kept the same, the rate at which product is formed will increase with the number of enzyme molecules present in the reaction system.

38. Test the aqueous solubility of the substance. Most proteins are soluble in water, whereas lipids are not.

39. $2000 \text{ kJ} \times \dfrac{1 \text{ mol ATP}}{30.5 \text{ kJ}} \times \dfrac{507.2 \text{ g ATP}}{1 \text{ mol ATP}} \times \dfrac{1 \text{ kg}}{10^3 \text{ g}}$

$= 33.3 \text{ kg ATP}$

40. Two dipeptides are possible. One possibility:

$$H_3N-\underset{\underset{H}{|}}{\overset{\overset{CH_3}{|}}{C}}-\overset{\overset{O}{\parallel}}{C}-OH \ + \ H_2N-\underset{\underset{H}{|}}{\overset{\overset{H}{|}}{C}}-\overset{\overset{O}{\parallel}}{C}-OH \longrightarrow$$

$$H_3N-\underset{\underset{H}{|}}{\overset{\overset{CH_3}{|}}{C}}-\overset{\overset{O}{\parallel}}{C}-\underset{\underset{H}{|}}{\overset{\overset{H}{|}}{N}}-\underset{\underset{H}{|}}{C}-\overset{\overset{O}{\parallel}}{C}-OH \ + \ H_2O$$

41. The extent to which the physical properties of a cell membrane are altered by a substance may depend on the solubility of the substance in the lipid bilayer. Beacause the interior of the lipid bilayer is a hydrophobic environment, nonpolar substances have the greatest chance of becoming incorporated into this protion of the cell membrane.

E. Essay

42. Enzymes are proteins that, like act as biological catalysts. They reduce the time required for a chemical reaction to reach equilibrium, but do not change the normal position of the equilibrium. Enzymes are not changed by the reactions they promote. The molecules on which an enzyme acts are called substrates. In an enzyme-catalyzed reaction the substrate binds to the active site on the enzyme form an enzyme-substrate complex. Next, bond-breaking and bond-making occur at the active site to produce the products of the reaction. Finally, the products dissociate from the enzyme leaving the enzyme free to bind new substrate and begin a second reaction cycle.

Chapter 24 Small-Scale Lab

Section 24.3 The Egg: A Biochemical Storehouse, page 774

Analysis

Sample answers are given.

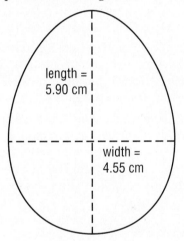

length = 5.90 cm

width = 4.55 cm

mass = 62.42 g

1. Shape Index $= \dfrac{4.55 \text{ cm}}{5.90 \text{ cm}} \times 100 = 77.1$

2. $V = 0.5236 \, lw^2 = (0.5236)(5.90 \text{ cm})(4.55 \text{ cm})^2$
$= 64.0 \text{ cm}^3$

$M = 0.5632 lw^2 = (0.5632)(5.90 \text{ cm})(4.55 \text{ cm})^2$
$= 68.8 \text{ g}$

$A = 3.138 \, [(5.90 \text{ cm})(4.55 \text{ cm})^2]^{2/3}$
$= 77.3 \text{ cm}^2$

3. The measured mass of 62.42 g is less than the calculated mass of 68.8 g by 6.4 g. The egg may have lost water over time.

4. $d = \dfrac{m}{v} = \dfrac{62.42 \text{ g}}{64.0 \text{ cm}^3} = 0.975 \text{ g/cm}^3$

This is less than the density of a freshly laid egg.

You're the Chemist

1. Weigh the egg once each day for two or three days. Typical eggs will loose 0.2 to 0.5 grams per day depending on the temperature at which they are stored.

2. Assume Step 1 reveals the egg loses 0.20 g per day.

   $$\text{Age of egg} = (68.8\ \cancel{g} - 62.42\ \cancel{g}) \times \frac{1\ \text{day}}{0.20\ \cancel{g}}$$
   $$= 32\ \text{days old}$$

3. Measure the volume of water displaced by the egg.

4. The larger the egg, the smaller the shape index. Extra large eggs tend to be more oblong than small eggs, which are rounder.

5. Extra large eggs are usually more than 70 grams, medium eggs are less than 50 grams.

6. HCl produces bubbles at the surface of the egg shell.
   $$2HCl + CaCO_3 \rightarrow CO_2 + H_2O + CaCl_2$$

7. Powdered milk + NaOH + $CuSO_4$ produces a violet color, a positive test for protein. Egg shell + NaOH + $CuSO_4$ produces a violet color, a positive test for protein.

8. Weigh an egg once a day for three days and store in a refrigerator between weighings. Weigh it once a day for three more days and store it at room temperature. The warmer the temperature the greater the mass loss.

Section Review 25.1

Part A Completion

1. radioactive
2. radioisotopes
3. nuclei
4. stable
5. energy
6. beta
7. Alpha
8. helium
9. electrons
10. metal foil
11. Gamma
12. mass
13. Lead
14. concrete
15. stop

Part B True-False

16. ST
17. NT
18. AT
19. NT
20. AT

Part C Matching

21. b
22. a
23. c
24. e
25. d

Part D Problems

26. a. $^{218}_{84}Po \rightarrow\ ^{4}_{2}He +\ ^{214}_{82}Pb$

    b. $^{210}_{82}Pb \rightarrow\ ^{210}_{83}Bi +\ ^{0}_{-1}e$

Section Review 25.2

Part A Completion

1. band of stability
2. beta
3. positron
4. rate
5. half-life
6. radioactive
7. billions
8. transmutation
9. radioactive decay
10. atomic numbers
11. synthesized

Part B True-False

12. NT
13. NT
14. AT
15. ST
16. ST

Part C Matching

17. c
18. e
19 b
20. a
21. d

Part D Questions

22. $\dfrac{60\ hr}{15\ hr} = 4$ half-lives; After 4 half-lives

    $1/2 \times 1/2 \times 1/2 \times 1/2 = 1/16$ of the original mass will remain. $1/16 \times 18.0\ g = 1.13\ g$

23. $2.0\ g \times \frac{1}{2} \times \frac{1}{2} \times \frac{1}{2} = 0.25\ g$ or 3 half-lives
    42 days $\div$ 3 = 14 days

Section Review 25.3

Part A Completion

1. fission
2. neutrons
3. fissionable atom
4. energy
5. moderation
6. absorption
7. fusion
8. mass
9. energy
10. hydrogen
11. helium

Part B True-False

12. ST
13. NT
14. NT
15. NT

Part C Matching

16. a
17. c
18. e
19. b
20. d

Part D Questions and Problems

21. a. 3   **b.** 4

22. a. slow fast-moving neutrons so they can be absorbed by the fuel atoms

     b. decrease the number of slow-moving neutrons and slow the chain reaction

Section Review 25.4

Part A Completion

1. ionizing
2. electrons
3. senses
4. Geiger
5. gas
6. scintillation
7. all
8. iodine-131
9. phosphorus-32
10. neutron activation

Part B True-False

11. AT
12. NT
13. ST
14. AT

Part C Matching

15. b
16. e
17. c
18. a
19. d

Part D Questions

20. b

21. Neutron activation analysis is used to detect trace amounts of elements in samples. Radioisotopes are used to study chemical reactions and molecular structures. Radioisotopes are used to diagnose and treat diseases such as cancer.

Practice Problems 25

Section 25.1

1. The atomic number increases by one; the mass number remains the same.
2. The atomic number decreases by two; the mass number decreases by four.
3. **a.** 28 protons and 36 neutrons
   b. 53 protons and 83 neutrons
   c. 79 protons and 116 neutrons
4. **a.** $^{14}_{7}N$ **c.** $^{0}_{-1}e$
   b. $^{237}_{93}Np$

Section 25.2

1. **a.** $^{208}_{87}Fr \rightarrow ^{4}_{2}He + ^{204}_{85}At$
   b. $^{7}_{4}Be + ^{0}_{-1}e \rightarrow ^{7}_{3}Li$
   c. $^{37}_{18}Ar \rightarrow ^{37}_{19}K + ^{0}_{-1}e$
   d. $^{17}_{9}F \rightarrow ^{17}_{8}O + ^{0}_{+1}e$
2. **a.** $^{3}_{1}H$ **d.** $^{144}_{58}Ce$
   b. $^{92}_{36}Kr$ **e.** $^{239}_{94}Pu$
   c. $^{30}_{15}P$
3. It takes five half-lives, or 820 s.
   $8.0 \text{ g} \rightarrow 4.0 \text{ g} \rightarrow 2.0 \text{ g} \rightarrow 1.0 \text{ g} \rightarrow 0.50 \text{ g} \rightarrow 0.25 \text{ g}$
4. $16 \text{ g} \rightarrow 8 \text{ g} \rightarrow 4 \text{ g} \rightarrow 2.0 \text{ g} \rightarrow 1.0 \text{ g}$
   Four half-lives = 4×17 days = 68 days
5. $\dfrac{51 \text{ min}}{5.1 \text{ min}} = 10$ half-lives. The mass would decrease by a factor of more than 1000.
   $\left(\dfrac{1}{2}\right)^{10} = \dfrac{1}{1024}$
6. The mass decreases by a factor of 1/8, or three half-lives. The half-life is $5.49/3 = 183$ s

Section 25.3

1. **a.** 2 $([1 + 235] - [90 + 144] = 2)$
   b. 3 $([1 + 235] - [87 + 146] = 3)$
   c. 4 $([1 + 235] - [72 + 160] = 4)$
2. $2.0 \times 10^7 \text{ kcal} \div 8.0 \text{ kcal/g} = 2.5 \times 10^6 \text{ g}$
3. $^{4}_{2}He$

Section 25.4

1. Radioisotopes replace non-radioactive isotopes in the structure of a compound without changing its chemical properties. Tracing the pathways of radioactive isotopes allows scientists to study reaction mechanisms and reaction rates.
2. Teletherapy is the use of gamma radiation to destroy cancerous tissue.

Interpreting Graphics 25

1. 8
2. 6; $^{238}_{92}U \rightarrow ^{206}_{82}Pb + 8\,^{4}_{2}He + 6\,^{0}_{-1}e$
3. 8 days = 2 half-lives; $20 \times \frac{1}{2} \times \frac{1}{2} = 5.0$ g
4. 20 minutes = 1 half-life; 1.0 mol = $6.0 \times 10^{23} \times \frac{1}{2} = 3.0 \times 10^{23}$ atoms
5. lead-210; The half-life of polonium-214 is insignificant compared to the half-life of bismuth-214.
6. Three half-lives = 15 days; $16 \text{ g} \rightarrow 8 \text{ g} \rightarrow 4 \text{ g} \rightarrow 2.0 \text{ g}$.

7. For heavier isotopes, such as lead-206, the stability ratio is about 1.5 neutrons to 1 proton. 124 n ÷ 82 p = 1.5

8. Uranium-238 has the longest half-life (4.5×10^9 yr); polonium-210 has the shortest half-life (1.6×10^{-4} s).

Vocabulary Review 25

1. b	5. i	9. k
2. l	6. d	10. f
3. g	7. e	11. h
4. a	8. c	12. j

Quiz for Chapter 25

1. d	5. a	8. b
2. b	6. d	9. a
3. c	7. c	10. a
4. b		

Chapter 25 Test A

A. Matching

1. a	5. j	8. f
2. i	6. e	9. h
3. g	7. d	10. b
4. c		

B. Multiple Choice

11. b	17. b	22. a
12. c	18. d	23. b
13. b	19. b	24. a
14. b	20. c	25. d
15. a	21. a	26. b
16. c		

C. Problems

27. **a.** $^{42}_{19}\text{K} \rightarrow {}^{\ 0}_{-1}e + {}^{42}_{20}\text{Ca}$
    b. $^{235}_{92}\text{U} \rightarrow {}^{4}_{2}\text{He} + {}^{231}_{90}\text{Th}$

28. If one-eighth of the sample remains, the isotope decayed through 3 half-lives.
    Three half-lives is 252 days, so one half-life period = 84 days.
    The half-life of scandium-42 is 84 days.

29. 40 days = 5 half-lives.
    $\frac{1}{32}$ of the original sample remains
    = 0.13 gram remaining.

D. Essay

30. The energy released from the sun is the result of a nuclear fusion, or thermonuclear reaction. Fusion occurs when two light nuclei combine to produce a nucleus of heavier mass. In solar fusion, hdrogen nuclei (protons) are fused to make helium nuclei. The reaction requires two beta particles.
    $4^1_1\text{H} + 2_{-1}^{\ 0}e \rightarrow {}^4_2\text{He} + \text{energy}$

Chapter 25 Test B

A. Matching

1. j	5. e	8. h
2. i	6. g	9. b
3. c	7. a	10. f
4. d		

B. Multiple Choice

11. a	16. d	21. d
12. d	17. b	22. d
13. c	18. a	23. d
14. b	19. a	24. a
15. a	20. c	25. d

C. Problems

26. **a.** $^{226}_{88}\text{Ra} \rightarrow {}^{222}_{86}\text{Rn} + {}^{4}_{2}\text{He}$
    b. $^{234}_{91}\text{Pa} \rightarrow {}^{234}_{92}\text{U} + {}^{\ 0}_{-1}e$
    c. $^{234}_{90}\text{Th} \rightarrow {}^{234}_{91}\text{Pa} + {}^{\ 0}_{-1}e$

27. 27.0 h/6.75 h = 4.00 half-lives
    Thus, $12.0\ \text{g} \times \frac{1}{2} \times \frac{1}{2} \times \frac{1}{2} \times \frac{1}{2} = 0.750\ \text{g}$

28. $\frac{0.125\ \text{g}}{4.00\ \text{g}} = \frac{1}{32}$ of the sample remains

    Since $\frac{1}{32}$ represents $\left(\frac{1}{2}\right)^5$, or 5 half-lives,

    $\frac{71.5\ \text{years}}{5\ \text{half-lives}} = 14.3\ \text{years/half-life.}$

D. Essay

29. **a.** Chemical reactions occur in an effort to attain stable electron configurations. Nuclear reactions occur in an effort to obtain stable nuclear configurations.

    b. Nuclear reactions release far more energy than typical exothermic chemical reactions.

c. Unlike chemical reactions, nuclear reactions are unaffected by changes in temperature, pressure, or the presence of a catalyst.

Chapter 25 Small-Scale Lab

Section 25.2 Radioactivity and Half Lives, page 809

Analysis

Sample data are provided.

Trial #	Number of flips	Number of heads
1	100	42
2	42	20
3	20	9
4	9	5
5	5	3
6	3	1
7	1	0

Figure A

1.

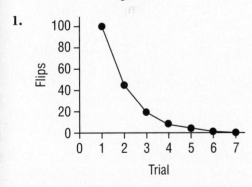

2. The rate of disappearance of heads is non-linear. The rate decreases over time.

3. For each flip the probability of a head is 0.50.

4. Each trial represents one half-life because the number of heads approximately halves for each trial.

You're the Chemist

1. Count the total number of even numbers that result in 100 rolls of the die. Roll the die again a number of times equal to the number obtained in the first trial. Do trials until the number of events equals zero. Plot number of evens vs. trial.

2. After 3.8 days, half the sample remains. After 7.6 days, one-fourth remains, and, after 11.4 days, one-eighth remains.

3. This time period is two half-lives (11,460 years/5730 = 2) of carbon-14. After two half-lives, one-fourth of the sample remains.